Magmas and magmatic rocks
An introduction to igneous petrology

Eric A. K. Middlemost

Department of Geology and Geophysics
University of Sydney

MAGMAS AND MAGMATIC ROCKS

An introduction to igneous petrology

LONGMAN
London and New York

Longman Group Limited
Longman House, Burnt Mill, Harlow
Essex CM20 2JE, England
Associated companies throughout the world

Published in the United States of America
by Longman Inc., New York

First published 1985

British Library Cataloguing in Publication Data
Middlemost, Eric A.K.
    Magmas and magmatic rocks : an introduction
    to igneous petrology.
    1. Magmatism
    I. Title
    552'.1   QE461
    ISBN 0-582-30080-0

Library of Congress Cataloging in Publication Data
Middlemost, Eric A.K., 1936–
    Magmas and magmatic rocks
    Bibliography: p. 235
    Includes index.
    1. Rocks, Igneous.   2. Magmatism.   I. Title.
QE461.M498   1986   552'.1   84-23358
ISBN 0-582-30080-0

Set in 9½/11pt. Linotron 202 Times
Produced by Longman Singapore Publishers (Pte) Ltd.
Printed in Singapore

CONTENTS

Contents

PREFACE

dents of petrology to heed some of the advice of that wise Dane, Petrus Severinus who, in his *Idea Medecinae Philosophicae* of 1571 (p. 73), counselled his readers to

... buy yourselves stout shoes, get away to the mountains, search the valleys, the deserts, the shores of the sea, and the deepest recesses of the Earth; mark well the distinctions between animals, the differences among plants, the various kinds of minerals, the properties and mode of origin of everything that exists. . . . Lastly, purchase coals, build furnaces, watch and experiment without wearing. In this way, and no other, will you arrive at a knowledge of things and of their properties.

The author is particularly grateful to Mr Len Hay for drafting the diagrams, and Miss S. M. Binns for her excellent typing.

The main purpose of this book is to give undergraduate, and postgraduate, science students a compendious account of current ideas, and speculations, on the origin and evolution of magmas and the magmatic rocks. In the past 25 years the horizon of petrology has expanded to accommodate a wide range of new information from both the Earth and the other terrestrial planets. This has made the content of petrology more interesting, but it has also made the literature of petrology much more voluminous and specialized. An attempt has been made to write a book that is complete within itself, so that a student, or general reader, with little knowledge of either petrology or chemistry, should be able to read and understand it without outside assistance. It is however suggested that the reader should possess a book on mineralogy, such as Deer, Howie and Zussman (1966) *An Introduction to the Rock-Forming Minerals*. The various concepts that are fundamental to an understanding of the magmatic rocks are developed using a step-by-step approach. One of the unifying themes in the book is that the models, proposed for the origin and evolution of magmas, can be strongly constrained by data from experimental petrology, physical chemistry, geochemistry and geophysics. The book contains long sections on magmas, magmatic differentiation and volcanology; and the discussion of these topics is followed by a series of shorter chapters that examine a variety of different magmatic rocks.

Although there are firm plans to undertake detailed studies of Venus, Mars, the Asteroids and Titan, before the end of this century, one must not conclude that petrology is becoming an armchair science. The writer would like all stu-

ACKNOWLEDGEMENTS

We are grateful to the following for permission to reproduce copyright material:
George Allen & Unwin Ltd for fig 3.3.4 adapted from fig 2.2 p 14 (Cox, Bell & Pankhurst 1979); Institut fur Geologie und Palaontologie for figs 3.2.1, 3.2.2, 3.2.3, 3.2.4 adapted from figs on pp 777–80 (Streckeisen 1974); International Union of Geological Sciences for fig 4.1.2 adapted from fig 4 p 18 (Chayes 1979b); the author, I Kushiro, R. B. Hargreaves & Princeton University Press for fig 1.4.2 adapted from fig 19 (Kushiro 1980); Lunar & Planetary Institute for fig 1.4.1 adapted from fig 3.1.12 (Basaltic Volcanism Study Project 1981); Mineralogical Society of America for fig 2.2.1 adapted from fig 1 p 283 (Roedder 1951); Oxford University Press for figs 5.4.1, 5.4.2 adapted from figs 1, 2 pp 350, 352 (Yoder & Tilley 1962), figs 3.1.1, 3.1.2 adapted from figs on p 99 (LeMaitre 1976a); Princeton University Press for fig 2.3.1 adapted from fig 5.5 (Osborn 1979); Springer-Verlag for fig 6.1.1 adapted from fig 2 p 66 (Peccerillo & Taylor 1976); University of Chicago Press for fig 7.7.1 adapted from fig on p 514 (Bowen 1937 & Shairer 1950); World Data Center A for figs 1.9.2, 1.9.3.

CHAPTER 1

MAGMAS

1.1 Rocks and magmas

In the past, rocks were usually regarded as aggregates of consolidated, naturally formed, inanimate matter from the Earth. Over the years this definition has been expanded to include unconsolidated materials, and natural, inanimate materials of extraterrestrial origin. A rock is now generally regarded as being a naturally formed body of solid, inanimate matter that has some degree of internal chemical (and usually mineralogical) homogeneity. Rocks are thus essentially the *solid stuff* of which planets, natural satellites and other broadly similar cosmic bodies are made. They are also much more than this as they provide the key to a whole universe of ideas about the origin of planets, the Solar System and, to a lesser extent, the cosmos. The present study is primarily concerned with the rocks that solidified from a hot (usually greater than 650 °C), molten, or partly molten, condition. All these *magmatic rocks* are igneous rocks (Latin *ignis*, fire). In Chapter 9 it will be shown that some of the rocks that are called igneous are not necessarily magmatic rocks but may be produced by extreme metamorphism.

Petrology is the study of the occurrence, composition, origin and evolution of rocks. When this science was named by Pinkerton in 1811, he used the term *petralogy*, and derived it from the classical Greek words *petra* meaning rock and *logos* meaning discourse. A full petrological description of an igneous rock should include a statement about the rock-unit in which it occurs, a record of the attitude and structure of the rock-unit, a report on the texture, physical appearance, mode (actual mineral and/or glass content), chemical composition and age of the rock; together with an account of its origin and evolution. If one examines this statement one finds that petrology consists of two components: (a) *petrography*, or the description and systematic classification of rocks; and (b) *petrogenesis* which is the study of the origin and evolution of rocks. The recognition that igneous petrology can be separated into these two sub-disciplines is important, because in the past, and even to some extent today, workers in these two fields have embraced different philosophies. Most early petrologists were essentially petrographers, and they described rocks in the field and laboratory using the concepts and words of everyday speech and affairs, and their petrogenetic ideas were often vague and speculative.

During the present century most igneous petrologists have come to accept that one of the most satisfactory ways of solving petrogenetic problems is to conduct laboratory experiments that reproduce the pressures and temperatures found in the various environments where igneous materials form and evolve. In order to set up their experiments and interpret their results, experimental petrologists have had to use the concepts and philosophy of physical chemistry. This approach to petrology was well illustrated by Norman L. Bowen (1928) in his book *The Evolution of Igneous Rocks*. Bowen (1928: 303) also broadened the scope of igneous petrology as he wished 'to establish the connection of igneous activity with ascertained facts regarding the nature of the Earth as a whole and if possible with the early history and ultimate origin of the Earth'. In more recent times the '*Basaltic Volcanism Study Project*' (BVSP 1981) has demonstrated that volcanism, and in particular basaltic volcanism, is a fundamental process in the evolution of not only the Earth but all the terrestrial planets.

Igneous petrology has thus grown from a science that was primarily concerned with describing individual rocks into one that gathers data from many related disciplines, such as experimental petrology, geochemistry, geophysics and volcanology, and used these data to develop hypotheses that account for the origin and evolution of igneous rocks on both the local and planetary scale. Experimental petrology is an essential part of igneous petrology because as Barth (1962a: 51) has observed, field and petrographic observations by themselves often do not provide conclusive proof of the igneous nature of a rock. The chemical compositions of igneous rocks are both complex and variable, but the study of large numbers of crystalline igneous rocks from a variety of localities has established that most of these rocks contain a limited number of phases (or minerals). This observation is usually interpreted as demonstrating that such rocks crystallized under equilibrium conditions (Bailey 1976a: 4). If most igneous rocks formed under equilibrium conditions, it follows that experimental petrology should be able to demonstrate whether, or not, a particular rock solidified from a hot molten, or partly molten, condition. Experimental studies should also limit the number of hypotheses that can be proposed for the origin of such rocks.

The sciences of igneous petrology, geochemistry, geophysics and volcanology are all interdependent. Geochemistry is essentially concerned with the abundance and distribution of the chemical elements, and their isotopes, in the minerals, rocks, ores, soils, waters and atmospheres of planetary bodies. It also stretches our minds and makes us think about how the chemical elements were created, and the relative abundance of these elements in the primordial solar nebula. Geophysics is primarily an investigation and interpretation of the physical properties of the planets. Volcanology is the study of volcanic phenomena wherever they are found.

Research into the origin and evolution of the Earth and the terrestrial planets (Mercury, Venus, Moon and Mars) is different from most other fields of study because it is concerned with enormous periods of time, the dissipation of vast amounts of heat, and usually also with the movement of huge amounts of material. Petrology is usually not troubled by problems related to the direction (or arrow) of time, because it is essentially a study of the rock-forming processes that occur sequentially on cooling and/or degassing planetary bodies. Isotopic age determinations have revealed that the age of the Earth, Moon and most meteorites is approximately 4.6 Ga (10^9 yrs, or giga earth-years). The vastness of this time-scale enables one to understand how planetary-forming processes can produce results that are inexplicable on the shorter time-scale of laboratory experiments, or human life-spans. In 1900, most informed, non-Hindu, people believed that the total span of earth-history was 100 Ma (10^6 yrs, or mega earth-years); however, the accepted duration of earth-history was soon expanded by the pioneering research of Rutherford and Soddy (1902), Boltwood (1907) and Arthur Holmes (1913), in the field of radioactive age determinations.

1.2 Concise history of igneous petrology

Many classical Greek and Roman authors described volcanoes, volcanic activity and earthquakes. Strabo, the Greek geographer and historian (63 BC–AD 20), described volcanic activity associated with Etna, Somma-Vesuvo and the Lippari Islands. He also suggested that volcanoes were natural safety valves through which fluids escaped. A detailed account of the AD 70 eruption of Somma-Vesuvius that destroyed Pompeii and Herculaneum is available because among those killed was the naturalist, Caius Plinius (Pliny the Elder). His nephew (Pliny the Younger) wrote two letters to the historian Tacitus in which he described (a) the eruption as seen from Misenum, and (b) the fate that befell Caius Plinius who visited the site of the eruption. In 1650 the geographer Varenius (Bernhard Varen) published his celebrated list of volcanoes and eruptions.

The eighteenth century saw the publication of the first detailed field descriptions of rocks, and the relationships that exist between different rock units. An example of such work is that of Johann Gottlob Lehmann (1700–67) who was a lecturer in mineralogy and mining in Berlin and St Petersburg (Leningrad). During the eighteenth century there were many passionate debates about the nature and origin of rocks. One of the major debates was between the *Neptunists* (e.g. Abraham Gottlob Werner, 1749–1817) on one side, and the *Vulcanists* (e.g. Jean Etienne Guttard, 1715–86 and Nicolas Desmarest, 1725–1815) and later the *Plutonists* (e.g. James Hutton, 1726–97) on the other. The *Neptunists* supported the ideas of Tobern Bergman (1735–84) that the rocks of the crust had all been deposited sequentially from, or precipitated out of, a primeval ocean. Both basalt and granite were regarded as being rocks that had precipitated out of the universal ocean (cf. Ospovat, 1971). Werner considered volcanoes to be curiosities caused by the subterranean combustion of coal. In 1752, Guttard studied the rocks of the

Auvergne region of central France and recognized many recently extinct volcanoes. He realized that the name of the ancient town of Volvic, which is found in this area, is derived from *volcani vicus*, or the seat of a volcano. Desmarest (1771) also worked in the Auvergne and he established that these volcanoes had produced a variety of different lavas that ranged in composition from dark basalts to lighter-coloured trachytes and phonolites. The plutonists proposed that the Earth formed from the solidification of hot molten materials and that granite was a hot intrusive rock. Hutton (1975) was particularly interested in the origin and evolution of the rocks and landforms found at the surface of the Earth. His published work shows a clear grasp of the concept that natural processes have gradually changed the surface of the Earth over long periods of time. He also compared and contrasted the irregular shapes and discordant contacts of many coarse-grained igneous bodies, with the more regular tabular form of most sedimentary bodies. He concluded that the igneous bodies were emplaced as hot mobile magmas (cf. Dott, 1969: 133). The term *magma*, and concept of a single dominant *primary magma* was introduced by G. Poulett Scrope in 1825.

Sir James Hall (1761–1832) was a contemporary and friend of Hutton, and he together with R. A. de Reaumur (1726), L. Spallanzani (1794) and George Watt (1804) pioneered *experimental petrology*. Hutton was opposed to the experimental approach and told Hall that he did not believe that one could learn what went on in the depths of the Earth 'by kindling a fire and looking into the bottom of a crucible'. After Hutton's death, Hall continued his experiments in earnest. He demonstrated that the textures of magmatic rocks are directly related to their cooling histories, and that temperatures of between 850° and 1400 °C were required to melt the common igneous rocks (cf. Eyles 1961). In his experiments, Hall used a primitive furnace, and gun-barrels for pressure-vessels. Ever since these pioneering days progress in experimental petrology has been directly related to improvements in experimental apparatus, and growth in our knowledge of physical chemistry. In the late nineteenth and early twentieth centuries the work of Daubree, Fouque, Michel-Levy, Lemberg, Vogt, Doelter and Morozewicz established the importance of experimental petrology in the study of the origin of igneous rocks and ore deposits (cf. Loewinson-

Lessing 1954: 42–8). The formal founding of the Geophysical Laboratory of the Carnegie Institution of Washington in 1905 was another important event in the history of this discipline, as the laboratory has produced invaluable data on equilibria in rock-forming and ore-forming systems. Most of the early results obtained by this laboratory were summarized in Bowen's (1928) remarkable book. Fifty years after the publication of this work, a new book called *The Evolution of the Igneous Rocks: Fiftieth Anniversary Perspective* (Yoder 1979) was produced which demonstrated that after fifty years the main petrogenetic questions discussed by Bowen are still pertinent to igneous petrology. The fiftieth anniversary of the publication of Bowen's book was also commemorated by a significant conference at which a distinguished group of scientists examined the nature of silicate magma and the physical processes associated with their generation, transport and crystallization (cf. Hargraves 1980). The main theme in Bowen's book was that most igneous rocks are derived from a single primary basaltic magma. He also proposed that this magma was produced by the partial melting of a deep-seated olivine-rich rock called peridotite. This concept was apparently first proposed by L. F. Harper (1915: 280) who stated that the basaltic rocks of the south coast of New South Wales, Australia, evolved from a magma that was generated 'more or less entirely from the fusion of a belt of coarsely crystalline ultra-basic rock' that envelops 'the metallic core of the Earth'.

In 1844, Charles Darwin (1809–82) proposed that different types of magmatic rocks may be derived from a single parent magma if the composition of the magma is changed by the crystallization and removal of one or more of the common rock-forming minerals. He suggested that this process would enable both trachytic and basaltic lavas to issue from the same volcanic vent. In 1851, R. W. Bunsen (1811–99) demonstrated that the chemical compositions of the magmatic rocks of Iceland could be expressed in terms of two primary magmas; one basic with a relatively low silica content, and the other silicic with a relatively high silica content. He also explored the idea that magmas may change in composition as the result of the assimilation of country rocks. Sartorius von Waltershausen (1853) also worked in Iceland and he proposed that the different igneous rocks were generated when fractures tapped compositionally-zoned magma chambers.

The first thin sections of rocks

In the 1850s, Henry Clifton Sorby (1826–1908) prepared the first thin sections of rocks suitable for microscopic study (cf. Sorby 1858). Thin sections are slices of rock approximately 0.03 mm thick; and when such slices are examined in transmitted light, most of the rock-forming minerals appear transparent or translucent, and their optical properties and textural relationships are readily observed. Ferdinand Zirkel (1828–1912) was one of the first to recognize the great value of thin sections. He, together with other workers such as H. Rosenbusch (1877b), A. F. Fouque and A. Michel-Levy (1879), E. Kalkowsky (1886), J. J. H. Teal (1888) and J. L. A. Roth (1879), published many important works on systematic petrography.

In 1893, petrology was formally recognized as a separate science with the establishment of a chair of petrology at the University of Chicago in the USA. J. P. Iddings became the first incumbent of this chair. Other milestones in the history of petrology were: (a) the publication by W. C. Brögger of the first part of his monumental work (1894–1933) on the igneous rocks of the Oslo region of Norway; (b) the publication in 1895 of Alfred Harker's widely-used textbook *Petrology for Students*: and (c) the publication in 1897 of Archibald Geikie's *The Ancient Volcanoes of Great Britain*. The latter book was published after G. P. Scrope's book entitled *Volcanoes: their phenomena, share in the structure and composition of the Earth's surface, and relation to its internal forces, with catalogue of all known volcanoes* in which he established that most of the volcanoes of Earth are distributed in discrete belts.

Petrology is usually regarded as having roots in both mineralogy and geology because rocks are both geological units and mineral associations. Information on the chemical composition of rocks has also been valuable in the development of petrological concepts. As early as 1861, J. Roth introduced a chemical classification of rocks, and in the late nineteenth and early twentieth centuries many methods of manipulating chemical data, and chemical classifications of rocks, were proposed (e.g. Loewinson-Lessing 1899; Cross, Iddings, Pirsson & Washington 1903; Osann 1919; Niggli 1920; von Wolff 1922). During the past century, significant improvements have been made in the methods used in the chemical analysis of silicate materials, and quantitative chemical data are now regarded as essential in discussing and solving many petrological problems. Experimental petrology also requires reliable chemical analyses of rocks, minerals and glasses.

The twentieth century

During the twentieth century there has been a huge increase in the number of people employed in the search for ore deposits, and in mapping and studying the rocks of the Earth. Drilling on land and beneath the oceans, collecting and processing geophysical, geochemical, tectonic and petrological data, interpreting aerial photographs and images obtained from artificial satellites, have all enhanced our perception of the surface of our planet as a mosaic of interacting discrete units. Alfred Lothar Wegener's (1915) book on *The Origin of Continents and Oceans* seems to have provided the leaven that made petrologists and others question the concept that the continents were immutably fixed in their positions. At first, workers were reluctant to accept Wegener's hypothesis because he envisaged the continents plowing through the relatively strong rocks of the oceanic crust. In the 1920s, Argand (1924), Du Toit (1927) and Holmes (1929) were the main advocates of *continental drift*: however, in the 1950s general interest in continental drift was revived with the publication by E. Irving (1956) and S. K. Runcorn (1956) of paleomagnetic data that substantiated the concept that drift had occurred between North America and Europe. Harry Hammond Hess introduced the concept of *sea-floor spreading* (cf. Dietz 1961 and Hess 1962), and in 1963 Vine and Matthews showed how the pattern of magnetic anomalies characteristic of the floor of the oceans could be related to the concept of sea-floor spreading. Late in the 1960s the hypotheses of continental drift and sea-floor spreading, together with the concepts of transform faults (cf. Wilson 1965a) and the underthrusting of oceanic lithosphere, were all combined to form the *plate tectonics hypothesis* (cf. Isacks & Molnar 1969; Le Pichon 1968; Mckenzie & Morgan 1969; Sykes 1969). In 1973, Le Pichon, Francheteau and Bonnin published their outstanding synthesis of this hypothesis.

A number of books that strongly influenced the development of igneous petrology were published during the first half of the twentieth century. These works included a number of general books on igneous petrology, such as: Alfred Harker (1909) *The Natural Histroy of Igneous Rocks*: Reginald Daly (1914) *Igneous Rocks and their Origin*; H. Rosenbusch and A. Osann (1923) *Elemente der Gesteinslehre*; G. W. Tyrrell (1926) *The Principles of Petrology*; S. J. Shand (1927) *Eruptive Rocks*; Reginald Daly (1933) *Igneous Rocks and the Depths of the Earth*; A. Rittmann (1936) *Vulkane und ihre Tatigkeit*; P. Niggli (1937) *Das Magma und seine Produkte*; T. F. W. Barth, C. W. Correns and P. Eskola (1939) *Die Entstehung der Gesteine; Ein Lehrbuch der Petrogenese*; F. J. Turner and J. V. Verhoogen (1951) *Igneous and Metamorphic Petrology*; T. F. W. Barth (1952) *Theoretical Petrology*; and a number of books on petrography, such as J. P. Iddings (1909) *Igneous rocks: Composition, Texture and Classification, Description and Occurrence*; A. Johannsen (1931–38) *A Descriptive Petrography of the Igneous Rocks* (Vols 1–4); and W. E. Tröger (1935) *Spezielle Petrographie der Eruptivgesteine*. These books are important because they synthesized the vast corpus of petrological writings that were then available, and in so doing revealed an array of petrological similarities and anomalies that would not otherwise have been readily perceived.

During the second half of the twentieth century there has been an information explosion in igneous petrology. Much of the new data has been gathered by multidisciplinary research programmes such as the *Upper Mantle Project*, the *Deep Sea Drilling Project* and the *Geodynamics Project*. These projects have demonstrated the close relationships that occur between particular igneous rocks and the various tectonic environments found on Earth. The data and materials obtained from the programmes designed to explore the Solar System have also provided many new insights of importance to petrology, particularly with regard to the nature of the processes that operated during the early stages in the evolution of the planets. This research has also established that plate tectonic activity is not a prerequisite for the evolution of magmatic rocks. The extraordinarily detailed petrographic geochemical and experimental studies carried out on the lunar rocks (cf. Taylor 1982) has had an important impact on petrology. For example, few Earth rocks had ever been examined in the same detail. This led to the *Basaltic Volcanism Study Project* (BVSP 1981) and the publication of a comparative study of basaltic volcanism on the terrestrial planets.

Pioneering petrological research is still being produced. For example, in 1969 Morris and Richard Viljoen published the first detailed petrographic and chemical descriptions of an important new suite of volcanic rocks that contained ultramafic members. The Viljoen brothers called these lavas with high MgO, high CaO: Al_2O_3 and low K_2O and TiO_2 contents, *komatiites*, after the Komati river valley in the Barberton Mountain Land of southern Africa where rocks of this suite crop out. Professor H. H. Hess, an expert on ultramafic rocks, visited the Komati river valley in 1969 and after examining critical exposures of rocks of the Komatiitic suite '. . . remarked enthusiastically that the peridotitic Komatiites were unlike any other ultramafics of which he was aware; different from Alpine or ophiolite peridotites and undoubtedly representing an important new class of extrusive peridotite with associated basalt' (Viljoen & Viljoen 1982: 13). Komatiites are important because they demonstrate that the Earth has contained, and may still contain, ultramafic magmas. They also show that during some stages in the evolution of the Earth, particularly during the Archaean, ultramafic lavas and volcaniclastic rocks were extruded. Rocks of the komatiite suite are now known from many areas of our planet.

1.3 Internal structure and thermal properties of the Earth

Seismology was originally the study of earthquakes, and it is now generally regarded as the study of the origin and propagation of elastic waves in planetary bodies. Such studies have revealed that the Earth is composed of three main layers, or shells (i.e. core, mantle and crust). The innermost layer is the core, and in 1914 Beno Gutenberg determined that the core–mantle boundary was at a depth of 2900 km. This boundary is now known as the Gutenberg discontinuity. Another major discontinuity was discovered in 1909 by Andrija Mohorovičić and

Table 1.3.1 The layers within the Earth (adapted from Bullen 1963)

Earth layers		Depth range (km)	
Crust	A	0–33*	Heterogeneous crust
	Mohorovičić discontinuity		
	B	33–400	Upper mantle
Mantle	C	400–1050	Transition zone ⎫
	D	1050–2900	Lower mantle ⎬ Deep Mantle
	Gutenberg discontinuity		
	E	2900–4980	Outer core (liquid)
Core	F	4980–5150	Transition zone
	G	5150–6370	Inner core (solid)

* The oceans average 3.9 km in thickness. The oceanic crust is usually between 5 and 8 km thick; and continent crust is generally between 25 and 90 km thick.

it separates the crust from the mantle. It is known as the Mohorovičić (Moho., or M.) discontinuity, and it is at a depth of approximately 35 km beneath the continents and 7 km beneath the ocean floor. In more recent times, Keith Bullen (1963) and others have divided the Earth into the seven layers shown in Table 1.3.1. The density of the rock-materials within each of these Earth shells increases with depth, and at each of the major seismic discontinuities there is a distinct change in the density of the rock-materials. At the Gutenberg discontinuity, for example, density is believed to increase from 5600 kg/m^3 at the bottom of the mantle to 10 000 kg/m^3 in the outer core. These variations in density result from either changes in bulk chemical composition and/or changes in the phases that are present. The Moho. discontinuity marks a change in chemical composition, and its nature will be discussed further in section 1.10; whereas the discontinuity at approximately 400 km probably occurs because olivine, the main phase in the upper mantle, becomes unstable at the pressure (14 GPa or 140 kb) encountered at this depth. Pressure or stress is measured in pascals (Pa) in the SI system and one pascal is equal to a force of one newton (N) per m^2. A gigapascal (GPa) is 10^{9}Pa, and ten kilobars (kb) are equal to one GPa.

According to Bott (1971: 176), the study of thermal processes within the Earth is one of the most speculative branches of geophysics. However, both igneous petrogenesis and tectonophysics (the study of the forces responsible for the movement and deformation of the crust of a planet) require data on the movement and distribution of heat within planetary bodies. Most

Table 1.3.2 Possible layers within the Moon (cf. Taylor 1982: 360)

Moon layers	Depth range (km)
Extensively fractured crust	0–20
Competent crust	20–70*
Upper mantle	70–480
Lower mantle	480–1100
Outer core (attenuating zone)	1100–1400
Inner core	1400–1738

* The far-side crust is approximately 10 km thicker than the near-side crust.

of the heat energy generated within the Earth at the present time is derived from the radioactive decay of long-lived isotopes; however, during the early stages of the history of the Earth other sources of heat may have been significant. According to Brown (1982a: 150) heat-flow measurements at the surface of the Earth vary from 30 to over 200 mW/m^2 (milliwatts per square metre), with a global mean of 60 mW/m^2. This gives an integrated heat-flow through the surface of the Earth of 10^{21} J/a (joules per year). The largest area of anomalously high heat-flow is at present over the East Pacific Rise, and it coincides with an area of rapid, presentday, sea-floor spreading. Other areas of presentday sea-floor spreading also show anomalously high heat-flow values; and it has been estimated that more than half of the presentday heat loss of the Earth takes place along active mid-ocean ridge-rift systems. Detailed studies have shown a systematic decrease in heat-flow values extending outwards from the mid-ocean ridge-rift systems (i.e. heat-flow is usually inversely proportional to the square root of the age of the oceanic lithosphere). Implicit in the plate tectonics model is the concept that hot mantle-derived magma is emplaced into the mid-ocean rifts: it cools, congeals, and continues to cool as it gradually migrates away from the ridge-rift system; and it is eventually resorbed into the mantle at convergent plate margins. This model also suggests that the origin, evolution and destruction of the ocean floor is part of a more extensive convective system that operates mainly within the mantle. Convection is essentially motion produced by buoyancy, with lighter material rising and denser material sinking.

Oxburgh (1981: 38) has compared convection in the Earth with convection in a vat of molasses that has a nearly uniform internal temperature distribution, and a fan blowing cold air across the upper surface. The upper layer is chilled. It becomes more dense and viscous and it sinks; however, the manner in which it sinks is controlled by the strength, or mechanical coherence, of the upper layer. This layer would generally slide into the vat as a coherent sheet and new hot material would well up to replace it at the surface. In order to explain the behaviour of continents one needs a more elaborate model because continental crust is thicker and more buoyant than ocean crust. As most of the major plates of the Earth contain both oceanic and continental domains, the process of subduction tends to operate efficiently when oceanic lithosphere forms the leading edge of the plate, but when continental lithosphere reaches this position subduction stops, and there is a planet-wide readjustment of plate motions.

The thermal characteristics of the continental lithosphere are quite different from those of the younger oceanic lithosphere. On a broad scale, the continental crust acts like a thick thermal blanket. It also contains an upper layer that has gradually acquired a relatively high concentration of heat-producing isotopes such as ^{40}K, ^{232}Th, ^{235}U and ^{238}U. In detail, the present-day heat-flow patterns of the continents are remarkably variable and complex. This is well illustrated by the map of *Terrestial heat flow in Europe* (Cermak & Hurtig 1979) which shows that in countries such as Italy heat-flow values may vary from less than 30 mW/m^2 to over 110 mW/m^2.

Some volcanic activity occurs in discrete areas within lithospheric plates, and such areas (e.g. Hawaii and Yellowstone in the USA and Jebel Marra in the Western Sudan) have been called *hot spots*. The concept of lithospheric plates moving over mantle hot spots has been advanced by Wilson (1965b) and others to explain the origin of the Hawaiian Archipelago and other linear chains of volcanic islands and seamounts. Morgan (1971: 42) proposed that these hot spots are 'manifestations of convection in the lower mantle' and that heat is brought up to the base of the lithosphere by 'deep mantle plumes'. It has been suggested that these deep mantle plumes originate in, or near, the boundary layer between the liquid outer core and the lower mantle.

Small planets such as Mercury and the Moon usually cool rapidly, and internally-driven magmatic activity is thus relatively short-lived. The thermal characteristics of the Earth have also changed with time. In the early Archaean there was a massive input of heat generated by processes, such as accretion, the formation of the core, and the decay of radioactive isotopes with both short and long half-lives. Subsequently

Table 1.3.3 Estimated temperatures and pressures within the Earth

Depth (km)	Temperature of rocks beneath oceans (°C)	Temperature of rocks beneath continental shields (°C)	Pressure Kilobars (kb)	Gigapascals (GPa)
50	860	570	14.5	1.45
100	1300	950	31	3.1
200	1580	1300	68	6.8
300	1700	1475	105	10.5
400	1775	1600	142	14.2
500	1830	1710	181	18.1
1000	2025	2025	395	39.5
1500	2240	2240	620	62.0
2000	2435	2435	868	86.8
2500	2635	2635	1126	112.6
3000	3000	3000	1440	144.0

there has been a steady decline in the amount of heat produced by the decay of radioactive isotopes: the amount is less than one-seventh of that produced when the Earth was first formed. Estimates of the mean temperatures and pressures that are currently expected at different depths within the mantle of the Earth are given in Table 1.3.3. Such information is of inestimable value in developing models that attempt to account for the origin, movement and evolution of magmas generated in the mantle.

1.4 The nature of magmas

Magma is essentially hot, naturally occurring mobile rock-forming material that is generated within a planet, natural satellite, or other cosmic body of broadly similar nature. An aura of uncertainty surrounds the term because magmas only exist beneath the surface. When extruded they not only become lavas and/or fragmental deposits, but they also release a variety of *fugitive constituents* that escape into the atmosphere and/or hydrosphere, or into space on the small airless planets. For example, some of the lunar lavas (i.e. Specimen 15016 which is a porphyritic vesicular basalt collected on the Apollo 15 mission) contain spherical cavities that formed around bubbles of gas. The composition of these fugitive constituents is now unknown, but it is most tantalizing to know that they were once part of a lunar magma. Shand (1950: 34) defined fugitive constituents as substances that occur in a magma before freezing sets in but are normally lost as it congeals. Magmas properly belong to the realm of theoretical petrology (cf. Barth 1962a). They are the most important concept in igneous petrology, yet thay cannot be examined in the field, collected, studied or directly experimented with.

During the twentieth century the concept of a *primary magma* has gradually been refined. The term now means a magma that has a chemical composition that has not changed since it was generated within the interior of a planet. In the past this term was regarded as being synonymous with *parental magma*, and both terms were mainly used to describe those magmas that produced large quantities of widely distributed rock that was of essentially uniform chemical composition. The term parental magma is now taken to refer to any magma from which one or more others have been derived. It is thus not necessarily a primary magma. In 1960, Kuno proposed that the compositions of different primary magmas were essentially controlled by the depths at which they were generated (or the depths at which they equilibrated with the essential phases in the upper mantle). This concept was supported by the pioneering experimental work of Yoder and Tilley (1962) who demonstrated that the thermal divides that separated different basaltic melts shift with changing pressures (see section 7.7). O'Hara (1965, 1968), however, revealed that the chemical compositions of the liquids in equilibrium with peridotites (i.e. upper mantle rock) at high pressures do not correspond to the compositions of the common basaltic lavas which at that time were regarded as congealed primary magmas. He explained this conundrum by suggesting that the chemical compositions of the primary magmas changed while in transit to the surface. Such changes were the result of the crystallization and removal of significant quantities of minerals, such as olivine. In Chapter 5 it will be argued that the chemical characteristics, that enable one to distinguish between the various types of basaltic rocks, are mainly determined by partial melting processes at various depths within the upper mantle; but it will also be argued that most of these rocks congealed from magmas that were modified in composition en route to the surface. It is important to search for and find primary magmas because they are uniquely able to provide substantial data about the region where they originated. The term primary magma should, however, be used with care, because as the authors of the *Basaltic Volcanism Study Project* (1981: 525) state, 'the unequivocal identification of a primary magma in any given tectonic environment or geographic region on the Earth is notoriously difficult'.

The *Basaltic Volcanism Study Project* (1981: 500–13) also demonstrated how a set of volcanic rocks can be used to determine the chemical and modal composition of the interior of a planet; and the following is an abridged account of this procedure. First of all those rocks that represent quenched liquids are identified. If the rocks are glassy or uniformly fine-grained, it is generally assumed that they represent quenched liquids; however, if the rocks contain larger crystals that crystallized out of the magma (phenocrysts) or crystals that are foreign to the magma (xenocrysts), then special experimental studies may be required to determine the composition of the liquid that was quenched to form these rocks. Once the quenched liquids have been identified, an attempt is made to discover whether they can be related to one another by low-pressure processes, or by processes that operated at lower pressures than those characteristic of the source region. If the liquids are so related, then the parental magma of these associated magmas is identified, and experiments are conducted to determine whether or not the parental magma is a primary magma.

It is usually reasonable to assume that primary magmas are in equilibrium with the essential minerals in the source region where they were generated; thus if one takes a liquid of the same composition as a particular primary magma and determines which mineral, or minerals, are the first to crystallize (i.e. liquidus minerals) over a range of pressures and temperatures, one is then able to identify some, or all, of the minerals (and their compositions) left as residues in the source region. Such an experiment also provides one with the ambient pressures and temperatures that are characteristic of the source region. This concept is illustrated by Fig. 1.4.1. which shows the different minerals which are first to crystal-

lize from a melt of basaltic composition over a wide range of temperatures and pressures. The figure also demonstrates that experimental petrology, by itself, is often unable to supply unique answers to the question of the physical and chemical character of a source region where primary magmas are generated. In this hypothetical example, the particular primary magma may have been generated in any one of five different physical environments. These environments are: (a) between 0.0 and 1.2 GPa (0–12 kb) and T_1 and T_2 leaving olivine in the residue; (b) at 1.2 GPa (12 kb) and T_2 leaving both olivine and clinopyroxene in the residue; (c) between 1.2 and 2.5 GPa (12–25 kb) and T_2 and T_3 leaving clinopyroxene in the residue; (d) at 2.5 GPa (25 kb) and T_3 leaving both clinopyroxene and garnet in the residue; or (e) above 2.5 GPa (25 kb) and above T_3 leaving garnet in the residue. The material used in Fig. 1.4.1 was lunar basalt, chosen because it has a relatively simple chemical composition compared to most igneous rocks from Earth.

Petrology has gleaned information from many disciplines, and it is now generally agreed that most Cenozoic (0–65 Ma) basaltic rocks from Earth were derived from magmas generated by partial melting in the upper mantle, and also that the mantle source rocks contained highly magnesian olivines (Fo_{94-90}). It is usually acknowledged that the primarily magmas responsible for the evolution of these basaltic rocks must have contained sufficient magnesium to have equilibrated at high pressures with olivines as magnesian as Fo_{90}, and they must have also been capable of equilibrating at high pressures with other residual phases such as orthopyroxene and/or garnet (cf. BVSP 1981: 508–9).

Magmas are generated, they move, evolve and their physical and chemical properties change; however, at present there are only very crude methods of directly monitoring these changes beneath the surface of a planet. Shaw (1980: 253) has declared that 'global seismicity is intimately and quantitatively tied up with the Earth's igneous history'; and that there is possibly 'a direct proportionality between mean annual volumes of magma ascent from melting sources in the mantle and mean annual volumetric moments of all earthquakes'. In a simple model of the evolving Earth in which time is contracted, the whole planet might be regarded as a huge heat engine that operates by the subtle interaction of physical and chemical processes

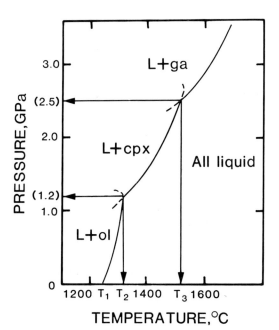

Fig. 1.4.1 Model liquidus mineralogy of a typical mare basalt at various temperatures and pressures. Adapted from BVSP (1981: p. 509). cpx = clinopyroxene, ga. = garnet, L = liquid and ol. = olivine.

that transform thermal energy into mechanical energy; and magma is a lubricating and possibly a driving fluid (cf. Oxburgh 1980: 161).

There is, however, irrefutable direct evidence that materials with the physical properties of magma exist within the Earth. The high attenuation of S-waves beneath some central volcanoes has, for example, been interpreted as indicating the presence of magma chambers. S-waves are seismic body waves that are propagated by a shearing motion that involves oscillation perpendicular to the direction of propagation. Such waves do not travel through liquids and they are attenuated by partially molten materials. Seismic studies in north-east Iceland have, for example, indicated the presence of a 4 km deep and 1.5 km broad magma chamber that lies 3 km beneath the caldera of Krafla volcano (Einarsson 1978: 187). This high-level volcanic focus has been studied through an inflation–deflation cycle, and detailed seismic monitoring has revealed that at times of deflation magma flows laterally out of the magma chamber and moves along fissures at a velocity of between 0.4 and 0.5 m/s (Einarsson & Brandsdottir 1980: 160). In September 1977 a most instructive event occurred. A batch of magma moved out from the magma chamber and encountered boreholes in the Namafjall geothermal field, and within 20 minutes 26 m^3 of basaltic magma (SiO_2 = 50.0 per cent, Na_2O = 2.34 per cent and K_2O = 0.37 per cent) moved up the 1138 m borehole and erupted. The pyroclastic rock that formed was extremely vesicular thus demonstrating that the magma contained fugitive constituents; and it cooled rapidly to form a glass in which were set a few crystals of olivine, plagioclase and augite. Larsen, Gronvold and Thorarinssen (1979: 710) estimated that the rock congealed at a temperature of between 1153° and 1158 °C.

Yoder (1976: 44–6) has reviewed the seismic evidence relating to the source of magmas within the Earth, and he (p. 55) concluded that 'magma may be generated in some broad regions extending generally from 50 to 170 km in depth', and in other local areas 'the source of magma may be as deep as 300–400 km'.

Viscosity

A chemical analysis of a magma does not describe it completely because magmas of the same bulk chemical composition have different physical properties at different pressures and temperatures. This is readily understood because differences in pressure and temperature may change not only the nature and abundance of the various phases present, but also the viscosity, density and structure (polymerization) of the magma. According to Williams and McBirney (1979: 20) viscosity is 'the most important physical property of magmas'. It is particularly important: (a) in the processes that separate magmas from the phases that remain in the source region; (b) in the ascent and emplacement of magmas; (c) in magmatic differentiation; and (d) in the diffusion of elements within magmas. Viscosity (η, eta) is the property of a fluid to offer internal resistance to flow, and it is often described as *internal friction*. Specifically, it is the ratio of shear stress to the rate of shear strain, and it is measured in newton seconds per square metre (Ns/m^2) (SI units) or poise (c.g.s. units). One poise is equal to 0.1 newton seconds per square metre. At 20°C glycerol has a viscosity of approximately 1.0 newton seconds per square metre (10 poises). Viscosity data are obtained from the study of lavas in the field, and also from laboratory measurements of both natural and synthetic materials. Such studies have demonstrated that in melts of the common igneous rocks, variations in viscosity are mainly due to changes in temperature, or differences in composition. Viscosity generally decreases with increasing temperature and pressure, and also with a lowering of the silica content of a melt. Scarfe and Hamilton (1980: 319) have studied the viscosities of the melts of a series of comagmatic lavas that have different SiO_2 contents. They discovered that in wholly liquid melts, the comendites (73.4 per cent SiO_2) have a higher viscosity than the hawaiites (47.8 per cent SiO_2), that 'at 1300° there is a difference of three orders of magnitude (10^2–10^5 poises) between the viscosities of the commendite and hawaiite'.

The *mare basalts* of the Moon have relatively low SiO_2 contents (37–49 per cent SiO_2); and experiments have shown that they extruded as extremely fluid liquids with viscosities of between 0.5 and 1.0 Ns/m^2 (5–10 poises). Such values are approximately an order of magnitude lower than those normally found in basalt flows on Earth. Taylor (1982: 331) has reported that the viscosity of the mare flows was 'comparable to that of heavy engine oil at room temperature'.

In order to understand the changes that occur in the viscosity of melts of the common igneous rocks, one has to examine the structure of these melts. It is easy to understand what the term structure means when discussing minerals because they consist of a systematic arrangement of atoms in a three-dimensional array. In the common silicate minerals, four oxygen ions are bonded to each silicon cation to form a tetrahedral configuration (that is the silicon–oxygen tetrahedron). Each oxygen ion also has the potential of being bonded to another silicon cation thus forming the characteristic chain, ring, sheet and framework structures of silicate minerals. The linking together of silicon–oxygen tetrahedra is usually called *polymerization*. X-ray and neutron diffraction studies have demonstrated that silicon–oxygen tetrahedra exist in melts of the common igneous rocks, and also that crystal-like, long-range (2 nanometre) ordering may persist within them (cf. Konnert & Karle 1972). It is now possible to construct models of the average structure of a magma of a particular composition at a given pressure and temperature (Hess 1980: 4). If one compares the structure of a number of melts of common igneous rocks with different SiO_2 contents, one discovers that as the SiO_2 content increases, the silicon – oxygen tetrahedra become more polymerized: network structures form, and increase both in size and complexity.

An examination of the structure of the melts described by Scarfe and Hamilton (1980) shows that the ratio of nonbridging oxygens to tetrahedrally coordinated cations in the hawaiitic melt is 0.75 as compared to 0.06 in the silica-rich comenditic melt. Comenditic melts are thus more polymerized and more viscous than hawaiitic melts. Measurements have also shown that rhyolitic melts of high SiO_2 content are more polymerized and viscous than andesitic melts of intermediate SiO_2 content, and the latter are more polymerized and viscous than basaltic that contain even less SiO_2. Ultramafic liquids, such as magnesium-rich komatiitic liquids, usually contain less SiO_2 and are significantly less viscous than basaltic liquids at the same temperature (cf. Nisbet 1982: 510) These interesting liquids will be discussed in Chapter 11.

Experiments have demonstrated that increases in temperature, and pressure, acting independently or together, can lower the viscosities of melts of the common igneous rocks, such as rhyolites, andesites, basalts and nephelinites (cf. Kushiro 1980: Scarfe 1981). Figure 1.4.2 shows the decrease in viscosity that would be

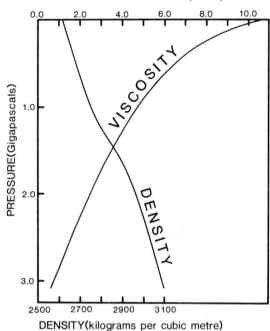

VISCOSITY(newtons seconds per sq.metre)

DENSITY(kilograms per cubic metre)

Fig. 1.4.2 Viscosity and density variations in an-olivine tholeiitic basalt melt from Hawaii. Adapted from Kushiro (1980: 116).

expected in an olivine tholeiitic basalt melt that was just kept at the temperature at which it remained wholly liquid (i.e. liquidus temperature), and pressure was increased from 0.0 GPa (0.0 kb) to 3.0 GPa (30 kb). At the surface the effective viscosity of such a melt is over 10 Ns/m² (100 poises), whereas at 3.0 GPa (30 kb) the viscosity is approximately 0.8 Ns/m² (8 poises). Yoder (1976: 175) has remarked that at high pressures (greater than 2.0 GPa) the effective viscosity of tholeiitic magma would be so low that once an interconnecting liquid network was established, the magma would 'literally squirt out of a containing rock under stresses of a few bars' (1 bar = 10^5 pascals).

At temperatures below the beginning of crystallization, the effective viscosity of a magma may increase with time (cf. Murase & McBirney 1973). If a magma is left undisturbed, the effective viscosity may continue to increase for many hours before reaching a steady value. According to Williams and McBirney (1979: 22–3), such increases in effective viscosity are usually the result of increases both in the proportion of crystals suspended in the magma and in the polymerization of the magma.

Volatile components

Minor changes in the chemical composition of a magma, such as in the abundance of the volatile components, or oxides of the alkali metals, may have significant effects on the physical characteristics (i.e. viscosity, polymerization and density) of the magma. The volatile components in a magma are those chemical components, such as H_2O and CO_2, that have vapour pressures that are sufficiently high for them to be concentrated in any gaseous phase that may occur. Hess (1980: 14) has shown that in a silica glass traces of H_2O are able to lower the viscosity by one order of magnitude, and that 'simply touching a pristine surface with a finger deposits sufficient alkali to cause the contaminated spot to devitrify'. If water is dissolved in a silicate melt, it increases the ratio of nonbridging anions to tetrahedrally coordinated cations, thus the melt becomes less polymerized and less viscous. Studies of: (a) fluid inclusions in minerals, (b) the volatile components found in common igneous rocks, and (c) the gases released during volcanic eruptions, all demonstrate that water and carbon dioxide are the most abundant volatile components in the igneous materials found at the surface of the Earth. Most papers that have examined the role of volatile components in the origin and evolution of magmas have emphasized the effect of H_2O in lowering the melting temperatures of the rock-forming minerals, and thus enhancing the possibility of magma generation by partial melting in the lower crust and upper mantle of the Earth. Tuttle and Bowen (1958) demonstrated that in the presence of H_2O, many crustal rocks begin to melt at temperatures and pressures that are readily attainable in the deeper parts of the continental crust. This study also revealed that such magmas are likely to be rhyolitic (granitic) in composition.

Studies of melts of igneous rocks have revealed that the solubility of H_2O increases with increasing pressure until a maximum value is reached; and that solubility is greater in rhyolitic melts than in andesitic melts, and greater in andesitic than in basaltic melts. For example, at a pressure of 1.0 GPa (10 kb) and a temperature of between 1000 and 1200 °C, a rhyolitic melt can dissolve approximately 21.0 wt% H_2O, whereas under the same physical conditions a basaltic melt can only dissolve approximately 14.0 wt% H_2O (cf. Sood 1981: 143). At high pressures the solubility of H_2O in ultramafic

melts is also very high; for example, above 2.0 GPa (20 kb) diopside and fosterite can dissolve over 20 wt% H_2O. CO_2 is generally considered to have a low solubility in silicate magmas at low pressures; however, Eggler (1973) and others have shown that at pressures above 1.5 Gpa (15 kb), significant amounts of CO_2 are soluble in silicate melts. For example, approximately 9.0 wt% CO_2 is soluble in olivine-bearing nephelinite melts at 3.0 GPa (30 kb). It is thus anticipated that if H_2O and CO_2 are available, they should both be highly soluble in the magmas normally generated in the upper mantle of the Earth.

Figure 1.4.2 also shows how the densities of olivine tholeiitic basalt glasses that congealed in the pressure range 0.0 to 3.0 GPa (30 kb) increased from 2830 kg/m^3 (2.85 g/cm^3) to 3080 kg/m^3 (3.08 g/cm^3: cf. Kushiro 1980: 117 and Kushiro et al., 1976:6355). Hess (1980: 117) has discussed the origin of these pressure-induced changes in the density of glasses and magmas. He states that the nature of the structural changes within a magma are not fully understood at present, because 'most observations of the melt and glass of jadeite and albite compositions suggest that the structural changes are mainly due to the shift of Al from 4-fold to 6-fold coordination; however, Raman spectroscopy on the jadeite glass does not support such coordination change, but suggests a cristobalite $\rightarrow$ coesite type structural change'. Cristobalite and coesite are polymorphs of SiO_2. Coesite is the high-pressure polymorph and it has a density of 2920 kg/m³ (2.92 g/cm³).

1.5 Magma generation

Many mechanisms are capable of producing primary magmas, and at different times during the evolution of a planet, particular mechanisms are dominant. At present on Earth, some of these mechanisms are specific to particular tectonic environments (for example, zones of plate convergence), whereas others are not. Immediately after the accretion of the terrestrial planets, their heat flow was much higher than at present. The lunar rocks, for example, contain convincing geochemical evidence of an early large-scale differentiation of that planet which resulted in the evolution of an Al, K, Th and U enriched highland crust. It has been estimated that the amount of heat required during this initial differentiation of the Moon is over three orders of magnitude more than that used to generate all the later mare basalts (cf. Taylor 1982: 243). Many petrologists believe that at the time of the initial differentiation, an outer layer of the Moon was melted to a depth of more than 400 km, and the initial differentiation took place in a *magma ocean*. At present the Jovian satellite Io has a mean global heat flow of approximately 2000 mW/m²which is over 30 times greater than the present mean global heat flow of Earth (cf. Beatty et al. 1981: 158). The high heat flow prolific volcanic activity on Io are examined in section 1.9, and it is proposed that *tidal heating* is probably the most important mechanism for generating primary magmas on this the most volcanically active planet in the Solar System.

Heat production within the Earth has declined steadily during the past 4.5 Ga. At present the crust and mantle are essentially composed of solid crystalline rocks. The low-velocity zone occurs in the mantle at depths of between 60 and 250 km, and it is the only extensive body of rock at near-melting-point temperatures. In the low-velocity zone there are three main methods of generating magma: (a) adding heat at constant pressure; (b) lowering the pressure at constant temperature; or (c) lowering the initial melting temperatures of the mantle rock by adding suitable materials such as volatile components. Most discussions of melting implicitly assume that it arises as the result of the addition of heat. At present, radioactivity is the major source of internal energy within the Earth. If the heat-producing nuclides were evenly distributed throughout a non-convecting mantle, one would expect volcanoes, which are the surface expression of the magma-producing processes, to have an essentially random distribution. However, at present most of the volcanoes of Earth are confined to a few relatively narrow belts that girdle the planet, as is shown in Fig. 1.5.1. This distribution pattern supports the concept that at the present time the Earth contains a convecting mantle.

When considering the physical nature of the upper mantle it is important to note that thermal conductivity changes with temperature (Lubimova 1958), and that within the Earth this physical property is calculated to reach a minimum in the uppermost mantle (70–100 km). Such a decrease in thermal conductivity may result in the accumulation of heat, and also assist in maintaining the low-velocity zone at a near-melting-point temperature (cf. McBirney 1963a: 6327).

Decompression melting results either from the relatively rapid upward movement of mantle material, or from a lowering of the lithostatic load that normally constrains mantle rocks. Convection within the mantle, or the ascent of a diapir (see section 1.6), both produce the first type of decompression melting. There is considerable evidence in support of the concept that convection is at present active within the mantle beneath oceans such as the North Atlantic. It is anticipated that the materials participating in the upward movement of such a convective system would undergo adiabatic decompression and this is likely to produce a moderately high degree of melting (cf. Tarney et al. 1980: 193). Adiabatic decompression means that decompression occurs without heat entering or leaving the system. The second type of decompression melting may occur when pressure in the uppermost mantle is relieved by arching, or faulting, in the overlying rocks (cf. Yoder 1952). Such processes may locally promote partial melting, and they may also generate local concentrations of volatile constituents from the underlying mantle (cf. Bailey 1964).

The influx of volatile components into essentially anhydrous rocks, that are at near-melting-point temperatures, reduces the melting temperature so that partial melting is likely to occur. This type of melting behaviour is well described for the simple system albite-H_2O (Burnham & Davis 1974) and albite-H_2O-CO_2 (Bohlen et al. 1982). On Earth this method of generating magma is important in areas of active subduction where one lithospheric plate descends beneath another, and volatile components are released from the descending slab of lithosphere (see Ch. 6). The introduced volatile components usually carry heat and this also aids partial melting. Bailey (1978: 11) has examined the general question of the degassing of the mantle, and has proposed that 'persistent and extensive fluxing of gases through a preferred channel system' (such as a continental rift system) 'must ultimately lead to thermal decomposition of volatile-bearing minerals, and melting'. He and others claim that the gases released from the deep mantle are likely to be rich in carbon (that is CO,CH_4), fluorine and chlorine, and also to be strongly reducing. It is proposed that in the upper mantle in areas of active subduction, and in the lower

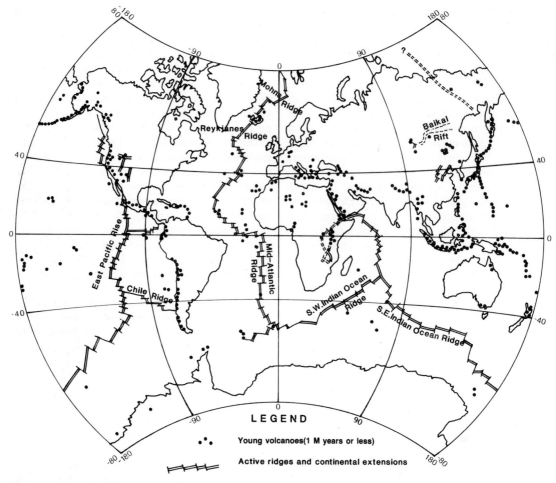

Fig. 1.5.1 The distribution of quaternary volcanic activity on Earth, including the belts of presently active ocean-floor spreading. Adapted from Lowman and Frey 1979: 30, 40 and 42; and Morris et al. 1979.

crust in areas of continental shield rocks, the gases derived from the deep mantle are likely to be oxidized to produce H_2O and CO_2. One would thus anticipate that in different tectonic environments the gases from the deep mantle would be oxidized at different depths.

Spera (1981) has discussed the nature of the low-viscosity fluids that are believed to produce metasomatism within the mantle of the Earth (cf. Ch. 13). He claims (p. 57) that these 'mantle metasomatic fluids' are rich in Fe^{3+}, Ti, K, Nb, REE, C, H, Cl, F, O and other large ion lithophile elements; and that they are likely to ascend isothermally at velocities of the order of 1 to 10 m/s, decompress, and transport both heat and mass. It is estimated that these mantle metasomatic fluids could transport approximately 85 petajoules (8.5×10^{16}J) per year. According to Spera (1981: 62), this amount of heat would be able to generate about 4.4×10^{11} kg of basaltic magma, and this is approximately the amount of 'alkaline magma' that is considered to be produced on Earth each year.

1.6 Melting processes

According to Yoder (1976: 105) there are four main physicochemical means of producing large volumes of relatively homogeneous magma: (a) batch melting; (b) fractional melting; (c) zone melting; and (d) disequilibrium melting. Yoder illustrated the concepts of batch and fractional melting by examining what might be called *the simple mantle-rock system*, forsterite (Fo) – diopside (Di) – pyrope (Py) at 4.0 GPa (40 kb). In the following discussion this system is regarded as an ideal ternary system, and composition M, which is plotted in Fig. 1.6.1, is considered to represent the composition of the rocks of the upper mantle of the Earth. If the temperature of a solid of composition M is raised to 1670 °C, melting begins and a liquid of composition E is produced; E is regarded as a eutectic which is the lowest melting point of any ratio of components in a system. In this system, E is the lowest melting point of the components forsterite, diopside and pyrope. At a eutectic, such as the one shown in Fig. 1.6.1, the addition or removal of heat produces an increase or decrease, respectively, in the proportion of liquid to solid phases. Such changes do not change the temperature of the system or the composition of any phases, including the liquid. Continued melting produces more liquid of composition E. The bulk composition of the solid phases moves towards R, and in so doing passes through successive compositions on the line MR. When approximately 30 per cent of the system is liquid, the bulk composition of the solid phases reaches R,

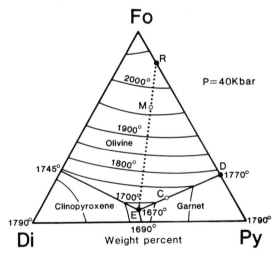

Fig. 1.6.1 The *simple mantle-rock system*, fosterite (Fo)–diopside (Di)–pyrope (Py) at 4.0 GPa (40 kb). E is the piercing-point composition. M is the estimated chemical composition of the upper mantle of the Earth. D is the composition of the liquid produced from the fractional melting of R. Adapted from Davis and Schairer 1965: 124; and Yoder 1976: 108.

and only two solid phases, garnet and forsterite, now remain in the system. The liquid (or magma) produced isothermally at 1670 °C may be removed either as a single batch or continuously as it is produced. Fractional melting, or fractional fusion, is the process whereby each infinitesimal amount of liquid is removed from the source rock as soon as it is formed. Such liquid is thus prevented from reacting further with the crystalline residue. The major element compositions of the initial magmas produced isothermally by either batch or fractional melting processes are identical to the eutectic composition; however, the trace element compositions of the magmas produced by the different melting processes may differ (cf. Yoder 1976: 110).

If the liquid in the system Fo – Di – Py is removed as it forms (i.e. fractional melting), then when it reaches R melting stops until the temperature is raised to 1770 °C. At this temperature, melting is resumed and the liquid has the composition D, and no liquid of intermediate composition is produced. This demonstrates that fractional melting can produce magmas of uniquely different composition from the same source region. If all of the initial liquid of E composition remains in contact with the residual solid phases (Fo and Py) and the temperature is raised, the composition of the liquid changes from E towards D. At C all the pyrope is melted, and with increasing temperature the composition of the liquid heads directly towards forsterite which is now the only remaining solid phase; whereas at M the whole system is liquid. It is thus demonstrated that a succession of liquid batches of different composition (i.e. from E via C to M) can be produced if the residual solid phases remain in equilibrium with an evolving liquid.

The system Fo – Di – Py at 4.0 GPa (40 kb) also demonstrates how large volumes of chemically homogeneous magma (i.e. 30 per cent liquid of composition E) can be produced. In natural systems this chemical homogeneity applies mainly to the major elements as trace element variations are often linked to the abundance of accessory phases such as phlogopite, richterite and apatite. According to Yoder (1976: 205) the melting behaviour of normal rocks from the upper mantle is essentially eutectic in character, and the first liquids form at the lowest temperature invariant point in the garnet peridotite system.

15

Zone melting

Zone melting is more than just an unconventional melting process. It was introduced by Harris (1957) as a method of concentrating the 'large ion lithophile elements' such as potassium. The term was originally used to describe an industrial process used in the purification of metals in which a zone of melting is passed along a bar of metal. The impurities are preferentially distributed into the liquid, and they are then swept along in the zone of melting as it moves from one end of the bar to the other. Harris (1957: 199) proposed that some magmas are generated deep within the mantle and, as they rise, the crystals at the top of such bodies of magma will be more soluble than those at the base because there is a drop in pressure from the bottom to the top of the magma body. If the composition of the magma is kept uniform by convection, then the magma will rise by solution-stoping with solid phases in the roof going into solution and equivalent amounts of material crystallizing at the base of the magma body. There should be little loss of heat, or diminution in the volume, of the magma if the mantle rocks are at their melting point. This is because the heat of solution of crystals at the top of the body is balanced by the heat of crystallization of the minerals deposited at the base of the magma. Harris (1957: 200) has also proposed that as a body of magma rises through the mantle by solution-stoping, the composition of the magma changes with the gradual introduction of those elements 'too large or too small, or differing too much in valency and bond type to replace the ions in the minerals being deposited, and not sufficiently abundant for their own mineral phases to crystallize'. The elements expected to concentrate in this manner include K, Rb, Cs, Ba, Pb, Zr, Th, U, Nb, Ta, P, C, H and Cl. Such elements are often called the *incompatible elements*. According to Cox et al. (1979: 31), an incompatible element is 'one which under given compositional conditions is excluded or largely excluded from the lattices of minerals crystallizing and therefore becomes concentrated in the liquid in a manner simply related to the amount of the original material crystallized'. An ideal incompatible element has a distribution coefficient, K^D (expressed as concentration of the element in the solid divided by concentration in the liquid), that approaches zero. The unique feature of zone melting is that it is able to concentrate incompatible elements from a large volume of essentially solid mantle material in a relatively small volume of magma.

A process called *wall-rock reaction* has many features in common with zone melting. It operates when a magma that is migrating towards the surface comes in contact with phases in the wall rocks with which it is not in chemical equilibrium. The magma melts and/or reacts with these phases thus modifying the composition of both the magma (i.e. contamination) and the enclosing wall rocks. During this reaction the incompatible elements present in the wall rocks may become preferentially concentrated in the magma.

Disequilibrium melting

All phases in a body of partially-molten rock from the upper mantle of the Earth are normally in elemental and isotopic equilibrium. Hart and Allègre (1980: 123) have, for example, estimated that if a body of mantle material (i.e. a diapir) was to rise through the upper mantle at a velocity of 0.1 m/a, it would only have to rise 4 km before 'complete intermineral equilibration' was established. Under the conditions normally prevailing in the upper mantle, it is likely that equilibrium is established within a diapir before significant amounts of magma are extracted. However, under special conditions, such as when a magma is rapidly generated and extracted from its source region, disequilibrium melting may occur.

It is thus proposed that a broad spectrum of different primary magmas can be produced by melting the normal upper mantle materials of the Earth, and that the exact composition of a particular magma essentially depends upon the amount of thermal energy available, the phases present at the site of melting, and the nature of the melting process. The foregoing discussion also illustrates the concept that a number of primary magmas of different chemical composition can originate from the same source region.

1.7 Movement and storage of magma

Volcanic eruptions imply that magma has moved through at least the uppermost layers of a planet, and seismic and other geophysical studies of volcanic areas, such as Hawaii, support this concept. Magma is transported at different velocities by a variety of mechanisms. It may, for example, rise as a large buoyant diapiric body of crystals and liquid, or it may be moved by a 'percolation process involving the evolution and interactions of transient conduit paths' that extend discontinuously from the source region to the surface (Shaw 1980: 205). When a rock begins to melt, the magma usually occupies a larger volume than the original source rock. This change in volume will eventually produce extensional rock failure in the source region. This is likely to result in an upward migration of liquid magma, because the normal gradients of pressure and stress in the source region are negative upwards, and liquid magma flow into regions of lower stress at greater speed than the surrounding deformable network of residual solid phases. A very small proportion of magma, dispersed as an interstitial phase in a rigid crystalline framework, might remain dynamically stable at depth. However, once a body of magma has segregated from the network of residual solid phases, it moves upwards by fracturing, or by deforming and moving aside the enveloping solid materials, or by solution-stoping.

The main forces that act within a planet and cause magma to rise are: (a) overburden squeeze; and (b) buoyancy (cf. Yoder 1976: 186–9). Overburden squeeze is considered to operate in brittle rocks in the lithospheres of planets. At any point X within the lithosphere of a planet there is normally a vertical pressure (or geostatic pressure) caused by the weight of overlying rocks. If a column of magma, with a lower mean density than the mean density of the overburden of rocks, was to form and extend from X to the surface, the magma in this column would be squeezed to the surface, 'and even to the summits of lofty volcanoes by the head of pressure due to the weight of the overlying rocks' (Holmes 1944: 478). Volcanologists (cf. Williams & McBirney 1979: 56) regard this model as too simplistic because it assumes that magma is able to stand in a long rigid-walled conduit; however, this model does reveal the nature of the process of overburden squeeze.

Buoyancy

Buoyancy is the upward thrust exerted on a body immersed in a fluid. For example, if a solid body of any shape and density is immersed in a fluid the buoyant force is the sum of the vectors of all the forces that the fluid exerts on the body. It is always upwards because the pressure underneath the body is greater than the pressure above it, whereas the pressures on the sides essentially cancel each other out. If the buoyant force is greater than the weight of an immersed body, the body will tend to move upwards; however, if the buoyant force is less than the weight of the body, the body tends to sink. Both the buoyant force and weight, which is also a force, can be measured in newtons. A newton is the force required to give a mass of one kilogram an acceleration of one metre per second per second. The weight of a mass m is equal to mg where g is the acceleration due to gravity. As the buoyancy of a body is equal to the weight of the fluid displaced by that body, it follows that if the gravitational force changes, the buoyant force will also change.

According to Newton's law of gravitation, every particle in the cosmos attracts every other particle with a force directly proportional to the product of the masses of the particles and inversely proportional to the square of the distance between them. This means that as the Earth has a mass 81.3 times greater than the Moon, the intensity of the gravitational field of the Earth is 81.3 times greater than the Moon, if the measurements are made outside of these planets and at the same distances from the centre of each planet. As the radii of the Moon and Earth are 1738 km and 6371 km respectively, and gravitational intensity weakens as the square of the distance, the surface gravity of the Earth is decreased as compared to the surface gravity of the Moon by a factor of 13.44 (i.e. $\frac{6371}{1738} \times \frac{6371}{1738}$); therefore, although the Earth has a mass that is 81.3 times that of the Moon, the surface gravity of the Moon is one-sixth that of the Earth ($\frac{81.3}{13.44} = 6.005$). However, when a body lies within a planet, the mass of the planet is distributed all around the body, and the gravitational force acting on the body is the sum of the vectors of all the gravitational forces acting on that body; thus as a body approaches the centre of a planet, the gravitational force acting on it tends to decrease, and at the centre the force becomes zero. This is because the mass of the planet is attracting the body in all directions away from the centre. In the Earth at present the distribution of mass is such that the gravitational force is essentially constant within both the crust and mantle, but it decreases steadily within the core (cf. Brown & Mussett 1981: 41). On all planets with different masses and/or different internal distributions of mass, the magnitude of the gravitational force will differ from the simple model postulated for the interior of the Earth.

Diapirs

Magmas are commonly said to move through the Earth as diapirs. The term diapir comes from the classical Greek words *dia* meaning through and *peiro* meaning piercing. Diapirs are thus bodies of rock and/or magma that are buoyant and move upwards, piercing the rocks above them. On Earth, diapirs are believed to travel through both the mantle and crust. Such diapirs may develop whenever a body of rock or magma is covered by denser rock materials that will yield to the buoyant force exerted by the body of low-density material. In areas such as the North German Plain of Europe and the Gulf Coast of North America, diapirs that are essentially composed of low-density (2200 kg/m^2) sedimentary rock-salt (halite, NaCl) thrust their way through beds of more dense sedimentary rocks. Salt diapirs are generally about 2 km in diameter and they rise from parental rock-salt beds that are normally 5–10 km beneath the top of the diapir. If the rock-salt was originally bedded, the internal structure of these diapirs is often revealed and found to be dominated by tight folds that may show evidence of multiple refolding. As long as a diapir remains attached to the layer from which it evolved, overburden squeeze on the parental layer helps force the proto-diapir upwards; however, once the diapir is detached from the parental layer it is moved upwards by buoyancy. Diapirs, such as salt diapirs, usually occur together with other diapirs in regular arrays.

Many large bodies of granite and granitic gneiss are considered to have been emplaced as diapirs. Ramberg (1970) has used models to demonstrate how such large batholithic bodies of essentially crystalline rock can force their way through crustal materials of broadly similar viscosity. He (285) claims that: (a) the manner in which igneous magmas (or crystal-mushes) move; (b) the paths they follow; and (c) the shapes they assume while in motion, are all directly related to the differences in viscosity between the moving materials and the surrounding rocks. If the viscosity contrast is large, as for example when a low-viscosity magma moves through more viscous crustal rocks, the flow pattern of the magma is strongly controlled by the structures and fractures found in the surrounding rocks; however, if the viscosity contrast is low, as for example when a granitic diapir is emplaced into rocks of broadly similar viscosity, then the shape and path of the rising diapir is not significantly affected by the nature of the structures it encounters in the surrounding rocks.

In south-east Papua New Guinea there are several domes of granitic gneiss, such as the Goodenough Dome, that are considered to have forced their way through to the surface by 'shouldering aside' the country rocks that originally enclosed them (cf. Ollier & Pain 1980: 38). These *surface-breaching domes* were emplaced in an extensional tectonic setting; and individually they are regarded as apical protuberances that extend upwards from much larger bodies of buoyant granitic material. Domes such as these are regarded as good examples of the importance of buoyancy in the emplacement of a wide range of granitic rocks.

It may be difficult to visualize how a large granitic diapir (10 km in diameter) can rise through solid rocks, such as those found in the upper crust of the Earth. The conundrum that the same rocks can apparently be both strong and weak is solved if one considers the effect of size on the stability of both structures and rocks. In his *Dialogues concerning two new sciences*, Galileo Galilei postulated that 'if one wished to maintain in a great giant the same proportion of limbs as found in ordinary man one must either find a harder and stronger material for making the bones, or one must admit a diminution of strength in comparison with men of medium stature; for if his height be increased inordinately he will fall and be crushed under his own weight' (cf. Hubbert 1937: 1516). It is thus found that strength and weakness are purely relative terms that have little meaning unless the size of the body is specified. According to Hubbert (1937: 1517), strength is a specific term describing a specimen of material of a given size, and the strength of a body of the same material of another size must be determined by experimentation. Generally the over-all strength of a body taken as a whole decreases with increasing size; and Ramberg (1967: 307) has stated that 'increasing geometric size increases the tendency of gravitational collapse and spreading and also raises the velocity of viscous flow as generated by gravity in dynamically similar structures of the same substances'

Large diapirs are believed to develop within the upper mantle of the Earth where they are important in the generation of the more abundant types of basaltic magma. Such diapirs may form as the result of the addition of heat and/or volatile components to a body of mantle rock. If partial melting occurs and a basaltic magma is formed, both the newly-formed liquid and the residual solid phases are likely to be less dense than the original undepleted mantle material. The liquid is less dense because it occupies a larger volume than the solid phases it replaces; whereas the residual solids are less dense because partial melting generally lowers the proportion of the dense minerals garnet and jadeite in the residual crystal mush, and it also changes the composition of the residual olivines and pyroxenes. The Fe/Mg ratio of these minerals decreases (that is, the liquid has a higher Fe/Mg ratio) and they become less dense. For example, the Mg-rich olivine, forsterite, has a density of 3200 kg/m^3, whereas the density of the Fe-rich olivine, fayalite, is 4390 kg/m^3. As both the liquid and the residual solids are less dense than the original undepleted mantle material, they are all likely to rise as a buoyant diapir through the overlying undepleted mantle.

As the diapir rises, the ambient pressure decreases and if the diapir does not lose too much heat to the surrounding mantle further partial melting will occur. The production of more liquid will increase the tendency of the liquid to segregate out of the crystal–liquid mush. Spera (1980: 305) has estimated that the rate of segregation between crystals and liquid in a mush consisting of 30 per cent liquid is 6500 times larger than in a mush with 2 per cent liquid. According to Williams and McBirney (1979: 47–18), any diapir that is at least partly melted when it reaches the base of the lithosphere must contain a large proportion of liquid by the time it reaches the upper brittle zone of the lithosphere.

Magma chambers

Geochemical, geophysical and petrological evidence all support the concept that reservoirs of

magma lie beneath many volcanoes. These magma chambers are believed to occur in many shapes and sizes: they probably range from single chambers to complex networks of interconnecting dykes and sills. Geophysical studies have shown that a pipelike structure extends from approximately 40 to 10 km beneath the summit of Kilauea Volcano, Hawaii, and that at depths of between 10 and 3 km there is a roughly pear-shaped magma chamber. Magma appears to be constantly moving up the pipelike duct and into the magma chamber where it is usually stored. Periodically, magma is released into the main vent, or into dykes that feed the rift zone of the volcano. According to Moore (1983: 139) there are several magma chambers beneath the lower east rift zone of this volcano, and they are repeatedly filled with magma that moves in from higher up the rift zone.

Seismic studies have also revealed a large magma chamber at depths of between 10 and 20 km beneath Bezymianny Volcano in Kamchatka, USSR (cf. Utnasin, et al. 1976: 129). Baker (1968: 74) attempted to determine the size, form and internal structure of the magma chamber that once existed beneath the now extinct south-western shield volcano on the island of Saint Helena in the South Atlantic. In his model the magma chamber had a maximum width of 19 km, a height of approximately 2 km, and it was situated approximately 2.5 km below the present surface. Baker also showed that this magma chamber was compositionally layered. Hildreth (1981: 10153) states that most non-basaltic magma chambers are thermally and compositionally zoned.

Some magma chambers are very large. It has, for example, been proposed that the Tharsis Dome on Mars (see Fig. 1.9.1) is evidence that a huge magma chamber once existed beneath the Tharsis volcanic province. Some petrologists believe that both the *continental flood basalts* and the *ocean-floor basalts* of Earth evolved in vast magma chambers. According to Cox (1980: 646), the continental flood basalts are derived from a primary magma of picritic (olivine-rich basalt) composition. This magma formed in the upper mantle, moved upwards until it encountered less dense crustal rocks, and then stopped and spread out to form a large reservoir. The magma cooled and *magmatic differentiation* (see Ch. 2) gradually produced a less dense basaltic residual liquid that accumulated at the top of the huge, deep-seated magma chamber. Periodically, batches of this differentiated magma, which has a lower density than the overlying crust, rose to the surface.

Some of the models that have been proposed to account for the origin of the ocean-floor basalts suggest that the magmas responsible for these rocks evolved in *periodically replenished magma chambers* that developed at shallow depths immediately beneath the crests of mid-ocean ridges. These models claim that under the conditions that usually obtain beneath active mid-ocean ridges, the periodic refilling of a magma chamber with new primary magma, and the mixing of old residual and new incoming magmas, enables the resulting composite magma to remain saturated in both olivine and plagioclase throughout most of the active life of the magma chamber (cf. O'Hara and Mathews 1981). They demonstrate that even if a magma chamber is the site of continuous fractional crystallization, the major element compositions of the liquids erupted can remain approximately the same if the following parameters are held constant: (a) the composition of the incoming magma; (b) the amount of magma supplied in each cycle of replenishment; and (c) the ratio of the amount of magma that crystallizes to the amount of magma that is removed from the magma chamber.

In the petrogenetic model that we have just examined it was assumed that there was a thorough mixing of the incoming magma with that resident already in the magma chamber. This is only one of many possibilities. If, for example, the incoming magma is less dense than the resident magma, it will rise; and depending on prevailing circumstances, such as: (a) the size and shape of the magma chamber; (b) the relative miscibility of the magmas; and (c) the magnitude of the differences in density and temperature between the magmas, there will be variable amounts of turbulent mixing between them. However, if the incoming magma is more dense than that resident, then there may be little mixing, and the incoming magma may form a pool at the base of the magma chamber. For example, a basaltic magma would not be able to force its way through a reservoir of less dense rhyolitic magma. Magma chambers that contain an upper layer of relatively low-density magma may thus act as efficient filters that prevent denser magmas from reaching the surface.

1.8 Emplacement of intrusive rocks

The manner in which magma moves through and is emplaced into the upper layers of a planet depends to a large extent on how the country rocks respond to the intruding magma. They may flow plastically or pseudoplastically away from the magma, or they may deform by fracturing. On Earth, seismic events may occur down to a depth of 700 km. This is usually interpreted as showing that brittle fracture may occur to this depth; however, plastic deformation may occur at relatively shallow depths as is shown by many granitic intrusions that appear to have been emplaced by forcibly compacting and radially distending the upper crustal rocks they encountered. There is also irrefutable field evidence that some fracture-fault systems have tapped sub-crustal magma. For example, the linear dyke swarms associated with the Tertiary volcanic and subvolcanic centres of western Scotland and Ireland indicate extensive fracturing and the tapping of large sub-crustal bodies of magma (cf. Speight et al. 1982: 456). At depth, dykes usually form when

Table 1.8.1 The form of common instrusions

Dykes (or **dikes**): are tabular, or wall-like, igneous intrusions that are usually steeply inclined and cut across the bedding or foliation of the country rocks.

Sills: are tabular igneous bodies that are usually flat-lying, and have been intruded parallel to the planar structures in the surrounding rocks. They are generally injected between bedded units, at relatively shallow depths within the upper crust.

Batholiths: are large, generally discordant, bodies of plutonic rocks that have an outcrop area that is greater than 100 km^2 (Classical Greek, *bathos*, depth).

Stocks: are small, generally discordant, bodies of plutonic rock that have an outcrop area that is less than 100 km^2.

Lopoliths: are large, generally concordant bodies of plutonic rocks that have a plano-convex or lenticular shape. They differ from sills in that they are depressed in the centre (Classical Greek, *lopas*, a basin).

Cone sheets: are conical dykes that converge towards a central point. In plan they usually occur as concentric sets of dykes arranged about and dipping towards a centre of igneous activity.

Ring dykes: are dykes that are arcuate or circular in plan. Their dip is vertical or inclined away from a local centre of igneous activity.

magma forcefully wedges open fractures, but in the near-surface environment the mechanism of emplacement is generally more passive with the magma filling open fissures. It has even been proposed that major fault-fracture systems may have controlled the distribution of the intrusive bodies that make up some of the huge linear granitic batholiths of Earth, such as the Coastal Batholith of Peru (cf. Pitcher 1979a: 645).

Epizone, mesozone and catazone

The study of the contacts and contact rocks that surround, and the structures that occur within, intrusive bodies, such as *stocks, batholiths* and *lopoliths* has shown that such bodies are emplaced by a variety of different mechanisms. It is also evident that the dominant mechanism associated with the emplacement of a particular intrusive body is usually determined by an interplay between the physical properties of the intrusive materials and those of the country rocks with which it is in contact. When considering the emplacement of plutonic bodies into the crust of the Earth it is convenient to divide the crust into a number of *intensity zones* (Buddington 1959: 676–7). Each zone has a characteristic range of temperatures and pressures, and the country rocks in these zones have distinctive styles of deformation. The position of these intensity zones is, however, not fixed either in space or time. For example, when the rocks in a segment of the crust are being *metamorphosed*, or subjected to an influx of heat and/or volatile components, changes take place in the location, shape and size of these intensity zones.

In the upper intensity zone, or *epizone*, the country rocks are essentially brittle (or have a low ductility), and contacts between intrusive bodies and country rocks are generally discordant. At intermediate depths, in the *mesozone*, the country rocks are more ductile, and the contacts between intrusive bodies and country rocks are usually partly discordant and partly concordant. In the deepest zone, or *catazone*, the country rocks are highly ductile and tend to deform plastically or pseudoplastically. In this zone the contacts between intrusive bodies and country rocks are generally concordant. *Ductility* measures the amount of deformation a rock can sustain before fracturing or faulting. The most important factors in determining the form of an intrusion are the differences in ductility and density between a magma and the country rocks that surround it (cf. Pitcher 1979a: 646)

The bulk chemical composition of the rocks in most lopoliths (see Table 1.8.1) is basaltic; however, individual lopoliths often contain layered igneous rocks (see Ch. 10). Detailed studies of the contact relationships between the country rocks and bodies that have traditionally been regarded as lopoliths has revealed that many of them are essentially funnel-shaped bodies; or as in some large lopoliths, such as the *Bushveld Igneous Complex* of South Africa, they consist of a cluster of comagmatic funnel-shaped intrusions. Regular funnel-shaped intrusions are considered to develop when magmatic pressure is exerted upwards (that is, point push) on brittle country rocks. The overlying rocks fracture, and the fractures follow the trajectories of the greatest principal stress axes. This produces a nest of fractures in the form of inverted cones and the magma, which is generally more dense than the country rocks, displaces the fractured rock upwards and occupies the funnel-shaped chamber as it forms (cf. Wager & Brown 1968: 541).

On Earth, highly fluid basaltic magmas are usually transported through the crust and are extruded at the surface. Evidence of the passage of such magmas is usually recorded by the presence of dykes, sills, plugs and, less commonly, funnel-shaped intrusions (see Table 1.8.1). For a number of reasons that will be discussed later, the more viscous and less dense magmas, such as the rhyolite–granite magmas, tend to form stocks and batholiths within the upper crust of the Earth. In the catazone these silicic magmas usually occur as large rounded *diapiric bodies*, but upon entering the mesozone the ductility of the country rocks decreases, and it is more difficult for the intrusive bodies to push them aside. Many granitic bodies, such as the individual plutonic bodies that compose the Coastal Batholith of Peru (Pitcher 1979a: 645), are found to have risen to a common shallow level in the crust. The granitic bodies emplaced into the epizone are usually relatively small, and their shape in plan is often polygonal. This shape demonstrates that their emplacement was controlled: (a) by fracture patterns of pre-intrusion age; or (b) by fractures induced by the act of intrusion. Detailed field mapping has revealed that the granitic rocks of the epizone and upper mesozone are generally emplaced by one, or more, of the following mechanisms: (a) *lateral magmatic wedging* (Pitcher & Read 1959: 298); (b) *doming of the roof rocks* (Buddington 1959: 736); (c) *piecemeal stoping* (Daly 1933: 267); (d) *ring-fracture stoping or cauldron subsidence* (Buddington 1959: 735–6); and (e) *fluidization-assisted intrusion* (Reynolds 1954: 577)

Magmatic stoping

Daly (1933: 267) introduced the term magmatic stoping, and he proposed that this process operated during the last stage in the emplacement of many stocks and batholiths. The term stoping was originally a mining term used to describe a method of extracting ore from an inclined underground ore-body by removing the ore in steps from a number of different levels. Daly used the term to describe the subsidence, or ascent, of blocks of country rocks enclosed within a magma that was of either higher, or lower, density than the engulfed blocks. Usually the blocks of country rock are denser than the magma; they sink down into it and are eventually assimilated by the magma. Daly (1933: 268) claimed that 'by continued fracturing of wall or roof, continued immersion of corresponding fragments, and continued subsidence of these fragments, the magmatic chamber is enlarged upward or sideways or in both senses'. If comparatively small pieces of country rock are engulfed, either singly, or in one or more 'showers', the process is called *piecemeal stoping. Ring-fracture stoping* and *cauldron subsidence* are extreme examples of magmatic stoping. They occur when a more or less cylindrical block of roof rocks is lowered into a magma chamber along steep ring-shaped fractures. Examples of the many different types of stoping have been described from the western cordillera of the Americas. Pitcher (1978: 166) claims that in the Coastal Batholith of Peru one can observe large tongues (or apophyses) of magmatic rock that congealed while in the process of prising off great slabs of country rock. Other outcrops are described as containing large numbers of xenoliths derived from disrupted slabs that spalled off the rocks that once formed the roof above the intruding plutonic body. Ring-fracture stoping is also found in the Coastal Batholith of Peru where, for example, the main bell-jar-shaped plutonic body in the Huaura ring-complex contains a large (2 km in diameter) central block of subsided rocks.

Many of the granitic rocks that were emplaced into the mesozone are surrounded by zones of contact metamorphism – metasomatism, and zones of local deformation. It is generally assumed that the sequence of mineralogical changes observed in a traverse across such *contact aureoles* reveals the response of relatively cool country rocks to a thermal, and possibly a chemical, gradient imposed by the emplacement of a relatively hot plutonic body. The size and nature of the contact aureole depends on the size, composition and temperature of the intrusion, and also on the composition, permeability and initial temperature of the country rocks.

Regular patterns of fractures, veins and/or dykes are commonly observed within stocks and batholiths of the mesozone and epizone, and also in the country rocks that surround them. Evidence of variations in the orientation of fractures with the passage of time is recorded by the cross-cutting nature of many of these sets of fractures, veins and dykes. A study of the orientation, abundance and continuity of such fracture patterns usually reveals that there were significant variations in the magnitude and orientation of the ambient stress field during the post-emplacement period of cooling. If the country rocks are permeable, the cooling process may be speeded up by the evolution of a thermal (or hydrothermal) convection system above the intrusion (cf. Hardee 1982: 179). The metamorphic – metasomatic and structural adjustments that occur within the contact zones surrounding mesozonal stocks and batholiths usually continue long after the main body of magma has crystallized.

Stocks and batholiths

With regards to the movement and emplacement of granitic stocks and batholiths in the catazone, it is generally assumed that the magma accumulated until it had sufficient buoyancy to penetrate the overlying rocks. It then rose and gradually became detached from the source region, and heated, deformed, compacted and displaced the surrounding rocks (cf. Hamilton & Myers 1967: 21). Such diapirs usually assume a streamlined shape similar to that of an inverted drop of water. On entering the mesozone the head of the diapir slows down relative to the tail, and the diapir flattens out and becomes mushroom-shaped (cf. Ramberg 1970). According to Pitcher

(1979a: 628), some tonalitic batholiths of the cir-cum-Pacific mobile belt approach 1000 km² in outcrop area; however, careful mapping often reveals that these large bodies consist of a series of smaller units, and individual units seldom exceed 300 km² in area. He also claims that granodiorite batholiths usually have a mean surface area of 150 km², whereas granites (sensu stricto) usually occur in stocks with a mean outcrop area of 80 km². The granitic, or *granitoid*, rocks are those plutonic rocks that normally contain more than 20 per cent modal quartz, and range in composition from the granites (sensu stricto) with their relatively high alkali feldspar/plagioclase ratio, via the granodiorites to the tonalites with low alkali feldspar/plagioclase ratios (cf. Ch. 3). Many large batholiths, such as the huge Coastal Batholith of Peru, consist of an extended cluster of smaller intrusions that coalesced after being channelled into the same zone of crustal weakness (cf. Cobbing & Pitcher 1972). Detailed study of such composite bodies usually reveals that hot basic magma was intruded first, and it heated and increased the ductility of the rocks that surround the conduit used by the later more voluminous intrusions of tonalite, granodiorite and granite.

In his modelling experiments, Ramberg (1970) has found that diapiric intrusions of the shape proposed for most granitic batholiths evolve as a consequence of a relatively low viscosity contrast between the intrusion and country rocks of the aureole that envelop them. Once a diapir has formed, the rate of ascent is largely independent of the physical state (liquid, crystal-mush or solid) of the body, because the rate of ascent is essentially controlled by the ductility of the rocks that envelop it, and the buoyancy of the body. Many granitic batholiths, particularly those found in the catazone and mesozone, were probably emplaced as mush of crystals lubricated by a water-rich granitic fluid. Harris et al. (1970) have demonstrated that hydrous granitic magmas are normally unable to remain liquid in the near surface environment of the Earth. This is because most granite (sensu stricto) magmas have the following properties: (a) they have minimum or near minimum melting compositions; (b) there is only a small interval between the temperature at which they are totally liquid and the temperature at which they are totally solid; and (c) the temperature at which they remain liquid is strongly depressed by the presence of water. In Section 1.4 it was established that water is highly

soluble in rhyolitic (granite) melts, and that the solubility of this component increases with increasing pressure until a maximum value is reached. Let us now follow the evolution of an ascending hydrous granitic magma. At the beginning of the journey it is not saturated in water, but as it rises to higher crustal levels the pressure decreases, and the magma becomes saturated in water because water is now less soluble in the magma. As the magma rises higher, the pressure decreases and a water-rich fluid phase separates from the magma. The exsolution of this fluid raises the liquidus temperature of the magma and it begins to crystallize. This process continues and the magma may eventually become a mush of crystals and liquid. In the catazone the escaping water-rich phase would permeate the surrounding country rocks, promote metasomatism, and help generate a more ductile aureole in advance of the intruding magma. In the less ductile mesozone the water-rich phase might generate discrete dyke-like bodies of aplite and pegmatite.

1.9 Volcanic eruptions and eruptive mechanisms

When magma penetrates the surface layer of a planet, it enters a new environment. There are few descriptions of the opening of new volcanic vents; however; Thorarinsson (1969) has provided a remarkable record of the development of a large *fissure eruption* in Iceland in 1783. The eruption began with the opening of the Laki (or Lakagigar) fissure. This was accompanied by the release of huge amounts of volcanic gases and the ejection of pyroclastic materials (see Table 1.9.1). The volcanic gases produced a bluish haze over Iceland and much of Europe. In Iceland, the ash carpeted the grazing lands and the gases stunted the vegetation, producing what has become known as the *haze famine*. This famine resulted in the death of about one-fifth of the population of eighteenth-century Iceland. After the initial gas-release stage, floods of basaltic lava poured from a 10 km long section of the fissure. Lava was erupted at a mean rate of approximately 2300 m³/s for 50 days; the maximum rate was probably four or five times this value. If it is assumed that the average width of the fissure was 4 m, then the average velocity of the magma up the fissure was approximately 0.3 m/s. Be-

Table 1.9.1 Nomenclature of pyroclastic materials (after Le Bas and Sabine 1980)

Pyroclasts: individual crystals, crystal fragments, glass and rock fragments generated by disruption as a direct result of volcanic action.

Agglomerate: pyroclastic rock whose average pyroclasts exceed 64 mm and in which rounded pyroclasts predominate.

Ash or dust particles: pyroclasts with mean diameters smaller than 0.0625 mm.

Ash grains: pyroclasts with mean diameters of between 0.0625 mm and 2 mm.

Block: pyroclast with a mean diameter exceeding 64 mm whose commonly angular to subangular shape indicates that it was ejected as a solid.

Bomb: pyroclast with a mean diameter commonly exceeding 64 mm; and it has a shape or surface texture that indicates that it was ejected in a wholly, or partially, molten condition.

Crystal tuff: tuff in which crystals and crystal fragments predominate.

Epiclasts: crystals, crystal fragments, glass and rock fragments that have been liberated from a pre-existing rock by weathering or erosion and transported by gravity, air, water or ice.

Fine ash-tuff (or **dust-tuff**): pyroclastic rock whose average pyroclast size is less than 0.0625 mm.

Lapilli: pyroclasts of any shape, with mean diameters of 2 to 64 mm.

Lapilli-tuff: pyroclastic rock whose average pyroclast size is 2 to 64 mm.

Pyroclastic breccia: pyroclastic rock whose average pyroclast size exceeds 64 mm and in which angular pyroclasts predominate.

Pyroclastic deposit: rock that contains more than 75 per cent by volume of pyroclasts.

Tephra: collective term for an unconsolidated deposit of pyroclasts.

Tuff (or **ash-tuff**): pyroclastic rock whose average pyroclast size is less than 2 mm.

Vitric tuff: tuff in which pumice and glass fragments predominate.

tween June and November 1783, about 11 km³ of lava flowed out of the fissure and covered an area of some 600 km². So much flowed into the Skafter valley that it was completely filled, and some spilled out over the surrounding countryside. Smaller, but similar, fissure eruptions have been described from a number of areas, such as the rift zones of Kilauea Volcano on Hawaii.

Ignimbrites

In early June 1912 another spectacular, but quite different, type of eruption took place at the head of the Ukak valley in the Aleutian Range in the Alaska Peninsula. Within a period of about 20 hours some 10 km³ of *pyroclastic flow materials* were expelled at a rate of approximately 140 000 m³/s. The ejected materials filled the upper Ukak valley and transformed it into a flat, barren plain that contained thousands of active fumaroles, or vents that emitted gases. Robert Griggs, the leader of the 1916 expedition to the area, called the pyroclast-filled valley the *Valley of Ten Thousand Smokes*. The pyroclastic rock that fills the valley is now usually called an *ignimbrite* (Latin, *ignis* fire and *nimbis* cloud). This term was introduced by P. Marshall (1932) to describe the extensive deposits of similar rocks found in the Taupo–Rotorua area of New Zealand. He postulated that ignimbrites were deposited from a hot, turbulent cloud of volcanic material. In 1935, Mansfield and Ross described similar rocks from south-eastern Idaho, USA: these rocks were called *welded tuffs*. Ignimbrites usually contain mostly tuff-sized pyroclasts, together with both smaller and larger materials. Such rocks are essentially pyroclastic flow deposits. They are ejected explosively from a volcanic vent, and they then travel downslope as a fluidized turbulent mixture of gas and pyroclasts. Walker (1982: 408) claims that 'practically nothing is known from direct observation about ignimbrite eruptions'; and that 'it is rather doubtful if observations sufficiently close to be useful are feasible'. It is sometimes claimed that ignimbrite eruptions are similar to *nuée ardente* (French, 'glowing cloud'). The latter are gravity-controlled avalanches of incandescent materials that travel as density flows down the steep sides of some volcanic cones; however, the *nuée ardente* that have been observed are several orders of magnitude smaller than normal ignimbrite eruptions.

Evidence of the turbulent nature of the fluidized systems that transport and deposit ignimbrites is revealed by their textures. The clasts that occur in the main body of a flow unit are usually unsorted according to size or shape; however, the upper portion of some flow units contain a concentration of pumice clasts, whereas the lowermost portion contains a concentration of denser lithic clasts. These differences are considered to be due to sorting according to density. Pumice rises, and the dense lithic clasts sink, in an active fluidized system (cf. Sparks et al. 1973).

The full sequence of volcanic events associated with the extrusion of the ignimbrites in the Ukak valley in 1912 is complex. This is because there was a simultaneous eruption of Mt Katmai some 12 km to the east of Novarupta which is believed to have been the main vent for the extrusion of the ignimbrites. Before June 1912, Katmai was an andesitic volcano with a 2300 m high cone. On 5 June, clouds of ash were observed above the Katmai area, and on the following day there were two enormous explosions, and a huge ash cloud showered ash over a large area of the Alaska Peninsula. This type of eruption is a Plinian eruption, and the different types will be discussed in the latter part of this chapter. On 7 June a third large explosion reverberated around Alaska. Eventually, approximately 2 m of ash accumulated at Kaflia Bay on the coast, and a few centimetres in Kodiak, 160 km away. Kodiak experienced total darkness for a period of 60 hours, and the surface of the surrounding sea, particularly in the Shelikof Strait between Kodiak Island and the mainland, was covered with floating pumice. When Griggs visited Katmai Volcano in 1916 he discovered that the upper 300 m of the cone was missing. It had been replaced by a roughly-circular caldera that was 3 km across and approximately 1 km deep. Smith (1960) has shown that most large-volume ignimbrite eruptions are associated with large caldera, or volcano-tectonic depressions, and that there appears to be a linear relationship between the size of the caldera and the volume of the resulting ignimbrite deposits.

Prior to the 1912 Katmai–Novarupta volcanic event, andesitic magma is believed to have been present in a high-level magma chamber beneath Katmai Volcano, and rhyolitic magma was present at a lower level some 12 km to the west. A system of fractures developed, and some of the andesitic magma drained downwards and westwards through an underground system of fissures. The andesitic magma mingled explosively with the rhyolitic magma, and the resulting *hybrid magma* rapidly foamed to the surface at the head of Ukak valley. A flood of streaky hybrid ignimbrite and pumice deposits soon filled the upper Ukak valley. As the andesite magma drained from beneath Katmai Volcano, it collapsed and ejected vast quantities of pyroclastic materials. Some of the ignimbrite flows found in the Ukak valley are composed chiefly of white rhyolitic clast, whereas others contain strongly-banded hybrid pumice in which the dark bands are andesitic and the light bands rhyolitic. After

the huge eruption of ignimbrite, Novarupta passed through an explosive phase during which it ejected large quantities of coarse pumice, but finally the eruption was terminated with the extrusion of a glassy dome which is now approximately 100 m high and 400 m in diameter (cf. Curtis 1968; Williams & McBirney 1979: 159).

Island-building eruptions

We have examined two very different types of eruptions in which floods of volcanic materials were extruded. At present, fissure eruptions are typical of the central neovolcanic zone of Iceland which is a subaerial section of the actively-spreading mid-Atlantic ridge system; where fissures are continuously developing and being filled with magma. Some of this material may reach the surface in volcanoes such as Hekla and Krafla, or flood out of fissures. Along the mid-ocean ridges, new ocean floor is continuously being generated by a similar process of fissure formation, magma emplacement and submarine eruptions. Not all submarine eruptions are confined to the mid-ocean ridges. Eruptions beneath the deep ocean are difficult to observe, because the overlying water hides such eruptions from view; and the pressure of water in the deep ocean may inhibit, or prevent, the explosive release of volcanic gases. According to McBirney (1963b) and others, explosive eruptions should not occur if vents are situated at depths greater than about 2000 m beneath the sea because the expansion of water vapour below this depth is not likely to be large enough to produce gaseous explosions. Submarine explosions do, however, draw attention to shallow submarine eruptions. There are many records of *island-building eruptions*; for example, the book by Simkin et al. (1981: 18) contains details of some 96 island-building eruptions. Many of these new volcanic islands are quickly eroded by the sea; for example, since 1950, Kavachi in the Solomon Islands has constructed a new subaerial edifice on eight separate occasions. Probably the best documented island-building eruption was the birth of Surtsey near the Westmann Islands south of Iceland (cf. Fridriksson 1975).

On the morning of 14 November 1963, some fishermen observed what looked like smoke rising from the sea. By the middle of the morning, a column of volcanic ash and gas had reached a height of 4 km above the sea, and materials were being erupted in at least two separate places. During the afternoon the erupted materials were observed being ejected from a fissure that was some 500 m long, and the column of ash and gases could now be seen from Reykjavik. On the following morning, the highest point on Surtsey was approximately 10 m above sea-level, and basaltic pyroclastic materials were being constantly erupted. Towards the end of 1963, the volcanic activity slowed down and the winter storms removed much of the tephra, or unconsolidated pyroclastic material. Sea water entered the volcanic vent producing explosions as the water was rapidly converted into steam. It is significant to note that the pyroclastic materials ejected by Surtsey are usually more highly fragmented than those found associated with eruptions of similar alkalic basalts on dry land. When only a moderate amount of water seeped into the active vent, the pulsating explosions ceased and there was a continuous uprush of pyroclastic materials including volcanic bombs. This eruptive activity was a type of lava-fountaining, but sea water was still able to cool the incandescent lava so that it was ejected as ash and scoria. By the end of March 1964, Surtsey had grown to cover an area of 1 km². On 4 April 1964, one of the vents developed a water-tight lining that excluded the sea. Lava fountains formed, and lava flowed over the tephra and protected it from further erosion by the sea. This effusive phase continued intermittently until May 1965, when the island covered an area of 2.5 km². Prior to the extrusion of lava, the pyroclastic materials on Surtsey were ejected from vents that developed low broad cones called *ash cones* or *tuff cones*.

Jökullhlaups

At present, subglacial eruptions are also characteristic of Iceland. However, during the Pleistocene, when much of the land surface of the Earth was covered by ice, this type of eruption was more common, and it must be the most common type of volcanic activity on the ice-covered planets of the Solar System. When a volcano erupts beneath an ice cap or ice sheet (that is, greater than 50 000 km² in area), large amounts of ice melt, and this water may flood adjoining lowlands. In Iceland, ice caps are known as *jökulls* and eruptions beneath the ice are known as *hlaups* (bursts), hence *jökullhlaups* are glacier

outburst floods induced by volcanic activity. It is difficult to visualize the volume of water released during a jökullhlaup. In the 1934 eruption of Grimsvötn Volcano beneath the Vatnajökul (Vatna ice cap in south-eastern Iceland), some 16 km³ of ice was melted which produced a flood of water of 100 000 m³/s for approximately two days. Such floods are able to carry huge loads of debris, and the coastal areas of south-eastern Iceland have been extensively modified by the deposits left behind by floods propagated by subglacial eruptions.

These jökullhlaup deposits are usually regarded as being a type of *lahar*. The term lahar is Indonesian and it describes a large mud flow, or debris flow, that is mostly composed of volcaniclastic detritus, and occurs on, or surrounding, the flanks of a volcano (cf. Neal 1976). Lahars associated with crater lake eruptions have probably caused more loss of life, and damage to property, than any other type of debris flow. Kelut Volcano in Java, Indonesia, has produced approximately thirty lahars in the past 1000 years, and it is regarded as being typical of the volcanoes that produce lahars by crater lake eruptions. Crater lake eruptions usually result from the explosive introduction of lava into the water of a summit crater lake. Between 1889 and 1980 Ruapehu Volcano on North Island, New Zealand produced thirty-seven crater lake eruptions (cf. Simkin et al. 1981: 44–5).

Most of the Earth's best-known volcanoes have produced central-crater eruptions, or central eruptions. Approximately half the eruptions recorded by Simkin et al. (1981: 17) are of this type. For example, between 1321 and 1980, Etna Volcano in Italy produced seventy-six central-crater eruptions; this volcano also produced 84 radial fissure eruptions in the period between 693 and 1979. Radial fissures develop in the flanks of many volcanoes; and radial fissure eruptions are recorded from approximately 5 per cent of the active volcanoes of the Earth. Other volcanoes that have had large numbers of radial fissure eruptions include Vesuvio in Italy and Kilauea in Hawaii. Some volcanic edifices that have been mainly produced by central eruptions are cut by circumferential or ring fissures; however, the presence or absence of these features is not recorded in the *Catalog of Active Volcanoes of the World*. This catalogue does, however, record eruptions in parasitic or eccentric craters. Such eruptions are associated with approximately 12 per cent of all active volcanoes of the Earth. For example, between 1768 and 1975, forty such eruptions were recorded from the Piton de la Fournaise Volcano, on the island of Reunion in the southern Indian Ocean.

The size of explosive volcanic eruptions

It is difficult to find objective criteria that can be used to measure the size of explosive volcanic eruptions. Walker (1980: 86–91) has proposed that such eruptions show five different kinds of *bigness*, namely magnitude, intensity, dispersive power, violence and destructive potential. The term magnitude is used to describe the total quantity of material extruded and/or energy released by an eruption. Intensity refers to the rate at which material, or energy, is released. Dispersive power refers to the area covered by erupted materials. Violence is mainly concerned with pyroclastic flow eruptions (cf. Wilson & Walker 1981: 441) as it reflects the vigour with which pyroclastic flows are ejected, or the momentum possessed by such flows or by pyroclasts in general. Destructive potential refers to the devastation, actual or potential, generated by an eruption.

In their description of the volcanoes of the world Simkin *et al.* (1981: 20–1) use a simple 0 to 8 volcanic explosivity index to describe the *size* of historic eruptions. The criteria used in this index include volume of ejecta, eruptive column height, duration of continuous blast, and qualitative eyewitness descriptions of eruptions. It is primarily a measure of the destructive potential of explosive eruptions. Voluminous quiet effusions of lava, such as the historic eruptions of Mauna Loa in Hawaii, are given volcanic explosivity indices of 0; however, in contrast to this, the eruptions attributed to the Taupo Volcanic Centre in New Zealand have a mean volcanic explosivity index of 5 (cf. Simkin et al. 1981: 43 and 88).

The main reason why it is difficult to classify eruptions is because they are extremely complex phenomena. During a single eruptive episode the character of an eruption may change, or different eruptive events may occur simultaneously on different parts of the same volcano. In the past it has been found convenient to classify the principal types of central eruptions into a sequence of progressively more violent explosive types. The members of such sequences were given names, such as *Hawaiian, Strombolian, Vulcan-*

ian, Plinian and even *Ultraplinian*. It is now possible to assign a volcanic explosivity index number, or series of numbers, to each one of these types of central eruptions.

Hawaiian eruptions

The ideal Hawaiian eruption is gently effusive with a volcanic explosivity index of 0 or 1. Such eruptions are typical of the youthful and mature stages in the growth of Hawaiian shield volcanoes, such as Mauna Loa. They usually begin with lava fountaining and flowing from a fissure in the summit caldera. As the gas content of the lava decreases, the fountains diminish in height; however, during some eruptions the lava may continue to well up quietly for a long time and thus flood the floor of the caldera and produce a *lava lake*. Radial fissures may also develop in the flanks of the volcano (cf. Carr & Greeley 1980). The term *shield* is applied to volcanoes, like Mauna Loa, that have broad, low profiles, and have the overall form of a flattened dome. Olympus Mons in the Tharsis region of Mars is the largest shield volcano known in the Solar System (see Fig. 1.9.1). It is more than 700 km in diameter and it rises to 24 km above the surrounding plains (cf. Carr & Greely 1980). Mauna Loa in Hawaii is the largest shield volcano on Earth; it is only 200 km in diameter and rises some 9 km above the floor of the Pacific Ocean.

Strombolian eruptions

Strombolian eruptions are named after the small (12.2 km^2) volcanic island of Stromboli which is the northernmost island of the Aeolian Archipelago to the north of Sicily in the Tyrrhenian Sea. An ideal Strombolian eruption has a volcanic explosivity index of 1 or 2. Such eruptions usually consist of frequent, small to moderate discharges of incandescent scoria and bombs. Francis (1976: 108) has described Strombolian eruptions as being a 'bit noisier' than Hawaiian eruptions but not particularly dangerous. The later statement is verified by the positions of the two main villages on the island of Stromboli as they are both approximately 2 km from the main active vent (cf. Vallari 1980). The materials ejected by Strombolian eruptions are usually basaltic, or andesitic, in composition; and as such materials are not ejected very far from the vent they tend to collect together to form scoria cones. Stromboli has an almost perfect conical form both above and below the sea. It is a *strato-volcano*, or composite volcano. The main edifice is constructed of alternating layers of lava and pyroclastic materials, and it is cut by a variety of dykes and sills.

Blackburn et al. (1976) have made a detailed study of the *mechanisms and dynamics of Strombolian activity*. According to them, this type of activity consists of a series of discrete explosions separated by periods of inactivity that vary in length from less than 0.1 s to several hours. At Stromboli on 25 April 1975 the explosions occurred at intervals of 12 minutes, from one, or more, of six vents; and the duration of individual explosions varied from 3 to 10 s. They propose that Strombolian explosions are largely the result of the bursting of individual bubbles, or clusters of bubbles, within the magma. In a column of magma, bubbles of those gases that are not particularly soluble in the magma, nucleate first. These nuclei grow as the more soluble, and more abundant, gas species diffuse into them. Eventually, large bubbles form and move through the rising magma leaching out smaller pockets of gas; when bubbles burst, the gas decompresses and escapes at a high velocity. On Earth the speed of the escaping gas, and entrained pyroclasts, is soon slowed down by atmospheric drag.

Vulcanian eruptions

Vulcanian eruptions are also named after a small (22 km²) volcanic island in the Aeolian Archipelago. Vulcano, the type volcano, is the southernmost island in the group and it has been intermittently active throughout history. It is believed to have been particularly active in classical Greek and Roman times. An ideal Vulcanian eruption has a volcanic explosivity index of 2, 3 or 4; it ejects moderately large volumes of pyroclastic material, and on Earth the height of the eruptive column is usually between 3 and 15 km. Vulcanian eruptions may be produced by magmas of many different compositions but they are usually felsic. The active vent on Vulcano is Fossa di Vulcano and forms a steep composite cone that lies within a large caldera. The pyroclastic materials and lavas of Fossa di Vulcano range in composition from K-rich, silica under-saturated leucite tephrites to highly potassic trachtes and rhyolites (cf. Vallari 1980: 47).

Vulcanian eruptions usually begin with a series of *phreatic explosions* that eject lithic debris from the volcanic conduit. Such phreatic explosions are usually caused by the heating and consequent rapid expansion of ground water due to the upward movement of magma. During the main phase of the eruption, vitric ash, lapilli and volcanic bombs are ejected. These pyroclastic air-fall deposits tend to be well bedded and sorted, and more widely dispersed than those associated with Strombolian eruptions. Pyroclastic flow and surge deposits may occur interbedded with the air-fall deposits (see Section 8.4). Many Vulcanian eruptive cycles end with the extrusion of thick flows of viscous felsic lava.

Plinian eruptions

The word Plinian was originally used to describe the AD 79 eruption of Vesuvio in Italy and commemorated Pliny the Younger's account of the eruption. The term Plinian eruption is now used to describe eruptions that are considered to be essentially similar to the AD 79 event. At present, such eruptions are usually defined as exceptionally powerful, continuous gas blast eruptions which eject copious pumice (cf. Walker & Croasdale 1971). An ideal Plinian eruption has a volcanic explosivity index of 4, 5 or 6, it ejects large volumes (1–10 km³) of pyroclastic materials, and on Earth it has an eruptive column that is over 15 km in height. Some are short-lived explosions of gas-rich, silicic magma that precede the quiet extrusion of more mafic lava. In 1947–48, Hekla in Iceland produced such an eruption. Other Plinian eruptions are of longer duration and eject large volumes of silicic pumice. Examples of the latter type include Crater Lake–Mount Mazama, Oregon, USA (4650 BC), Santorini, Greece (1470 BC) and Krakatau, Sunda Strait, Indonesia (AD 1883). All these eruptions had volcanic explosivity indices of 6.

Modern examples of Plinian eruptions include Bezymianny Volcano in Kamchatka, USSR, and Mount St Helens, Washington, USA (cf. Gorschkov 1959; Eichelberger & Hayes 1982). On 30 March 1956 an explosion, with a volcanic explosivity index of 5, blew the upper 200 m off the 3102 m high cone of Bezymianny Volcano. The blast was not vertical but inclined to the east at an angle of between 30–40° to the horizon.

The eruption column expanded and eventually reached a height of 38 km. Trees up to 25 km from the vent were felled by the force of the initial blast. Approximately 4 km³ of pyroclastic material were ejected over an area of 57 000 km². At Mount St Helens the blast, or surge, event can be separated from the more typical Plinian phase. At 8.32 on 18 May 1980, a 5.1 magnitude earthquake occurred at a shallow depth beneath the cone of the volcano. This triggered a 2.3 km³ landslide on the bulging north slope of the cone. Within seconds, a blast issued from the new scarp created by the landslide, and it swept northwards as a high-velocity, debris-laden cloud. This cloud laid down a deposit containing fragments of the old cone, organic debris and juvenile microvesicular dacite. In the valleys near the volcano these ground-surge deposits were soon overlain by pyroclastic flow deposits of similar chemical composition and air-fall deposits from the expanding eruption column above the volcano. According to Decker and Decker (1981), the thermal and mechanical energy released at Mount St Helens on 18 May 1980 was approximately 1.7×10^{18} joules, and it was released over a 9-hour period (that is, 5×10^{13} J/s or watts). The eruption column reached altitudes in excess of 20 km for much of the day, but began to wane at 17.30 hours. High-altitude winds blew to the north-west and by mid-morning ash was falling in central Washington State; and by 15.00 hours on 18 May the town of Spokane, 430 km north-east of the volcano, experienced darkness produced by the blowing and falling ash. According to Eichelberger and Hayes (1982: 7727), the initial devastating blast, or surge, phase in the 18 May eruption of Mount St Helens was triggered by the landslide that 'reduced the confining pressure on a magmatic and/or hydrothermal reservoir within the cone and resulted in rapid expansion of gases contained within this system'. After the explosive eruptions of June, August and October 1980, a volcanic dome developed in the crater of Mount St Helens (see Section 8.4); and during the following two years each new eruption resulted in the addition of another small (1×10^6 to 4×10^6 m³) lobe of dacitic lava to the surface of the growing composite dome. According to Swanson et al. (1983), before each of these eruptions there was a brief period of tumescence, or swelling, and this process has added some 15 per cent to the volume of the dome. In January 1983 the volcanic dome was approximately 600 m long, 500 m wide and 205 m high, and it had a volume in excess of 30×10^6 m³.

Ultraplinian eruptions

The volcanic explosivity indices of ultraplinian (or Toba-type) eruptions are significantly larger than the AD 79 eruption of Vesuvio. It is proposed that this class of eruption has a volcanic explosivity index of 7 or 8, ejects more than 10 km³ of pyroclastic materials, and on Earth the eruptive column injects significant volumes of pyroclastic material into the stratosphere. Eruptions of this explosivity are generally associated with volcano-tectonic depressions rather than positive volcanic landforms. Walker (1981a: p. 328) has shown that the most powerful and violent Plinian and ultraplinian eruptions produce unimpressive-looking pyroclastic deposits in the area immediately surrounding the vent. The dispersal of pyroclastic products in ultraplinian eruptions is usually so widespread that the deposits in the area close to the vent are generally not sufficiently thick to balance the subsidence resulting from the removal of magma. Walker (1981) regards the Taupo Volcanic Centre as an *inverse volcano* with the vent in a depression (Lake Taupo) surrounded by a low plateau of pyroclastic materials. Walker (1980: 69) regards the *Taupo pumice* of approximately AD 186 as a product of an ultraplinian eruption, because although 'the maximum thickness is only 1.8 m, the volume is 24 km³, and about 80 per cent of this has fallen at sea farther than 220 km from source'. The only historical ultraplinian eruption was that of Tambora Volcano in the Lesser Sunda Islands, Indonesia in 1815. According to Simkin et al. (1981: 22 and 57), this eruption had a volcanic explosivity index of 7 and produced more than 100 km³ of pyroclastic materials.

A very large ultraplinian eruption is believed to have issued from the Toba Volcano – tectonic depression in northern Sumatra, Indonesia in approximately 73 000 BC. This eruption produced the Toba rhyolitic tephra layer which occurs on Sumatra and also in deep-sea sediment cores over vast areas in the north-eastern Indian Ocean (cf. Westerveld 1952). According to Ninkovich et al. (1978: 1), the 73 000 BC eruption of the Toba Volcanic Centre produced a caldera that was 100×30 km in area, rhyolitic pyroclastic-flow deposits that cover an area of 20 000 km², and a submarine tephra layer that blankets an area in excess of 5 million km². The volume of rhyolitic material ejected by this ultraplinian eruptive event was greater than 1000 km³ of dense rock. The size of this volcanic event can be gauged if it is compared with the 1470 BC eruption of Santorini in Greece. The latter is regarded as important because it is often claimed that it was directly, or indirectly, responsible for the sudden collapse of the Minoan civilization on Crete to the south of Santorini (cf. Vitaliano 1973: 179). This ultraplinian eruption, however, produced only 13 km³ of dense rock.

Another large ultraplinian eruption is believed to have produced the Los Chocoyos Ash that was ejected from Atitlan Volcano in Guatemala approximately 85 000 years ago (cf. Rose et al. 1979). It is the most extensive silicic pyroclastic deposit in northern Central America; it contains more than 200 km³ of dense rock; and it is found in deep-sea cores from the Pacific Ocean, the Gulf of Mexico and the Caribbean Sea.

Extraterrestrial volcanic landforms

Thus far our discussion of volcanic activity has been mainly concerned with the Earth; however, all the terrestrial planets, together with the Jovian satellite Io, display surface features that are currently interpreted as being of volcanic origin. In recent years the study of extraterrestrial environments, landforms and materials has forced volcanologists to re-examine their ideas on eruptive mechanisms and the origin of volcanic landforms. This is because on the various planetary bodies studied at least some of the parameters that are significant during the extrusion and dispersal of volcanic products differ from those found on Earth, whereas others are essentially the same. Examples of such parameters are surface gravity, radius of curvature of the planet, chemical composition of the volcanic material, the presence or absence, and nature, of atmospheres and hydrospheres. If the same amount of pyroclastic material was ejected from similar volcanic vents on a number of different planets, the heights reached, and the distances travelled by the particles, would be a function of the velocity at which they were ejected, the surface gravity of the particular planet, and surface forces, such as atmospheric or hydrospheric drag, acting on the particles (see Table 1.9.2). Whitford-Stark (1982: 114) has calculated that if a particle 1 cm in diameter, with a density of 2.5×10^3 kg/m³, is ejected at 600 m/s, at an ejection angle of 45°, from a land surface on Earth, it will travel 0.25 km. If, however, the Earth did not have an atmosphere, the same particles ejected under the same conditions would travel 36 km. On the Moon, where the surface gravity is one-sixth of that on Earth and there is essentially no atmosphere or hydrosphere, a similar particle ejected under the conditions proposed above would travel 950 times further than on Earth. It is thus evident that volcanic landforms constructed of pyroclastic materials on the Moon should be quite different in shape from their counterparts on Earth (cf. McGetchin & Head 1973).

One would thus expect different volcanic landforms to evolve on planets with different atmospheric densities at their surfaces (see Table 1.9.2). Atmospheres not only impose drag on particles in ballistic flight, but they also help propagate eruption columns. For example, the volatile constituents escaping from a lunar volcano would not be confined by atmospheric pressure, nor would there be any turbulent mixing between the eruption column and the non-

Table 1.9.2 Some basic facts about the terrestrial planets

	Mercury	Venus	Earth	Moon	Mars
Mass ($\times 10^{24}$ kg)	0.33	4.87	5.97	0.073	0.64
Equatorial radius (km)	2439	6050	6378	1738	3398
Mean density (kg/m³)	5420	5250	5520	3340	3940
Equatorial surface gravity (m/s²)	3.78	8.60	9.78	1.62	3.72
Equatorial escape velocity (km/s)	4.3	10.3	11.2	2.38	5.0
Surface temperature (°K)	100–625	753	295	100–385	250
Mean distance from the Sun ($\times 10^6$ km)	57.9	108.2	149.6	149.6	227.9
Surface atmospheric pressure (Pa)*	10^{-7}	9.0×10^6	1.0×10^5	10^{-9}	6.0×10^{-2}

* Note: 1 millibar (mb) = 100 pascals (Pa) = 100 N per m².

existent atmosphere. Conditions would be quite different on Venus as its atmosphere is approximately a hundred times more dense than that of the Earth. Atmospheric drag would be high, but escaping volcanic gases would be buoyed up by the dense atmosphere.

The distribution of volcanoes is strongly influenced by the nature and extent of crustal fractures. It is postulated that most of the fractures that controlled volcanic activity on the Moon were produced by *impact cratering by meteoroids*. Similar cratering and fracturing of the crust was probably important on Earth during the early Archaean. At present, the active volcanoes of Earth are mainly found at plate boundaries (see Fig. 1.5.1), or less frequently along major intraplate fractures. Such fractures are often spaced at intervals that are directly related to the thickness of the lithosphere (cf. Vogt 1974; Mohr & Wood 1976). On a dynamic planet such as Earth, the distribution of volcanoes keeps changing, whereas on a planet such as Mars, where plate tectonics probably never operated, volcanic landforms are significantly different and often much larger. It has, for example, been proposed that some Martian shield volcanoes remained in a fixed position over an active source of upwelling magma for periods of the order of hundreds of millions of years (cf. Francis 1981: 236).

Martian volcanoes

According to the authors of the *Basaltic Volcanism Study Project* (1981: 772), 'Mars has a rich and diverse array of volcanic landforms that range in size from several hundred kilometers across down to the resolution limit of available images'. These landforms are unevenly distributed across the surface of the planet, and it is convenient to divide the planet into two distinct regions, or hemispheres. Most of the southern hemisphere is densely cratered, and the terrain resembles the lunar highlands. It is generally believed that this terrain formed very early in the history of Mars. The sparsely-cratered volcanic plains of the northern hemisphere stand between 2 and 3 km lower than the southern plains. They are mainly covered by volcanic flows and wind-blown deposits. In a few areas, spectacular volcanic landforms rise above these northern plains. These are mainly shield volcanoes and generally occur in either the Tharsis volcanic province,

centred at 10 °N and 110 °W, or the Elysium volcanic province, centred at 25 °N and 210 °W. The Tharsis is the largest province and comprises all the volcanic materials of the Tharsis Dome (see Fig. 1.9.1). It includes Olympus Mons in the north-western edge of the dome and Alba Patera on the northern edge. The dome is an elongate topographic bulge that is over 7 km high and more than 7000 km long. It is cut by an extensive system of radial fractures and embellished with a variety of spectacular volcanic landforms. The volcanoes of the Elysium province are also situated on a huge dome, 2000 km across and 5 km high.

Alba Patera (40 °N, 110 °W) only rises to an elevation of 5 km above the surrounding plains, yet it has the largest outcrop area of all the Martian volcanoes. It is at least 1100 km in diameter, and the central caldera complex is approximately 150 km in diameter. Many faults and fractures, including a prominent ring fracture, cut the edifice. The gentle slopes of the volcano are covered by many different types of flows. Some have been called *sheet flows* which have well-developed lobate flow-fronts, and they are usually several hundred km long and tens of km wide. Other flows have been described as *tube-fed flows*; they now appear as radial lines of ridges and partly collapsed tubes. According to the authors of the BVSP (1981: 780), the extensive flow sheets formed as the result of the rapid eruption of large volumes of lava, whereas the tube-fed flows formed when large volumes of lava were extruded at a slower rate.

Paterae (Latin, *patera*, saucer) of different ages have been described from many parts of Mars (cf. Mutch et al. 1976). The characteristic features of this volcanic landform are: (a) they have less vertical relief relative to their outcrop area than the shield volcanoes; (b) they have central depressions that are large compared to their overall size; and (c) their overall form is like an inverted saucer. Most paterae occur in the Tharsis and Elysium provinces; however some, such as Apollinaris Patera (8 °S, 186 °W), occur within the ancient cratered terrain.

In the Tharsis province, three huge shield volcanoes, known as Ascreus Mons, Pavonis Mons and Arsia Mons, occur on a south-west–north-east trending line that crosses the Tharsis Dome (see Fig. 1.9.1). This trend is parallel to a major fracture system that continues both to the north-east and south-west of the line of volcanoes. These volcanoes are huge by Earth standards:

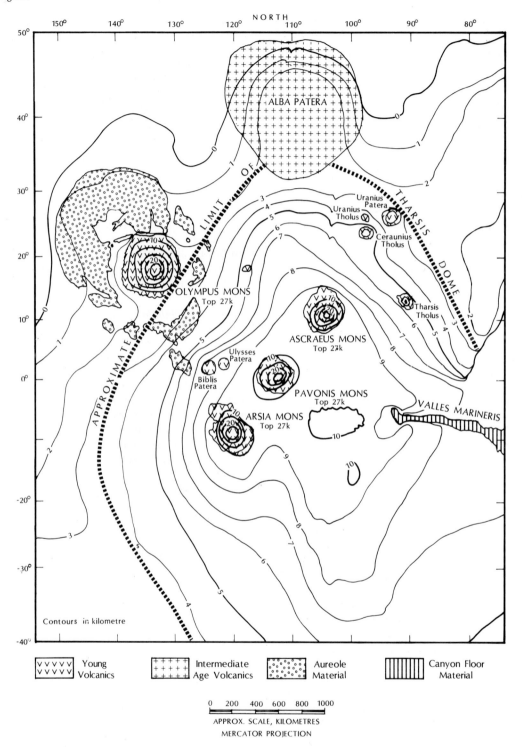

Fig. 1.9.1 The Tharsis Dome region of Mars, showing the relationship between the dome and the Tharsis Montes shield volcanoes (Ascraeus Mons, Pavonis Mons and Arsia Mons), and the Valles Marineris. This sketch map also shows the form and relative sizes of Olympus Mons and Alba Patera. Adapted from the *Geologic Map of Mars* by Scott and Carr (1978).

they are approximately 400 km in diameter and rise some 17 km above the surrounding plains. Olympus Mons, the tallest volcano on Mars (24 km) is situated 1600 km north-west of these volcanoes. At present, this huge volcano has an estimated volume of approximately 2.6×10^6 km^3. Olympus Mons has gently sloping flanks that become less steep in the summit area and in the distal zone. The central zone contains a complex summit caldera composed of several coalescing depressions (see Fig. 1.9.2). On the upper flanks of the volcano there are a series of roughly concentric terraces that are typically 15–50 km across and separated from one another by a sharp break in slope. The presence of numerous narrow lava flows give photographs of Olympus Mons a radial texture that extends outwards from the summit caldera. A spectacular, roughly circular, escarpment, that is generally between 1 and 4 km high and approximately 550 km in diameter, surrounds most of the volcano (cf. Morris & Dwornik 1978). In many places, lava flows drape over the escarpment and extend several tens of km beyond it. Most of the volcanic features of the main edifice are similar to those found on shield volcanoes from Earth, and are thus consistent with the model that they formed as the result of the slow accumulation of fluid lava of low viscosity and low yield strength. A feature of Olympus Mons that appears to have no counterpart on Earth is its *aureole*. This consists of blocks of textured, or grooved, terrain that surround the main edifice and extend for up to 1000 km from the summit caldera. The origin of the aureole is not known, but it has been suggested that it might represent: (a) a series of eroded ash-flow tuffs; (b) a number of gigantic lahars; or (c) jökullhlaup deposits.

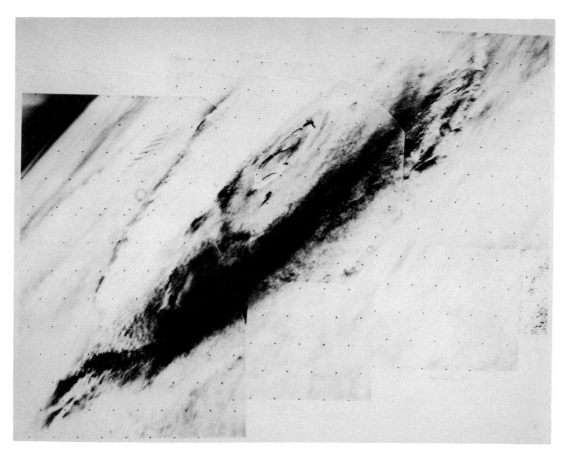

Fig. 1.9.2 An oblique view of the summit of Olympus Mons Shield Volcano, Mars, showing the complex summit caldera that is more than 75 km in diameter. This Viking photograph has been provided by the 'U.S. National Space Science Data Center through the World Data Center-A for Rockets and Satellites' (Viking, 17444).

The three shield volcanoes of the Tharsis Dome are all broadly similar to Olympus Mons, yet they all have some minor distinctive characteristics. Their main edifices are between 350 and 450 km across, and their summits stand approximately 17–19 km above the surrounding plains. They all have complex summit calderas and flanks with average slopes of 4–6°. Arsia Mons, for example, has a summit caldera that is 110 km in diameter, and is surrounded by concentric faults. There are also many graben-like structures and embayments on the flanks of the edifice. The embayments are the source of numerous flows that are interpreted as being younger than the main shield-building event. According to Carr and Greeley (1980: 179), each of these volcanoes follows an essentially similar evolutionary trend. First, the construction of the main shield. This event was probably accompanied by repeated subsidence of the central zone to form the summit caldera. In the late stages of shield construction, eruptions were mainly confined to the north-east and south-west flanks and the shield became considerably modified by these eruptions from eccentric, or parasitic, vents. These vents supplied vast amounts of lava that flowed over the surrounding plains and buried the distal zone of the original edifice. The central and proximal zones of the original edifice were also modified by concentric and radial fractures and the formation of pitcraters.

Another Martian landform that appears to have been produced by a central eruptive mechanism is the *tholus* (Latin, *tholus*, dome). The term tholus is recognized by the International Astronomical Union as an isolated domical mountain, or hill, on Mars. On Earth, volcanic domes that occur inside the caldera of volcanoes are sometimes called *tholoids*. The tholi of Mars are usually smaller and have steeper slopes than the shield volcanoes; their flanks tend to be convex-upward. Examples occur in both the Tharsis and Elysium volcanic provinces. Ceranius Tholus (24 °N, 97 °W) occurs in the northern part of the Tharsis province, and it is a good example of this volcanic landform (see Fig. 1.9.3). It has a mean diameter of approximately 100 km, and lava flows, lava channels and collapsed lava tubes can be observed radiating out from the central caldera. Hecates Tholus (30 °N, 212 °W) in the Elysium province is larger, and it is approximately 180 km in diameter and 6 km high.

Cinder and spatter cones are not abundant on Mars. It is evident from the present photographic coverage that the major volcanic landforms do not contain the large numbers of eccentric, or parasitic cones, that are found on many of the large volcanoes of Earth. This probably means that the Martian lavas were erupted in such a fluid state that their contained gases escaped without generating explosive activity, or that the lavas originally had low volatile contents as compared to similar materials from Earth. With regard to cinder cones, it must be appreciated that Mars has a low surface gravity, a thin atmosphere and experiences occasional high winds, thus pyroclastic materials are likely to be widely dispersed. However, in the summit caldera of Arsia Mons (9 °S, 120 °W) one can recognize a fissure vent surrounded by spatter rings and/or spatter ramparts. Spatter is an accumulation of very fluid pyroclasts; and such pyroclasts often become welded together.

Venusian volcanoes

Venus and Earth have similar radii, masses and densities. These data, together with the data gleaned from limited studies of Venusian surface materials, have resulted in the proposal that Venus is a differentiated Earth-like planet with a crust mantle and core. The high surface temperature (470 °C) and surface atmospheric pressure (over 90 times greater than Earth) of Venus should greatly affect the shape of Venusian volcanic landforms. On Earth, a volcanic eruption analogous to an eruption on the surface of Venus would occur at a depth of 1 km beneath the sea. As we have already noted in the section on *island-building eruptions*, eruptions taking place at such pressures are normally non-explosive. If, however, pyroclastic materials were ejected into the Venusian atmosphere they would be strongly affected by both atmospheric drag and buoyancy. The presumed difference in density between volcanic gases and the atmosphere would be greater than on Earth, and convective thrusting might carry ejecta to great heights. Atmospheric drag would, however, rapidly slow down any materials in ballistic flight. It is anticipated that most Venusian eruptions would be of the effusive type, and the mobility of this lava would be greatly enhanced by the high surface temperatures and pressures, because both of these parameters would reduce the effective viscosity of the lava. The high pressure would also inhibit

Fig. 1.9.3 A moderate resolution view of Ceranius Tholus (24 °N, 97 °W) which is located in the northern part of the Tharsis province of Mars, and it shows radial lava flows, lava channels, and partly collapsed lava tubes on the flanks of the volcanic edifice. The elongate impact crater on the northern flank of the tholus has been breached by a lava flow that issued from a vent at the summit. Frame dimensions are 220 km × 236 km. This Viking photograph has been provided by the 'U.S. National Space Science Data Center through the World Data Center-A for Rockets and Satellites' (Viking, 516 A 24).

degassing which is a significant cooling mechanism on Earth (cf. BVSP 1981: 788–90).

Orbital radar has revealed that Venus contains at least two large shield-shaped landforms in the Beta Regio highlands. It has been claimed

that the landforms are large shield volcanoes with extremely low profiles. One of these, Theia Mons, has a summit depression which has been interpreted as a caldera. Both Theia Mons and Rhea Mons rise to an elevation of approximately

5 km above the surrounding plains and their flanks coalesce to form an elevated region that is approximately 800 km long. A number of other landforms on the surface of Venus such as Maxwell Montes, the highest point yet found on the planet, and Atla Regio on the eastern site of Aphrodite Terra, are at present tentatively regarded as being of volcanic origin. There is strong circumstantial evidence in support of the hypothesis that there are at present active volcanoes on Venus. This evidence consists of (a) reports of the injection of huge amounts sulphur dioxide into the Venusian atmosphere in the latter half of 1978, and (b) the discovery of the clustering of electrical discharges (lightning) in areas, such as the Beta Regio highlands, which contain young-looking volcanic landforms (cf. Anderson, 1984). Lightning is frequently associated with volcanic activity on Earth. A detailed study of the surface features of Venus will have to await future orbital radar imaging probes, such as VOIR.

Lunar volcanoes

From the Earth, the Moon is observed to have two main types of surface morphology: there are light-coloured, densely-cratered *highland* areas; and dark-coloured, relatively smooth, level, low-lying plains. The latter are known as *maria* (Latin, *mare*, sea), because Galileo Galilei (1610) believed that they were seas. Most of the maria are on the Earth-facing side of the Moon. The rocks that occupy this region are generally basaltic in composition and are called *mare basalts*. These basalts are the most impressive volcanic unit on the Moon, although they occupy only 17 per cent of it total surface area. Mapping of the surface rocks and landforms has revealed that the mare basalts crop out in three of the morphologic regions of the Moon: (a) as flows filling the centres of large circular multiringed basins such as the huge Mare Imbrium, or in concentric troughs that surround such circular basins, such as the Lacus Veris trough which borders the Mare Orientale; (b) as floods of lava that cover large irregular depressions such as the Mare Tranquillitatis; and (c) as relatively small rock units in the highlands, or on the floors of craters such as Plato.

One of the most striking morphological features of the maria are long, *sinuous scarps* or terraces. They are interpreted as congealed fronts that were once at the head of floods of basalt.

In the Mare Imbrium, such scarps may be up to 60 m high. Another prominent morphological feature of the maria, and also of the highland areas that adjoin the maria, are the *sinuous rilles*. Hadley Rille, which was studied during the Apollo 15 landing, is 135 km long. It has a meandering course and averages 1.2 km in width and 370 m in depth. Although the sinuous rilles are much larger than the lava channels and collapsed lava tubes found on Earth, they closely resemble these features. A large number of dome-shaped landforms occur both in the highlands and in the maria. Many of these edifices have regular forms; that is, they are circular in plan, 3–17 km in diameter and up to several hundred metres in height. Their flanks generally slope at less than 5°, and are convex in profile. Many of these domes have summit craters which are generally larger than those found in similar volcanic landforms from Earth. Large shield volcanoes such as those of Earth and Mars are not found on the Moon. A variety of volcanic domes, together with some volcanic cones, occur in the Marius Hills area (15 °N, 50 °W) of the Oceanus Procellarum. The volcanic cones occur in a range of sizes; however, the largest only reach a height of 500 m; these are interpreted as cinder or spatter cones that evolved from a magma with a relatively low volatile content.

On the *Geologic Map of the near side of the Moon* (Wilhelms & McCauley 1971) there is a rock unit called *dark mantling material*, and the type area is given as north-west of the crater Sulpicius Gallus (20 °N, 10 °E). Dark mantling deposits have been described from a number of areas of the Moon, including the Taurus–Littrow Valley which was the Apollo 17 landing site. In this valley the dark mantling materials were found to consist of small black and orange glass spheres. These spheres are interpreted as having formed by the eruption of a jet, or spray, of lava droplets (that is, a fire fountain).

Analysis of the morphologic and petrologic characteristics of the mare basalts indicates that they were usually extruded as massive outpourings of fluid, volatile-poor lava. However, the process of filling the mare basins took place over an extended period of time, between 4.1 and 2.5 Ga. Most of the feeder vents that have been identified consist of major crustal fractures associated with the major multiringed basins, or with smaller impact craters within the maria. Pyroclastic eruptions occasionally accompanied the larger eruptions of lava, and they probably demonstrate that volatiles were locally important. The scarps or terraces within the maria indicate that some of the flows were at least 50 m thick; however, overall the mare basalts represent but a surface veneer as they are seldom thicker than 2 km. There is strong geochemical and petrographic evidence in support of the concept of nonmare volcanism, particularly during the early history of the Moon. At present there is little morphologic information that is of use in reconstructing this episode in the volcanic evolution of the planet (cf. BSVP 1981: 749–64).

Volcanism on Mercury

High-resolution images of the whole of Mercury are not as yet available. Most of the images that have been obtained show terrain similar to that of the lunar highlands. There are no large shield volcanoes such as those on Venus, Earth and Mars: and as yet no unambiguous volcanic landforms have been described that are similar to those found in the lunar maria.

Volcanism on Io

Io is approximately the same size (equatorial radius 1816 km) and mean density (3500 kg/m³) as the Moon. During the Voyager I encounter with Jupiter in March 1979, Io was studied for a period of 6.5 days, and nine separate eruption clouds were observed (cf. Strom et al. 1981: 8593). Four months later, during the Voyager II encounter, eight of these volcanoes were still active. The eruption clouds of Io range in height from about 60 to over 300 km, and between 60 and 1100 km in diameter. It is estimated that the pyroclasts ejected by these eruptions were transported at velocities of between 0.4 and 1.0 km/s. Numerous surface deposits that appear to be similar to those associated with the active eruption clouds are interpreted as marking the sites of other recent eruptions. Most of the active and recent eruptions have occurred in the equatorial regions of the planet. According to Strom et al. (1981: 8619), the shapes of the eruption clouds appear to be related to the shapes of the vents. Highly symmetrical, umbrella-shaped eruption clouds seem to originate from circular to elliptical vents or calderas, whereas very diffuse eruption clouds appear to originate from long fissures. Some reach so high that they are regarded as the probable source of the large doughnut-shaped ring of atoms that surrounds Jupiter in the position of the orbit of Io.

There are many caldera on the surface of Io, and the largest is approximately 200 km in diameter. All of these caldera are apparently rimless, but they usually have steep inner walls and flat floors. Their shapes are highly variable and about half have flows associated with them, often several hundred km long and tens of km wide. It has been proposed that some flows formed as the result of lava overflowing from a lava lake. In recent maps of Io (cf. Briggs & Taylor 1982: 196–7), most of the volcanic landforms on this planet have been called paterae. Examples of such patera include Dazhbog Patera, with its large central caldera, and Loki Patera.

The volcanic activity responsible for generating the huge, long-lasting eruption clouds of Io is quite different from that normally found on Earth. On Earth, steam-blast eruptions that can produce ejection velocities of 0.5–0.6 km/s usually operate for only a few minutes. On Io at least eight eruptions have continued at high levels of activity, with ejection velocities of between 0.4–1.0 km/s, for at least 4 months, and probably much longer. This demonstrates that Io must have large reservoirs of volatiles that are able to supply gases to the vents for long periods of time. Consolmagno (1979: 397) has shown that the volcanoes of Io must be essentially anhydrous if the present high levels of activity have been sustained for a long period. No primordial gases would be expected to remain. It has been proposed that the volatile substance driving the explosive volcanoes of Io is elemental sulphur, possibly assisted by SO_2. There is now no doubt that sulphur is extremely abundant on the surface of Io. It is also likely that some of the lava flows observed are composed of sulphur. Flows of this composition are rare on Earth; however, the strato-volcano Siretoko-Iwo-Zan in Hokkaido, Japan, extruded some 200 tonnes of molten sulphur in 1936, and Kirishima Volcano, Kyushu, Japan has extruded molten sulphur on a number of occasions.

It has been estimated that the total heat flow on Io is approximately 2 W/m² (Matson et al. 1981: 1664). This value is much larger than the average for both the Earth (0.06 W/m²) and Moon (0.02 W/m²), and it implies that much of the interior of Io is at least partially molten. It is believed that the large amount of heat dissipated by Io comes from the following sources:

(a) the decay of radioactive isotopes; (b) the tidal stresses generated within Io by the interplay between the huge and nearby mass of Jupiter, and the other Galilean satellites of Jupiter, particularly Europa; and (c) the dissipation of electromagnetic energy inside Io as it moves through the powerful magnetic field that surrounds Jupiter.

Many models have been proposed to explain the volcanic activity that is characteristic of Io (cf. BVSP 1981: 692–3). Most of these models postulate that large areas of the planet are covered in a layer of solid sulphur and/or sulphur compounds. In some models it is proposed that hot, possibly basaltic, magma rises up into this layer where it vaporizes the sulphur and/or sulphur compounds. This produces the explosive type of volcanism found on Io. After such an explosion, or succession of explosions, a stream of liquid sulphur may flow from the active vent. Other workers have proposed that the explosive volcanism found on Io is essentially due to the presence of liquid SO_2 beneath a thin, solid upper crust. If this crust is ruptured, liquid SO_2 is ejected; it encounters very low atmospheric pressures and volatilizes explosively. In the cold atmosphere, the vapour soon condenses and forms small particles of SO_2-ice that eventually shower down on the surface of the planet. The colours that are characteristic of the surface of Io are yellow, orange and black. According to Carl Sagan (1981: 157–8),

'the pattern of colours that we see on Io resembles closely what we would expect if rivers and torrents and sheets of molten sulphur were pouring out of the mouths of the volcanoes: black sulphur, the hottest, near the top of the volcano; red and orange, including the rivers, nearby; and great plains covered by yellow sulphur at a greater remove'.

1.10 Mantle of the Earth

In Section 1.3 it was disclosed that the mantle is the second major shell of the Earth: it constitutes 84 per cent of the volume and 67 per cent of the mass of our planet. In most tectonic discussions the crust, and the relatively thin (10–50 km) uppermost layer of the mantle, are regarded as a single relatively strong unit known as the *litho-sphere*. Below this layer there is a structurally weak layer known as the *asthenosphere*, and it is on this layer that the lithospheric plates are considered to slide. The asthenosphere is also the layer in which isostatic adjustments occur. Such adjustments are required in order to maintain an equilibrium (comparable to floating) among lithospheric units of different mass and density. It is often assumed that the asthenosphere which is a tectonic concept, and the *low-velocity zone* which is a geophysical concept, are essentially the same. The low-velocity zone is generally some 100 km thick, and seismic waves usually travel within it at velocities (that is, 7.7 km/s) that are approximately 6 per cent slower than in the outermost mantle. However, on a global scale the physical properties, thickness and depth of this zone varies greatly. It is well developed in active tectonic regions, but poorly developed in old continental cratonic areas. Another property of the low-velocity zone is that it strongly attenuates seismic waves, which is interpreted as indicating that it usually contains a relatively small volume (≈ 1 per cent) of widely-disseminated melt.

The upper mantle has not as yet been directly sampled, thus a variety of indirect methods are used in attempts to discover its modal and chemical composition. Geophysical measurements, such as seismic velocity studies, set broad limits as to the composition of the upper mantle, and they also enable petrologists to recognize petrologically significant physical features, such as the low-velocity zone. The mean density of the upper mantle can be estimated by using the concept of isostasy, and comparing detailed gravity and seismic data from normal oceanic and continental sections through the crust and upper mantle. Such investigations have yielded densities that range from 3240 kg/m³ (3.24 g/cm³) to 3320 kg/³ (3.32 g/cm³ (cf. Ringwood 1975: 78–85). This range in densities is consistent with an upper mantle composed of peridotite (cf. Woollard 1970).

Studies of the abundance of the chemical elements in the Sun, meteorites (particularly carbonaceous chondrites) and other bodies of the Solar System have resulted in the production of cosmic abundance tables (see Table 1.10.1). These data, together with data on the physical properties of the mantle, have enabled geochemists to develop models of the chemical composition of the mantle (cf. Ringwood 1975). Petrologists have used petrographic, chemical

1 Phonolitic pyroclastic beds of Quaternary age that form part of the crater ring of the Laacher See Volcano in the East Eifel district of West Germany. This exposure in the Wingertsberg Quarry contains a lower essentially horizontally bedded sequence that is mainly composed of air-fall and pyroclastic flow deposits that are locally disrupted by bomb-sags, and a less regularly bedded upper sequence that contains primary structures characteristic of surge-deposits. See Section 12.1.

2 A congealed and subsided basaltic lava lake that developed in the Halemaumau vent within the caldera of Kilauea Volcano, Hawaii. This photograph was taken in 1975. See Section 1.9.

3 Recent black phonolitic lavas that spread out radially from the summit vent of the Teide strato-volcano, Tenerife in the Canary Archipelago. Stubby, steep-fronted, phonolitic flows can be observed on the Montaña Blanca to the east (or right) of Teide. See Sections 4.2 and 12.2.

4 The view to the east, from the summit of Teide stratovolcano, showing Montaña Blanca and the older bedded pyroclastic rocks and lavas of the arcuate Portillo-Tauce escarpment. This escarpment marks the edge of a huge collapse caldera that developed prior to the construction of the Teide volcanic edifice. The black blocky lavas in the foreground are phonolites and they overlie lighter pyroclastic rocks and brown phonolitic lavas. See Sections 4.2 and 12.2.

5 A lava gutter, or channel, that developed in the 1949-west basanitic flows on San Miguel de La Palma in the Canary Archipelago. Such gutters usually occur in areas where the lava flowed down a steep slope. See Section 12.2.

6 The eroded remains of volcanic plugs and dykes of sodic trachyte within the complex central core of the Middle Miocene Warrumbungle Volcano of the Coonabarabran district, New South Wales, Australia. See Sections 7.6 and 7.8.

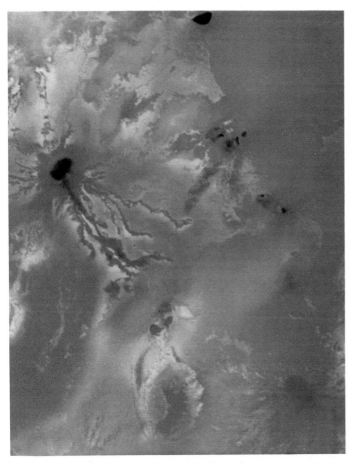

7 A view of the surface of Io which is the innermost Galilean satellite of Jupiter, showing Ra Patera (8°S lat., 326° long.). The dark spots are volcanic vents with radiating lava flows of sulphur. The width of this picture is approximately 900 kilometres. See Section 1.9. This Voyager I photograph has been provided by the "U.S. National Space Science Data Center through the World Data Center – A for Rockets and Satellites" (Voyager I, P-21277).

8 Shapes taken by magmas that have cooled within the crust. See Table 1.8.1 for a description of the shapes and sizes of the common magmatic intrusive bodies. (No. 65, Van Rose and Mercer: *Volcanoes*, HMSO: Institute of Geological Sciences) (Reproduced by permission of the Director, British Geological Survey (NERC) NERC Copyright reserved).

9 Igneous activity: magma generation and emplacement related to plate boundaries (No. 55, Van Rose and Mercer: *Volcanoes*, HMSO: Institute of Geological Sciences). (Reproduced by permission of the Director, British Geological Survey (NERC) NERC copyright reserved). See Section 4.3.

10 The deeply dissected pyroclastic flow deposits that crop out in the Valley of Ten Thousand Smokes, Alaska. In June 1912 some ten cubic kilometres of ignimbrites were extruded in this area of the Katmai National Monument. See Section 1.9 for a full description of this eruption. (Photograph by Winfield Parks (c) 1975 National Geographic Society).

Table 1.10.1 Abundance of the elements

Element	Cameron 1982 (atoms/10^6 Si)	Anders & Ebihara 1982 (atoms/10^6 Si)	Orgueil CI chondrite Anders & Ebihara 1982	Unfractionated REE Anders & Ebihara 1982 (p.p.b.)
1 H	2.66×10^{10}	2.72×10^{10}	2.02%	
2 He	1.8×10^9	2.18×10^9	56 μl/kg	
3 Li	60	59.7	1.59 p.p.m.	
4 Be	1.2	0.78	26.7 p.p.b.	
5 B	9	24	1.25 p.p.m.	
6 C	1.11×10^7	1.21×10^7	3.45%	
7 N	2.31×10^6	2.48×10^6	3180 p.p.m.	
8 O	1.84×10^7	2.01×10^7	46.4%	
9 F	780	843	58.2 p.p.m.	
10 Ne	2.6×10^6	3.76×10^6	203 nl/kg	
11 Na	6.0×10^4	5.70×10^4	4830 p.p.m.	
12 Mg	1.06×10^6	1.075×10^6	9.55%	
13 Al	8.5×10^4	8.49×10^4	8620 p.p.m.	
14 Si	1.00×10^6	1.00×10^6	10.67%	
15 P	6500	1.04×10^4	1180 p.p.m.	
16 S	5.0×10^5	5.15×10^5	5.25%	
17 Cl	4740	5240	698 p.p.m.	
18 Ar	1.06×10^5	1.04×10^5	751 nl/kg	
19 K	3500	3700	569 p.p.m.	
20 Ca	6.25×10^4	6.11×10^4	9020 p.p.m.	
21 Sc	31	33.8	5.76 p.p.m.	
22 Ti	2400	2400	436 p.p.m.	
23 V	254	295	56.7 p.p.m.	
24 Cr	1.27×10^4	1.34×10^4	2650 p.p.m.	
25 Mg	9300	9510	1960 p.p.m.	
26 Fe	9.0×10^5	9.00×10^5	18.51%	
27 Co	2200	2250	509 p.p.m.	
28 Ni	4.78×10^4	4.93×10^4	1.10%	
29 Cu	540	514	112 p.p.m.	
30 Zn	1260	1260	308 p.p.m.	
31 Ga	38	37.8	10.1 p.p.m.	
32 Ge	117	118	32.2 p.p.m.	
33 As	6.2	6.79	1.91 p.p.m.	
34 Se	67	62.1	18.2 p.p.m.	
35 Br	9.2	11.8	3.56 p.p.m.	
36 Kr	41.3	45.3	8.7 nl/kg	
37 Rb	6.1	7.09	2.30 p.p.m.	
38 Sr	22.9	23.8	7.91 p.p.m.	
39 Y	4.8	4.64	1.50 p.p.m.	
40 Zr	12	10.7	3.69 p.p.m.	
41 Nb	0.9	0.71	250 p.p.b.	
42 Mo	4.0	2.52	920 p.p.b.	
44 Ru	1.9	1.86	714 p.p.b.	
45 Rh	0.40	0.344	134 p.p.b.	
46 Pd	1.3	1.39	557 p.p.b.	
47 Ag	0.46	0.529	220 p.p.b.	
48 Cd	1.55	1.69	673 p.p.b.	
49 In	0.19	0.184	77.8 p.p.b.	
50 Sn	3.7	3.82	1680 p.p.b.	
51 Sb	0.31	0.352	155 p.p.b.	
52 Te	6.5	4.91	2280 p.p.b.	
53 I	1.27	9.90	430 p.p.b.	
54 Xe	5.84	4.35	8.6 nl/kg	
55 Cs	0.39	0.372	186 p.p.b.	

Table 1.10.1 (*Cont'd*)

Element	Cameron 1982 (atoms/10^6 Si)	Anders & Ebihara 1982 (atoms/^{6} Si)	Orgueil CI chondrite	Unfractionated REE Anders & Ebihara 1982 (p.p.b.)
56 Ba	4.8	4.36	2270 p.p.b.	
57 La	0.37	0.448	236 p.p.b.	236
58 Ce	1.2	1.16	619 p.p.b.	616
59 Pr	0.18	0.174	90 p.p.b.	92.9
60 Nd	0.79	0.836	462 p.p.b.	457
62 Sm	0.24	0.261	142 p.p.b.	149
63 Eu	0.094	0.0972	54.3 p.p.b.	56.0
64 Gd	0.42	0.331	196 p.p.b.	197
65 Tb	0.076	0.0589	35.3 p.p.b.	35.5
66 Dy	0.37	0.398	242 p.p.b.	245
67 Ho	0.092	0.0875	54 p.p.b.	54.7
68 Er	0.23	0.253	160 p.p.b.	160
69 Tm	0.035	0.0386	22 p.p.b.	24.7
70 Yb	0.20	0.243	166 p.p.b.	159
71 Lu	0.035	0.0369	24.3 p.p.b.	24.5
72 Hf	0.17	0.176	119 p.p.b.	
73 Ta	0.020	0.0226	17 p.p.b.	
74 W	0.30	0.137	89 p.p.b.	
75 Re	0.051	0.0507	36.9 p.p.b.	
76 Os	0.69	0.717	669 p.p.b.	
77 Ir	0.72	0.660	473 p.p.b.	
78 Pt	1.41	1.37	953 p.p.b.	
79 Au	0.21	0.186	145 p.p.b.	
80 Hg	0.21	0.52	390 p.p.b.	
81 Tl	0.19	0.184	143 p.p.b.	
82 Pb	2.6	3.15	2430 p.p.b.	
83 Bi	0.14	0.144	111 p.p.b.	
90 Th	0.045	0.0335	28.6 p.p.b.	
92 U	0.027	0.0090	8.1 p.p.b.	

The abundances of the gases He, Ne, Ar, Kr and Xe for the Orgueil CI chondrite are given in nl/kg (nanolitres per kilogram) or μl/kg (microlitres per kilogram) at standard temperature (0 °C) and pressure (1.01325 × 10^5 Pa). p.p.m. = parts per million (10^6), p.p.b. = parts per 'billion' (10^9).

and isotopic data obtained from rocks that are considered to have congealed from primary magmas, together with special experimental studies, in order to develop independent models of its chemical and modal composition. Occasionally solid materials, that are interpreted as having once been part of the upper mantle, are discovered at the surface. Most of these samples occur as blocks, or slices of ultramafic rock that have been thrust, or obducted, onto, or into, the crust (see Ch. 11). *Obduction* is the overthrusting of a slab of oceanic lithosphere onto the leading edge of a plate of continental lithosphere. Such tectonic events may result in slabs of sub-oceanic upper mantle material being thrust onto the surface of the Earth. Samples of upper mantle rocks, from beneath the continental crust, are usually obtained as xenoliths in volcanic/-subvolcanic rocks, such as kimberlites, carbon-atites, alkalic basalts and a variety of other 'alkaline rocks'. Further chemical and modal data on the upper mantle can be obtained from the study of other ultramafic rocks, such as the Tinaquillo Peridotite of Venezuela. Rocks from this complex are usually interpreted as being emplaced directly from the mantle in a hot quasi-solid diapir.

Xenoliths (or nodules) provide the freshest samples of the mantle. Many of these contain evidence of decompression reactions, such as disequilibrium partial melting. It is widely accepted that xenoliths are usually transported rapidly to the surface. Velocities of the order of 0.01–0.5 m/s have been proposed for the xenoliths in alkalic basalts (cf. Spera 1980) and between 7 and 20 m/s for those in kimberlites (cf. Anderson 1979). If the upward movement of these xenolith-bearing magmas was this rapid, it is probable that their compositions have not been significantly modified during transit to the surface; thus volcanic rocks that carry xenoliths of mantle origin generally have primary, or near primary, compositions. This concept implies that not all primary magmas are necessarily picritic, or komatiitic, in composition.

Spinel lherzolites

The most abundant and widespread group of xenoliths derived from the upper mantle are spinel lherzolites. They are usually found in alkalic basalt eruptive centres, and their host rocks are commonly basanites or nephelinites. Both of these host rocks are feldlspathoid-bearing rocks of basaltic character (see Ch. 3). Lherzolites are *two-pyroxene peridotites*, thus their essential minerals are olivine, orthopyroxene and clinopyroxene. Xenoliths of relatively fresh spinel lherzolite set in a scoriaceous basanitic host rock are, for example, found at Kilbourne Hole, New Mexico, USA. Most of the reference suite of spinel lherzolites used in the Basaltic Volcanism

Study Project (1981: 283–4) were collected from this locality. The modal compositions of these lherzolites fall within the following range: forsteritic olivines 60–70 per cent; aluminous enstatite 10–30 per cent; aluminous chrome diopside 8–12 per cent; aluminous chrome spinel 3–13 per cent; together with minor amounts of sulphides and glass. Table 1.10.2 contains the mean chemical composition of the spinel lherzolite xenoliths from Kilbourne Hole, and Maaløe and Aoki's mean value for 384 spinel lherzolites from both continental and oceanic areas. Maaløe and Aoki (1977: 179) regard their value as representative of the composition of the uppermost mantle above the asthenosphere.

Garnet lherzolites

The xenoliths found in the rare rock called *kimberlite* are particularly important in our search for the composition of the upper mantle, because kimberlitic magmas are generated at depths of at least 150 km, and the xenoliths they contain may have been plucked from anywhere within a

Table 1.10.2 Possible major element compositions of the upper mantle

	1	2	3	4	5	6	7
SiO_2	44.48	44.20	46.93	44.10	45.83	43.59	45.1
TiO_2	0.1	0.13	0.04	0.11	0.09	0.03	0.2
Al_2O_3	3.34	2.05	1.66	3.60	1.57	1.27	4.6
Cr_2O_3	0.46	0.44	0.49	0.88	0.32	0.43	0.3
ΣFeO	8.72	8.29	6.13	14.12	6.90	5.71	7.9
MnO	0.13	0.13	0.11	0.17	0.11	0.07	0.1
NiO	0.26	0.28	0.26	nd	0.29	0.31	0.2
MgO	39.24	42.21	41.16	33.45	43.41	48.39	38.1
CaO	3.14	1.92	0.92	2.90	1.16	0.21	3.1
Na_2O	0.27	0.27	0.18	0.21	0.16	0.06	0.4
K_2O	0.03	0.06	0.12	0.03	0.12	0.07	0.02
P_2O_5	0.01	0.03	0.03	0.01	0.04	0.00	0.02
H_2O^+	nd	nd	1.57	nd	nd	nd	—
CO_2	0.03	nd	0.09	nd	nd	0.07	—
SUM	100.23	99.95	99.69	99.58	100.0	100.21	100.0

1. Mean chemical composition of eight spinel lherzolite xenoliths from Kilbourne Hole, New Mexico, USA (after BVSP 1981: 288)
2. Mean chemical composition of 384 spinel lherzolite xenoliths (after Maaløe and Aoki 1977: 165)
3. Mean chemical composition of four garnet lherzolite (sensu lato) xenoliths from Matsoku Kimberlite, Lesotho (after BVSP 1981: 288)
4. Chemical composition of a garnet lherzolite (senu stricto) xenolith from Matsolu Kimberlite, Lesotho. This rock contains 42.0 per cent olivine, 38.4 per cent orthopyrozene, 9.2 per cent chromium diopside and 10.4 per cent garnet. After Cox, Gurney & Harte 1973: 93, Spec. No. LBM 12.
5. Mean chemical composition of sixty-one garnet lherzolite (sensu lato) xenoliths (after Carswell 1980: 135). Analysis recalculated on a H_2O and CO_2 free basis
6. Chemical composition of a garnet-spinel harzburgite found in carbonatite from the Lashaine Volcano, northern Tanzania (after BVSP 1981: 288)
7. Chemical composition of the 'average mantle pyrolite' (after Ringwood 1975: 188)

Table 1.10.3 Some trace element data in p.p.m. on xenoliths from the upper mantle

	1	3	6		1	3	6
C	122	295	269	La	0.17	2.12	0.59
S	140	75	49	Ce	0.39	5.25	0.64
Sc	14.43	7.9	6.4	Nd	—	—	—
Cr	3082	3340	2970	Sm	0.26	0.38	0.075
Co	109	94	103	Eu	0.11	0.12	0.024
Ni	2010	1986	2435	Yb	0.34	—	0.047
Zn	44	31	30	Lu	0.057	0.012	0.008
Ge	860	700	620	Hf	0.15	0.21	0.13
Se	32	8.5	2.2	Re	0.16	0.12	0.009
Pd	5.7	5.1	0.09	Os	3.1	6.1	0.059
Ag	8.2	5.1	1.3	Ir	3.7	7.0	0.052
Cd	49	80	9	Au	1.0	1.19	0.37
In	12	2	2	Tl	1.1	15	4.2
Sb	2.6	6.0	—	Bi	1.7	5.5	1.0
Te	11.6	4	2	Th	0.24	0.34	0.17

1. Mean values for spinel lherzolite xenoliths from Kilbourne Hole, New Mexico, USA (after BVSP 1981: 291 & 298)
3. Mean values for garnet lherzolite (sensu lato) xenoliths from Matsoku Kimberlite, Lesotho (after BVSP 1981: 291 & 298)
6. Garnet-spinel harzburgite from Lashaine Volcano, northern Tanzania (after BVSP 1981: 291 & 298)

relatively thick segment of sub-continental upper mantle. Xenoliths generally comprise no more than 5 per cent of the volume of kimberlites; however, in a few exceptional diatremes (or breccia-filled volcanic pipes), such as the Matsoku Pipe in Lesotho, they may make up 20 per cent of the volume of the rock (cf. Dawson 1981: 2). The most abundant types of mantle-derived xenoliths found in kimberlites are garnet lherzolites and *harzburgites*. According to the data provided by Mathias et al. (1970: 85–9), xenoliths of garnet lherzolite (sensu stricto) have the following mean modal compositions: forsteritic olivine (plus altered olivine) 56 per cent; aluminous enstatite 25·per cent; aluminous chrome diopside 9 per cent; chrome pyrope garnet (plus reaction rims) 7 per cent; together with other minor phases. Differences are often found in both the modal compositions and the compositions of their constituent minerals. According to Dawson (1981: 2), this type of xenolith contains five different types of garnet, five different kinds of orthopyroxene and five different types of clinopyroxene.

Accessory minerals that are likely to occur in garnet lherzolite xenoliths include phlogopite, sulphides, carbonates and chrome-rich spinel; diamonds have been found in a very few specimens. According to Shee et al. (1982: 86), the compositions of the minerals found in the diamondiferous garnet lherzolites of the Finsch Kimberlite of S. Africa are consistent with them

having equilibrated in the diamond stability field of 5.0–6.0 GPa (50–60 kb) and 1100 °C. Most garnet lherzolites are considered to have equilibrated at temperatures of between 900 and 1400 °C, and at pressures that are equivalent to depths of between 120 and 170 km. Gurney and Harte (1980) have proposed that those that equilibrated at the high end of this temperature range formed within high-temperature aureoles that developed around ascending high-temperature diapirs. Mean chemical compositions of garnet lherzolites are given in Tables 1.10.2 and 1.10.3; and the chemical compositions of selected minerals from these rocks are given in Table 1.10.4.

Harzburgites

Harzburgites are peridotites that are chiefly composed of olivine and orthopyroxene. Xenoliths of this composition are abundant in many kimberlites. They are particularly abundant if one uses the formal classification of ultramafic rocks given in Chapter 3, because this requires all lherzolites to carry more than 5 per cent modal clinopyroxene. According to Dawson et al. (1980: 325), only sixteen of the ninety-seven published modes of 'garnet lherzolite xenoliths' from southern Africa contain more than 5 per cent clinopyroxene. The four 'garnet lherzolites' from Matsoku Kimberlite, Lesotho, which are mentioned in column 3 of Table 1.10.1, all contain

Table 1.10.4 Chemical composition of selected minerals obtained from mantle-derived xenoliths

| | U.M.6. | | | | U.M.19 (After B.V.S.P., 1981, p. 287 | | | |
	Olivine	Opx	Cpx	Spinel	Olivine	Opx	Cpx	Garnet
SiO$_2$	40.1	54.3	51.9	0.06	40.3	57.5	55.7	41.9
TiO$_2$	—	0.17	0.50	0.17	0.02	0.03	0.09	0.13
Al$_2$O$_3$	0.05	4.5	7.5	58.1	—	0.77	2.48	19.7
Cr$_2$O$_3$	0.04	0.18	0.70	9.1	0.03	0.39	2.60	5.8
ΣFeO	10.4	6.5	3.0	11.1	7.5	4.6	2.43	7.3
MnO	0.21	0.09	0.05	0.04	0.07	0.07	0.09	0.35
MgO	48.6	32.7	15.6	20.9	50.3	34.9	16.3	20.5
NiO	0.34	0.16	0.04	0.49	—	—	—	—
CaO	0.07	0.79	19.3	—	0.08	0.48	18.7	5.2
Na$_2$O	—	0.10	1.7	—	—	0.14	2.5	—
SUM	99.81	99.49	100.29	99.96	98.3	98.88	100.89	100.88

Opx = Orthopyroxene and Cpx = Clinopyroxene
U.M.6: Chemical composition of minerals from a spinel lherzolite (sensu lato) xenolith from Kilbourne Hole, New Mexico, US of A (after BVSP 1981: 286).
U.M.19: Chemical composition of minerals from a garnet lherzolite xenolith from Matsoku Kimberlite, Lesotho (After BVSP 1981 p. 287).

less than 4 per cent clinopyroxene (cf. BVSP 1981: 296), and are thus garnet-clinopyroxene harzburgites, or garnet lherzolites (sensu lato). It has already been noted that the average garnet lherzolite contains approximately 9 per cent diopside and 7 per cent garnet. As these minerals are the only essential minerals in this rock that contain CaO, it can be calculated, using the chemical data in Table 1.10.4, that such a rock would contain just over 2 per cent CaO, and also that all lherzolites (sensu stricto) must contain more than 1 per cent CaO.

Most models of the upper mantle beneath continental cratonic areas include a layer of less dense harzburgite between the denser garnet lherzolites and the Moho (that is, between approximately 35–120 km). Dawson et al. (1980: 330) have demonstrated that there are two main types of harzburgites: one is highly refractory, but the orthopyroxene in the other type contains appreciable amounts of Na, Ca, Al and Cr, and is thus capable of yielding significant amounts of basaltic or picritic magmas by partial melting.

Many petrologists who have worked on peridotitic xenoliths from kimberlites believe that these various types of peridotite are related to one another. The parental rock is usually described as a *fertile garnet lherzolite* that contains appreciable amounts of garnet and diopside, together with minor amounts of accessory minerals such as phlogopite. When a basic, or ultrabasic, magma is extracted from the fertile parental ma-

terial, a series of residual rocks are left behind. The compositions of these more refractory, and usually less dense, rocks are directly related to the amount of melt removed from the fertile parental material. One would expect the residual peridotites to range in composition from garnet lherzolites that are slightly depleted in garnet, diopside and accessory minerals, via garnet harzburgites, to highly refractory harzburgites and dunites. Dunites are peridotites that are almost entirely composed of olivine (see Ch. 3).

Eclogites

Eclogites usually form only a small proportion of the xenoliths found in kimberlites; however, in some rare pipes, such as Obnazhennaya (USSR), Orapa (Botswana), Rietfontein (S. Africa) and Roberts Victor (S. Africa), they are the most abundant type. The essential minerals in these eclogites are garnet and omphacitic clinopyroxene; accessory minerals include kyanite, corundum, coesite (a high-pressure phase of SiO$_2$), diamond and/or graphite, rutile, sulphides, amphibole and mica. According to Dawson and Stephens (1975; 1976), these eclogites contain six distinct types of garnet and seven chemically-distinct varieties of clinopyroxene. The clinopyroxenes vary from chromiferous diopsides, that are indistinguishable from the minerals found in the garnet lherzolites, to jadeites with high sodium and aluminium contents. Eclogites and basalts usually have similar major element compositions.

Glimmerites

Xenoliths that contain a high percentage of phlogopite are found in many kimberlites from southern Africa and Yakutia, USSR. Such xenoliths are called glimmerites, or rocks of the MARID-suite. Glimmerite (German, *glimmer*, mica) is a general name for igneous rocks that contain a high percentage of biotite-phlogopite. MARID is both a mnemonic and an abbreviation for *mica* (Phlogopite) + *amphibole* (potassic-richterite) + *rutile* + *ilmenite* + *diopside* which are the main minerals found in this suite of rocks. Other minerals found in these rocks include olivine, apatite, sphene, zircon, perovskite, sulphides and carbonates. It is generally proposed that these upper mantle glimmerites are produced by either: (a) metasomatism of normal upper mantle materials; or (b) the crystallization of magma derived from kimberlitic magma (cf. Dawson 1980: 186–7). MARID suite materials occur not only as complete xenoliths, but also as veins and less regular patches within xenoliths of upper mantle peridotites. Detailed studies of MARID suite materials indicate that they crystallized from fluids that were enriched in O, F, Na, Al, P, Cl, K, Ca, Ti, Mn, Fe, Rb, Sr, Y, Zr, Ba, light R.E.E., Ta, Th and U (cf. BVSP 1981: 304).

Sub-continental upper mantle

The xenoliths from volcanic/subvolcanic rocks demonstrate that the sub-continental upper mantle is mineralogically complex and chemically heterogeneous. In the uppermost mantle there is usually a layer of harzburgite that persists to a depth of between 100 and 120 km. It is underlain by a layer that contains both garnet-clinopyroxene harzburgite and garnet lherzolite. These rocks grade into one another and gradually increase in density with depth. Fertile garnet lherzolite is the most dense of these materials. Small bodies of eclogite and glimmerite probably occur in both major layers of the sub-continental upper mantle. The hydrous minerals are probably amphiboles and high-titanium phlogopite in the harzburgite, and low-titanium phlogopite in

the garnet lherzolite. A significant proportion of the hydrous minerals probably occur in small bodies and veins of glimmerite. Calcite is the main CO_2-bearing mineral in the harzburgites, and it is probably replaced by dolomite and magnesite at greater pressures (cf. Wyllie 1979b). Detailed studies of the mineral assemblages and textures found in xenoliths demonstrate that parts of the upper mantle have been subjected to thermal metamorphism, metasomatism and shearing. It is proposed that the continental lithosphere may in some areas restrict the escape of volatile components derived from the deep mantle. This results in metasomatism and the replenishment of the sub-continental mantle in the incompatible elements.

Sub-oceanic upper mantle

Even if the chemical compositions of the upper mantle materials beneath continental cratonic areas and ocean basins were similar, there would be differences in their modal compositions, and thus in their melting characteristics. This is mainly because the uppermost mantle beneath the oceans is much nearer the surface, and the phases it contains equilibrated at lower pressures that the phases characteristic of the uppermost mantle beneath continental cratonic areas. Garnet lherzolite that was stable at 3.0 GPa (30 kb) would become spinel lherzolite at approximately 2.5 GPa (25 kb), and a plagioclase lherzolite at pressures of less than 0.9 GPa (9 kb) (cf. Kushiro & Yoder 1966).

Most petrologists (cf. Presnall et al. 1979: 27 –8) believe that the magma from which the mid-ocean ridge basalts (MORB) evolved, equilibrated with the solid phases in the mantle at a pressure of less than 0.9 GPa (9 kb) and a temperature of between 1200–50 °C. In this petrogenetic model these voluminous magmas would be generated in the uppermost mantle environment where either plagioclase lherzolites, or spinel lherzolites, might exist. It is probable that beneath the mid-ocean ridges, upper mantle materials rise towards the surface in the ascending limb of a convection current. Relatively small amounts of melting take place at depths greater than 30 km (0.9 GPa), but at this depth there is an increase in the amount of partial melting. This increase in the volume of the magma facilitates its separation from the source materials. These source materials become depleted in some of the components found in basalt, and a refractory harzburgite develops in the uppermost mantle beneath the oceanic crust. It is thus suggested that beneath the crust in relatively stable oceanic regions there is a 20 km thick layer of harzburgite (10–30 km), followed by a 30 km layer of spinel lherzolite (sensu lato). Much of this latter layer is probably slightly depleted in the basalt-forming components. At 60 km the spinel lherzolite (sensu lato) is transformed into a garnet lherzolite (sensu lato) assemblage. The low-velocity zone begins at a depth of approximately 90 km and in this zone the garnet lherzolite, or garnet harzburgite, is partially melted.

Pyrolite

The *pyrolite model* is often mentioned in geochemical and petrological discussions of the composition of the upper mantle. Ringwood (1962) coined the term pyrolite to describe the chemical composition of a hypothetical fertile pyroxene + olivine + pyrope garnet rock of the upper mantle. This composition is obtained by mixing together depleted upper mantle material and the magmatic material supposedly extracted from it. Ringwood (1975: 180) states that 'the composition of pyrolite is defined by the property that it is required to produce a basaltic magma upon partial melting, leaving behind a residual refractory peridotite'. A variety of different pyrolite compositions have been proposed; and the following are examples: (a) 3 parts Alpine peridotite and 1 part Hawaiian tholeiite; (b) 99 parts Lizard peridotite and 1 part nephelinite; and (c) 83 parts residual harzburgite and 17 parts mid-ocean ridge basalt. The chemical composition of the *average pyrolite* is given in Table 1.10.2.

Geochemistry of the upper mantle

During the past 4.5 Ga, three major reservoirs with distinct chemical compositions (core, mantle and crust) have evolved within the Earth. Geochemical studies have provided much valuable information about the composition and evolution of these major layers. For example, in the physical and chemical environment of the upper mantle, elements such as Fe, Co, Ni, Ge, Pd, Re, Os, Ir and Au are regarded as being *siderophile* (Goldschmidt 1923). Such elements have relatively weak affinities for oxygen and sulphur, but are readily soluble in molten iron. It is thus anticipated that during the core-forming process these siderophile elements would be preferentially incorporated into the core. If one examines the proportions (ratios) in which these elements are present in mantle materials (see Table 1.10.2), one finds that they are essentially similar to the proportions found in primitive chondritic meteorites. As it is unlikely that the partition coefficients of all these siderophile elements are similar, it is usually concluded that a significant proportion of the highly siderophile elements were added to the upper mantle by an influx of chondritic meteoritic material after core formation. Chou (1978) has estimated that the addition of 1 per cent of primitive meteoritic material (Cl carbonaceous chondrite) to the Earth after the main core-forming process had taken place would supply the siderophile elements required. The relatively high mantle abundances of Ni, Co, Ge and other moderately siderophile elements are interpreted as indicating that there was an initial partitioning of these elements into silicates during core formation, followed by relatively minor, late-stage enrichment in components derived from primitive chondritic meteorites (cf. BVSP 1981: 297–304).

Isotopes

Nearly all elements found in nature are mixtures of several isotopes. Isotopes of the same element have similar electron configurations, and thus similar chemical properties; however, such isotopes have different atomic weights because they contain different numbers of neutrons in their nuclei. The physical properties of isotopes of the same element are essentially the same, except for those properties determined by the mass of the isotope. These physical differences are only significant in the isotopes of the light elements (for example, H, C, N, O), because the difference in mass between isotopes of these elements is large. Deuterium (^2H), for example, has twice the mass of common hydrogen (^1H). The physical differences between isotopes of the heavier elements, such as strontium, is comparatively small because the relative difference between the mass of ^{86}Sr and ^{87}Sr is small. Isotopes that are radioactive are called *radioisotopes* or radionuclides (for example, ^{40}K, ^{87}Rb), and they produce *radiogenic isotopes* (for example, ^{40}Ar, ^{87}Sr). Those that do not undergo radioactive decay are the *stable isotopes*.

At present the only stable isotopes that are used in the study of igneous rocks are of light elements, such as H, C, N, O and S (cf. O'Neil 1979: 246–50). Differences in mass between isotopes of a particular light element mean that molecules containing the lighter isotopes have greater internal vibrational energy than those containing heavier ones. For example, water molecules containing the more abundant light isotopes (^{1}H and ^{16}O) require slightly less energy to vaporize than those containing heavier isotopes (^{2}H and/or ^{18}O); thus during the evaporation of normal water, the molecules that contain the lighter isotopes vaporize more readily than those containing heavy ones. This is why the water vapour in the clouds is usually isotopically lighter than sea water. Stable isotopes are particularly useful in the study of low-temperature processes, such as the alteration of magmatic rocks, because isotope fractionation is greater at low than at high temperatures. The alteration of basalt may, for example, produce new minerals such as chlorites, zeolites and clay minerals. These minerals form at low temperatures and have higher ^{18}O/^{16}O ratios than are characteristic of fresh basaltic rocks derived from the upper mantle. Most fresh upper mantle materials have uniform ^{18}O/^{16}O ratios (that is δ^{18}O = 5.5 to 5.7 per cent). Delta (δ) values are all calculated relative to an international standard. The oxygen standard is *Standard Mean Ocean Water* (SMOW), and the δ-values for ^{18}O are calculated as follows:

$$\delta^{18}O = \left(\frac{^{18}O/^{16}O \text{ sample}}{^{18}O/^{16}O \text{ SMOW}} - 1\right) \times 1000 \, ^0/_{00}$$

Samples that have positive δ-values are thus isotopically heavier than SMOW. Oxygen isotopic studies are also of great assistance in detecting crustal assimilation, or contamination, of primary magmas, because most crustal rocks of the Earth have relatively high δ^{18}O values.

Radiogenic isotopes are particularly important in the search for the chemical composition of the upper mantle because one would expect the isotopic ratios of the heavier elements to be essentially unchanged by the normal chemical fractionation processes that occur during the origin and evolution of magmas. In the past the relatively low ^{87}Sr/^{86}Sr ratios (0.702–0.707) of most volcanic rocks derived from magmas em-

placed through the oceanic crust were assumed to indicate: (a) that the mantle had a uniformly low ^{87}Sr/^{86}Sr ratio; and (b) that the Rb/Sr ratio of the upper mantle had been low since the formation of the mantle. Most geochemists now reject this simple, single-stage model for the evolution of the upper mantle. For example, the MOR basalts exhibit significant trace element and isotopic heterogeneity. If these heterogeneities had been established at the time of formation of the Earth, then each segment of the upper mantle with a discrete Rb/Sr ratio could conceivably be a separate single-stage subsystem; however, if this had occurred, then all the data points on a ^{87}Sr/^{86}Sr v. Rb/Sr diagram should lie on the same isochron with a slope age of approximately 4.55 Ga (that is, the age of the Earth). The MOR basalts and most of the basaltic rocks from oceanic islands lie well off the 4.55 Ga isochron. Most MOR basalts plot to the left of the 4.55 Ga isochron; and if they were derived from a magma with a normal upper mantle Rb/Sr ratio, they now contain more ^{87}Sr than their contained ^{87}Rb could have produced since the accretion of the Earth (see Table 1.10.5). This anomaly is readily explained if the Rb/Sr ratio of the upper mantle had been reduced from an initially higher value. The Rb/Sr ratio would be reduced by the removal of magma from the upper mantle, because rubidium is a more incompatible element than Sr, and it is thus preferentially incorporated into magmas. The Sm/Nd system usually shows the reverse behaviour as neodymium is generally more incompatible than samarium (see Section 1.6 and Table 1.10.5).

Radiogenic isotopes should theoretically enable one to evaluate how the composition of a particular portion of a planet has changed with time. Such changes are readily depicted on isotope evolution diagrams (for example, ^{87}Sr/^{86}Sr v. Age). Isotopic studies of the Earth are currently directed towards trying to discover how and why the compositions of the crust and upper mantle differ from that of the bulk composition. On an isotope evolution diagram, the slope of any positively inclined straight line shows the rate of increase through time of the isotope ratio portrayed in the diagram. On a ^{87}Sr/^{86}Sr evolution diagram, the data points for the bulk composition of the Earth form a straight line that commenced at 0.699 (^{87}Sr/^{86}Sr) and 4.55 Ga and extended to 0.705 (^{87}Sr/^{86}Sr) at the present time (BVSP 1981: 1010). Present day crustal rocks generally have higher Rb/Sr ratios and will con-

Table 1.10.5 Radioactive decay schemes used in geochronology and isotope geochemistry

Radioactive isotope	Present isotopic abundance (atoms %)	Disintegration mode	Disintegration constant (lambda per year)	Half-life ($T\frac{1}{2}$)	Radiogenic isotope	Radiogenic isotope abundance (atoms %)	Ratio measured
^{40}K*	0.01167	K capture	5.81×10^{-11}	1.25×10^{9}	^{40}Ar	99.6	^{40}Ar/^{36}Ar
^{87}Rb	27.85	beta	1.42×10^{-11}	4.88×10^{10}	^{87}Sr	7	^{87}Sr/^{86}Sr
^{147}Sm	14.97	alpha	6.54×10^{-12}	1.06×10^{11}	^{143}Nd	12	^{143}Nd/^{144}Nd or ^{143}Nd/^{146}Nd
^{232}Th	≈ 100	chain	4.95×10^{-11}	1.40×10^{10}	^{208}Pb	52	^{208}Pb/^{204}Pb
^{235}U	0.72	chain	9.8485×10^{-10}	7.04×10^{8}	^{207}Pb	22	^{207}Pb/^{204}Pb
^{238}U	99.28	chain	1.5512×10^{-10}	4.47×10^{9}	^{206}Pb	25	^{206}Pb/^{204}Pb

* Approximately 10.5 per cent of ^{40}K decays by K capture to ^{40}Ar, and 89.5 per cent of ^{40}K decays by beta disintegration to ^{40}Ca: $\varkappa^{40}$K $= 5.543$ $\times 10^{-10}$/a, $\varkappa^{40}$K^{e} $+ \varkappa^{40}$K^{e} $= 5.81 \times 10^{-11}$/a, and $\varkappa^{40}$K$^{B^-}$ $= 4.962 \times 10^{-10}$/a. K capture is an abbreviation for the process whereby the nucleus of an atom captures an electron from the innermost electron shell or K shell.

sequently evolve along steeper trajectories on a $^{87}Sr/^{86}Sr$ evolution diagram. Rocks from the upper mantle that have Rb/Sr ratios that are less than the bulk composition of the Earth will evolve along trajectories that are less steep than the bulk composition. A strontium isotope evolution diagram of all published data (BVSP 1981: 1010) shows a significant dispersion of the data points for rocks younger than 2.0 Ga. This dispersion may be related to a real increase in mantle isotopic heterogeneity with time, or it may signify an increasing tendency towards involvement of old sialic crust in the processes of magma generation. If all the published initial Nd isotopic ratios are plotted on a Nd evolution diagram (BVSP 1981: 1009), one discovers that the data points for the Archaean and early Proterozoic rocks fall on a single straight line. The data points on lead isotope evolution diagrams, however, do not show this tendency to converge in the Archaean. Possibly the simplest interpretation of these data is that in the Archaean the upper mantle was relatively homogeneous for Sr and Nd but heterogeneous with respect to Pb. The early Pb isotope heterogeniety may well have been produced by the core-forming process (cf. Allègre et al. 1979).

Strontium and neodymium isotopic studies have also shown: (a) that mantle metasomatism, with the introduction of incompatible elements, has been recently active in the upper mantle; and (b) that mantle metasomatism is often a precursor of intraplate, alkaline magmatism (cf. BVSP 1981: 304–5). For example, isotopic studies by Menzies and Murthy (1980) of pargasite spinel lherzolite xenoliths, and the host basanite, from Nunivak Island, Alaska, USA, have demonstrated that the $^{87}Sr/^{86}Sr$ ratios of the pargasitic amphibole from the xenolith (0.70270–0.70337) are identical to those of the enclosing basanite (0.70251–0.70322). The Nd isotopic composition of the Nunivak amphiboles and micas is also identical to that of the host basanite ($^{144}Nd/^{143}Nd = 0.51303$). Mantle metasomatism may greatly increase the incompatible element content of a source region; thus allowing alkalic magmas to be generated from a higher degree of partial melting than is usually considered likely. If some parts of the upper mantle are heterogeneous on a small scale, and contain veins and small bodies of rock enriched in the incompatible elements, then one would expect the trace element and isotopic compositions of the magmas generated in such heterogeneous

source regions to be affected by one or more of the following: (a) the modal, chemical and isotopic compositions of the metasomatic veins; (b) the size and spacing of the veins; (c) the degree of initial isotopic disequilibrium between the introduced metasomatic minerals and the essentially dry mantle mineral assemblage; and (d) the age of the veining (cf. BVSP 1981: 306).

It has long been established that the various basaltic rocks have different isotopic and trace element abundance patterns. One of the aims of petrology is to discover how, when and where these *geochemical signatures* originate. Even in the supposedly simple oceanic environment there are clear distinctions between the isotopic patterns characteristic of MOR basalts and the basalts from most oceanic islands. Typical MOR basalts usually reveal the following rations: $^{87}Sr/^{86}Sr < 0.7030$, $^{206}Pb/^{204}Pb < 18.7$ and $^{143}Nd/^{144}Nd > 0.51305$; whereas most oceanic island basalts contain the following ratios: $^{87}Sr/^{86}Sr > 0.7030$, $^{206}Pb/^{204}Pb > 18.5$ (except Hawaii) and $^{143}Nd/^{144}Nd < 0.51305$ (cf. BVSP 1981: 991). Basalts from islands that straddle areas of sea-floor spreading, such as Iceland and the Azores in the Atlantic, usually display a fairly regular transition from MOR basalt ratios to oceanic island basalt ratios. If the definition of MOR basalt is modified to exclude all those areas of sea-floor spreading that contain oceanic islands, it is found that the isotopic distinction between MOR basalts and oceanic island basalts extends to other trace elements as well. MOR basalts are normally depleted in the incompatible elements (or *large-ion-lithophile elements*) such as K, Rb, Sr, Y, Nb, Cs, Ba, REE, Ta, Pb, Th and U, relative to the oceanic island basalts; and the MOR basalts are also more depleted in the following element ratios: Ba/Sr, Cs/Rb, Rb/K, Nb/Zr and light REE/heavy REE (see Ch. 5). These data are usually interpreted as indicating chemical heterogeneity in the mantle. O'Hara (1980) has, however, proposed an alternative explanation; and it is that oceanic island rocks may be derived from magmas that were contaminated by pre-existing crustal materials (such as hydrothermally-altered basaltic rocks and sedimentary materials) during their stay in high-level magma chambers.

Mantle heterogeneity

There are often significant variations in incompatible element abundances, incompatible element ratios, and in isotopic ratios controlled by these elements, in volcanic rocks extruded in similar tectonic settings. These geochemical differences are interpreted as indicating that the upper mantle is chemically heterogeneous, and in some regions of the upper mantle heterogeneities may persist in essentially closed systems for long periods of time (cf. Boettcher & O'Neil 1980). Peridotitic xenoliths from kimberlites in southern Africa and Yakutia, USSR, show that the upper mantle beneath these particular continental areas is compositionally heterogeneous on the scale sampled by the kimberlites. Further circumstantial evidence of mantle heterogeneity is provided by the common observation that there are conspicuous regional variations in the type and abundance of metalliferous ore deposits. It is often proposed that geochemical anomalies in the mantle (that is, chemical heterogeneities) have influenced the abundance and distribution patterns of these deposits (cf. Watson 1980). The following are some of the models proposed to account for the heterogeneous nature of the upper mantle: (a) heterogeneities are inherited from the heterogeneous accretion of the Earth; with, or without, the influx or additional chondritic meteorites after the formation of the core; (b) heterogeneities are produced by the core-forming process; (c) heterogeneities are produced by the evolution of the continental crust; (d) heterogeneities are produced by the subduction of hydrous crustal materials; (e) heterogeneities are produced by the generation and movement of magmas; and (f) the percolation of fluids through the upper mantle may affect the abundance and distribution of the incompatible elements. There are also processes that will tend to remove heterogeneities within the mantle and they are essentially convection and diffusion. The former mixes mantle materials slowly, but on a large scale; whereas the latter is probably inefficient in the solid mantle, but can readily homogenize materials during partial melting.

Simple model of the upper mantle

It is proposed that the upper mantle of the Earth is roughly layered. At depths greater than 60 km (sub-oceanic mantle) to 120 km (sub-continental mantle), the main rock types are garnet lherzolites and garnet-clinopyroxene harzburgites. In many areas, particularly beneath old continental cratonic areas, this layer is overlain by a mixed layer that contains both barren and fertile harzburgite. Beneath the young oceans, there is usually a layer of spinel lherzolite between the garnet lherzolites (sensu lato) and the harzburgites. Plagioclase lherzolite is probably only occasionally found in the uppermost mantle beneath the oceanic crust. Different types of chemical heterogeneities occur at a variety of scales, and they are superimposed on this large-scale layering. Many of these heterogeneities exist, and are still being created, because the Earth has a dynamic, convecting mantle that interacts with the crust and possibly the core. The mantle gains heat, and possibly volatile components from the core; and subduction enables it to acquire hydrous, altered volcanic and sedimentary materials from the crust. Some of the eclogite xenoliths found in kimberlitic rocks probably represent the partially melted and metamorphosed remnants of subducted basaltic rocks from the oceanic crust. A wide variety of magmas with different major and trace element compositions are generated within the mantle; and the components in these magmas are either transported out of the mantle and into the crust, hydrosphere, and atmosphere, or they remain in the mantle where they congeal to form veins or rocks (for example, eclogite or glimmerite) and promote heating and metasomatism.

The deep mantle of the earth

In Table 1.3.1 the mantle was divided into three main layers called B, C and D. Layer C occurs between the upper and lower mantle and it is also known as the *transition zone*. Seismic velocity profiles show discontinuities at the top and bottom of this layer (that is, at 400 and 1050 km), and also at a depth of approximately 650 km. Both this zone and the *lower mantle* (1050–2900 km) are believed to have bulk chemical compositions that are similar to those of the upper mantle (see Table 1.10.2), thus the seismic discontinuities which correlate with jumps in the density-depth profile probably represent changes in the phases present at these various depths. Most of the significant phase change reactions in the mantle are *reconstructive transformations*, in which the high- and low-pressure polymorphs are structurally very different (for example, the quartz-to-stishovite transformation). The 400 km discontinuity is now usually explained as the transformation of normal olivine to a denser phase with a spinel-like structure, together with the transformation of the pyroxenes to denser phases with garnet-like structures. At 650 km, the spinel-like phases are probably transformed into more densely-packed strontium-plumbate type structures, and the garnet-like phases are probably transformed into ilmenite and/or perovoskite type structures. These phases persist to a depth of 1050 km where they are probably transformed into 'complexes of compounds such as $MgAl_2O_4$ and $MgSiO_3$ in calcium ferrite and perovskite structures, respectively' (Brown & Mussett 1981: 132). These phases are probably the dominant minerals throughout the whole lower mantle (cf. Ringwood 1975: 325–539).

1.11 Selected references

Brown, G. C. & Mussett, A. E. (1981) *The Inaccessible Earth,* George Allen & Unwin, London.

Hargraves, R. D. (ed.) (1980) *Physics of Magmatic Processes*, Princeton University Press, Princeton, New Jersey, USA.

Loewinson-Lessing, F. Y. (1954) *A Historical Survey of Petrology*, Oliver & Boyd, Edinburgh.

Taylor, S. R. (1982) *Planetary Science: A Lunar Perspective*, Lunar and Planetary Institute, Houston, Texas, USA

Williams, H. & **McBirney, A. R.** (1979) *Volcanology*, Freeman, Cooper & Co., San Francisco, California, USA.

CHAPTER 2

MAGMATIC DIFFERENTIATION

2.1 The diversity of magmatic rocks

There are large numbers of different types of magmatic rocks; however, when their abundance and distribution is examined, most of these rocks are found to occur not alone, but in association with other magmatic rocks. Such *rock associations* keep recurring both in space and time. According to Bowen (1928: 3), rocks 'that have been intruded at a definite period, tend to exhibit certain similarities of mineral or chemical composition which persist even in the presence of diversity and which mark them off more or less distinctly from the rocks of another region or from rocks of the same region intruded at another period'. Individual members of a rock association usually evolve from the same parental magma. The evolution of different magmatic rocks from a common parental magma is called *magmatic differentiation*; and the processes responsible for the evolution of these various rocks are called the *processes of magmatic differentiation* (cf. Bowen 1928: 3). Some of the best examples of rock associations generated by magmatic differentiation occur within layered intrusions (see Ch. 10), or as sequences of diverse volcanic rocks that occur in a single volcanic edifice.

The formation of the core and mantle was probably the first major differentiation process within the Earth. This separation essentially occurred because metal sulphides and ultramafic liquids are *immiscible*. In many smelting processes, immiscibility produces this type of differentiation, which results in a liquid rich in metals separating cleanly from a silicate slag. Immiscibility between silicate, oxide and sulphide liquids

has been recorded in many experimental systems (cf. Roedder 1979). In the field, many intrusions of silicate rocks have been found to contain layers, globules or blebs of sulphides. Such materials have, for example, been described from Sudbury in Canada, Insizwa in South Africa and Skaergaard in Greenland (cf. Wager & Brown 1968). *Liquid immiscibility* is only one of a number of magmatic differentiation processes that may occur in wholly liquid magmas.

2.2 Differentiation in wholly liquid magmas

Liquid immiscibility may occur during cooling or heating; and it consists of the separation of an initially homogeneous liquid into two compositionally distinct liquid phases (see Fig. 2.2.1). The concept of magmatic differentiation by liquid immiscibility, or *liquation differentiation*, was proposed at an early date in the history of petrogenesis by petrologists such as Scrope (1825), Dana (1849) and Durocher (1857) (cf. Loewinson-Lessing 1954: 72–3). These early petrologists used silicate liquid immiscibility in magmas to explain the juxtaposition of rocks such as basalts and rhyolites, and also the apparent dearth of associated rocks of intermediate chemical com-

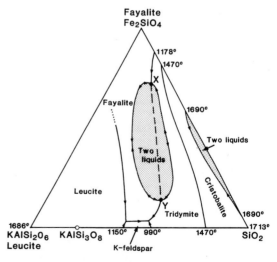

Fig. 2.2.1 A phase diagram of the system Fe_2SiO_4-$KAlSi_2O_6$-SiO_2 at 0.1 MPa (1 atmosphere), showing two stable liquid immiscibility fields. The line XY gives the compositions of the two immiscible liquids in equilibrium with each other and with fayalite and tridymite (Modified from Roedder 1951).

position. In 1927, Greig described experimental evidence of immiscibility in silicate melts. He studied anhydrous systems, and his data seemed to show that liquid immiscibility only occurred in melts with compositions that were unlike those of the common magmatic rocks, and at temperatures that were excessively high (1700 °C) for normal magmas. In more recent times, experimental studies have shown that liquid immiscibility can occur at lower temperatures (for example, 1000–1200 °C) in a variety of hydrous silicate systems (cf. Roedder 1979). It has also been demonstrated experimentally that the addition of some minor oxides (for example, P_2O_5 and TiO_2) is able to expand the field of liquid immiscibility in many silicate systems (cf. Mysen et al. 1981). According to Visser and Koster van Groos (1979: 1173), the addition of P_2O_5 to some silicate melts extends the pressure range, as well as the composition field, of liquid immiscibility in some silicate systems.

Once liquid immiscibility occurs, droplets of the minor liquid phase become suspended in the major phase. The densities of the two immiscible liquids may vary by as much as 400 kg/m³ (0.4 g/cm³: McBirney & Nakamura 1974) or even 870 kg/m³ (0.87 g/cm³: Philpotts 1972). Normally one would expect a rapid separation of the liquids, because: (a) the geometries of the immiscibility fields usually imply that a relatively large amount of the minor phase is able to form within a small temperature interval; (b) relatively little latent heat is removed during the formation of immiscible liquids; and (c) globules of each liquid phase will coalesce if they touch, and such a process increases the average size of the globules thus speeding up the separation of the liquids in a gravitational field (cf. Roedder 1979: 34–5).

The mare basalts provide good examples of natural, late-stage liquid immiscibility. In the *mesostasis*, or last-formed interstitial materials, of some of these rocks there are two co-existing glasses separated by sharp contacts. One glass has high SiO_2 (76 per cent) and K_2O (6.6 per cent) values, whereas the other glass has low SiO_2 (46 per cent), Al_2O_3 (3.1 per cent) and K_2O (0.3 per cent) values, but high FeO (32 per cent), CaO (11.3 per cent) and TiO_2 (4.3 per cent) values. If one calculates the potential mineral compositions of these glasses (that is, C.I.P.W. norms: see Ch. 3), the high-Si glasses are found to contain over 50 per cent normative quartz and approximately 40 per cent normative orthoclase,

whereas the high-Fe glasses contain approximately 75 per cent normative pyroxene. In a number of papers, Roedder and Weiblen (1970; 1977) have proposed that at a late stage in the crystallization of the mare basalts the interstitial melt became greatly enriched in Fe and K. This residual liquid then split into high-Si and high-Fe immiscible liquids. The high-Fe liquid that came into contact with pyroxene, crystallized to form a high-Fe rind on the pyroxene crystals, leaving the high-Si liquid to form a glassy mesostasis. Fragments of this rhyolitic (high-Si) glass occur in the lunar 'soils', and they have given rise to the proposal that there may be *lunar granites*.

Since the discovery of late-stage liquid immiscibility in mare basalts, evidence of similar late-stage liquid immiscibility has been described from a number of basaltic rocks from Earth. For example, the mesostasis of many basaltic rocks from the Deccan Flood Basalt Province of India contain two evidence of immiscible silicate liquids. According to De (1974: 471), these glasses are usually found in the triangular, rectangular or polygonal interstitial spaces between laths of plagioclase. The minor liquid phase now occurs as dark-coloured globules of glass enclosed in a base of lighter-coloured, or colourless, glass. As silicate liquid immiscibility is now known from the basalts of the Deccan Flood Basalt Province, De has proposed that liquid immiscibility may play a significant role in the late-stage differentiation of other magmas of similar chemical composition that cooled and congealed in a closed system. De has also suggested that the iron enrichment of the ferrodiorite specimens of the Upper Zone of the Skaergaard Intrusion of Greenland may be partly due to the settling of immiscible silicate liquid globules enriched in iron. McBirney and Nakamura (1974) prepared melts with chemical compositions intermediate between the Fe-rich gabbros and granophyres (silicic rocks) of the Skaergaard Intrusion. Their experiments showed that when such melts were held for periods of 1 to 10 hours at temperatures of between 5 and 10 °C above the liquidus of the melt, it unmixed to produce two immiscible liquids. One liquid was similar in chemical composition to the Fe-rich gabbros and the other the granophyres of the intrusion. McBirney and Nakamura (1974: 352) concluded that the small granophyric dykes and sills within the gabbros of the Upper Zone of the intrusion 'could have separated as immiscible liquids during the differentiation of the gabbroic magma'.

Table 2.2.1 Immiscible liquids in basaltic rocks from the Hawaiian Archipelago. Chemical analyses of rocks (R), their average mesostases (Mes), and immiscible iron-rich (Fe) and silica-rich (Si) glasses

	1				2				3			
	R	Mes	Fe	Si	R	Mes	Fe	Si	R	Mes	Fe	Si
SiO_2	48.88	67.8	40.8	77.0	49.89	61.8	40.2	74.8	51.18	63.9	39.3	72.2
TiO_2	2.12	2.4	6.3	0.3	2.41	1.9	4.6	0.4	2.10	2.3	5.8	1.3
Al_2O_3	15.57	9.4	3.1	11.5	14.48	9.7	4.1	13.0	14.07	9.9	2.8	12.2
Fe_2O_3	1.63				2.30				1.35			
FeO	9.48	11.2	35.6	3.2	9.12	12.0	28.3	2.2	9.78	13.1	35.4	5.4
MnO	0.17	0.0	0.4	0.0	0.18	0.0	0.4	0.0	0.17	0.1	0.4	0.0
MgO	8.59	0.0	0.9	0.0	7.37	0.5	1.3	0.0	7.78	0.4	1.4	0.1
CaO	10.55	4.5	8.0	3.1	10.60	4.5	10.2	1.7	10.83	4.3	0.4	2.6
Na_2O	1.89	2.5	1.3	3.4	2.16	2.5	0.0	3.9	2.39	3.0	9.4	3.9
K_2O	0.10	0.3	0.1	0.4	0.34	2.0	0.5	2.8	0.44	1.6	0.5	2.0
P_2O_5	0.23	1.4	4.1	0.3	0.24	2.3	4.5	0.0	0.15	1.3	4.3	0.0
H_2O^+	0.85				0.66				0.10			
H_2O^-	0.30				0.11				0.01			
Remainder		0.5	0.0	0.8		3.3	5.9	1.2		0.1	0.3	0.3
	100.36	100.0	100.6	100.0	99.85	100.0	100.0	100.0	100.40	100.0	100.0	100.0
% Mesostasis	22				25				22			

1. Tholeiitic basalt from Kohala Volcano, Hawaii (after Philpotts 1982: 207, No. 3)
2. Tholeiitic basalt from Kauai Island, Hawaiian Archipelago (after Philpotts 1982: 207, No. 6)
3. Olivine basalt from Kilauea National Park quarry, Hawaii (after Philpotts 1982: 207, No. 9)

Table 2.2.1 gives the chemical compositions of the basaltic host rocks, and the immiscible glasses found in the mesostases, of a series of basalts from the Hawaiian Archipelago (cf. Philpotts 1982: 207). In all the examples given one of the immiscible liquids is iron-rich (that is, FeO 28.3–35.6 per cent), whereas the other is silica-rich (that is, SiO_2 72.2–77.0 per cent).

Experimental studies have also demonstrated that a Fe-rich basaltic residual liquid develops after about 95 per cent of a mid-ocean ridge (MOR) basalt has crystallized. At low pressures, and at a temperature of 1010 °C, this residual liquid splits into: (a) a more Fe-enriched basaltic liquid; and (b) a silicic liquid. Dixon and Rutherford (1979), who did these experiments, claim that the silicic rocks (dacites and tonalites or plagiogranites) of the ocean crust are derived from an immiscible liquid that evolved late in the crystallization history of a magma with a bulk composition similar to the MOR basalts.

Many komatiitic lavas from Canada and South Africa contain large numbers of spheroidal bodies that are often called varioles or ocelli. These spheroidal bodies have sharp contacts with their host rocks, and generally have low-K rhyolitic compositions. A number of petrologists have proposed that they were generated by liquid immiscibility. Unfortunately most of these variolitic lavas have been metamorphosed since their extrusion in the Archaean, and their original compositions cannot be readily determined.

Both field and laboratory studies have established that liquid immiscibility occurs during the formation of at least some magmatic rocks, and it may occur in many more. The nature of the process is such that the preservation of unambiguous evidence of liquid immiscibility is only to be expected in rocks that congealed under relatively exceptional conditions. For example, a sharply-defined meniscus between two compositionally distinct glasses is clear evidence of liquid immiscibility; however, such evidence would be readily destroyed by crystallization, or the separation of the liquids into discrete bodies. According to Roedder (1979: 48), there is evidence for liquid immiscibility in a wide range of magmatic rocks. These rocks include low-K ultrabasic and basic komatiites, high-K feldspathoid-bearing basalts, high-Al olivine-bearing subalkalic basalts, normal and high-Fe subalkalic basalts, nephelinites and various high-Ti mare basalts. Roedder (1979: 47) suggests that immiscibility in silicate liquids usually yields a 'felsic, alkali-aluminosilicate melt and a mafic melt rich in Fe, Mg, Ca and Ti'. There is some evidence that the felsic rocks generated by liquid immiscibility may have trace element abundance patterns that are different from those of felsic rock generated by other differentiation processes. This is a field that requires further detailed study. Philpotts (1982: 201) states that 'immiscible liquids are present in sufficient amounts in so many volcanic rocks that magma unmixing should be considered a viable means of differentiation during the late stages of fractionation of common magmas, at least at low pressures'.

Soret effect, thermal diffusion – convection and gaseous transfer

Some of the other magmatic differentiation processes that may operate in completely molten magmas include: (a) the *Soret effect* (Tyrrell 1916); (b) *thermal diffusion–convection* (Wahl 1946); (c) the migration of ions and molecules in response to pressure gradients and buoyancy; and (d) *gaseous transfer* or *volatile transfer* (Fenner 1926: 743–4). The Soret effect is the tendency of liquids (including magmas) that contain gradients in temperature to develop gradients in composition. In the late nineteenth century this effect was regarded as being one of the main causes of magmatic differentiation. Bowen (1915), however, claimed that it was of no practical importance. Wahl (1946) combined the Soret effect with convection, and proposed that his process of thermal diffusion–convection was a significant cause of magmatic differentiation. Little is known about the actual molecular or ionic species that diffuse through structured, multicomponent, silicate magmas; thus it is difficult to assess the significance of gravity in the diffusion of ions and molecules of different density in them. On planets that are more massive than the Earth this process may be of great importance. It is proposed that a variety of different molecules and ions migrate through most bodies of magma; and they move at different rates in response to thermal and pressure gradients, and differences in density. Once a compositional gradient develops in a body of magma, ions and molecules (complexes) may also migrate differentially in response to this new gradient.

Gaseous transfer from lower to higher levels in a body of magma occurs whenever the internal gas pressure is sufficient to produce a separate gas phase. The efficacy of gases as agents of magmatic differentiation lies both in their ability to remove materials when they escape from a magma and in their ability to selectively transfer material from lower to upper levels in a magma chamber. A gas bubble rising through a magma may scavenge other volatile components, including the alkali metals, from the various parts through which it passes. Some trace elements, such as Sc, Y and the R.E.E., have a tendency to form complexes with OH and F, and they may also migrate upwards with the volatile components (cf. Hildreth 1979: 70).

Convection-driven thermogravitational diffusion

In 1976, Shaw et al. (1102) introduced what they called a *thermogravitational mechanism* to account for the systematic variations in chemical composition that develop in large bodies of silicic magma. They introduced this differentiation process because they found that some ash-flow deposits, such as the voluminous Bishop Tuff of the Long Valley Caldera, California, USA, show systematic chemical gradients that cannot readily be explained by: (a) fractional crystallization; (b) differences inherited from parental magmas; or (c) a combination of these processes. According to them, compositional and thermal gradients existed in the magma prior to the precipitation of any crystals. Their petrogenetic model is corroborated by the low phenocryst contents of the extrusive rocks, and the systematic increase in extrusion temperatures of the different rock units within eruptive sequences, as revealed by iron–titanium oxide geothermometers.

Hildreth (1979: 43) proposed that the hydrous silicic magma that evolved in the upper part of the Long Valley Caldera magma chamber was produced by the 'combined effects of convective circulation, internal diffusion, complexation, and wall-rock exchange'. He called this process *convection-driven thermogravitational diffusion*. It is essentially a combination of convection, or the transference of heat by the actual movement of magma, and the various diffusion processes that may operate in a magma; and it was originally developed in order to explain how thermal, compositional and isotopic gradients can be periodically re-established in a magma chamber after the removal of large batches of magma. It is essentially a differentiation process that generates compositionally-zoned magma chambers. This process not only operates in the huge magma chambers that produce voluminous ash-fall and ash-flow deposits, but it probably also operates in relatively small sub-volcanic magma chambers, where it may generate the silicic rocks of the basalt–hawaiite–mugearite–benmoreite–trachyte–comendite association (see Ch. 7). Hildreth (1981: 10153) holds the extreme view that 'every large eruption of nonbasaltic magma taps a magma reservoir that is thermally and compositionally zoned'. Broadly similar differentiation processes are, however, believed to operate in basaltic and ultrabasic magmas. These processes will be discussed later in this chapter under the heading of *multidiffusion*.

2.3 Fractional crystallization

The crystallization histories of most magmas is complex. This is mainly because either *equilibrium crystallization* or *fractional crystallization* may occur; and the importance of the one *vis-à-vis* the other may change as crystallization proceeds. In equilibrium crystallization the minerals that precipitate from a cooling magma react continually with the magma; whereas in fractional crystallization these minerals are prevented from reacting (or equilibrating) with the magma. Fractional crystallization consists of separating minerals from a residual magma, and it is readily accomplished by the mantling, or the mechanical removal, of minerals. The former process occurs when a crystal is covered by an overgrowth and it is thus unable to react with the magma. In the latter process, minerals may, for example, precipitate, and then sink onto the floor of a magma chamber, where they are covered by other crystals and prevented from reacting with the residual liquid. Fractional crystallization is an important magmatic differentiation process because it is able to produce a series of residual liquids that have different compositions as compared to their parental magmas. Evidence that supports fractional crystallization is found in the chemical compositions of the mesostases of many porphyritic basic and intermediate volcanic rocks, which are significantly more differentiated (that is, enriched in SiO_2, Na_2O and K_2O and depleted in MgO and CaO) than the bulk chemical compositions of these rocks (see Table 2.2.1).

The reaction principle

In order to comprehend the nature of the crystallization processes that occur in magmatic rocks, one has to understand the concept of the *reaction series*, or *reaction principle* (Bowen 1922). Reaction relations between crystals and liquids are common both in natural and experimental silicate systems. Bowen (1928: 54) claimed that the reaction principle was of 'the utmost importance in connection with the problems of fractional crystallization in silicate systems'; and he recognized two different types of reaction series, a *continuous reaction series* and a *discontinuous reaction series*. The plagioclase feldspars are a good example of a continuous reaction series, as the reaction of the early-formed Ca-rich crystals with the residual liquids takes place without any abrupt phase changes. If perfect equilibrium (that is, complete reaction) is maintained among the phases of a continuous reaction series, the crystals remain homogeneous, and at any specific temperature and pressure all the crystals have identical compositions. Complete reaction is, however, usually not achieved during cooling because: (a) diffusion in solids tends to be slow relative to the rate of crystal growth; and (b) crystals are often separated from the main body of liquid (fractional crystallization). A well-studied example of a discontinuous reaction pair is olivine–pyroxene in the system Mg_2SiO_4–SiO_2 (Bowen & Andersen 1914); whereas the common ferromagnesian minerals form a discontinuous reaction series at low pressures (see Fig. 2.3.1).

In order to provide a 'concrete' illustration of the importance of the reaction principle in petrogenesis, Bowen (1928: 60) produced Fig. 2.3.1a. It is an idealized model of the low-pressure crystallization of subalkalic basaltic magma. An important feature of this diagram is the gradual convergence of the ferromagnesian minerals of the discontinuous reaction series, and the plagioclase feldspars of the continuous reaction series. Bowen recognized that the minerals that crystallized after the convergence formed in a different manner from those of the converging reaction series; that is, they formed at relatively low temperatures from a residual liquid. Figure 2.3.1a was devised to illustrate the

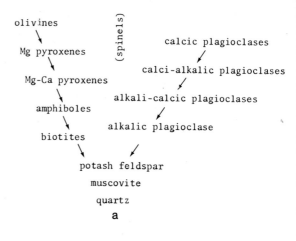

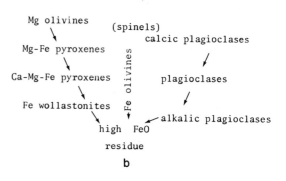

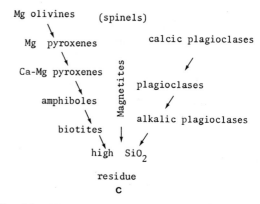

Fig. 2.3.1 Reaction series for subalkalic igneous rocks at low pressures: (a) Reaction series (after Bowen 1928: 60); (b) reaction series in a closed system (after Osborn 1979: 145); (c) reaction series under oxygen-buffered conditions (after Osborn 1979: 145).

manner in which subalkalic basaltic magmas generally crystallize; it does not imply that all Mg pyroxene is derived by reaction from olivine, or that all hornblende is derived by reaction from Mg–Ca pyroxene. Magmas of different composition, or similar magmas crystallizing under different physical conditions, may directly precipitate a variety of different minerals.

Osborn (1979: 166) reviewed the reaction principle fifty years after the publication of Bowen's book on *The Evolution of Igneous Rocks*, and he concluded that 'Bowen's sense of the importance of the reaction between crystals and liquid has been borne out by the continuing experimental work of the past fifty years'. Figures 2.3.1b and 2.3.1c are both from Osborn's paper (145). The first of these figures illustrates the crystallization of a subalkalic basaltic magma at low pressures when the system is closed to the entry of oxygen; whereas the second figure (2.3.1c) illustrates the crystallization of similar magma at low pressures, under oxygen-buffered conditions (that is, the partial pressure of oxygen remains high, and magnetite is likely to form). At medium (0.8 2.0 GPa or 8–20 kb) and high (>2.0 GPa) pressures most magmas, including subalkalic basaltic magmas, have significantly different reaction relations and crystallization histories. For example, in basaltic liquids at high pressures, garnet is usually the liquidus phase, and a basaltic magma crystallizing at this pressure will contain the minerals characteristic of eclogite (see Section 1.10).

An examination of the various reaction series portrayed in Fig. 2.3.1 reveals that under the conditions prevailing in Fig. 2.3.1b fractional crystallization, with the removal of the early-formed olivines, Mg pyroxenes and calcic plagioclases, will generate a differentiated residual liquid that is impoverished in MgO and CaO, and enriched in SiO_2, total Fe, Na_2O and K_2O. However, if the same magma crystallized under oxygen-buffered conditions (Fig. 2.3.1c), the residual liquid resulting from fractional crystallization would be impoverished in MgO, CaO and total Fe, and enriched in SiO_2, Na_2O and K_2O.

Filter press

Lava lakes

Lava lakes are regarded as 'natural laboratories' for studying cooling, crystallization (particularly fractional crystallization) and differentiation in magmas at low pressures (cf. Wright et al. 1976;

Helz 1980). Eruptions of Kilauea Volcano, Hawaii, have produced three accessible lava lakes (Kilauea Iki, Alae and Makaopuhi West Pit). The liquidus temperatures of each of these bodies of basaltic lava is at, or above, 1200 °C; the solidus temperatures are all near 980 °C; and the interface between rigid 'crust' and fluid lava occurs at approximately 1070 °C. Most cooling is by conduction, through the upper crust of the lava lakes.

In August 1963 the eruption of Kilauea Volcano ponded a tholeiitic basaltic flow in the bottom of Alae Crater, forming a 15 m deep lava lake (cf. Wright & Peck 1978). Detailed studies of (a) drill cores and (b) the *liquid oozes* that flowed into the drill holes and were later cored, have revealed the following crystallization sequence in the Alae lava lake: olivine (Fo_{80}) is the first mineral to crystallize at about 1190 °C; it is closely followed by augite (Wo_{40} $En_{48.8}$ $Fs_{11.2}$) at 1180–5 °C, plagioclase An_{70} at 1165–70 °C; ilmenite (Ilm_{90} Hem_{10}) first appears at 1070 °C, pigeonite at about 1050 °C, magnetite at 1030 °C and apatite at 1010 °C. During crystallization the plagioclase feldspars change in composition from An_{70} to an average of An_{59} in the congealed basalts. Small quantities of sodic plagioclase and alkali feldspar are found in the mesostasis of some of the congealed basalts. Olivine ceases to crystallize at about 1100 °C when it has a composition of Fo_{65}. During the crystallization of the silicates, but before the precipitation of the Fe–Ti oxides, the residual liquid changes in composition and becomes slightly depleted in SiO_2, significantly depleted in Al_2O_3, MgO and CaO, and enriched in total Fe, Na_2O, K_2O, P_2O_5 and TiO_2. After the Fe–Ti oxides begin to crystallize, Al_2O_3 shows little change in abundance, MgO and CaO continue to be depleted, and SiO_2, Na_2O, K_2O and P_2O_5 are all enriched in the residual liquid. TiO_2 and total Fe reach a maximum and then decrease in abundance. P_2O_5 is progressively enriched in the residual liquid, until apatite begins to crystallize. The residual liquid is now represented by a colourless glass that makes up about 6 per cent by weight of the crystallized basalt. This glass contains more than 75 per cent SiO_2, and it has the chemical composition of a rhyolite. All the congealed Hawaiian lava lakes contain coarse-grained *segregation veins* of more differentiated rock. These veins are similar in composition to the liquid oozes that form during drilling, and they are probably generated by the filtration of a residual liquid through a crystal mush (that is, filter pressing).

Stokes' Law

The first minerals to crystallize in basaltic magma at low pressure (see Fig. 2.3.1) are generally more dense than the circumjacent liquid, and thus have a tendency to sink. Bowen (1915: 190–1) claimed that he was able to demonstrate experimentally that olivine and pyroxene sink, and tridymite floats, in melts belonging to the system diopside–forsterite–silica. The movements of crystals in liquids is often analysed by using *Stokes' Law*. Stokes proposed that a small sphere falling under the action of gravity, through a viscous medium, ultimately reaches a constant velocity that is equal to

$$v = 2gr^2(d_1-d_2)/9\eta$$

where g = gravitational acceleration, r = radius of the sphere, d_1 = density of the sphere, d_2 = density of the medium, and η (eta) = the coefficient of viscosity of the medium. Although Stokes' Law relates to the movement of small spheres in Newtonian fluids, it draws attention to the importance of crystal size in determining the rate at which crystals move through a magma. According to Hess (1960: 142), a plagioclase crystal (density 2680 kg/m^3 or 2.68 gm/cm^3) that has a radius of 2.1 mm, a pyroxene crystal (3280 kg/m^3) that has a radius of 0.72 mm, and a chromite crystal (3980 kg/m^3) that has a radius of 0.56 mm, will all sink at the same rate of approximately 100 m/a in a magma that has a density of 2580 kg/m^3 and a viscosity of 300 Ns/m^2 (3000 poises).

When considering the movement of crystals in basaltic magmas, the plagioclase feldspars are of particular interest because at low pressures the liquidus plagioclases are more dense than most basaltic magmas, but if pressures are increased the density of the magma increases at a faster rate than the plagioclase crystals. At a pressure of approximately 0.7 GPa (7 kb), plagioclase tends to float in normal basaltic magma (cf. Kushiro 1980: 113). Even at low pressures, some minerals such as leucite (density = 2485 kg/m^3) and minerals of the sodalite group (density = 2300–2500 kg/m^3) may be less dense than the magma they precipitate from. Such minerals may float upwards, and possibly concen-trate at the top of a magma chamber. The leucite-rich rock *italite* may have formed in this manner. Komatiitic magmas have high densities at low pressure (2700 kg/m^3 at 0.1 MPa) and even greater densities at depth. Nisbet (1982: 508–9) has estimated that at 5.0 GPa (50 kb), komatiitic magmas and olivine crystals would have similar densities, and at greater pressures olivine would float in a komatiitic magma. In 1939, Wager and Deer (282–3) suggested that as crystallization proceeded in the Skaergaard Intrusion of East Greenland, the residual magma became more dense (that is, more iron-rich) than the precipitating plagioclase. Experimental studies (cf. McBirney & Noyes, 1979) have confirmed this concept, and it is now established that the plagioclase in the Skaergaard Intrusion was less dense than its parental liquids during the formation of practically the whole of the exposed part of the layered series of rocks. This concept of *plagioclase flotation* is probably applicable to most layered intrusions that developed iron-rich residual liquids.

Non-Newtonian liquids

It is often postulated that not all magmas behave like *Newtonian liquids* in which the rate of shear strain is proportional to the shear stress. Magmas that are highly polymerized and/or contain more than a few percent of crystals by volume may behave rheologically like *non-Newtonian liquids*. They may, for example, behave like a *Bingham plastic*. Crystals, or xenoliths, suspended in such a magma must exceed a critical size before they can move through it. This is because a Bingham plastic has a finite yield strength (cf. Spera 1980: 285). The amount of data on the yield strengths of natural silicate melts is at present limited. Experimental measurements reported by McBirney and Noyes (1979: 496) have shown that the yield strengths of basaltic and andesitic magmas increase sharply when these liquids begin to crystallize and minerals appear in the magma. They propose that as heat is lost through the boundaries of a cooling body of magma, a growing crystal exerts an increasing gravitational stress on the circumjacent liquid. The crystal will either float or sink, at a rate governed by the properties of the liquid, and the size and density of the crystal. As the temperature of a normal magma falls, the number and size of suspended crystals increases, and the viscosity and yield strength of the crystal–liquid suspension (or magma) increases. If the stress exerted by some or all of the crystals is greater than the yield strength of the liquid, the crystals either float or sink; but if the stress is less than the yield strength of the liquid, the crystals become trapped in the congealing magma. According to McBirney and Noyes (1979: 498), the gravitational stress exerted by a crystal rises as its radius increases, but this increase does not normally occur as rapidly as the exponential increase in the yield strength of the magma, over the same temperature interval.

Flow Differentiation

Magmatic differentiation in a moving magma

The composition of a magma may change while it is moving through the lithosphere. Some of the more important processes that produce these changes are as follows: (a) the crystallization and sinking of early-formed crystals; (b) the nucleation of crystals on conduit walls; (c) wall-rock reaction; and (d) the escape of volatile components that are no longer soluble in a magma that has risen to higher levels and lower ambient pressures. The very act of moving a liquid containing suspended crystals through a conduit tends to produce a concentration of crystals in the central part of the flow. Baragar (1960: 1631–2) introduced this concept in order to explain why there was a marked increase in the number and size of the 'feldspathic clots' at the centre of many of the gabbroic sills in the Labrador Trough of Canada. He proposed that the clusters of feldspar crystals were moved towards the centre of a conduit by a process that was analogous to the one that operates during the flow of dilute suspensions of wood fibres in a smooth pipe. The wood fibres move away from the sides of the pipe and concentrate towards the centre. Bhattacharji and Smith (1964: 150) studied this non-gravitative method of concentrating crystals within a magma, and called it *flowage differentiation*. The process has also been studied by Barriere (1976) who concluded that flowage differentiation can only operate successfully in channelways that are less than 100 m wide. He also found that the process operates on all solid particles irrespective of their shape and size. The germ of the idea of flowage differentiation was published by Bowen (1928: 158) in his description of the origin of the picritic dykes associated with the central plutonic complex of Skye, Scotland. Many dykes and sills contain segregation, or layers, of early-formed crystals that are believed to have been concentrated by flowage differentiation. An example of a large sill of this type is the Whin Sill in the north of England. According to Dunham and Strasser-King (1981: 27–8), this sill contains no evidence of crystal settling. Flowage differentiation concentrated the early-formed crystals towards the centre of the sill; and crystal settling was inhibited by high viscosity caused by the presence of a large volume of crystals.

Bottom-crystallization

In the past many authors (for example: Tyrrell 1916: 123–8; Bowen 1919: 411–23; Walker 1940: 1083–9) have proposed nonconvective cooling, together with crystal settling from the top of a magma body, as a possible mechanism for magmatic differentiation and layering in basaltic sills. In this type of cooling model, crystallization is considered to take place at the top of the sill because most heat is lost through the roof-rocks. The latter concept is generally valid because, as Lovering (1935: 86) has demonstrated, the temperature of the country rocks below a crystallizing sill is eventually likely to exceed the temperature in the magma itself. In a convecting magma, however, the thermal gradients, and sites of crystallization, may be quite different. Jackson (1961: 94–5) explored the concept of a convecting body of magma in which both the composition and temperature become relatively homogeneous. Under these conditions, the most propitious place for crystallization to occur is at the base of the body of magma, where the pressure is highest. Jackson (1961: 94) has proposed that after the emplacement of a body of magma, such as the one that was the precursor of the thick (8 km) sill-shaped Stillwater Complex of Montana, USA, there is an initial chilling of the magma against the country rocks; then a system of convection currents becomes established; and gradually a zone of major crystallization develops on, or near, the floor of the magma chamber. In relatively thin sills, or in bodies of magma that have become small as the result of crystallization, the conditions may not be suitable for bottom-crystallization.

Convection currents in magmas

In 1939, Wager and Deer (262–77) proposed that *convection currents of variable velocity* played a significant role in the cooling and differentiation of the Skaergaard Layered Intrusion of East Greenland. In a later paper, Wager (1963: 4) suggested that during the cooling of this intrusion 'two different sorts of currents existed simultaneously'. One was a slow (0.06 m/hr) and fairly continuous convective circulation; whereas the other was an *intermittent density current* of relatively small volume that periodically plunged down the outer margin of the body of magma at velocities of the order of 125 m/hr. Wager's model implied that many of the crystals that nucleated in the cooler roof areas of the magma chamber would either become an essential part of the density currents or they would become entrained in the slower-moving convective currents. The liquid in the descending currents would be relatively cool and this, together with the increasing ambient pressure, would promote growth among the crystals contained in the downward-moving currents. However, the growth of any other crystals that formed towards the top of the magma chamber and sank directly into the main body of hot magma would be retarded, or they might even be incorporated into the magma by reactive solution. If convection currents, such as those postulated by Wager and Deer (1939), were to carry crystals across the floor of a magma chamber and then let them gradually settle on the bottom, it is difficult to understand why this process should consistently produce uniform accumulations of crystals that are arranged in parallel units of relatively constant thickness (cf. McBirney & Noyes 1979: 531).

In order to account for the regular repetition of layers of rocks of different composition found in many layered intrusions, Hess (1960: 133–7) and others have proposed that the upward component in convection current may provide a mechanism for separating sinking minerals of different size and density (that is, winnowing). He (134) claims that 'if motion in the magma is not constant in velocity and direction, rhythmic layering will result, provided only that the two or more crystalline phases involved have considerably different settling velocities'. When discussing the Ultramafic Zone of the Stillwater Complex of Montana, Jackson (1961: 96) proposed that these rocks were produced by *variable-depth convection*. He proposed, as has already been noted, that most crystallization and settling took place from a stagnant layer at the bottom of the Stillwater magma chamber. Periodically, however, this layer heated up and became unstable, and the convective system operating above it increased in size and swept it aside. Fresh, cooler magma now formed a new stagnant layer, and started a new cycle of crystallization and settling. In any body of magma that crystallizes from the bottom upwards, the successive layers of minerals cover up, and eventually seal off, the underlying layers, thus promoting fractional crystallization. Some magma chambers develop a relatively thick mush of essentially unconsolidated crystals at their base, and the expulsion of the interstitial, or intercumulus, liquid between the crystals is a particularly powerful mechanism for promoting fractional crystallization. Irvine (1980a: 367) claims that the vertical alignment of olivine crystals in some of the rocks of the layered series of the Muskox Intrusion, Canada, was produced by the upward flow of expelled interstitial liquid.

Magmatic density currents

It has been proposed that *magmatic density currents* produced some of the layers, particularly the size-graded layers, and the scouring and slumping found in layered intrusions. Examples of these features are particularly well developed in the Duke Island Ultramafic Intrusion of southeastern Alaska (cf. Irvine 1963). This complex intrusion is of particular importance as it contains many *graded fragmental layers*, and it is believed that magmatic density currents distributed, sorted and size-graded the rock fragments (pyroxenites) found in these layers. Magmatic density currents usually develop when magma immediately below the roof of a magma chamber cools, crystals nucleate and grow, and thus the upper layer of magma becomes more dense than the main body. Eventually this gravitationally unstable layer cannot be supported by the underlying magma and it surges downwards at a velocity that is much greater than the settling rate of the individual crystals. It is usually postulated that such magmatic density currents move down the sides of magma chambers and then spread rapidly over the floor before they come to rest. Irvine (1980b) has studied density currents under laboratory conditions; and he has shown how they deposit graded layers. He has also shown how they can entrain and transport low-density crystals downwards through a denser magma (that is, plagioclase in an iron-rich basaltic magma).

Diffusion

Double diffusion in a gravity field

In recent years a number of petrologists (cf. Irvine 1980a; McBirney & Noyes 1979; Rice 1981) have attempted to evaluate the nature of the convective systems that evolve in density-stratified magmas, and the part played by convective systems in changing, and enhancing, density stratification. The flow phenomena found in liquids that contain thermal and compositional gradients have also been studied experimentally (cf. Turner & Gustafson 1978). It is, for example, known that when hot saline water is released at the bottom of a body of cooler and less saline water, the properties of salinity and temperature have opposing effects on the density of the introduced liquid. High salinity makes the liquid more dense, whereas the thermal expansion produced by the higher temperature makes it less dense. During the mixing of the introduced liquid into the main body of liquid, there is a *double-diffusive* effect, because heat and salt diffuse into the surrounding liquid at different rates (that is, heat normally diffuses at a greater rate than salt). If, for example, hot saline water was to move upwards through a body of sea water that had a stable density gradient, the introduced liquid would rise until its density matched that of the surrounding liquid, and it would then spread out horizontally. The introduced liquid would still be hot and saline relative to the surrounding liquid, and a *diffusive interface* would develop above it. Heat would be exchanged relatively rapidly through the diffusive interface, and that part of the introduced liquid that had given up some of its heat would now be more dense than the liquid below it. This density inversion would probably be resolved by the downward movement of the more saline liquid.

It is claimed that double-diffusive processes are able to generate, and maintain, the system of layering found in the hot, nearly saturated brine deposits of the Red Sea. Recently the concept of *double-diffusive convection* has been used to account for a variety of features found in layered intrusions. According to Irvine (1980a: 365), when double-diffusive (or multidiffusive) convection operates in a magma it becomes 'gravitationally stratified on a local scale in such a way that it is subdivided into several (in some cases many) roughly horizontal layers comprised of numerous small, irregular convection cells'. Each separately convecting layer is likely to become relatively uniform in temperature and composition; and the magma body as a whole will then tend to have step-like gradients in temperature and composition. Between the horizontal layers of convecting liquid there are relatively thin layers of static liquid which form diffusive interfaces through which heat and mass (chemical components) are exchanged. The layered structure is relatively long lasting because heat is conducted through the diffusive interface at a greater rate than the chemical components can diffuse through the interface. This means that as heat moves through the diffusive interface, it reduces the density of the liquid in the layer above, but increases it in the layer below; and it is essentially these density differences that drive the convection cells that operate in each layer.

According to Irvine (1980a: 367), double-diffusive convection occurred in the Muskox Intrusion of Canada. Heat was mainly lost via the roof rocks; and within the main body of magma, changes in composition associated with fractional crystallization at the bottom, the mixing of liquids at intermediate levels, and contamination at the top, are transmitted upward and downward by convection and diffusion. Irvine also claims that the convection in the bottom-most layer of magma is coupled to an upward flow of intercumulus liquid that is squeezed out of the pile of cumulus crystals that collect at the base of the magma chamber. A *cumulus crystal* is one that precipitates directly from a magma and is not modified by later crystallization; and a *cumulate* is a magmatic rock formed by the accumulation of such crystals.

Diffusion

Multidiffusion

Double diffusion is likely to operate in relatively simple chemical systems (that is, between bodies of water with different temperatures and salinities); however, in most natural magmas, *multidiffusion* is more likely to occur, with a number of different chemical components being exchanged at different rates through the diffusive interface (cf. Rice 1981: 408). According to McBirney and Noyes (1979: 547), the initial layering in bodies of magma that are eventually to become layered intrusions may have formed above the crystallizing base of the magma chamber, at a time when the magma at that level was wholly liquid. Then with further bottom-crystallization, the floor of the magma chamber would rise, the temperature decline, and crystals would nucleate and grow in the convecting layers within the density-stratified magma. McBirney and Noyes (1979: 547) state that if one was to consider the various factors operating before and during the crystallization of a large body of magma, one would have to include multidiffusion convection, nucleation, growth and the settling of crystals. It is not difficult to imagine how sensitive the geometry and compositions of individual layers would be to minor differences in these complexly related variables.

Muskox Intrusion

The intricacy of the relationship between the various differentiation processes that operate separately, or jointly, in the cooling of a large body of magma will now be illustrated by examining the evolution of the Muskox Intrusion, which is situated south of Coppermine in the Canadian Arctic. It is essentially a funnel-shaped intrusive body that consists of two marginal zones, a layered series and a roof zone that is extensively charged with xenoliths. Rocks of the layered series occur in a trough-shaped body surrounded by the other units. They are about 1800 m thick, and range in composition from dunite at the base, via peridotite and various pyroxenites and gabbros, to a granophyre (silicic rock) at the top. The layered series has two notable features: (a) the dominance of olivine cumulates; and (b) the systematic repetition of rock types. Olivine cumulates make up over 60 per cent of the layered series of the Muskox Intrusion and, according to Irvine (1980a: 331), 'olivine by itself forms more than 50 per cent of the (layered) series by volume'. The layered series thus contains more olivine than could possibly be produced by the fractional crystallization of a basaltic magma in a closed magma chamber (that is, not enough MgO). Irvine and Smith (1967: 48) divided the layered series into twenty-five repetitive units, or *cyclic units*, and proposed that each of these formed as the result of the introduction of separate batches of magma. Each new influx of magma displaced and moved most of the residual magma in an upward direction.

A detailed study of the compositional variations found in the cyclic units of the layered series has shown that 'the chemical breaks between the cyclic units are constantly up-section from the modal breaks' (Irvine 1980a: 341). This discrepancy is most readily explained by postulating that the composition of the cumulus crystals is changed by reaction between the crystals and an intercumulus liquid that migrates up through the crystal mush. It is proposed that as the pile of crystal grows on the floor of the magma chamber, the load at any particular level within it increases, and this causes the framework of self-supporting crystals to gradually collapse. There is consequently a tendency for the hydraulic pressure on the intercumulus liquid in the lower levels of the crystal mush to increase, and force the liquid to rise to higher levels. This process has been called *self-imposed filter pressing*; and in the Muskox Intrusion it is believed to produce *infiltration metasomatism*. Irvine (1980a: 359) claims that during the accumulation of the layered series of the Muskox Intrusion the unconsolidated crystal mush extended to a depth of up to 300 m below the depositional surface, and the intercumulus liquids filtered upwards through the pile of cumulus crystals for distances of over 100 m. The concept of a thick pile of unconsolidated cumulus crystals is relatively new, as in the past most petrologists (cf. Wager & Brown 1968: 274) have postulated relatively thin ($\approx$3 m) layers of unconsolidated crystals. Irvine (1980a: 359) also claims that the synformal structure of many of the large-layered intrusive bodies is partly attributable to the preferential compaction of their more slowly-cooled interior parts.

The following are the main reasons why Irvine (1980a: 368) claims that double-diffusive (or more likely multidiffusive) convection occurred during the cooling of the Muskox Intrusion: (a) evidence that the magma was repeatedly stratified in composition and temperature in the manner required to produce double-diffusive convection; (b) individual cyclic units are exceptionally well differentiated, and they give the impression that 'each time a layer increment of crystals was fractionated from the liquid, the compositional changes resulting from its removal were rapidly transmitted through the whole of the residual liquid, as would be expected if this liquid were undergoing double-diffusive convection'; (c) the observation that the rocks of the layered series of the intrusion terminate against the marginal zones rather than lapping up over them. The latter observation is most readily explained if local convection current within individual layers of a stratified magma removed cooled liquid from the bounding walls of the magma and transferred it inwards. Although Irvine (1980a and b) is a strong advocate of the concept that certain types of small-scale layering in ultramafic–mafic intrusions are produced by current transport and the deposition of crystals, he claims that most thickly-layered to massive bodies of cumulates are probably produced by the growth of cumulus minerals either in situ or within a few centimetres of the floor of the magma body. He (1980a: 369–70) also suggests that multidiffusive convection is probably 'a principal mechanism in the fractional crystallization of magmas'. This process is also particularly valuable in providing a suitable mechanism for transmitting the effects of *magma mixing* and *assimilation* through a cooling body of magma.

It has already been postulated that infiltration metasomatism probably occurred in the unconsolidated crystal mush that develop at the base of the Muskox Intrusion. This process is likely to produce rocks that have previously been called *adcumulates*, because the cumulus crystals in such rocks have developed overgrowths that appear to have been added after their deposition. The concept of *adcumulus growth* was introduced to account for the origin of *monomineralic rocks*, such as anorthosites (plagioclase rocks), pyroxenites and dunites in layered intrusions. Petrographic studies have, however, shown that adcumulates (sensu stricto) are not particularly common in layered intrusions. According to Irvine (1980a: 371), adcumulus growth occurs deep in the pile of cumulus crystals, and it may extend hundreds of metres below the depositional surface. The process operates because the crystal mush compacts under its own weight and the cumulus crystals develop overgrowths as they are constantly bathed in a flow of migrating intercumulus liquid. Much has still to be discovered about the composition and temperature of such migrating liquids.

In this chapter, the following differentiation processes have been examined: (a) liquid immiscibility; (b) the Soret effect; (c) gaseous transfer; (d) convection-driven thermogravitational diffusions; (e) multidiffusion; (f) crystal settling with, or without, convection or density currents; (g) self-imposed filter pressing; and (h) infiltration metasomatism and adcumulus growth. However, there are many more variables that may influence the course of magmatic differentiation in an essentially stationary body of magma, and they include: (a) the size and shape of the magma chamber; (b) the position of the magma chamber within the lithosphere, as this will determine the ambient pressure regime in which the magma crystallizes, and the ability of the country rocks to dissipate heat; (c) the shapes as well as the sizes of the various solid phases that occur within the magma; (d) whether, or not, the minerals aggregate into clusters and thus form *mats* or *rafts* that settle with greater velocities than they would as individual crystals; (e) changes in the density, polymerization and/or viscosity of the magma as crystallization proceeds; (f) variations in the rate at which different minerals nucleate; (g) whether, or not, the contents of the magma chamber was subjected to shock waves, movements or pressures produced by tectonic processes; and (h) whether the materials in the magma chamber form an open or closed chemical system. With regard to the question of whether a particular magma chamber is an open or closed chemical system, it is important to consider: (a) that many magma chambers are of the periodically replenished, periodically tapped, continuously fractionated type (see Section 1.7); (b) that chemical changes that may at first appear to be minor, such as changes in the partial pressure of oxygen, may induce large changes in the final products of magmatic differentiation (see Figs 2.3.1b and c); and (c) that if a magma becomes *contaminated*, the change in chemical composition may produce sudden changes in the phase, or phases, being precipitated. The latter process has been used by Irvine (1981: 320) to account for the chromite-rich layers in the Muskox Intrusion. Prior to the precipitation of the chromite-rich layer, the magma was crystallizing both olivine and chromite. However, when the magma assimilated silica-rich material, the resulting *hybrid magma* had a chemical composition that was well within the chromite liquidus field; thus, for a short time only, chromite was precipitated.

2.4 Mixing of magmas

Since the time of Bunsen (1851), it has often been proposed that the rocks with compositions intermediate between the basalts and the rhyolites are products of magma mixing. In more recent times, Eichelberger (1975: 1981) has, for example, proposed that many andesites and dacites are produced by the mixing of 'primary basaltic and rhyolitic magmas'. He specifically suggested that the dacitic rocks of the Glass Mountain of northern California, USA, were generated by the contamination of a rhyolitic magma by basaltic lavas from the Medicine Lake Highland Shield Volcano. McBirney (1980) has critically examined the concept of magma mixing; and he concluded that the variations in composition normally found in rocks of the high-alumina basalt, andesite, dacite, rhyolite (or calc-alkalic suite), are difficult to explain, if the rocks of this suite are products of the mixing of two genetically unrelated magmas of different composition and density. He claims that most of the petrographic and chemical features proposed as evidence of magma mixing, such as disequilibrium, can be explained by the eruption and mixing of magmas from a compositionally-zoned magma chamber. Magma mixing has also been invoked to explain the association of basic and silicic glasses in the mesostasis of some volcanic rocks; however, such glasses are now usually interpreted as congealed immiscible liquids.

Rocks from many layered intrusions contain evidence that supports the concept of the mixing, or blending, of either: (a) separate batches of magma; or (b) liquids of the same parentage that are at different stages of differentiation. The latter process can readily be visualized as occurring in subvolcanic magma chambers and vents, when fresh and more primitive magma is added to residual, fractionated magma. Keith et al. (1982) have proposed that the Stillwater Intrusion of Montana, USA, developed from two magmas with distinctly different chemical compositions. One magma, which they called Uo, gave rise to the rocks of the ultramafic lineage, whereas the other, known as Ao, gave rise to the rocks of the anorthositic lineage (see Chs 10 and 11). It is proposed that the sulphide minerals that host the platinum-group elements in the platinum-bearing reef of this intrusion represent an immiscible liquid that developed as the result of the mixing of the Uo and Ao magmas. Most of the platinum-group elements were derived from one of the magmas, whereas the sulphur came from the other; thus prior to mixing, the concentration of the platinum-group elements in the first magma was not limited by sulphide-saturation equilibrium. It is claimed that although the Uo and Ao

magmas began to mix while they were at their respective liquidus temperatures, the hybrid magmas so produced would be at temperatures well above their liquidi. Such *superheated* magmas would tend to assimilate the rocks they came into contact with; and the resorption so produced may be responsible for the so-called *pothole structures* found in some layered intrusions, such as the Bushveld Layered Complex of S. Africa.

A remarkable example of the mixing of silicate liquids of different composition can be observed in the Gardiner River rhyolite–basalt complex in Yellowstone Park, Wyoming, USA (cf. Fenner 1938; 1944; Wilcox 1944). This volcanic complex contains many examples of hybrid rocks produced by the mixing of rhyolitic and basaltic materials. Fenner (1938) obtained bulk chemical analyses of eighteen samples of rock that cover the whole compositional range from basalt to rhyolite. When these data are plotted on a silica variation diagram, the data points for the various oxides follow straight lines. Wilcox (1944) has shown that these straight oxide-abundance-lines are what one would expect if the various intermediate rocks had been produced by mixing together a fluid rhyolitic lava and a simultaneously-erupted fluid basaltic lava. The straight MgO and CaO lines are, for example, quite unlike the lines one would expect in a suite of rocks produced by fractional crystallization (see Fig. 2.6.1). More recently, Miesch (1976) has used *Q-mode factor* (*vector*) *analysis* to test the hypothesis that the intermediate rocks of this complex were generated by the mixing of two end-member liquids. His *factor-variance diagram* shows that two end-members could account for 97 per cent, or more, of all the chemical variation in six of the major oxides (namely, SiO_2, Al_2O_3, FeO, MgO, CaO and K_2O), for 85 per cent of the variation in Na_2O, 28 per cent in Fe_2O_3, but very little in H_2O^+. It is thus concluded that the main petrogenetic process in the evolution of the Gardiner River rock series was the mixing in varying proportions of basaltic and rhyolitic liquids; however, in order to account for the variations in Na_2O, Fe_2O_3 and H_2O^+, one has to also postulate an ancillary process such as post-congelation alteration.

Magma mixing does not always result in a simple linear combination of the chemical components in the two magmas as occurred in the Gardiner River rock series. If one, or both, of the magmas contain crystals, and the crystals are not in equilibrium with the new hybrid magma, they will react or be resorbed; and the bulk composition of a particular hybrid magma will depend on the proportions of the various liquid and solid components it incorporates; and such a hybrid magma may not be a simple intermediate mixture of the two end-member magmas.

Another well-known hybrid rock crops out within an irregular ring-dyke in the Western Red Hills, on the island of Skye in north-western Scotland. It is quartz monzodioritic in composition, and it is well exposed on a prominent peak that is called Marsco. The hybrid rock is called marscoite (Harker 1904: 175), and it contains xenocrysts and/or phenocrysts of quartz, alkali feldspar and plagioclase (An$_{50}$) set in a groundmass of oligoclase, iron-rich amphibole, alkali feldspar, Fe–Ti oxides, quartz and acicular apatite. Marscoite is believed to be the product of the mechanical mixing of a granitic magma with an iron-rich basaltic magma (cf. Sabine & Sutherland 1982: 543).

Evidence of the mixing of magmas is also found in many epizonal and mesozonal granite–granodiorite batholiths (see Section 9). These plutonic rocks contain *enclosures* of congealed, generally finer-grained, magmatic materials that tend to have compositions that are intermediate between basalt and the host granitic rock (for example, enclosures of medium- to fine-grained monzodiorites, quartz monzodiorites or quartz monzonites).

2.5 Assimilation

Assimilation is the incorporation and digestion of foreign, usually solid, material by a magma. In the past it was widely believed that many igneous rocks, and even suites of igneous rocks, evolved as the result of the assimilation of continental crystal rocks by primary magmas (cf. Daly 1933). Such views should not surprise one because no body of magma is ever completely independent of the wall rocks that contain it. This concept is elegantly illustrated by Fratta and Shaw (1974) and Dostal and Fratta (1977), who studied the trace element abundance patterns in a basaltic dyke that had been emplaced into country rocks that contained markedly different chemical compositions. The dyke is approximately 10 m wide; and in areas where it intrudes granitic gneiss it contains significantly

higher concentrations of K, Rb, Ba, Li and Ti than in areas where it intrudes country rocks of more basic composition. Some petrologists would call the process that changed the composition of this dyke *wall-rock-reaction*, rather than assimilation.

The main reason why assimilation is not a major process in the evolution of magmatic rocks is that there is an enormous discrepancy between the specific heat capacities of silicate magmas and the heats of solution of silicate country rocks (that is, 1 : 350; cf. Bowen 1928: 184). It is estimated that a magma would normally have to be at a temperature of some 300 °C above its liquidus if it was to assimilate crystalline materials of the same mass as itself; that is, even when the crystalline materials are preheated to their melting temperatures. There is, however, no evidence that magmas normally contain significant amounts of *superheat*; and even if they contain superheat, this would normally be dissipated before the composition of the whole magma could be significantly changed. In some bodies of magma, however, convection currents may supply enough heat for the local assimilation of country rocks, particularly at contacts.

The manner in which igneous materials are assimilated will be considered by examining what happens during the assimilation of igneous rock-forming minerals. When such minerals are assimilated, the process may be considered to operate in one of three ways, depending on whether the mineral is: (a) a phase the magma may have crystallized earlier but is no longer precipitating (that is, earlier in the reaction series); (b) a phase the magma is currently precipitating; or (c) a phase that the magma may precipitate at a late stage in its cooling history (late in the reaction series). In the first example, the magma is unable to melt the mineral, and thus reacts with it; in the second example, the mineral is stable in the magma, and the assimilation process increases the volume of that mineral without altering the composition of the liquid part of the magma; whereas in the third example, there is normally *reactive solution* of the mineral by the magma. Bowen (1928: 221) has shown that a granitic–rhyolitic magma saturated in biotite cannot dissolve olivine or pyroxene (that is, minerals that occur earlier in the reaction series), but it can react with them in an attempt to convert them into biotite. On the other hand, a subalkalic basaltic magma will react with xenoliths of granitic composition (that is, minerals that occur later in the reaction series), and the reaction will be such that the chemical components of the xenoliths are incorporated into the magma, and there is an accompanying precipitation of their heat equivalent in liquidus phases. Provided that conditions are suitable, the granitic xenoliths that pass into solution tend to augment the volume of normal granitic–rhyolitic differentiates that are later formed by fractional crystallization of the hybrid magma. Bowen (1928: 187) summarized these concepts by stating that 'any magma will tend to make inclusions over into the phase or phases with which it is saturated, in so far as the composition of the inclusions will permit . . . also that any magma saturated with a certain member of a reaction series is effectively supersaturated with all higher members of the reaction series'. He ends his chapter (1928: 223) on *the effects of assimilation* by stating that 'it is doubtful whether the presence of foreign matter is ever essential to the production of any particular type of differentiate': however, a rider should be added to this statement to acknowledge that assimilation is often required to account for the rocks found near igneous contacts.

The assimilation of xenoliths of sedimentary, or metamorphic, origin is often complicated, because these materials may contain phases that do not belong in the reaction series for subalkalic magmatic rocks; and sedimentary rocks, such as sandstones and limestones, have extreme chemical compositions as compared to the common magmatic rocks. When quartz-rich xenoliths are engulfed in subalkalic basaltic lava (McBirney 1979: 316), the earliest stages in the assimilation process consist of the formation of rims of glass that 'penetrate along grain boundaries and fractures, and as the process of solution advances, the grains of quartz are reduced to rounded and embayed remnants surrounded by pale brown glass and a corona of augite'. In his pioneering study of the *transfusion of quartz xenoliths in alkali, basic and ultrabasic lavas*, Holmes (1936) demonstrated that such xenoliths do not melt directly to a liquid of their own composition. He showed that the glass rims around the xenoliths contained chemical components that could only have been introduced from the host magma. Such rims usually contain regular gradients in composition that contain a complete spectrum of concentrations, from an inner silica-rich zone to an outer zone with a composition that approaches that of the liquid fraction of the host magma.

In the past it has often been proposed that the assimilation of carbonate rocks might result in the desilication of magmas, and the generation of *feldspathoidal alkaline rocks* (cf. Daly 1910; Shand 1945). For example, if an alkalic basaltic magma was to assimilate carbonate xenoliths, the addition of calcium would probably increase the amount of augite and anorthite precipitated; and this would deplete the magma in those components of augite and anorthite that are not present in the xenoliths; that is, Si, Fe, Al and possibly Mg. Watkinson and Wyllie (1969) have examined *phase equilibrium studies bearing on the limestone-assimilation hypothesis*, and they concluded that limestone assimilation would consume a large amount of heat from the host magma. As there is a thermal barrier at low pressures that prevents silica-oversaturated magmas from moving into the silica-undersaturated field, it is suggested that under normal circumstances that assimilation of limestone by a subalkalic basaltic magma, or any other silica-oversaturated magma, is not likely to produce significant quantities of silica-undersaturated magma.

Assimilation normally increases the mass of solid phases precipitated by the participating magma; however, once chemical equilibrium is re-established in the magma, it is usually difficult to use major element abundance data to demonstrate that assimilation has occurred; however, this restriction does not necessarily apply to trace element abundance data. The assimilated material might, for example, contain distinctive concentrations, or ratios, of the incompatible elements; and if these elements were not removed by the precipitating phases, the added trace elements might provide irrefutable evidence of assimilation (see the next section of this chapter on mass balance mixing). In many areas, such as East Africa, where limestone assimilation was supposed to have generated *feldspathoidal alkaline rocks*, detailed field and trace element studies have demonstrated conclusively that the so-called xenoliths of sedimentary limestone, that have been described as occurring in these rocks, are intrusive *carbonatites* (see Ch. 14).

Anatexis is a process that has much in common with assimilation; and it is involved with the production of magmas, particularly granitic magmas, by the selective fusion of crustal rocks. According to some petrologists, anatexis is the normal consequence of extreme regional metamorphism; whereas others maintain that anatectic magmas obtain at least some of their heat, and even some of their mass, from the emplacement of hot, usually basic, magmas into the crust. This topic will be examined in Chapter 9.

2.6 Variation diagrams and mass balance mixing models

In the first chapter of his book on the evolution of the igneous rocks, Bowen (1928) discussed the *diversity of igneous rocks* as found within *rock associations*; and he demonstrated the continuous nature of the variations in chemical composition that are usually found within such associations. He also showed how effective *variation diagrams*, such as Fig. 2.6.1, are in illustrating the chemical relationships among the members of a rock association. Variation diagrams also enable one to explore the compositions and quantities of phases that have to be added, or subtracted, from an evolving magma to produce the next magma in the *liquid line of descent* (Bowen 1928: 114). Diagrams, particularly variation diagrams, are of great importance in igneous petrology because they portray the relationships between real rocks, not the trends in ideal chemical systems. Petrologists seem to like to use these diagrams because, as Rene Thom (1975) has shown, our qualitative grasp of form and geometric order goes deeper than our quantitative grasp of numbers and magnitude. All the possible variations in magmatic differentiation are great, yet for most magmatic rock associations there is a 'normal line of descent'

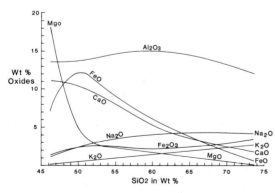

Fig. 2.6.1 Silica variation diagram of the subalkalic (tholeiitic) suite of Iceland (data from Jakobsson 1980: 59).

(Bowen 1928: 114). It is as though an evolving magma follows a *stable pathway of change*. Thom has shown that similar topological patterns of behaviour occur in many different natural processes. It is suggested that the liquid lines of descent in most magmatic rock associations follow unique pathways through compositional space, and these pathways have what Thom calls 'structural stability'.

The *liquid line of descent*, or the *liquid path*, refers to the trend in composition followed by residual liquids that evolve as a result of the differential withdrawal of chemical constituents from these liquids as a magma crystallizes. One would, however, generally expect a magmatic rock to form from the congealation of a residual liquid, together with some of the crystals that had crystallized earlier suspended in it. If these crystals represent all the solid material that separated from a less differentiated liquid of the same comagmatic series, then the bulk composition of the rock will fall onto the liquid line of descent; however, if the congealed rock only contains some of these crystals, or other crystals have been added to it during magmatic differentiation, its composition will depart from the liquid line of descent. In the past, many studies of the evolution of magmatic rocks, including studies of slowly-cooled plutonic rocks, have been based on chemical analyses of individual members of rock associations in the belief that bulk chemical compositions of the various members of an association represent compositions on a liquid line of descent. When studying porphyritic volcanic rocks it is now possible to determine the chemical composition of both the mesostasis and the phenocrysts; however, such detailed studies often reveal that the rocks being studied evolved in an even more complex manner than previously anticipated, as the mesostasis may be heterogeneous and the phenocrysts compositionally zoned (cf. Wilcox 1979).

Mass balance mixing models

Variation diagrams may be used to simulate graphically the addition (phenocrysts, xenocrysts, xenoliths or batches of magma), or subtraction (minerals or immiscible liquids), of phases from a magma; and when so used they demonstrate the ability, or inability, of these processes to account for the chemical differences that exist between the members of a rock association. Such diagrams provide a clear picture of the chemical changes that take place when a single phase is added, or subtracted, from a magma (see Fig. 2.6.2); however, variation diagrams are often difficult to interpret when a number of phases have to be added, and/or subtracted, at the same time. Fortunately, computers, and least-squares mass balance mixing programs, such as XLFRAC (Stormer & Nicholls 1978) and GENMIX (Le Maitre 1981), are able to handle magmatic differentiation models that contain many phases, and have complex differentiation histories. According to Stormer and Nicholls (1978: 143), their program can be used to test fractional crystallization (by subtraction, or addition, of chemically-analysed phenocrysts

or cumulate minerals), assimilation (by addition of chemically-analysed country rocks or xenoliths), fractional melting (by subtraction of xenocrysts or refractory residual rocks from an assumed parental material) and magma mixing (see the worked example in Table 7.8.2). They also state (143) that the concept of mass balance can be informally described as 'some of it, plus the rest of it, equals all of it' (that is, andesite + olivine + pyroxene = basalt). Mass balance mixing programs are usually able to produce a number of arithmetically sound models; however, before accepting the model with the best fit (that is, lowest sum of the residuals squared), one should ascertain that this model makes petrological and geochemical sense. It must also be remembered that the least-squares method requires the system being modelled to have fewer phases (minerals) than chemical components (oxides).

In 1974, Wright (246) used a least-squares procedure to quantitatively model magmatic differentiation in the Columbia River volcanic rocks of north-western USA. He showed that the differentiated Umatilla basaltic icelandite (SiO_2

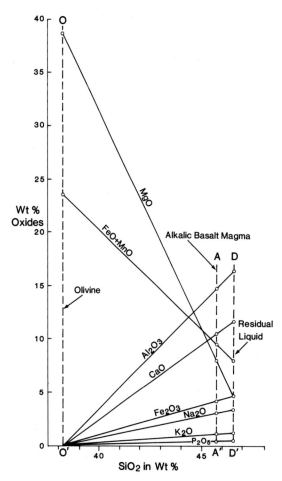

Fig. 2.6.2 Silica variation diagram of an alkalic basaltic magma (AA') from which 10 per cent olivine ($Fo_{66.7}$) has been removed. DD' is the composition of the residual liquid.

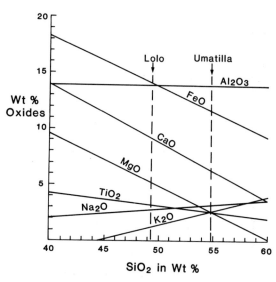

Fig. 2.6.3 This silica variation diagram shows how difficult these diagrams are to interpret when more than one phase is added, or subtracted, during magmatic differentiation. In this example, approximately 4 per cent olivine, 19 per cent augite, 25 per cent plagioclase and 7 per cent Fe-Ti oxides have to be removed in order to generate a residual liquid of the composition of the Umatilla basaltic icelandite from the Lolo basalt (cf. Wright 1974).

= 54.7 per cent, MgO = 2.7 per cent) might represent a residual liquid formed after crystallization of 55 per cent of a parental magma of the composition of the Lolo basalt (SiO_2 = 49.2 per cent, MgO = 5.3 per cent). In detail, the solution obtained is as follows: 100 per cent Lolo basalt = 44.8 per cent Umatilla basaltic icelandite + 3.8 per cent olivine (Fo_{64}) + 18.7 per cent augite + 25.2 per cent plagioclase (An_{55}) + 7.0 per cent Fe–Ti oxides + 0.7 per cent apatitie (see Fig. 2.6.3). The minerals used by Wright in this mixing model were similar to the microphenocrysts found in the sparsely porphyritic Umatilla basaltic icelandite.

Trace element modelling

In igneous petrology, *trace elements* are usually regarded as being either the non-essential elements in a mineral or those elements that are present in igneous rocks in concentrations of less than approximately 0.1 per cent by weight. Trace elements that are frequently used in petrogenetic discussion include the following: vanadium (V = 135 p.p.m.); chromium (Cr = 100 p.p.m.); cobalt (Co = 25 p.p.m.); nickel (Ni = 75 p.p.m.); rubidium (Rb = 90 p.p.m.); strontium (Sr = 375 p.p.m.); yttrium (Y = 33 p.p.m.); zirconium (Zr = 165 p.p.m.); niobium (Nb = 20 p.p.m.) barium (Ba = 425 p.p.m.); the lanthanides or rare earth elements (R.E.E.); lead (Pb = 13 p.p.m.); thorium (Th = 7.2 p.p.m.); and uranium (U = 1.8 p.p.m.). The numbers in brackets are the crustal abundances of these elements in parts per million (after Mason & Moore 1982: 46–7). Trace elements such as these can be used to place more constraints on partial melting, and magmatic differentiation, models. For example, during the fractional crystallization of a magma, a trace element will distribute itself between the magma

and the various minerals in such a way that the *mineral/magma distribution coefficients* (concentration in mineral/concentration in liquid = K_D) of the trace element for the individual minerals will be constant (cf. Arth 1976; Cox et al. 1979: 332–59; Henderson 1982: 88–101; see Table 2.6.1). In principle, distribution coefficients can be determined: (a) by measuring trace element abundances in both the phenocrysts and the mesostasis of glassy volcanic rocks; or (b) by studying trace element distribution behaviour in synthetic silicate melts. In practice, it is often difficult to obtain reliable estimates of the distribution coefficients for many trace elements, because distribution coefficients may change in response to changes in temperature, pressure, oxygen fugacity, types of phases present and magma composition; and it is not always easy to establish: (a) the number of phases present in a rock (for example, the mesostasis may contain two types of glass, or the zircon and apatite crystals may be too small to recognize); and (b) that the trace element compositions that were determined for the various phases, represent the exact compositions of these phases as they were when they were in chemical equilibrium with one another.

Kyle (1981: 490–4) has used major element data, and a mass balance mixing program, to develop a series of models that attempt to describe the fractional crystallization of a hyperalkalic (basanite to phonolite) suite of rocks from Ross Island, Antarctica (see Fig. 2.6.4). He then used trace element data, and the appropriate mineral–liquid distribution coefficients, to test the various fractional crystallization models, and he found overall agreement between the trace element abundances predicted by the arithmetically-acceptable mass balance fractional crystallization models and the actual trace element abundances found in the various differentiated rocks of the suite. It is interesting to

Table 2.6.1 Examples of mineral/liquid distribution coefficients for five selected trace elements in basaltic magmas (after Henderson 1982: 91)

Element	Olivine	Orthopyroxene	Clinopyroxene	Amphibole	Plagioclase
Cr	2.1	≈10	8.4	≈1.0	n.a.*
Rb	0.006	≈0.025	0.04	0.25	0.10
Sr	0.01	≈0.015	0.14	0.57	1.8
Ba	0.006	≈0.013	0.07	0.31	0.23
Sm**	0.009	0.05	0.9	0.91	0.08

* Not available.
** Sm is the rare earth element, samarium.

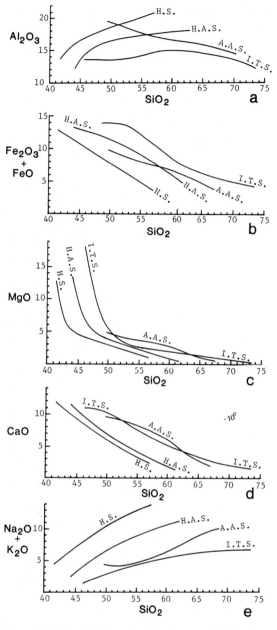

note that over 75 per cent of the fractionation from basanite to phonolite occurs in the step from basanite to silica-undersaturated hawaiite.

2.7 Selected references

Bowen, N. L. (1928) *The Evolution of the Igneous Rocks*, Princeton Univ. Press, Princeton, New Jersey, USA.

Jackson, E. D. (1961) Primary textures and mineral associations in the ultramafic zone of the Stillwater Complex, Montana, *US Geol. Surv. Prof. Pap., 358.*

Wager, L. R. & Brown, G. M. (1968) *Layered Igneous Rocks*, Oliver & Boyd, Edinburgh.

Yoder, H. S. (ed.) (1979) *The Evolution of the Igneous Rocks: Fiftieth Anniversary Perspectives*, Princeton Univ. Press, New Jersey, USA.

Fig. 2.6.4 (a–e) Five related silica variation diagrams illustrating magmatic differentiation in four different suites of igneous rocks. H.S. is a hyperalkaline suite of rocks from Ross Island, Antarctica (data from Kyle 1981: 478–9). H.A.S. is the Hawaiian alkalic suite (data from Macdonald 1968: 502–3). A.A.S. is an Aleutian orogenic andesite suite of rocks (calc-alkalic; data from Marsh, 1982: 108). I.T.S. is the Icelandic tholeiitic suite that contain anorogenic icelandites (data from Jakobsson 1980: 59).

CHAPTER 3

CLASSIFICATION OF IGNEOUS ROCKS AND MAGMAS

'Personally, I doubt that an exact petrological classification of igneous rocks can ever be attained. We may arrive at some sort of approximation to an orderly arrangement for the purposes of petrographic description and petrological discussion, which might by courtesy be called a classification . . .' (H. S. Washington 1922: 801).

3.1 General statement

An ideal classification of rocks should enable one to place individual rocks in groups; and then arrange the groups in an order that is relatively easy to remember, and also directs attention to relationships between the different groups. In the past, many hundreds of different names have been used in igneous petrography; and many of these names 'emphasize petty differences between one rock and another, while ignoring fundamental points of resemblance' (Shand 1950: 207). This is the very antithesis of classification. At present it is difficult to reform igneous nomenclature because the names of many of the common rocks have been used, and abused, for such a long time. For example, the rock names basalt, granite and syenite have all been used for hundreds of years, and they are now usually held in such reverence that they dominate most systems of classification, instead of the classification dominating the names. There have been a number of attempts to redefine, or rearrange, existing names, but such endeavours have generally failed because, as Chayes

(1979a: 521) has remarked, there are no widely-accepted criteria for deciding whether modifications of the names already in the public domain are actually in the public interest.

However, only a relatively few (approximately 50) of the many (approximately 800) igneous rock names are frequently used in the literature of petrology (see Ch. 4); and as many of the commonly used rock names have been widely used for many years, it is desirable to collect and process all the quantitative and descriptive data that have accumulated on these rocks. Using this data-base, one is then able to arrive at a consensus view on what petrologists have in the past understood by these rock terms. Le Maitre (1976a), for example, compiled a file of some 25 924 major element analyses of igneous rocks, and from this huge volume of data established the mean chemical compositions and standard deviations of some thirty-eight common igneous rocks. The publication of Le Maitre's work, and other similar works (for example, Chayes 1975), has made most petrologists re-think their approach to the classification of igneous rocks. However, it must be recognized that the following concepts are implicit in what one might call the Le Maitre approach to the study of igneous rocks: (a) past usage of terms, such as basalt, is the key to understanding how these terms should be used at present; and (b) most workers who publish chemical analyses of igneous rocks are able to name them 'correctly'.

It is significant to note that Le Maitre's mean basalt composition is similar to the mean value obtained by Manson (1967: 236) who used a comprehensive major element and normative mineral screen to define basalt. The major premise in Manson's approach is that at any particular time, one can obtain a broad consensus among petrologists as to the major element and/or normative limits they would set to define the common igneous rocks. Such limits may be broad for individual parameters, but when many such parameters are used together they are able to define a rock type quite closely. Table 3.1.1 provides an example of a simple chemical screen. This method of defining the common igneous rocks has much to recommend it, as the definition of a particular rock can be gradually revised in the light of new knowledge.

Igneous rocks are usually defined as those rocks that solidified from a hot (usually greater than 600 °C), molten, or partly molten condition. When one attempts to apply this definition

Table 3.1.1 A simple chemical screen that defines the post-Archaean basalts of Earth (after Middlemost 1980: 53)

Oxide	More than (%)	Less than (%)
SiO_2	44.0	53.5
Al_2O_3	10.5	21.5
FeO	2.5	15.0
CaO	5.0	15.0
Na_2O	1.0	3.9
K_2O	0.0	2.5
Total H_2O	0.0	2.0

to real rocks, one discovers that in the plutonic realm it is often difficult to establish criteria for deciding whether particular crystalline rocks are either igneous or metamorphic; whereas in the surficial realm it may be difficult to decide whether pyroclastic materials are of igneous or sedimentary origin. Many pyroclastic rocks should properly be regarded as being both igneous and sedimentary. For example, the same bed of pyroclastic material might be regarded as a volcanic rock that was extruded from a particular volcano, and also as a unit of clastic material that filled a basin. All pyroclastic rocks can be readily named using the system proposed by Le Bas and Sabine (1980: 389–91; see Table 1.9.1). Laboratory experiments usually provide conclusive proof as to whether a rock is of igneous origin or not; and most igneous petrologists would agree with Shand's (1940: 231)

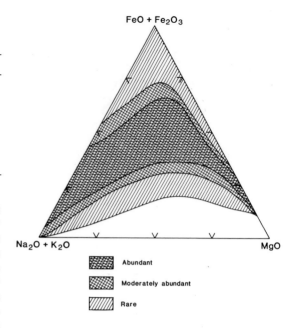

Fig. 3.1.2 Scatter-plot of all available chemical analyses of igneous rocks on a $(Na_2O + K_2O)-(FeO + Fe_2O_3)-MgO$ triangular diagram. (Adapted from Le Maitre 1976a: 599).

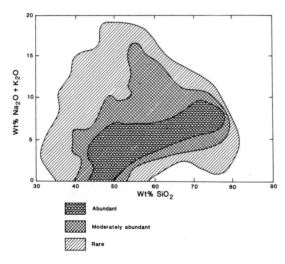

Fig. 3.1.1 Scatter-plot of all available chemical analyses of igneous rocks on an alkali silica diagram (Adapted from Le Maitre 1976a: 599).

statement that 'what the petrographer cannot learn through the microscope, he must be prepared to seek in the crucible'.

Igneous rocks are difficult to classify in an unambiguous manner because they are part of a single, irregular, yet gradational series (Iddings 1903: 66), and the boundaries set up between different rock types are essentially arbitrary. A scatter-plot of all available igneous rock analyses on an alkali silica diagram, or a $(Na_2O + K_2O) - (FeO + Fe_2O_3) - MgO$ triangular diagram (see Figs 3.1.1 and 3.1.2) clearly demonstrate this; and these diagrams also show a strong clustering of data points in the basalt–gabbro and rhyolite–granite positions in compositional space. Although the chemical compositions of the common igneous rocks grade into one another, this does not imply that they occupy all of compositional space; on the contrary, they occupy only a limited volume of contiguous compositional space. If one examines Figs 3.1.1 and 3.1.2 in conjunction with the data on the means and standard deviations of the abundant oxides in the 'average igneous rock' (Table 3.1.2), one gets some insight into this concept.

Table 3.1.2 The chemical composition of the 'average' igneous rock in Wt%

	1	*2*	*s**
SiO_2	57.03	58.28	10.38
TiO_2	1.05	1.07	1.10
Al_2O_3	15.02	15.33	3.86
Fe_2O_3	2.90	2.99	2.28
FeO	4.63	4.84	3.50
MnO	0.14		
MgO	5.06	5.17	6.84
CaO	6.13	6.25	4.22
Na_2O	3.50	3.58	1.87
K_2O	2.45	2.50	1.97
H_2O^+	1.12		
H_2O^-	0.13		
P_2O_5	0.26		
CO_2	0.15		
Total	99.57	100.01	

1. Chemical composition of the 'average' igneous rock (after Le Maitre 1976a: 599). Total number of analyses 25 924.
2. Same data as in 1 recalculated to 100 per cent after removing MnO, H_2O^+, H_2O^-, P_2O_5 and CO_2.
Note: H_2O^- is the amount of hygroscopic moisture given off when a sample is heated at 110 °C, whereas H_2O^+ is the *combined water* that is driven off at higher temperatures (cf. Groves 1951: 94–104).
s* = Standard deviation of chemical analysis 2.

Systems of igneous rock classification

There are many comprehensive systems of igneous rock classification that use the actual mineral composition, or *modes*, of unaltered rocks (for example: Johannsen 1931; or Streckeisen 1967; 1973; 1974; 1978; 1980). Such modal classifications are useful in succinctly communicating petrographic ideas, and they are also important because they goad petrographers into producing precise descriptions of the rocks they study. However, in such classifications the individual rock types are usually rigidly defined; and many of the rock names used were introduced, and defined, at a time when petrology was essentially a descriptive science and a branch of *natural history*. Such systems of classification tend to inhibit petrogenetic discussions. Modal classifications are also of little use in naming glassy or crypto-crystalline rocks.

Present-day igneous petrology requires at least two systems of rock classification, that is: (a) a quantitative modal and/or chemical (possibly normative) system that can be used in petrography; and (b) a flexible system that brings together those igneous rocks that are considered to have evolved under broadly similar conditions. The latter system is essential in petrogenetic discussions, and it should change as petrogenetic theory changes and evolves in response to new petrological discoveries and experimental studies.

Critical phase petrology

A strong case can be argued for using a third system of classification concurrently with the two systems already mentioned. This third system of classification would be used to study specific assemblages of intimately associated and roughly contemporaneous igneous rocks. Many such igneous complexes contain a variety of different rock types that grade into one another. In mapping these complexes, one has to attempt to integrate both the petrography and structure of the rocks, and this is most readily achieved by employing the methods of *critical phase petrology* (Shand 1942: 414; 1950: 929; Hess 1960: 51; Jackson 1967: 23–4). In this method of classification, one records the appearance and/or disappearance of certain phases (that is, minerals) that are considered important in the interpretation of the evolution of a suite of igneous rocks. Shand (1950: 929) demonstrated that this approach to rock classification was able to lessen the 'exaggerated importance' of feldspars in most modal classifications, and it also directed attention towards other minerals that are stable for only a limited time during the crystallization of a magma.

Critical phase petrology has been successfully used by Shand (1942) to integrate the petrography (Rogers 1911) and structure (Balk 1927) of the peridotite–pyroxenite–norite–diorite Cortland Complex to the south of Peekskill, New York. The technique has also been used in mapping larger bodies of layered igneous rocks. Hess (1960: 51), for example, introduced the term *phase layering* to describe the abrupt appearance or disappearance of a crystalline phase, or phases, during the crystallization of a magma; wheras Jackson (1967: 24) used the term *phase contact* to describe the boundary plane between layers of rock that contain different critical phases, such as chromite, clinopyroxene or quartz. The mapping of critical phases in igenous complexes is broadly analogous to the mapping of *index minerals*, and *lines of equal grade*, in metamorphic petrology.

Plutonic and volcanic magmatic rocks

If one attempts to devise a practical classification of igneous rocks, one soon discovers that many of the problems that confront orthodox systems of igneous rock classification can be circumvented if one separates the volcanic from the plutonic rocks. These two groups of rocks generally cool, and congeal, at different rates; and this cooling tends to occur in different physical and often chemical environments. Plutonic magmatic rocks are generally medium- to coarse-grained crystalline rocks that may grade into contiguous crystalline metamorphic rocks. Many volcanic rocks are partially, or wholly, glassy and/or fragmental, and the phenocrysts/megacrysts they contain are often not a clear guide to the overall composition of the rock. It thus seems rational to use modal criteria to classify plutonic rocks that contain easily recognizable minerals, and chemical criteria to classify volcanic rocks. It is anticipated that ultimately chemical or quasi-chemical (essentially normative) methods will be used to classify all igneous rocks.

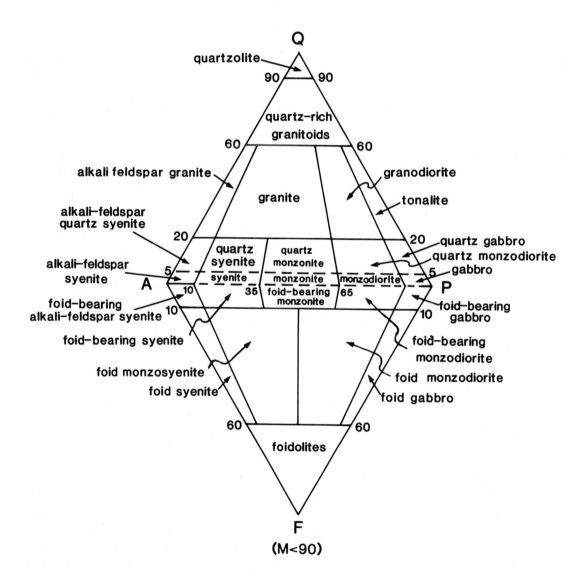

Fig. 3.2.1 General modal classification and nomenclature of the *plutonic rocks* (after Streckeisen 1974: 777).

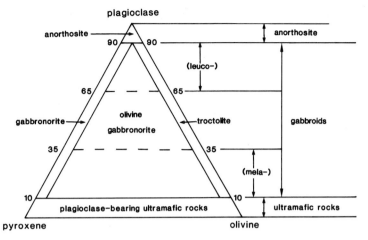

Fig. 3.2.2 General modal classification and nomenclature of the *gabbroic rocks* (after Streckeisen 1974: 780).

3.2 Classification of plutonic rocks

In 1973 the *International Union of Geological Sciences subcommission on the systematics of igneous rocks* (Streckeisen 1973; 1974; 1976; 1980) introduced a new modal classification of the plutonic rocks. The classification uses the following minerals and mineral groups: Q = quartz or high-temperature forms of SiO$_2$; A = alkali feldspars (orthoclase, microcline, perthite, sanidine, anorthoclase, albite (An$_{00-05}$); P = plagioclase (An$_{05-100}$) and scapolite; F = feldspathoids (leucite and pseudoleucite, nepheline, sodalite, nosean, hauyne, cancrinite, analcime, etc.); and M = mafic and related minerals (micas, amphiboles, pyroxenes, olivines), opaque minerals (Fe–Ti oxides), accessory minerals (zircon, apatite, titanite), epidote, allanite, garnets, melilites, monticellite and primary carbonates. Rocks that contain 90 per cent, or more, M are classified using the relative abundances of their mafic minerals; whereas, all rocks that contain less than 90 per cent M are classified, and named, according to the position they occupy in the double triangle QAPF (see Fig. 3.2.1). Prior to being plotted on the QAPF diagram, the values of the light-coloured constituents are recalculated to total 100 (that is, Q + A + P = 100, or A + P + F = 100).

Gabbroic rocks

Superficially this classification of the plutonic rocks appears to be simple and comprehensive;

unfortunately, it is neither. For example, the area adjoining the P-corner of the QAPF diagram is nominally called the *gabbro-field*; however, it contains many of the most abundant plutonic rocks, such as gabbro (pl. + cpx ± ol.), norite (pl. + opx ± cpx), anorthosite (pl.), troctolite (ol. + pl.), hornblende gabbro (pl. + cpx + hb) and gabbronorite (pl. + cpx + opx). In the general classification of plutonic rocks, all of those that plot within the area adjoining the P-corner of the QAPF diagram are called *gabbroic rocks*, and the nomenclature used to describe them can be defined by using the supplementary diagrams shown in Figs 3.2.2 and

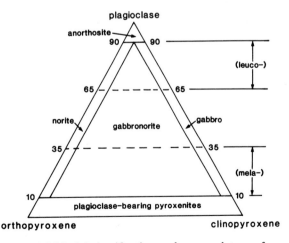

Fig. 3.2.3 Modal classification and nomenclature of the *orthopyroxene-bearing gabbroic rocks* (after Streckeisen 1974: 780).

3.2.3 (that is, pl.–px–ol. and pl.–opx–cpx triangular diagrams).

Ultramafic rocks

In the Streckeisen (1974) classification, the plutonic rocks that contain 90 per cent, or more, of the M-component are called *ultramafic rocks*. Not all petrologists would agree with this definition because the ultramafic rocks are often defined as being those that have a *colour index* (that is, M-value) that is greater than 70 (for example Wyllie 1967: 1). It is recommended that all rocks that have M-values greater than 70 should be called *melanocratic* (that is, melanocratic gabbro, a gabbro in which M is between 70 and 90). A significant proportion of the ultramafic rocks are essentially composed of olivine, orthopyroxene and clinopyroxene. Such rocks can be further subdivided using Fig. 3.2.4. The *kimberlites*, which are another petrologically important group of ultramafic rocks, will be defined and discussed in detail in Chapter 13.

The present discussion of the classification of igneous rocks is mainly concerned with the magmatic silicate rocks that are common on Earth. *Non-silicate magmatic rocks* that contain less than 20 per cent SiO_2 (cf. Middlemost 1972: 385) include those rocks that are essentially composed of carbonates (carbonatites), magnetite (magnetites), sulphur and apatite, and they will be discussed in Chapters 11 and 14.

3.3 Classification of volcanic rocks

If one wishes to use the same method of classification for all the many different types of volcanic rocks (including ash-beds and glassy lava flows), then a chemical system of classification appears to be the only real choice. Textural and structural criteria may be useful in augmenting such a classification. For example, a number of different volcanic materials with dacitic chemical compositions might be described as: (a) holocrystalline dacites; (b) vitrophyric dacites; (c) glassy dacites; or (d) dacitic coarse tuffs.

A problem that commonly arises when using chemical data in the classification of magmatic rocks is that those with broadly similar major element compositions may contain different amounts of volatile components, particularly H_2O and CO_2, or they may be chemically altered. Small amounts of primary H_2O and/or CO_2 (usually less than 1.5 per cent) are found in many magmatic rocks; however, much of the volatile content recorded in igneous rocks was introduced by secondary alteration processes. It is now a common practice to manipulate chemical data prior to their use in the classification of rocks. The volatile components are, for example, removed from the list of oxides, and the sum of the other oxides is then recalculated to equal 100. This procedure raises the abundances of the remaining oxides, and it also tempts petrologists into using data from altered and/or metasomatized rocks in the same manner as they would use

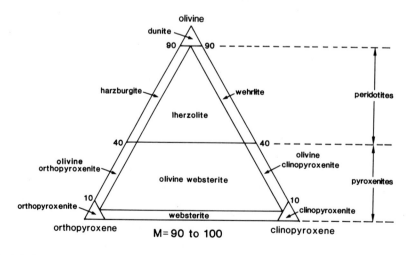

Fig. 3.2.4 Modal classification and nomenclature of the *ultramafic rocks* composed essentially of olivine, orthopyroxene and clinopyroxene (after Streckeisen 1974: 779).

data from unaltered rocks. If the volatiles are removed from the common volcanic rocks, it is found that the SiO_2 values of phonolite, trachyte, rhyolite, dacite and trachyandesite are usually increased by between 1.0 and 1.5 per cent, and the $(Na_2O + K_2O)$ values are increased by between 0.15 per cent (for dacite) and 0.33 per cent (for phonolite). The SiO_2 value of andesite increases by approximately 0.9 per cent and that of basalt by 0.85 per cent; and the $(Na_2O + K_2O)$ value of andesite increases by approximately 0.11 per cent, and basalt by only 0.08 per cent. In the simple chemical classification given in Fig. 3.3.2, all chemical analyses of magmatic rocks that contain more than 2.0 per cent $(H_2O + CO_2)$ are rejected and regarded as altered rocks, unless there is strong contrary evidence.

According to Le Maitre (1976a: 599), the *average igneous rocks* contains 1.12 per cent H_2O^+, 0.13 per cent H_2O^- and 0.15 per cent CO_2. His data also shows that the only normal unaltered igneous rocks that contain significantly more water than these values are the nepheline syenites (mean 1.30 per cent H_2O^+ and 0.27 per cent H_2O), phonolites (1.57 per cent H_2O^+ and 0.37 per cent H_2O^-), leucite basalts (1.75 per cent H_2O^+ and 0.37 per cent H_2O^-) and the nephelinites (1.65 per cent H_2O^+ and 0.54 per cent H_2O^-). The syenites (mean 0.28 per cent CO_2) and the nephelinites (0.60 per cent CO_2) contain significantly more CO_2 than the average igneous rock.

The Fe_2O_3/FeO ratio

Many igneous rocks are oxidized by secondary alteration and thus their Fe_2O_3/FeO ratio increases, and this has a significant effect on the normative mineral composition of the rock. The oxidized rock will contain more normative magnetite ($Fe^{+2}Fe^{+3}_2O_4$), thus less FeO will be available to form silicate minerals such as diopside, hypersthene and olivine. If a smaller than normal proportion of these silicates form, an excess of SiO_2 will appear in the norm of the oxidized rock. Oxidation can result in a basaltic rock changing from being nepheline normative to being hypersthene, or even quartz normative. In order to overcome this problem, and also to establish suitable FeO and Fe_2O_3 values for XRF analyses of rocks in which only total iron is determined, a number of arithmetic computations have been proposed as methods of standardizing the ferric iron contents of magmatic rocks. One

method that is commonly used is to choose the Fe_2O_3/FeO ratio of the least oxidized sample in a group of samples, and adjust the other ratios to this value. Irvine and Baragar (1971: 526) set an upper limit on Fe_2O_3 by using the equation: $\%Fe_2O_3$ in rock = $\%TiO_2$ in rock + 1.5. If the analysed value of Fe_2O_3 was less than $\%TiO_2$ + 1.5, no change in the Fe_2O_3 was made; if it was greater, the 'excess' was converted to FeO. Le Maitre (1976b: 185–9) made a detailed study of the oxidation problem in magmatic rocks. He examined the actual abundance and distribution of FeO and Fe_2O_3 in a large number (25 894) of igneous rocks, and he found that: (a) the mean *oxidation ratios* [wt% FeO/(FeO + Fe_2O_3)] of the common igneous rocks ranged from 0.38 to 0.77; (b) the basic rock types have higher mean oxidation ratios than the acid types; and (c) the mean oxidation ratio is higher in the plutonic rocks as compared to their volcanic equivalents. Figure 3.3.1 is an alkali silica diagram on which lines of equal oxidation ratio have been plotted, and it can be used if any adjustments have to be made to the Fe_2O_3 values in chemical analyses of magmatic rocks. Many of the pre-Tertiary continental flood basalts have, for example, high Fe_2O_3 contents and high Fe_2O_3/FeO ratios. Such

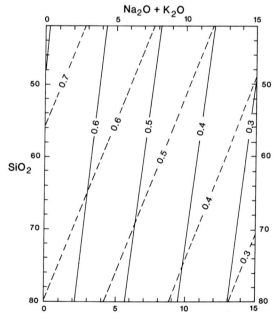

Fig. 3.3.1 Alkali silica diagram showing *lines of equal oxidation ratio* (wt. % FeO/FeO + Fe_2O_3) for the plutonic rock (solid lines) and volcanic rocks (dashed lines) (adapted from Le Maitre 1976b: 189).

high values have to be adjusted downwards before these rocks can be classified, or their normative compositions calculated. In the BVSP (1981: 68) the iron values of rocks of this type from north-eastern Minnesota, USA, were adjusted so that the Fe_2O_3/FeO ratio was equal to 0.2 by weight. Some studies of silicate melt structures suggest that there are inherently different oxidation states for alkaline, silica-undersaturated and silica-saturated magmas.

Silica saturation

In his study of the volcanic rocks of Italy, Herman Abich (1841) established the importance of silica saturation in the classification of igneous rocks. This concept has been used in most later classifications. Shand (1950: 226), for example, divided the igneous rocks into *undersaturated*, *saturated* and *oversaturated* rocks: and defined the oversaturated rocks as those that contained free silica of primary origin; the saturated rocks as those that contained neither free silica nor any undersaturated minerals; and the undersaturated rocks as those that consist either wholly, or in part, of unsaturated minerals. There is also a widely-used system for classifying igneous rocks that is based on their SiO_2 content, and it divides them into *ultrabasic, basic, intermediate* and *silicic* (or *acidic*) rocks. The boundaries between these four major rock groups are usually taken as being approximately: (a) 44–5 per cent SiO_2; (b) 51–4 per cent SiO_2; and (c) 60–5 per cent SiO_2, respectively. In Fig. 3.3.2 these boundaries are placed at 44 per cent SiO_2, 53.5 per cent SiO_2 and 62 per cent SiO_2.

Normative classifications

Not all chemical classifications of igneous rocks use major element data directly. For example, the classification introduced by Cross, Iddings, Pirsson and Washington (C.I.P.W.) in 1902, and which is broadly similar to an earlier classification of Osann, used a standard method of recalculating rock analyses so as to form a set of standard or *normative minerals*. The relative proportions of these normative minerals, together with other chemical criteria, are then used to classify igneous rocks. At present this elaborate classification is seldom, if ever, used; but the C.I.P.W. method of calculating the *norm* of a rock is widely used. Many modern petrologists do not express the relative proportions of the normative minerals in weight percentages as in the original C.I.P.W. norm, but use *molecular norms* or *cation norms*. One of the main advantages of these other types of norms is that the proportions of the opaque minerals (that is, Fe–Ti oxides) are closer to volume percentages, and thus the relative proportions that we observe in the rocks. Yoder and Tilley (1962: 352) used C.I.P.W. normative minerals in their classification of basalts (see Section 5.4); and many petrologists use norms to determine whether a rock is normatively saturated, oversaturated or undersaturated in silica. Both the *differentiation index* and the *crystallization index* use normative minerals; and C.I.P.W. norms have been widely used in various classifications of igneous rocks. The differentiation index is a numerical expression of the extent to which a magma has differentiated, and it represents the sum of the weight percentages of normative quartz, orthoclase, albite, nepheline, leucite and kalsilite (Thornton & Tuttle 1960); whereas the crystallization index represents the sum (in weight per cent) of normative anorthite, magnesian diopside, forsterite and normative enstatite converted to forsterite, together with magnesian spinel calculated from normative corundum in ultramafic rocks (Poldervaart & Parker 1964: 281).

The differentiation index is based on *petrogeny's residua system* ($NaAlSiO_4 - KAlSiO_4 - SiO_2$ (that is, nepheline – kalsilite – quartz; Fig. 7.7.1); and it contains the phases that are usually found in the final residual magma generated by magmatic differentiation; whereas the crystallization index is linked to *petrogeny's primitive system* ($CaAl_2Si_2O_8 - CaMgSi_2O_6 - Mg_2SiO_4$ (that is, anorthite – diopside – forsterite)), and it contains the phases that usually crystallize during the early stages in the differentiation of basaltic magma. The differentiation index (D.I.) is often particularly useful in dividing up suites of volcanic rocks that issued from the same volcano. For example, in the suite alkalic basalt→trachyte, the *alkalic basalts* generally have a D.I. of less than 35; the *hawaiites* of 35 or more, but less than 50; the *mugearites* of 50 or more, but less than 65; the *benmoreites* of 65 or more, but less than 75, and the *trachytes* of 75 or more.

In 1920, Paul Niggli proposed a simple

method of recalculating rock analyses so as to form a set of partial molecular norms, or *Niggli values* (that is: si, al, fm, c, alk, k and mg). These Niggli values can be used to determine the *magma type* to which a particular igneous rock belongs (Burri 1964: 76–84). More recently, Rittmann (1973) has introduced a new, elaborate method of recalculating rock analyses to form molecular norms. These *Rittmann norms* are innovative in that Rittmann attempts to apportion molecular orthoclase (Or), albite (Ab) and anorthite (An) between potassium feldspar and the plagioclase feldspars in the ratios that he regards as normal in stable mineral assemblages in magmatic rocks. In classifying igneous rocks, Rittmann uses a QAPF diagram similar to the one used by Streckeisen (1967) in his modal classification of the plutonic rocks.

Streckeisen (1978; 1980) has extended his modal classification of plutonic rocks (Fig. 3.2.1) to include the volcanic rocks; and in his 1978 paper (2–7) he suggested that the following rock names are equivalent to one another (plutonic rocks are on the left-hand side):

(a) alkali feldspar granite = alkali feldspar rhyolite
(b) granite = rhyolite
(c) granodiorite and tonalite = dacite
(d) alkali feldspar quartz syenite = alkali feldspar quartz trachyte
(e) quartz syenite = quartz trachyte
(f) quartz monzonite = quartz latite
(g) quartz monzodiorite = andesite
(h) quartz gabbro = (tholeiitic) basalt
(i) alkali feldspar syenite = alkali feldspar trachyte
(j) syenite = trachyte
(k) monzonite = latite
(l) monzodiorite = andesite
(m) gabbro = basalt
(n) foid-bearing alkali feldspar syenite = foid-bearing alkali feldspar trachyte
(o) foid-bearing syenite = foid-bearing trachyte
(p) foid-bearing monzonite = foid-bearing latite
(q) foid-bearing monzodiorite = hawaiite and mugearite
(r) foid-bearing gabbro = alkali basalt
(s) foid syenite = phonolite
(t) foid monzosyenite = tephritic phonolite
(u) foid monzodiorite = phonolitic tephrite
(v) foid gabbro = tephrite, and
(w) foidolite = foidite

Chemical classifications of volcanic rocks

In the past many different criteria have been used in the chemical classification of volcanic rocks. Two criteria that have been widely used are (a) silica content and (b) degree of alkalinity. The use of silica in the classification of igneous rocks is particularly appropriate because it is the dominant oxide in the common magmatic rocks of Earth, and the silica content of a melt exerts considerable control over the physical nature and structure of the melt. It is also important to take Na_2O and K_2O into account as these oxides, together with silica, essentially determine the silica saturation of the common magmatic rocks, and they also enable one to determine whether a rock is subalkalic, alkalic or hyperalkalic (see Fig. 3.3.2). This is because the SiO_2, Na_2O and K_2O contents of a rock usually determine the quantity and type of felsic minerals that form (note that the chief felsic minerals are quartz, the feldspars and the feldspathoids). Alumina, CaO and MgO are generally the next most important oxides in determining the gross chemical, and modal character, of the common magmatic rocks.

Figures 3.3.2, 3.3.3 and 3.3.4 illustrate some of the many simple chemical classifications of volcanic rocks that use alkali silica diagrams. In the present work, Fig. 3.3.2 will be used as an initial classification of the abundant types of volcanic rocks found within the accessible crust of the Earth. This classification can be augmented by other chemical criteria, and the expanded classification can then be used to define some of the less abundant, yet petrologically important, volcanic rock types.

It is recognized that in classifications such as those shown in Figs 3.3.2, 3.3.3 and 3.3.4, 'patterns can be created by divisions which are more or less arbitrary' (De Bono 1977: 35); and once these divisions are established they become self-perpetuating because mean values of the newly-defined rock types are calculated and used to describe idealized examples of these rocks. In order to minimize this effect, and also to show that real volcanic rocks grade one into the other, areas of overlaps have been established between the different major rock types shown in Fig. 3.3.2. Rocks that plot into area 'a' are called transitional basalts; area 'b' contains basaltic andesites; and area 'c' contains andesitic dacites. Appropriate compound names can be given to

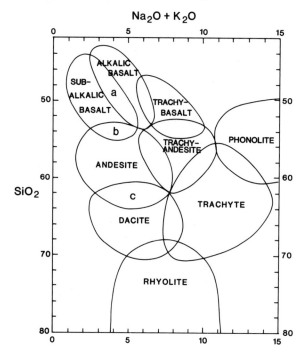

Fig. 3.3.2 Chemical classification and nomenclature of the *common volcanic rocks*. (Adapted from Middlemost 1980: 54).

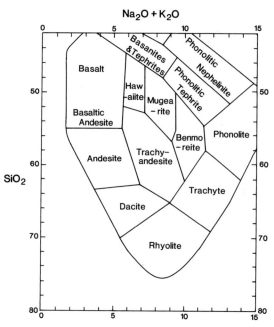

Fig. 3.3.4 Chemical classification and nomenclature of the *normal* (non-potassic) *volcanic rocks* (adapted from Cox; Bell and Pankhurst 1979: 14).

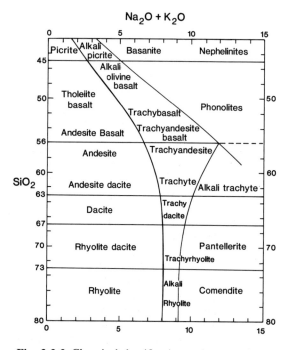

Fig. 3.3.3 Chemical classification and nomenclature of the *volcanic rocks* (adapted from Kremenetskiy Yushko and Budyanskiy 1980: 58).

the rock types that fall within the other areas of overlap. Some petrologists regard the basaltic andesites as an important group of rocks, and propose that they should be allocated a relatively large area on the alkali silica diagram (that is, subalkalic rocks that contain between 52 and 56 or 57 per cent SiO_2; cf. Innocenti et al. 1982: 334).

It is often petrologically desirable to subdivide some of the major rock types defined in Fig. 3.3.2. For example, the trachybasalts are readily separated into trachybasalts (sensu stricto) and hawaiites. In the *hawaiites* the Na_2/K_2O ratio is usually 2.0 or greater, whereas in the *trachybasalts* this ratio is usually less than 2.0 (see Ch. 7). The andesites (sensu lato) may be separated into *andesites* (sensu stricto) that usually have a $Al_2O_3/(Fe_2O_3 + FeO)$ ratio of 2.0 or greater and *icelandites* that usually have a $Al_2O_3/(Fe_2O_3 + FeO)$ ratio that is less than 2.0. Trachyandesite can be divided into *benmoreite* and *tristanite*; the former usually have a Na_2O/K_2O ratio of 1.5 or greater, whereas the tristanites have a Na_2O/K_2O ratio that is usually less than 1.5. Both the trachytes and the rhyolites can be divided into peralkaline and normal rock types. The peralkaline rocks are defined as

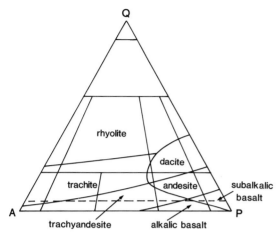

Fig. 3.3.5 This diagram has been produced by using data from magmatic rocks for which both chemical and modal information is available. All the rocks have been classified twice, once using the chemical classification of volcanic rocks given in Fig. 3.3.2, and a second time using the QAPF modal classification. The diagram shows the fields occupied by the volcanic rocks as defined by the chemical classification when they are plotted onto the QAP triangle of the QAPF diagram.

being those in which the molecular proportion of alumina is less than that of soda and potash combined (Shand 1950: 229). For most practical purposes magmatic rocks may be regarded as peralkaline if their Al_2O_3 contents in weight per cent are less than their $(1.6\ Na_2O + 1.1K_2O)$ contents in weight per cent. Such peralkaline rocks are undersaturated in alumina, and they usually contain soda-pyroxenes and/or soda-amphiboles and other soda-rich minerals (see Ch. 7). The basaltic rocks are divided into a number of discrete rock types in Chapter 5.

An interesting chemical classification of the igneous rocks has been proposed by Roche and Leterrier (1973), and Roche et al. (1980). The igneous rocks are classified using what they call a R1 R2 diagram in which R1 = 4Si − 11(Na + K) − 2(Fe + Ti) and R2 = 6Ca + 2Mg + Al. The values Si, Na, K, etc. are expressed as *atomic equivalent numbers* multiplied by 1000 (cf. Burri 1964: 42). The following are some of the advantages claimed for the Roche and Leterrier classification: (a) the two chemical parameters R1 and R2 are simpler to calculate than the C.I.P.W. norm; (b) the classification uses all the major elements, except oxygen; (c) it does not require elements such as Fe to be partitioned

between the oxide and silicate minerals, nor does it require the partitioning of albite between plagioclase and the alkali feldspars; and (d) it is able to classify the volcanic and plutonic rocks with equal facility. It has, however, yet to be demonstrated that the R1 R2 diagram is superior to the much simpler total alkali silica diagram in the classification of magmatic rocks. Roche et al. (1980: 200) have used data from the CLAIR and PETROS geochemical data files to test the validity of their classification. They found that 69 per cent of the volcanic rocks and only 57 per cent of the plutonic rocks received the same name from the R1 R2 diagram classification, as the name recorded in the data files. They claim (194) that these relatively large differences in classification are essentially due to 'semantic noise'.

There are also a number of specialized chemical classifications of particular groups of igneous rocks, including those proposed by Church (1975), O'Connor (1965), Taylor (1969; see Fig. 6.1.1), Pearce and Cann (1973) and Floyd and Winchester (1975). The two latter systems use the so-called *immobile elements* such as Ti, Zr, Y, Nb and P; and they attempt to classify rocks, particularly basaltic rocks, that have experienced low-grade metamorphism, alteration or mild metasomatism.

Modal and chemical classifications compared

It is common practice to use modal classifications, such as the one proposed by Streckeisen (Fig. 3.2.1), to define the plutonic rocks, particularly the abundant quartz-bearing varieties; whereas a chemical classification is used to define the finer-grained and/or glassy volcanic equivalents of these rocks. Any rational discussion of the origin of igneous rocks requires that the equivalence between the rocks in the two systems should be precisely established. One should, however, not expect an exact correspondence between a simple chemical classification (Fig. 3.3.2) and the QAPF classification (Fig. 3.2.1), because the minerals that go to form the A, P and F parameters of QAPF have variable chemical compositions. Modal and major element data have been used to construct Figs 3.3.5 and 3.3.6, and they show the fields occupied by the volcanic rocks plotted on a QAP diagram, and the fields occupied by the plutonic rocks plotted on an alkali silica volcanic rock classification diagram. From these figures it is

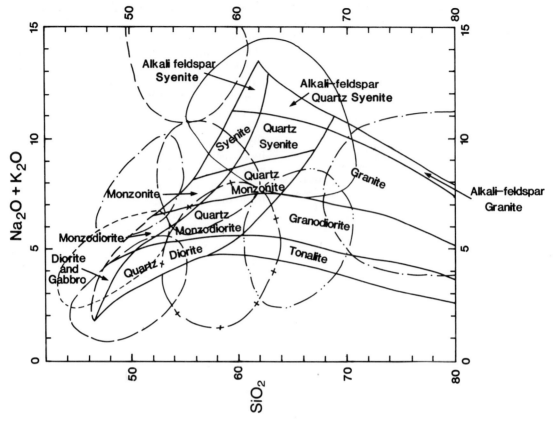

Fig. 3.3.6 This diagram uses the same data as Fig. 3.3.5; however, in the present diagram the compositional fields occupied by the plutonic rocks as defined by the QAPF modal classification are plotted onto a diagram (Fig. 3.3.2) used in the chemical classification of volcanic rocks.

evident that: (a) rhyolite is equivalent to granite, alkali-feldspar granite and SiO_2-rich granodiorite; (b) dacite is equivalent to tonalite and normal granodiorite; (c) trachyte is equivalent to alkali-feldspar syenite, alkali-feldspar quartz syenite, syenite, quartz syenite and the alkali-poor quartz monzonites; (d) andesite is essentially equivalent to quartz monzodiorite (quartz gabbro) and quartz diorite (quartz gabbro); and (e) basalt is essentially equivalent to gabbro (diorite) and monzogabbro (monzodiorite). Figure 3.3.5 is particularly interesting as it shows the basalts and andesites occupying distinct, but contiguous, areas in the QAP diagram.

This chapter has attempted to show how the common magmatic rocks of the Earth are classified. It has also demonstrated: (a) that it is difficult to classify all the magmatic rocks using the same methods of classification; and (b) that over the years an extensive and complex petrographic nomenclature has evolved that contains many

rock names that are difficult to directly relate to the systems of classification in current use. Electronic computers can, however, be used to store and manipulate large amounts of petrological data; and this technique has enabled petrologists to establish that there are only a relatively small number of rock names that are frequently used in petrology (cf. Chayes 1975). Computers have also enabled petrologists to set discrete limits on the domain in compositional space occupied by the various rock types for which suitable compositional data are available.

3.4 Selected references

Burri, C. (1964) *Petrochemical Calculations*, Israel Program for Scientific Translations, Jerusalem.

Johannsen, A. J. (1931) *A Descriptive Petrography of the Igneous Rocks*, Vol. 1, Introduction, textures, classification and glossary, The University of Chicago Press, Chicago, Illinois, USA.

Le Maitre, R. W. (1976a) The chemical variability of some common igneous rocks, *J. Petrol.*, **17(4)**, 589–637.

Streckeisen, A. (1974) Classification and nomenclature of plutonic rocks, *Geol. Rundsch.*, **63(2)**, 773–86.

Streckeisen, A. (1978) Classification and nomenclature of volcanic rocks, lamprophyres, carbonatites and melilitic rocks, *Neues Jahrb. Mineral., Abh.*, **134(1)**, 1–14.

CHAPTER 4

ABUNDANCE AND DISTRIBUTION OF MAGMATIC ROCKS

4.1 Abundance

When considering the abundance of the magmatic rocks, one has to examine their abundance relative to the other major groups of rocks (the sedimentary and metamorphic rocks); and also the relative abundances of the different types of magmatic rocks. Blatt and Jones (1975: 1085–8) studied the relative abundances of the major groups of rocks exposed on the land surfaces of the Earth, and they estimated that 66 per cent of this area was covered by sedimentary rocks, 15 per cent by Precambrian crystalline rocks, 9 per cent by intrusive rocks, 8 per cent by extrusive rocks, and 2 per cent by metamorphic rocks. When the ages of the sedimentary rocks are reviewed, it is found that the relationship, between age and area of outcrop, can be described by a decay curve with a half-life of 130 Ma; that is half of these sedimentary rocks are younger than the Early Cretaceous. Magmatic rocks are, however, the most abundant group of rocks within the accessible crust of the Earth.

Although there are some 800 different igneous rock names, relatively few of these are frequently used at the present time. For example, 225 different words appear as nouns in the 10 870 rock names given to the chemical analyses stored in Chayes' (1975: 545) data-base of Cenozoic volcanic rocks; and only two of these names occur more than 2000 times. The two common volcanic rocks are *basalt* and *andesite*. Seven names occur between 200 and 1999 times: *basanite, dacite, phonolite, rhyolite, trachyandesite, trachybasalt* and *trachyte*. Fifteen names occur between 56 and 199 times: *ankaratrite, ankaramite, comendite, diabase, dolerite, latite,*

leucitite, limburgite, mugearite, nephelinite, oceanite, plagiliparite, rhyodacite, tephrite and *tholeiite*. Three of the names in this latter group (diabase, dolerite and tholeiite) normally relate to rocks of basaltic composition.

In 1914, Daly estimated the relative abundance of the various igneous rocks by using planimetric measurements of the areas occupied by these rocks on geological maps. This study demonstrated that most of the volcanic rocks found on the land surfaces of the Earth are basaltic or andesitic in composition, whereas most plutonic rocks are granitic or granodioritic in composition. These conclusions are supported by the SiO_2 frequency distribution curves of igneous rocks produced by such workers as Richardson and Sneesby (1922), Ahrens (1964) and Chayes (1975; 1979b). Richardson and Sneesby published a SiO_2 frequency distribution curve of all the rocks contained in Washington's (1917) compendium of 'Chemical Analyses of Igneous Rocks' (see Fig. 4.1.1). This diagram shows a broad centrally-located minimum, with maxima (or statistical modes) at 52.5 per cent SiO_2 (gabbro–basalt) and 73.0 per cent SiO_2 (granite–rhyolite). Ahrens demonstrated that if SiO_2 frequency distribution curves were constructed for individual rock types, the basalt maximum was at 48.4 per cent SiO_2, and that both the granite and rhyoliote maxima were at 73.0 per cent SiO_2. He also showed that when a single SiO_2 frequency distribution curve is constructed for the granites and granodiorites, the maximum (or statistical mode) is at 73 per cent SiO_2, and the curve has a strong negative skewness. Chayes (1979b: 18) constructed a SiO_2 frequency distribution curve for his collection of 10 869 chemical analyses of Cenozoic volcanic rocks. This curve (Fig. 4.1.2) shows a strong positive skewness; it has a maximum at approxi-

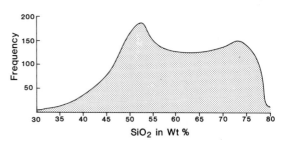

Fig. 4.1.1 Frequency distribution of SiO_2 in igneous rocks (adapted from Richardson and Sneesby 1922: 306).

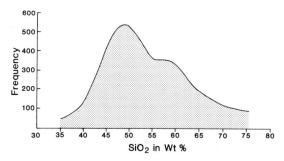

Fig. 4.1.2 Frequency distribution of SiO_2 in 10 869 chemical analyses of Cenozoic volcanic rocks (adapted from Chayes 1979b: 18).

mately 49 per cent SiO_2 (in the basalt field) and then decreases to very low values at 75 and 35 per cent SiO_2.

If one constructs a SiO_2 frequency distribution curve for the plutonic rocks using the data in Le Maitre's (1976a) paper, it is immediately evident that the curve is bimodal. The chief maximum is in the granite field, and a secondary maximum occurs in the gabbro–norite field. The ten most abundant plutonic rocks in Le Maitre's compilation are granite, gabbro, granodiorite, diorite, syenite, monzonite, norite, websterite, harzburgite and lherzolite.

4.2 Distribution

A remarkable large-scale feature of the Earth is the contrast between the continental land masses and the floors of the ocean basins. The 4.6 km difference in altitude between the average height of the continents and the average depth of the ocean basins developed because the continental crust contains a much greater thickness of low-density rocks than the oceanic crust, and *isostatic compensation* has elevated and maintained the elevation of the continents. This topographic asymmetry is typical of all the terrestrial planets. For example, the lower-lying lunar maria mainly occur within the Earth-facing hemisphere, and highlands that stand approximately 5 km higher than the maria are typical of the lunar far-side. The older heavily-cratered southern hemisphere of Mars stands approximatedly 3.5 km higher than the relatively smooth volcanic plains of the northern hemisphere. Venus also has highland, or continental areas, such as Ishtar Terra and

Aphrodite Terra. It is thus found that large-scale topographic asymmetry can evolve on planets where there is no evidence of subduction, or the magmatic activity characteristically associated with subduction.

The Earth is an active planet and when discussing the present distribution of magmatic rocks it is convenient to divide its surface into six major regions: (a) continental shield areas; (b) active continental margins and island arcs; (c) continental rifts and palaeorifts; (d) active mid-oceanic ridges and oceanic crust; (e) aseismic ridges; and (f) oceanic islands and sea-mounts.

Continental shield areas

The continental shield areas have been relatively stable over long periods of time, and they generally contain nuclei of Archaean age. Such areas occupy approximately 20 per cent of the surface of our planet. Their mean altitude above sea-level is 0.7 km, and the M-discontinuity lies at a mean depth of approximately 35 km below sea-level. In these shield areas the mean thickness of sedimentary cover is 0.5 km, and below this discontinuous layer, rocks of the granite–granodiorite–tonalite association usually predominate (cf. Poldervaat 1955: 124). In most areas this granitic layer is less than 10 km thick. It often lies on rocks that are interpreted as being medium- to high-pressure *granulite facies* materials that may be depleted in elements such as K, Th and U (Heier 1973: 174–87). The concept of a metamorphic layer depleted in the common heat-producing radioactive isotopes is supported by heat-flow data, and also by direct evidence gleaned from the study of xenoliths contained within alkalic basalts, such as those from the Massif Central of France and other areas (cf. Dostal *et al.* 1980: 38).

The Archaean rocks (pre-2.6 Ga) of continental shield areas may be regarded as the archives of our planet as they contain the only petrographic records of the early history of the Earth. These records demonstrate that the Archaean differed significantly from the Phanerozoic (post-570 Ma), because: (a) it was probably a time of heightened igneous activity; and (b) it contains some distinctive magmatic rocks and rock associations. Discussions about this eon in Earth history have stimulated much petrological interest. This is because other planetary bodies, such as the Moon, contain well-preserved records of this initial stage in planetary evolution. Probably the best-documented body of ancient rocks found on Earth crop out in the Godthaab and Isua areas of West Greenland (Moorbath et al. 1972; Escher & Watt 1976: 18–75). The oldest rocks in West Greenland consist of a 3.8 Ga old volcano–sedimentary sequence which was deposited on crustal material of unknown composition. These supracrustal rocks were later intruded, or invaded, by voluminous gneissic rocks, such as the 3.75 Ga old *Amitsoq Gneiss*. During the Archaean, the concentration of radiogenic isotopes, and consequently the rate of heat production, was several times greater than it is at present. Heat production on this scale would probably inhibit the formation of continental lithospheric plates of similar thickness to those found at present. Some petrologists (for example, Hargraves 1976) believe that in the Archaean: (a) the mantle was hotter; (b) the crust was scum-like and world-wide in extent; (c) mantle convection was vigorous; and (d) the dominant tectonic regimen was *viscous drag subduction* similar to that observed in the surface crust of present-day lava lakes. This tectonic style probably changed at the beginning of the Proterozoic, with the emergence of relatively large granitic continental crustal blocks and the cooling of the upper mantle enabling the modern style of subduction to commence. Trace element studies of sedimentary rocks of various ages indicate that mafic rocks were more abundant on the surface of the continental crust in the Archaean than in post-Archaean times. There was also a sharp increase in Th and U abundances in sedimentary rocks at about the time of the change from the Archaean to the Proterozoic (2.6 Ga; McLennan et al. 1980: 1833). The latter observation probably means that there was a significant increase in the abundance of granitic rocks at the surface in the late Archaean. Experimental studies (Green 1975) have demonstrated that the Mg-rich basic and ultrabasic komatiitic lavas that are characteristically found in most Archaean areas probably erupted at high temperatures ($\approx$1650 °C). This is interpreted as further evidence in favour of the model that heat production, and dissipation, was particularly high in the Archaean.

Anorthosites form a minor but distinctive component in most Archaean terrains. Windley (1970) has proposed that some of these rocks evolved in much the same way as the lunar anorthosites, and they thus represent fragments of the primordial crust of the Earth. Geochemical data does not, however, support the concept that extensive areas of the crust were once composed of anorthositic rocks. Most of the anorthosites found on Earth formed during the Proterozoic, particularly between 1.4 and 1.5 Ga; and some petrologists (cf. Bridgwater & Windley 1973; Weibe 1980) have postulated that they evolved from a magma that was produced during a widespread heating event that melted crustal materials such as basic gneiss (see Ch. 10). Another interesting petrological anomaly is the relatively low proportion of hyperalkalic magmatic rocks (that is, basanites to phonolites) in the Archaean and early Proterozoic. Most of the hyperalkalic leucite-bearing rocks are of late Mesozoic or Cenozoic age (cf. Gupta & Yagi 1980).

In post-Archaean times the continents have gradually grown out from their Archaean nuclei, and the magmatic rocks that have been extruded and intruded during this process are essentially similar to those that are presently forming in active continental margins and island arcs. The continental flood basalts (see Ch. 5), and the magmatic rocks associated with continental rifting, are notable exceptions.

Active continental margins and island arcs

The seismically-active continental margins and island arcs include the *Cenozoic fold-belts* that border some of the continents, and the zones of active continental collision. Such areas are usually belts associated with active plate convergence and subduction. The latter process tends to assist in the generation of a broad spectrum of comagmatic volcanic and plutonic rocks. In detail the tectonic environments, and the magmatic response to these environments, varies in different parts of an active continental margin. In the Peruvian Andes, the continental crust is thick, the mean altitude of the surface is high, and the *Benioff seismic zone* has a low angle of inclination. According to Dewey (1980), this type of tectonic environment produces *compressional volcanic arcs* that contain little overt magmatic activity; however, the magmatic rocks that are produced in this environment are mainly plutonic, and those rocks that reach the surface tend to be silicic in composition. In stark contrast, the *intra-oceanic island arcs*, such as the Marianas and Tongas, evolved on oceanic crust and are associated with steep Benioff seismic zones. The rocks that evolve in this essentially *extensional environment* are mainly basaltic in composition. Extension occurs where the overriding plate retreats from the oceanic trench line, or the subduction hinge retreats at a faster rate than the overriding plate is able to advance (cf. Dewey 1980: 562). Subduction in areas that are intermediate between these two extremes, such as are found in central America, tends to generate magmatic rocks of intermediate, usually andesitic, composition. Despite the diversity of magmatic rocks produced along active continental margins and island arcs, there is often a systematic increase in the imcompatible element abundances that are found in magmatic rocks of similar SiO_2 content, as one proceeds away from convergent plate boundaries in areas above active Benioff seismic zones. This empirical correlation (see Fig. 4.2.1) supports the petrogenetic model that processes within, or associated with, subducted slabs of oceanic lithosphere trigger magmatic activity. The dehydration of hydrous phases contained in the descending slab of crust releases water and possibly other volatile components, and it is this that triggers magma production (see Section 6.6). Old metasomatized oceanic crust would probably contain about 5 per cent water, and more Na, K and other incompatible elements, than fresh MOR basalt.

It is usually convenient to divide the overriding plate at convergent plate margins into three regions: the fore-arc, the *volcanic-arc* and the *back-arc* region. The fore-arc region is also known as the *arc trench gap*. It is located between the oceanic trench and the volcanic front, and the latter is the trenchward limit of the stratovolcanoes of the volcanic-arc. The back-arc region lies behind the volcanic-arc, and it is often difficult to define this region accurately because it may also contain volcanic activity. For example, in the Tonga region of the south-western Pacific, andesite stratovolcanoes dominate the volcanic-arc, but submarine basalts are also being extruded in the actively-spreading back-arc basin. West of this region in Vanuatu (New Hebrides) basaltic rocks dominate both the volcanic-arc and back-arc region. The volcanic rocks of the back-arc region may be subalkalic or alkalic, but they normally differ in isotopic and trace element composition from the magmatic rocks of the volcanic-arcs (cf. Gill 1981: 140).

The active continental margins include those zones on the surface of the Earth where conti-

nental lithospheric plates are in collision. At present an extensive *continent–continent collision zone* extends from the Alps in southern Europe through Turkey and Iran to the Himalayan mountain system of Asia. Active collision zones develop when lithospheric plates converge, and the oceanic crust between the approaching continental blocks is removed by subduction. The collision usually begins when rocks of a continental block with a passive margin (that is, Atlantic-type) encounter an actively-subducting trench at the margin of the other continental block (Cordilleran-type). Buoyancy prevents either of the continental blocks being subducted; but the rocks in the collision zone are deformed, and thrust-sheets may develop. Eventually the collision zone develops into a belt of thickened crustal rocks that are characterized by faulting and uplift. The structures that develop are complex, and essentially depend upon the physical properties of the rocks in the colliding blocks and also the geometry of the colliding continental margins. Andesitic magmas are often emplaced during the early stages of the collision, and more silicic magmas generally evolve as the collision progresses. Some of the latter magmas may be products of the partial fusion of crustal rocks. Alkalic rocks may be extruded, or intruded, into local areas of crustal extension or lateral faulting (cf. Thorpe 1982).

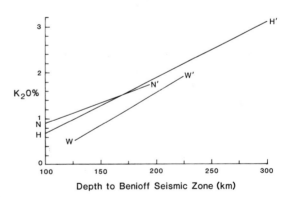

Fig. 4.2.1 Relationship of potassium content of andesitic lavas at a constant SiO_2 content ($SiO_2 = 55$ per cent) to the depth of the Benioff seismic zone beneath island arcs. Trend lines NN′ and HH′ are averaged results from a number of island arcs compiled by Nielson and Stoiber (1973) and Hatherton and Dickinson (1969), respectively. The trend line WW′ is from Whitford and Nicholls (1976) and it is for their 'preferred data' for the Sunda Arc in Java and Bali, Indonesia.

Continental rifts and palaeorifts

According to Burke (1978: 1), 'rifts are places where the entire thickness of the lithosphere has ruptured under tension'. Active continental rifts are not as common as oceanic rifts (see Fig. 1.5.1); however, the rocks found associated with them are more likely to be preserved in the geological record. When discussing palaeorifts, one has to recall that successful rifting results in the evolution of an ocean, and it is the failed rifts, or failed rift-arms, that are usually preserved within the continents. At present we do not know whether the active Ethiopian, or Baikal, rifts will continue developing and become active mid-ocean ridge-rift systems, or whether they will fail to develop and thus remain within the continents. Burke (1976: 96) has shown that the total length of failed rifts associated with the opening of the Atlantic Ocean greatly exceeds the length of ocean margin formed by the rupture of the former super-continent. If the East African rift is successful in producing an ocean, one can infer from the example of the Atlantic that at least half of the presently active rifts in Africa will be left as failed intra-continental rifts.

The modern African rift system has been active for some 20 Ma. It is claimed that 20 Ma ago the African continent came to rest over an upwelling mantle convection system (Thiessen et al. 1977: 503). This resulted in the evolution of one, or more, broad domical structures, such as the one Gass (1970) called the *Afro-Arabian Dome*. The lithosphere was thinned, and a triple-rift system developed (Burke 1978: 4). Abnormally thin crust is usually found under rifts; and the upper mantle materials under such anomalous crust are generally of lower than normal density with low-velocity seismic characteristics. Rifting generally occurs along pre-existing zones of weakness.

Continental rifts and palaeorifts generally contain alkalic to hyperalkalic rocks; however, lesser volumes of sub-alkalic rocks are also found in this environment. Most of these rocks do not contain any conclusive evidence of reaction with continental crustal materials; and the most common form of igneous intrusion in rift valleys is the *axial dyke* (Burke 1978: 5). Continental rifts usually have the following geochemical characteristics: (a) alkalinity decreases with time; and (b) alkalinity increases with distance from the rift axis (Neumann & Ramberg 1978: 419).

Rifts and/or palaeorift have been described from both Mars and Venus (cf. Mutch et al.

1976: 77). The Valles Marineris on Mars is a huge system of canyons that extends over more than a quarter of the equatorial girth of the planet; it is over 400 km long, up to 700 km wide and 6.5 km deep. The great rift valley of Venus lies to the east of Aphrodite Terra and is over 2200 km long and 280 km wide. Both of these huge extraterrestrial palaeorifts are interpreted as being extensional features, and they probably indicate that dynamic processes have operated deep within the interiors of these planets.

Active mid-oceanic ridges and oceanic crust

Active mid-oceanic ridges, and normal oceanic crust, covers over half the surface of the Earth. The ocean floor, exclusive of the ridges and seamounts, is normally covered by approximately 4.5 km of water and 0.6 km of sedimentary material. Beneath the pelagic (deep-sea) sediments, and above the M-discontinuity, the rocks are essentially MOR basalts together with coarser grained rocks of broadly the same chemical composition (cf. Hekinian 1982). This layer is normally about 5.7 km thick. It contains lesser volumes of alkalic basalts, silicic differentiates and ultramafic cumulate materials. The exact composition and nature of the 'Mid-Ocean Ridge' basalts is discussed in Chapter 5. Normal oceanic crust is created in the rift zones that bisect mid-ocean ridges at divergent plate boundaries. This is the most productive type of volcanism found on Earth at the present time, and circulating sea-water plays a significant role in cooling these magmatic materials. According to Fyfe (1980: 78), between 30 and 40 per cent of the heat generated at mid-oceanic ridges is removed by circulating waters that can penetrate as deep as 5 km into the brecciated and fractured oceanic crust. This water-cooling process also produces a significant exchange of elements between the newly-formed crust and sea-water. Volatiles, and elements such as Na, K and U, are added to the MOR basalt, and it may become a spilite. Spilites are essentially altered basalts in which the original feldspar has been albitized. Such rock usually also contains other secondary minerals such as chlorite, calcite, epidote, chalcedony and/or prehnite. Block and Bischoff (1979), for example, claim that as much as half of the potassium that is annually carried into the sea is metasomatically fixed in the altering oceanic basaltic crust. Another characteristic of the rocks of the oceanic crust is that they are relatively young and seldom exceed 200 Ma in age.

Aseismic ridges

As their name indicates, most aseismic ridges are essentially stable ridges that rise from the ocean floor. According to Hekinian (1982: 141) they comprise about 25 per cent of the present submarine surface of the oceans. They are normally linear volcanic chains, that rise some 2000–4000 m above the floor of the surrounding ocean basins. Such ridges are typically between 700 and 5000 km long and 250 and 400 km wide. Most are attached to a continent; and in the past some of them may have acted as land bridges across parts of the oceans (such as the Iceland–Faeroe Ridge). The origin of aseismic ridges is controversial, because it is not known whether: (a) they were generated by hot *mantle plumes* rising under a moving oceanic plate; or (b) they represent a line of volcanoes that developed on a major fault and/or fracture zone. The Ninety–East (aseismic) Ridge in the Indian Ocean is one of the few that has been studied in detail; however, the ages of the rocks obtained from this ridge do not fit into the pattern expected of materials generated by a simple hot mantle plume model.

Gravity and seismic studies have revealed that aseismic ridges are usually underlain by a 15–30 km thick crustal layer. The volcanic rocks collected from these ridges tend to resemble those from oceanic islands and seamounts, rather than the usual rocks of the ocean floor. There is also evidence of geochemical and petrological links between the volcanic rocks of the aseismic ridges and the oceanic islands with which these ridges are associated. For example, the Walvis Ridge which extends for approximately 3000 km, from the Mid-Atlantic Ridge near Tristan da Cunha to the coast of Namibia, contains a suite of rocks that are significantly enriched in potassium (cf. Hekinian 1982: 164); and such potassium-enrichment is also a geochemical feature of both Tristan da Cunha and Gough Island, which lie at the south-western end of this aseismic ridge. The Iceland–Faeroe Ridge and the Ninety–East Ridge both contain basalts as well as rocks called *oceanic andesites*. The latter rocks have a similar chemical composition to the *icelandites*. It is interesting to note that the Iceland–Faeroe Ridge meets Iceland near the site

of Thingmuli Volcano which is the type locality for the icelandites (cf. Carmichael 1964: 442). The high proportion of differentiated (intermediate) rocks found on aseismic ridges is interpreted as showing that the rocks associated with these ridges evolved in an environment where magmatic differentiation occurred without being interrupted.

Oceanic islands and Seamounts

Oceanic islands and seamounts occur in all the oceans and contain a remarkably wide range of different magmatic rocks. A few of these islands and seamounts are essentially fragments of continental crust. For example, the islands of the Seychelles Group, that lie to the east of Mombasa in the Indian Ocean, contain a variety of granitic rocks, and some of these granites are Precambrian in age (Baker & Miller 1963). Another small continental fragment that contains Precambrian basement rocks is the Rockall Plateau, south-east of Iceland in the North Atlantic. This seamount is essentially composed of basaltic rocks that are intruded by more differentiated rocks, such as the aegirine granite found on the small island of Rockall (Sabine 1960; 1965).

Another unusual group of oceanic islets are St Peter and St Paul Rocks. They are located 80 km north of the equator, and close to the axis of the Mid-Atlantic Ridge (Tilley 1947; Hess 1954; Melson et al. 1967; Melson et al. 1972). The most abundant rock type on these islets is a mylonitized spinel peridotite, but lherzolites with the following mineral assemblage, forsteritic olivine, aluminous enstatite, aluminous diopside, and chromian spinel, also occur. Such rocks are believed to have formed in the upper mantle, and they were subsequently brought to the surface along major oceanic fracture zones (that is St Paul Fracture Zone) that contain *transform faults*. Transform faults are essentially strike-slip faults that offset, and are usually at right angle to mid-ocean ridges. This means that they offset the zone of ocean floor spreading, and in the area between the offset ridge-crests the plates on either side of the transfrom fault slide past each other as the ocean spreads. Fragments of ultramafic mantle may also be associated with island-arcs where they are emplaced by obduction or the thrusting of oceanic crust and mantle onto another more buoyant lithospheric plate (Coleman 1971: 1212). Examples of such materials are found in New Caledonia in the south-western Pacific (cf. Avias 1977).

When volcanic islands are mentioned, one usually thinks of the volcanically-productive islands of Iceland and Hawaii. Both of these islands are, however, atypical of oceanic islands in general, as they contain vast quantities of tholeiitic basalt. Iceland is unique in that the central neovolcanic zone of the island is the surface exposure of the Mid-Atlantic Ridge. Both geological and geophysical evidence suggests that Iceland is rifting apart, and the fissures that are so generated are filled with magma as they form. The pattern of crustal growth in Iceland is revealed by magnetic studies (Piper 1971) that show that the neovolcanic zone is spreading at 12 mm/a. The lavas of Iceland are particularly interesting as their SiO_2 frequency distribution curve is strongly bimodal. Approximately 85 per cent of the lavas are basalts, and 12 per cent rhyolites (Sigurdsson & Sparks 1981: 41). It is proposed that the basaltic rocks of the neovolcanic zone congealed from magmas generated in a divergent plate-rifting environment, whereas a significant proportion of the icelandites, dacites and rhyolites congealed from magmas generated by the sub-lithospheric process responsible for the production of the Iceland–Faeroe Ridge.

If one was looking for a group of typical oceanic islands, one might well choose the western islands of the Canary Archipelago, in the North Atlantic, off the coast of North Africa. The islands of Tenerife, Gomera, Hierro and La Palma are all at slightly different stages in their volcanological and erosional evolution, and if they are all considered together one can develop a model of what a typical volcanic oceanic island is like. The rocks on such a model island would consist of: (a) olivine-rich basaltic rocks, often regarded as accumulative basalts; (b) sodic alkalic basalts, often basanitic in composition; (c) hawaiite; (d) mugearite; (e) benmoreite; and (f) phonolitic trachytes (see Ch. 7: cf. Mitchell-Thomé 1976: 153–246). In 1925, Daly reported that on the oceanic islands that contain trachytes, both basaltic and trachytic rocks were much more common than rocks of intermediate composition. This apparent paucity of intermediate rocks has been called the *Daly Gap* (see section 7.5).

Many volcanic islands, or groups of islands, have their own particular petrographic characteristics. For example, Tristan da Cunha and Gough Island in the South Atlantic contain suites of potassic alkalic rocks (cf. Mitchell-Thomé 1970: 224–305); whereas the igneous rocks of the Cape Verde archipelago in the North Atlantic, off the coast of Senegal, consist mainly of silica-undersaturated alkalic rocks that include nephelinites, ijolites and even carbonatites (cf. Mitchell-Thomé 1976: 247–319).

In the Pacific Ocean there are many linear chains of volcanic islands, such as the Hawaiian, Society and Marquesas; and the age of the volcanic rocks in these chains generally decreases in an east–south-east direction (Wilson 1963; Shaw & Jackson 1973). The origin of these linear chains is probably linked to the motion of the Pacific plate over a series of relatively fixed, sublithospheric melting anomalies. Over large areas of the central Pacific a variety of silica-undersaturated alkalic volcanic rocks are found on both islands and seamounts; and according to Jackson and Schlanger (1976: 915), most of these rocks evolved during periods of uplift after the main volcanic edifice had been constructed.

Menard (1964: 57) has estimated that in the Pacific Ocean there are the remains of some 3000 submarine volcanoes that rise to more than 1 km above the normal level of the ocean floor. Another 4000 similar volcanic edifices probably rise above the floors of the other oceans of our planet. At present, little is known about the petrography of most seamounts: it is usually not known whether they evolved by following the Hawaiian model and are thus mainly constructed of tholeiitic basalts with but a capping of more alkalic material; or if they followed the Tenerife model, and are mainly composed of alkalic basalts and differentiates of alkalic basalt magma.

It has also been proposed that the oceanic islands and seamounts that formed near mid-ocean ridges are mainly composed of subalkalic basaltic rocks; whereas those that originated further away from the ridges, on cooler and thicker lithospheric plates, are constructed of rocks that evolved from magmas that were generated at greater depths, and are therefore likely to be more alkalic in composition. McBirney and Gass (1967) have, for example, shown that islands such as Easter Island, that lie near the crest of the East Pacific Rise (mid-ocean ridge), carry subalkalic or transitional basalts that differentiate to rhyolite, whereas islands, such as the Cook Islands and Tahiti, that are over 3500 km west of the divergent plate boundary carry strongly alkalic, silica-undersaturated rocks.

4.3 A dynamic model of the Earth

The preceding examination, of the temporal and spatial distribution of magmatic rocks on Earth, provides insights into the present operation of the Earth as a heat-engine and producer of magmas. A more complete model of the dynamic processes that operate within our planet can be obtained by also considering the present distribution of: (a) heat-flow values (that is, where the igneous action is taking place, or will take place); (b) earthquake focii (where rocks and/or magmas are on the move); (c) active, dormant and recently extinct volcanoes (where the igneous action is, or has been operating recently); (d) total-field magnetic anomalies on the ocean floor (the changing shape of the oceans and seas); (e) major tectonic features, such as rifts, transform faults and active fold-belts; and (f) relative movements between different lithospheric plates. The simplest dynamic global model contains six main components: (a) the generation of new lithosphere at divergent plate boundaries (see Ch. 5); (b) the upwelling of magma, and the generation of a variety of igneous rocks, in intraplate environments that lie above thermal or degassing anomalies in the mantle, or fractures in the lithosphere (Turcotte & Oxburgh 1973); (c) the subduction of oceanic lithosphere and the concomitant evolution and extrusion of a variety of basaltic, andesitic, dacite and rhyolitic materials, together with the generation and emplacement of the rocks of the granite→granodiorite→quartz diorite→diorite association; (d) complex deformation and magmatic activity in active continental collision zones (see Ch. 6); (e) obduction, with the thrusting onto a lithospheric plate of relatively thin slabs of oceanic crustal and mantle rocks; and (f) the transformation of young fold-belts into relatively stable continental shield areas as the result of denudation at the surface, underplating of the base of the crust, and the evolution of a variety of crystalline rocks such as granites, anorthosites and granulites (cf. Windley 1977). There is probably a progressive magmatic and tectonic evolution, from the development of active continental margins, where subduction is taking place, through to continent–continent collisions which occur when subduction has consumed an ocean. Such collisions generally produce uplift, crustal shortening, thrusting, and minor volcanic and plutonic activity. The partial fusion of continental crustal rocks may occur within such collision zones (see Section 8.5). An inactive continent–continent collision zone is known as a *suture zone*, and examples of such sutures are found in the Ural Mountains of central Russia, the Caledonian mountains of Scandinavia, Britain and Newfoundland, and the Appalachian mountains of eastern North America. The simple dynamic model of the Earth that has just been presented is capable of explaining, in broad outline, the distribution, and in some cases the abundance, of the common igneous rocks; but it does not account for their origin. The petrogenesis of these rocks will be examined in the chapters that are to follow.

The model that has been presented is essentially a steady-state model that describes what happened on Earth during the Cenozoic. It does not attempt to describe the conditions that existed when the first igneous rocks solidified, on a hot and probably rapidly convecting planet, nor does it hint at the conditions that are likely to prevail in the future, when the planet is essentially degassed, heat-flow is significantly lower, the lithosphere is thicker and the mantle is more viscous. If we are to understand the origin and evolution of igneous rocks on our planet, we will have to construct thermal and chemical models capable of describing the past, present and future evolution of the Earth; and an attempt will be made to do this in Chapter 15.

4.4 The crust of the Earth

The crust makes up only 0.42 per cent of the mass of the Earth. In the past, most attempts at estimating the average composition of the crust assumed that the bulk was essentially similar to that of the average igneous rock. Implicit in such models is the concept that both the sedimentary and the metamorphic rocks are insignificant in abundance, and also that they are all ultimately derived from primary igneous rocks (Clarke & Washington 1924). However, this simple model is flawed, as it is now believed that much of the lower continental crust has gradually evolved into an incompatible element depleted layer that is essentially composed of refractory minerals. Smithson and Decker (1974: 221) have, for example, proposed that normal continental crust consists of 8 km of supracrustal rocks, such as volcanic rocks, shales, sandstones and their metamorphic equivalents, 8 km of migmatites and granites, and 18 km of granulites. If these granulites are depleted in incompatible elements, they are likely to produce little radiogenic heat, and this is in accord with presentday models of heat-flow within the crust. Most petrologists, however, believe that the chemical composition of the lower continental crust is hetereogeneous, and probably consists of interlayered bodies of granulites, gneisses, anorthosites and amphibolites that are deformed and intruded by a variety of igneous and meta-igneous rocks (cf. Smithson & Brown 1977).

Seismic studies have shown that the oceanic crust is layered, and in most oceanic basins there are three main layers. Layer one is approximately 0.3 km thick, and it is essentially composed of sedimentary materials. Layers two and three have mean thicknesses of 1.4 and 4.7 km respectively, and the seismic velocities that are characteristic are consistent with them being composed of mafic and ultramafic rocks. Layer two is usually regarded as being composed of MOR-type basalt; whereas layer three is considered to consist of two units: (a) an upper unit that contains a complex swarm of basaltic dykes; and (b) a lower unit that is essentially composed of gabbro and interlayered gabbroic and ultramafic rocks. The rocks of layer two and the upper part of layer three have usually been altered as the result of metasomatic reaction with circulating brine.

Table 4.4.1 provides two estimates of the overall chemical composition of the crust of the Earth, together with estimates of the chemical composition of: (a) the upper continental crust; (b) the lower continental crust; and (c) the crust of the oceans. It is immediately evident that nine elements make up more than 99 per cent of the crust, and that oxygen is the most abundant of these. If the chemical compositions of the crust and upper mantle are compared (see Tables 1.10.2 and 4.4.1), one discovers that the crust as a whole is significantly enriched in Si, Ti, Al, Ca, Na and K, and strongly depleted in Mg. It is difficult to estimate the major element composition of the crust; however, it is much more difficult to estimate the trace element abundances of this

Table 4.4.1 Average chemical composition of the crust of the earth (%)

	1	2	3	4	5
SiO_2	55.24	55.2	65.4	56.88	48.17
TiO_2	0.86	1.6	0.7	0.73	1.40
Al_2O_3	14.55	15.3	14.8	14.43	14.90
Fe_2O_3	2.42	2.8	1.4	2.37	2.64
FeO	5.86	5.8	3.3	5.64	7.37
MnO	0.16	0.2	0.1	0.14	0.25
MgO	5.37	5.2	2.3	4.97	7.42
CaO	8.12	8.8	4.0	7.14	12.19
Na_2O	2.44	2.9	3.3	2.39	2.58
K_2O	1.61	1.9	3.4	1.90	0.33
H_2O^+	1.46	—	0.6	1.56	1.05
P_2O_5	0.17	0.3	0.2	0.16	0.22
CO_2	1.44	—	—	1.37	1.35
	p.p.m.		p.p.m.	p.p.m.	p.p.m.
F	300	—	720	310	200
Cl	300	—	320	400	—
Th	5	—	11	5.7	0.45
U	1.5	—	3.5	1.5	0.26

1. Mean composition of the crust (after Ronov and Yaroshevskiy 1976: 106–7).
2. Mean composition of the crust (after Poldervaart 1955: 133).
3. Mean composition of the upper continental crust (after Wedepohl 1971: 61–5).
4. Mean composition of the lower continental crust (after Ronov and Yaroshevskiy 1976: 106–7).
5. Mean composition of the crust of the oceans (after Ronov and Yaroshevskiy 1976: 106–7)

shell of the Earth. Most tables that purport to give the abundances of the trace elements in the crust were prepared by mixing together in fixed proportions (that is, 1 : 1 or 1 : 2) the trace element compositions of 'average' granitic and basaltic rocks (cf. Ahrens & Taylor 1961; Vinogradov 1962; Taylor 1979).

4.5 Selected references

Mason, B. & **Moore, C. B.** (1982) *Principles of Geochemistry*, John Wiley & Sons, New York, USA

Windley, B. F. (1977) *The Evolving Continents*, John Wiley & Sons, London.

CHAPTER 5

THE BASALT CLAN

5.1 General statement

'Basalts have erupted on Earth throughout known geologic history and on the Moon for more than a billion years before it became quiescent 2.5 to 3 billion years ago (2.5 to 3.0 Ga). From the Earth today to the small asteroid Vesta 4.5 billion years (4.5 Ga) in the past, on Mars, Venus and Mercury, the generation of basalts has spanned the history of the Solar System and an enormous range of planetary mass. Basaltic volcanism is a fundamental process, the expression of stages of partial melting in the evolution of terrestrial planets' (BVSP 1981: xxvii). Basaltic magmas are regarded as 'probes of chemical compositions and physical conditions in planetary mantles that are hidden from direct observation by depth and time' (op. cit.).

The basalts of Earth are so abundant, and their chemical compositions so restricted, that they are often interpreted as having congealed from primary magmas, or slightly modified primary magmas, that were generated by a relatively simple reproducible process within the upper mantle. On the terrestrial planets, basaltic volcanism is regarded as the most accessible of the major processes responsible for their thermal and chemical evolution. The term *clan* is used to describe any group of magmatic rocks that are closely related by chemical composition; the basalt clan contains a number of different types of rocks that are broadly similar in their major element compositions, yet contain subtle innate differences in both their chemical and modal compositions. The significance of these subtle chemical differences emerges when one studies the chemical composition of the more differentiated rocks that commonly occur in close temporal and spatial association with particular basaltic rocks; that is, a quartz normative basalt is likely to produce a rhyolitic differentiate, whereas a nepheline normative basalt may produce a phonolitic differentiate. We often classify basalts by the company they keep.

Basalt is an old term, and it was used in the first century by Caius Plinius (or Pliny the Elder) in his *Natural History* (AD 77); the term was introduced into geology by Georg Bauer Agricola in the middle of the sixteenth century. Basalts are generally regarded as fine-grained, or glassy, mafic volcanic rocks that are essentially composed of plagioclase (usually labradorite), and one or more pyroxenes, together with lesser amounts of Fe–Ti oxides. In order to classify a rock as being a basalt (sensu stricto), one usually has to know both its silica content and modal composition (cf. Streckeisen 1979: 332). The IUGS subcommission on the systematics of igneous rocks acknowledged that it was difficult to distinguish between andesites and basalts, and recommended that two criteria should be used; that is, silica content and colour index. Basaltic or andesitic rocks that have a colour index of over 40, and contain less than 52 per cent SiO_2 (anhydrous basis), are called basalts (sensu stricto); whereas those transitional volcanic rocks that have a colour index of less than 40, yet contain less than 52 per cent SiO_2, are called *leucobasalts*. According to the Basaltic Volcanism study Project (1981: 2), 'basalts are characterized by Fe, Ca and Mg contents commonly in the range 5–15 wt% oxide and by SiO_2 contents generally in the range 38–53 wt%'. The project authors have also established that colour index, and plagioclase compositions, may be unreliable criteria in the classification of basaltic rocks. It is difficult to determine the colour index of many basalts because they often contain a high percentage of uncrystallized material. The silica value of 38 per cent is regarded as much too low for the normal basaltic rocks of the Earth; and a silica value of 44 per cent is probably a more suitable lower limit for the post-Archaean basaltic rocks of Earth.

Basalt nomenclature

In 1922, Washington (800) showed that the basaltic rocks are readily divided into at least two different groups: 'the *plateau basalts*, which are high in iron, and the *cone basalts*, which are low in iron and relatively high in magnesia and lime'. He also added the rider that his classification did not preclude the possibility that there were other groups of basalts such as 'those high in *soda* and grading into nephelite (nepheline) tephrites, and those high in potash and grading into leucite tephrites'. Washington's plateau basalts are what are now usually called *continental flood basalts*. At approximately the same time as Washington published his paper on plateau basalts, Bailey et al. (1924) were studying the volcanic rocks on the island of Mull in the British Tertiary Province (cf. Brown 1982: 345–50); and in their *Mull Memoir* they recognize nine *magma types*. The magma types that they considered to be genetically related were linked into a number of magma series; chemical criteria were used to define the magma types. This study of the volcanic rocks of Mull demonstrated 'that basalt is not a single entity, but that several basalt magmas need to be defined in relation to their derivative magmas' (Brown 1982: 346). The two main basaltic magma types recognized by Bailey et al. (1924) were called: (a) the *Plateau Magma Type* which is now regarded as being a nepheline-normative, *alkalic basaltic magma*; and (b) the *Non*-Porphyritic Central Type which is now regarded as being a hypersthene and/or quartz normative *tholeiitic basaltic magma*. It is thus found that Washington's plateau basalt is a tholeiitic basalt, whereas the rock that congeals from the Plateau Magma Type of Mull is an alkalic basalt.

In his paper on 'Trends of differentiation in basaltic magmas', W. Q. Kennedy (1933: 240) proposed that there are two main types of primary basaltic magmas. One is the *Olivine–basalt magma type*, and the other is the *tholeiitic magma type*. He (241) proposed that when the olivine–basalt magma type congealed, the essential minerals were 'olivine, augite, basic plagioclase and iron ore (Fe–Ti oxides). The pyroxene is a diopsidic or basaltic augite, often a titaniferous variety. A little residual, interstitial material may be present and this is of alkaline nature, without free quartz.' Kennedy (241) described the rock that would congeal from the tholeiitic magma type as being essentially composed of 'pyroxene, basic plagioclase and iron ore (Fe–Ti oxides). Olivine is either completely absent or present in very subordinate amount. Characteristically an interstitial, acid residuum is developed which may be glassy but is dominantly quartzo-feldspathic. The pyroxene belongs typically to the enstatite-augite (pigeonite) series of lime-poor pyroxenes.' He (243–4) also proposed that the composition of late differentiates of basaltic magmas 'depends primarily on the nature and composition of the parent basalt magma'; and that the late differentiates of the olivine–basalt magma type usually contain alkali feldspars and feldspathoids, whereas the late differentiates of the tholeiitic magma type normally contain silica minerals.

In 1950, Tilley wrote a stimulating paper on the evolution of magmas. He (39) was particularly interested in the chemical composition of the volcanic rocks of the Hawaiian archipelago, because the parental magmas of these rocks had evolved in 'an oceanic area characterized by the absence of a sialic underlayer'; and the evolution of the silica-saturated and oversaturated rocks had to be discussed without any appeal to the assimilation of sialic materials (see Section 9.1). Tilley (41) called the volcanic rocks that erupted during the early stages in the evolution of the archipelago, the *tholeiitic series*. This series contained olivine-bearing picritic (or oceanitic) basalts, olivine-free saturated basalts and oversaturated basalts. He called the younger rock association that ranged in composition from ankaramites, alkali olivine basalts, hawaiites, mugearites, and benmoreites to trachytes, the *alkali series*. An alkali silica diagram was used to demonstrate that the rocks of each series were chemically distinct from one another. Since Tilley's pioneering paper many petrologists (for example: De Long & Hoffman 1975; Macdonald 1968; Macdonald and Katsura 1964) have used an empirical boundary line on an alkali silica diagram to show the fields occupied by the alkalic (above the line) and sub-alkalic (below the line) basaltic rocks (see Fig. 3.3.2). Tilley (1950: 54) also discussed the basaltic rocks found in orogenic belts, and he noted that they 'include a wide variety of types, those most characteristically developed showing a high alumina content'. He (55) regarded the latter basalts as having chemical compositions akin to the *Porphyritic Central Magma Type* of Mull. Nockolds (1954: 1019), in his compilation of the chemical compositions of igneous rocks, divided the basaltic rocks into tholeiitic basalts, alkali basalts and *central basalts*; and he claimed that his central basalts are 'found in association with the typical calc-alkali andesites, dacites and rhyodacites at volcanic centres'. In a later paper, Nockolds and Le Bas (1977: 311) have suggested that 'the term central basalt is now considered to serve no further useful purpose, and it is recommended that the term be abandoned'; and 'the basalts of this group should be and are better known as *calc–alkali basalts*'. The mean chemical composition of this type of basalt is given in Table 5.1.1. In 1960, Kuno (121) divided the aphyric basaltic rocks of Honshu and Izu Islands, Japan, into three groups, '*tholeiite* with low Al_2O_3 and alkalis, *alkali basalt* with variable Al_2O_3 and higher alkalis, and *high alumina basalt* with higher Al_2O_3 and intermediate alkalis. Kuno (122) claimed that the Al_2O_3 content of the high alumina basalt is 'generally higher than 17 per cent and rarely as low as 16 per cent'; and that the minerals found in the high alumina basalts are intermediate between those found in the tholeiitic basalts and the alkali basalts. The chemical compositions of the calc–alkali basalts of Nockolds and Le Bas (1977: 312) and the high alumina basalts of Kuno (1960: 125) are essentially the same (Table 5.1.1). In more recent times, two more types of basalt have been widely recognized on the Earth: (a) the low-K mid-ocean ridge, or *MOR basalts*; and (b) the Mg-rich Archaean *komatiitic basalts*.

A number of petrologists (cf. Chayes 1966) have given apposite reasons why the term *thol-*

eiite should be expunged from igneous petrology; however, this term, and a number of terms derived from it, are at present still in common use. The term is, for example, frequently used in the Basaltic Volcanism Study Project (1981). In 1840, Steininger used the term tholeiit (or tholeiite) to describe a group of basic to intermediate, high-level rocks that crop out on the Schaumberg, near the village of Tholey on the border between Saar and Rheinland, West Germany. Over the years the term tholeiite has been used in a variety of different ways. Chemical analyses of the igneous rocks from Tholey (cf. Jung 1958: 163) show them to be altered rocks with relatively high Fe_2O_3/FeO ratios, and high H_2O contents. They are essentially subalkalic basic to intermediate rocks with variable Al_2O_3 contents; and their mean chemical composition (Jung 1958: 177, and Table 5.1.1) is that of an *icelandite* (see Ch. 6). It is considered appropriate to retain the concept of the *tholeiitic rock series*, but to look to other areas to find fresh rocks to typify this rock series. Table 5.1.1 contains the mean chemical composition of the tholeiitic basalts of Hawaii.

At present there are two approaches to the problem of the classification of the basaltic rocks of the Earth. They are either considered to belong to a specific rock association, or they are regarded as having evolved in a specific tectonic and/or thermal environment. These different methods of classification do not always complement one another; for example, the rocks of the basalt–trachyte association are extruded in both continental and oceanic environments. The following are some of the more common rock associations that contain basaltic rocks: (a) calc–alkalic basalt–andesite–dacite–rhyolite; (b) tholeiitic basalt–icelandite–dacite–rhyolite; (c) alkalic (or transitional) basalt–hawaiite–mugearite–benmoreite–sodic trachyte–(comendite); (d) alkalic basalt–trachybasalt–tristanite–potassic trachyte; and (e) foid-bearing basalt (basanite)–phonolitic tephrite–tephritic phonolite–phonolite. Some of the more important tectonic and/or thermal environments of the Earth where basaltic rocks are extruded are as follows: (a) the Archaean which was essentially a high-temperature environment; (b) belts of continental distension and rifting; (c) mid-ocean ridges; (d) seismically-active continental margins and island-arcs; and (e) oceanic intraplate volcanic areas including aseismic ridges, oceanic islands and seamounts.

Table 5.1.1 Major element compositions of various basaltic rocks (%)

	1	2	3	4
SiO_2	51.31	50.2	54.53	49.4
TiO_2	0.88	0.75	1.50	2.5
Al_2O_3	18.60	17.6	16.38	13.9
Fe_2O_3	2.91	2.8	4.86	3.0
FeO	5.80	7.2	3.98	8.5
MnO	0.15	0.25	—	0.2
MgO	5.95	7.4	4.37	8.4
CaO	10.30	10.5	7.64	10.3
Na_2O	2.93	2.8	3.23	2.2
K_2O	0.74	0.40	1.80	0.4
H_2O^+	0.30	—	—	—
P_2O_5	0.12	0.14	0.23	0.3

1. Mean chemical composition of the calc-alkali basalts (N = 48) (after Nockolds and Le Bas 1977: 312).
2. Mean chemical composition of the high alumina basalts of Japan and Korea (N = 11) (after Kuno 1960: 141).
3. Mean chemical composition of the high-level intrusive rocks of the Schaumberg near Tholey, West Germany (type tholeiite: N = 5) (after Jung 1958: 177).
4. Mean chemical composition of the tholeiitic basalts of Hawaii (N = 200) (after Macdonald 1968: 502).

In the past decade many studies have been made of the basaltic rocks of the Moon, and to a lesser extent those of Venus and Mars; and it is now realized that basaltic volcanism is a fundamental process in the evolution of the terrestrial planets. Discussions on the nature and origin of the extraterrestrial basaltic rocks have changed forever the way we perceive basaltic rocks. Basalt is now regarded as having a specific, and important, petrological niche in the development of the Earth; and it is proposed that rocks that occupy a similar petrological niche on other planets, but have slightly different chemical compositions as compared to the basaltic rocks of Earth (for instance, the rocks of the lunar maria), should also be called *basaltic rocks*.

5.2 Modal composition

As we have already noted, basalts are usually composed of plagioclase and one, or more, pyroxenes; and these essential minerals are usually set in a glassy, or fine-grained, groundmass. Olivine may be present. Ca-poor pyroxenes and olivine are critical phases in the modal classification of basalts, because the stability of the Ca-poor pyroxenes, relative to olivine, is dependent on the silica content of the magma. Ca-poor pyroxenes, such as hypersthene, or pigeonite, are typical of the tholeiitic basalts; and in such rocks one may find evidence of a reaction relation between olivine and the residual magma to form Ca-poor pyroxene. Olivine commonly occurs in alkalic basalts, where it essentially takes the place of the Ca-poor pyroxenes (cf. Morse 1980: 212). In alkalic basalts, olivine usually occurs, both as a phenocryst and as a phase within the groundmass. Many alkalic basalts contain clinopyroxenes that have a relatively high Ti content and a characteristic violet-purple pleochroism (that is, titanaugite). The plagioclases in the alkalic basalts are characteristically richer in both Na_2O and K_2O than those in the tholeiitic basalts, and their mean plagioclase composition is approximately An_{52}. Alkali feldspars and/or feldspathoids occur in the groundmass of many alkalic basalts.

Olivine and spinel (Cr–Al varieties) are co-liquidus phases in most of the *Hawaiian tholeiitic basalts*. Many of these tholeiitic basalts also contain phenocrysts and microphenocrysts of Ca-poor pyroxene (Wo_{4-5} En_{76-80} Fs_{16-19}) and clinopyroxene (Wo_{35-42} En_{46-51} Fs_{9-17}). The olivine and Ca-poor pyroxene may form a reaction pair, with the latter replacing the former. The BVSP (1981: 177) authors have described overgrowths of clinopyroxene on orthopyroxene in a tholeiitic basalt from Mauna Loa, and they have proposed that the order of crystallization in this specimen was chromite $\rightarrow$ olivine $\rightarrow$ orthopyroxene $\rightarrow$ (clinopyroxene + plagioclase). In many specimens, most of the plagioclase and clinopyroxene (Wo_{40-35} En_{50-42} Fs_{10-25}) occur as intergrown phases in the groundmass.

The *Hawaiian alkalic basalts*, such as the rocks from Hualalai Volcano (BVSP 1981: 177), usually contain olivine phenocrysts. They may contain clinopyroxene–plagioclase glomerocrysts and clinopyroxene microphenocrysts, set in a groundmass of olivine, plagioclase, clinopyroxene and titanomagnetite. Chrome spinel is regarded as the liquidus phase; and in the alkalic basalt specimens from Hualalai Volcano studied by the BVSP, the order of crystallization is chrome spinel $\rightarrow$ olivine $\rightarrow$ clinopyroxene $\rightarrow$ plagioclase $\rightarrow$ titanomagnetite. Some of the alkalic basalts from Hawaii contain phenocrysts of both olivine and plagioclase, and in such rocks plagioclase is considered to have crystallized after olivine but before clinopyroxene.

Spinels from the Hawaiian tholeiitic basalts have higher Cr_2O_3 and higher $Cr/(Cr + Al + Fe^{3+})$ ratios than the spinels from the Hawaiian alkalic basalts (cf. BVSP 1981: 178). Olivines from the tholeiitic basalts range in composition from Fo_{89} to Fo_{70} with a frequency maximum at Fo_{82} and a mean of Fo_{84}; whereas the olivines in the alkalic basalt range in composition from Fo_{87} to Fo_{34}, and their mean composition is $Fo_{71.5}$. In many of the Hawaiian tholeiitic basalts, plagioclase is a late-crystallizing phase with a limited compositional range (An_{68}–An_{50}). The Hawaiian alkalic basalts usually contain more plagioclase than the tholeiitic basalts. Their plagioclase phenocrysts range in composition between An_{72} to An_{58}, and their groundmass plagioclases are usually more sodic. For example, the plagioclase laths in the groundmass of *hawaiite* from Mauna Kea Volcano have compositions that range from An_{54} to An_{39}. The Hawaiian tholeiitic basalts usually contain augite, hypersthene and/or pigeonite; whereas the Hawaiian alkalic basalts usually contain salite which is enriched in Ca, Fe^{2+} and Ti relative to the clinopyroxenes in the tholeiitic rocks. Amphibole (that is, kaersutite) and phlogopite are recorded from the alkalic basalts. Fe–Ti oxides may occur as late-crystallizing phases in both the tholeiitic and alkalic basalts of the Hawaiian Islands. Some of the tholeiitic basalts do not contain these minerals and they are believed to be derived from liquids that were quenched at relatively high temperatures before they could form.

The *mid-ocean ridge basalts* (MORB) are essentially *tholeiitic* in composition and they display a variety of textures. They are frequently porphyritic; and their phenocryst assemblages tend to include; (a) olivine ± spinel; (b) plagioclase plus olivine ± spinel; or (c) plagioclase, olivine plus clinopyroxene. Most MOR basalts have the following order of crystallization; olivine (± spinel) → plagioclase → clinopyroxene. The compositions of the olivines range from Fo_{91} to Fo_{65}, and the forsteritic cores of many of the olivine megacrysts are too Mg-rich to be in equilibrium with the bulk composition of the rock. Magnesian–chromian spinel preceded, or crystallized simultaneously with, the forsteritic olivines. Experimental studies have demonstrated that the composition of the spinel is highly sensitive to the oxygen fugacity of the parental magma. The plagioclase in the MOR basalts varies greatly in composition, as it ranges from An_{88} in some of the megacrysts to An_{40} in some of the interstitial plagioclase crystals. The cores of some of the plagioclase megacrysts are too Ca-rich to be in equilibrium with the bulk composition of the rock. Clinopyroxene is common in all but the most fine-grained and glassy MOR basalts, and it usually occurs in the groundmass intergrown with plagioclase. According to the BVSP (1981: 137), the most commonly observed clinopyroxenes have compositions that cluster around Wo_{30-40} En_{50} Fs_{10-15}. Low-calcium compositions are rare, and iron-rich compositions only occur in late-stage interstitial pyroxenes. Skeletal Fe-Ti oxides (usually titanomagnetite) are late-crystallizing phases in the more slowly-cooled MOR basalts.

Most of the thick flows of *continental flood basalt* have ophitic textures. Glass and devitrified materials may make up between 10 and 30 per cent of these rocks. According to the BVSP (1981: 43), the structural and textural characteristics of these basalts generally indicate that they congealed from very fluid, generally aphyric lavas that were probably extruded in a slightly superheated condition. These rocks are typically *olivine tholeiitic basalts* that contain between 8 and 15 per cent olivine, together with plagio-

clase, augite, interstitial pigeonite, ilmenite and titanomagnetite. The mesostasis often contains apatite, potassium–feldspar and quartz after tridymite. Plagioclase phenocrysts with bytownitic cores (An_{80-85}) and labradoritic rims (An_{50-66}) occur in some flows, but the feldspars typically occur in the groundmass, or as small laths, and they are usually labradoritic in composition. More sodic feldspars are generally found in the associated flood icelandites (see Ch. 6). Augite (Wo_{40} En_{42} Fe_{18}) is the typical pyroxene, but pigeonite and orthopyroxene are also found. For example, in the Keweenawan flood basalts of North America (BVSP 1981: 65), interstitial pigeonite occurs in most samples, but in some the last pyroxene to crystallize is an orthopyroxene in the bronzite–hypersthene range. Similar orthopyroxenes have also been described from the Karroo continental flood basalt province of southern Africa (cf. Walker & Poldervaart 1949: 635–8). The compositions of the olivines generally range from Fo_{63} to Fo_{72}.

5.3 Geochemistry

Manson (1967) was the first to try to obtain an objective overall picture of the chemical variations that occur in the basaltic rocks of Earth. His study attempted to simultaneously evaluate the variations found in the twelve most abundant oxides contained in the basaltic rocks. As it is difficult to represent so many variables simultaneously, he used *factor analysis* to express rock analyses in terms of a reduced number of vari-

Table 5.3.1 Mean chemical composition of the basalt clan (N=1996) (after Manson 1967: 235)

	$\bar{x}$ (%)	s
SiO	49.2	3.23
TiO_2	1.9	1.03
Al_2O_3	15.8	2.13
Fe_2O_3	3.0	1.35
FeO	8.0	1.90
MnO	0.17	0.10
MgO	6.6	2.11
CaO	10.0	1.46
Na_2O	2.7	0.76
K_2O	1.0	0.65
P_2O_5	0.33	0.25
H_2O^+	0.9	0.73

Table 5.3.2 Chemical composition of selected basaltic rocks from Earth

	1(%)	2(%)	3(%)	4(%)	5(%)	6(%)	7(%)	8(%)	9(%)	10(%)
SiO_2	47.04	48.13	50.19	50.17	49.21	51.75	46.88	50.4	51.31	45.68
TiO_2	1.00	0.60	1.51	3.15	1.39	2.07	2.03	0.80	0.88	2.58
Al_2O_3	8.24	12.21	15.15	13.23	15.81	13.81	13.69	19.5	18.60	14.68
Fe_2O_3	1.50	0.64	5.51	3.52	2.21	2.48	2.41	2.70	2.91	3.58
FeO	11.70	10.61	5.82	10.71	7.19	8.35	9.86	6.60	5.80	8.14
MnO	0.28	0.20	0.15	0.22	0.16	0.17	0.17	0.16	0.15	0.17
MgO	13.38	10.07	5.91	4.41	8.53	7.25	9.78	4.45	5.95	8.92
CaO	10.43	10.23	9.13	8.20	11.14	10.57	10.81	11.2	10.30	10.44
Na_2O	1.30	2.28	2.71	2.85	2.71	2.31	2.47	2.65	2.93	3.11
K_2O	0.10	0.03	0.62	1.26	0.26	0.42	0.68	0.56	0.74	1.30
P_2O_5	0.08	0.06	0.17	0.67	0.15	0.24	0.24	0.15	0.12	0.52
H_2O^+	3.20	4.56	1.92	0.85	—	0.19	—	0.54	0.30	0.87
CO_2	0.16	0.09	0.13	0.05	—	0.06	—	0.05	—	—
Total	98.41	99.71	98.92	99.29	—	99.67	99.02	99.76	99.99	—
p.p.m.										
Sc	31.6	41.8	30.7	36.7	40.6*	29.5	30.1	25	32.0	26.2
Cr	1460	750	124	34.0	296	350	560	15	160	563
Co	—	—	48.7	—	—	—	—	—	—	—
Ni	580	150	110	—	123	—	—	18	50	90
Cu	—	—	—	—	87	—	—	77	—	—
Zn	—	—	—	—	122	—	—	70	—	—
Ga	13	15	—	24	18	20	19	17	—	—
Rb	0.8	0.9	8	33	2*	6.9	15	8.6	23	40
Sr	69	45	184	301	123	344	359	520	428	842
Y	17	14	—	41	43	23	21	18	22	25
Zr	—	—	150	—	100	129	166	44	71	213
Cs	0.07	0.04	—	0.4	—	—	—	0.18	—	—
Nb	1.5	3.0	8	—	4.6*	9	16	1.75	2.7	84
Ba	—	1.17	—	600	12	—	—	77	260	600
La	4.18	—	16.1	26.6	—	9.38	12.5	5.22	—	—
Ce	12.7	3.47	37.2	60.1	11.0*	25.0	29.0	13.5	29.3	96.8
Sm	2.99	1.35	5.37	8.58	3.26*	4.80	4.38	2.48	3.78	8.87
Eu	0.99	0.45	1.48	2.55	—	1.70	1.43	0.85	—	—
Tb	0.62	0.36	0.92	1.44	—	0.81	0.69	0.47	—	—
Yb	1.80	1.48	3.24	4.05	3.22*	2.00	1.88	2.07	2.31	0.89
Lu	0.26	0.23	0.49	0.62	—	0.29	0.26	0.31	—	—
Hf	1.91	1.05	4.5	5.37	2.44*	3.48	3.00	1.42	2.23	6.36
Pb	5	3	—	9	2	<1	<1	3.1	—	—
Th	0.36	0.15	2.8	4.18	0.26*	0.56	1.20	0.52	1.26	4.5

1. Archaean komatiitic basalt from Munro Township, Ontario, Canada (BVSP 1981: 15, ACH-13).
2. Archaean magnesian basalt from Munro Township, Ontario, Canada (BVSP 1981: 14, ACH-9).
3. Continental flood basalt from the Keweenawan lavas of the North Shore Volcanic Group, Minnesota, USA (BVSP 1981: 67, KEW-15). This rock also contains 1.76 per cent H_2O^-.
4. Continental flood basalt from the Columbia River Province, USA (BVSP 1981: 82, CP-6, Roza Member of the Wanapum Basalt Formation).
5. Mean chemical composition of MOR basalt from the mid-Atlantic Ridge (Melson & Thompson 1971: 429; N = 33). *These values were obtained from Pearce 1982: Table 1.
6. Tholeiitic basalt from Mauna Loa Volcano, Hawaii, 1859 eruption (BVSP 1981: 166, HAW-4).
7. Alkalic basalt or alkali olivine basalt, Hualalai Volcano, Hawaii, prehistoric eruption (BVSP 1981: 166, HAW-12).
8. High-alumina island-arc basalt from Duaga Island, Witu Islands, Papua New Guinea (BVSP 1981: 200, IA-6). This rock also contains 0.18 per cent H_2O^-.
9. Mean chemical composition of calc–alkali basalt. Major elements from Nockolds and Le Bas 1977: 213, and trace elements from Pearce 1982: Table 1.
10. Mean chemical composition of alkaline basalt. Major elements from Chayes 1975: 548. Note Chayes (1975: 547) defines the *alkaline basalts* as basalts that (a) contain normative nepheline, or (b) contain neither normative nepheline or quartz, but his ol'–hy' discrimant (Dc) is negative; that is, Dc = hy' + 0.134 ol' − 26.942, where hy' = 100hy/(ol + di + hy), ol' = 100 ol/(ol + di + hy). The trace elements were obtained from Pearce 1982: Table 1.

ables. In order to define the basaltic rocks, he (221) used an empirical chemical screen. This, comprehensive screen contained 33 items. Items 1 to 16 set limits on the various oxides (for instance, SiO_2 less than 56.00 per cent, Al_2O_3 between 10.50 and 22.00 per cent, and CaO between 5.00 and 15.00 per cent); whereas the remaining items set a variety of different normative limits (for instance, normative quartz has to be less than 12.50 per cent). The concept of using a *chemical screen* to define a particular rock type, or group of rocks, is important to petrology, because the major premise in this approach is that, at any particular time, one can obtain a consensus among petrologists as to the oxide and/or normative limits they would set to define a particular rock, or group of rocks. Such limits may be broad for individual parameters, but when they are all taken together they provide a method of defining what a specific rock type means to petrologists at that particular time.

Manson attempted to obtain chemical data on the basaltic rocks from all over the Earth; unfortunately his data-base contains insufficient information on the basaltic rocks of South America and the floor of the oceans. Table 5.3.1 gives his mean chemical composition of the basaltic rocks of the Earth. These data have proved to be particularly valuable as they show that the silica contents of the basaltic rocks fall within a restricted range (that is, $\bar{x} = 49.2$ per cent, $s = 3.23$); and one is thus able, for example, to use silica content as a parameter for separating the basalts from the andesites. Manson also found complete chemical gradation between the different basaltic rocks, with the notable exception of the *leucite basalts*. He also concluded that MgO and Al_2O_3 showed the most significant variations of all the major oxides found in the basaltic rocks.

5.4 The simple basalt system

Norms are not only of inestimable value in comparing glassy or partly glassy rocks with holocrystalline rocks, but they also provide an important link between natural rocks and experimental systems that would otherwise have to be defined by their chemical composition. There are a number of problems associated with the use of C.I.P.W. norms; for example, if there is an error in the determination of Na_2O, this error is in-

creased by a factor of eight during the calculation of normative albite (cf. Church 1975: 258). The norms of altered rocks can be misleading (see Section 3.3).

In 1962, Yoder and Tilley published their important paper on the origin of basaltic magmas, and in this they introduced the concept of the *basalt tetrahedron*. The end-members of this quaternary system are forsterite, diopside, nepheline and quartz. They regarded this system as a simple model for a wide range of different basaltic rocks because the various types of basalt essentially consist of plagioclase and clinopyroxene, together with lesser amounts of one or more of the minerals olivine, orthopyroxene, nepheline, quartz and the Fe–Ti oxides. In the basalt tetrahedron (Fig. 5.4.1), olivine is represented by *forsterite*; plagioclase is represented by *albite* which lies on the line Ne–Qz by virtue of the reaction $NaAlSiO_4$ (Ne) + $2SiO_2$ (Qz) = $NaAlSi_3O_8$ (Ab); clinopyroxene is represented by *diopside* at the top of the tetrahedron, whereas the orthopyroxene, *enstatite*, lies between forsterite and quartz by virtue of the reaction Mg_2SiO_4 (Fo) + SiO_2 (Qz) = $2MgSiO_3$ (En); *quartz* represents all the SiO_2 phases in the basalts, and *nepheline* represents the feldspathoids. Yoder and Tilley's drawing of the basalt tetrahedron was cut by two planes: one (Fo–Di–Ab) was labelled *critical plane of silica undersaturation*; whereas the other (En–Di–Ab) was la-

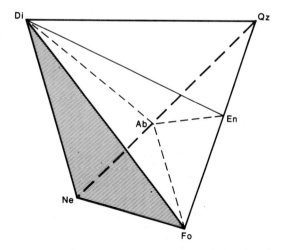

Fig. 5.4.1 Schematic representation of the *basalt tetrahedron*. Di–En–Ab is the plane of silica saturation, and Di–Fo–Ab is the critical plane of silica undersaturation (adapted from Yoder and Tilley 1962: Fig. 1).

belled *plane of silica saturation*. Basalts with compositions that plotted on the nepheline side of the plane Fo–Di–Ab would be normatively nepheline-bearing and undersaturated in silica, whereas those with compositions that plotted on the quartz side of the plane En–Di–Ab would be normatively quartz-bearing and oversaturated in silica. One should note that this simple basalt system does not contain iron.

Yoder and Tilley (1962) also introduced a *generalized simple basalt system* (Fig. 5.4.2) in which the normal minerals found in basalts, that is olivine, clinopyroxene, orthopyroxene and plagioclase, are substituted for the chemically pure end-members, forsterite, diopside, enstatite and albite. It is particularly convenient to use this generalized system when discussing the major element composition and origin of the basaltic rocks. Yoder and Tilley (1962: 352) used it to divide the basaltic rocks into the following groups:

(a) *tholeiite (oversaturated)*, contains normative quartz and hypersthene;

(b) *tholeiite (saturated)*, contains normative hypersthene but no normative quartz (that is, it lies on the plane of silica saturation);

(c) *olivine tholeiite*, contains both normative hypersthene and olivine;

(d) *olivine basalt*, contains normative olivine but no normative hypersthene or nepheline (that is, it lies on the critical plane of silica undersaturation);

(e) *alkali basalt*, contains normative olivine and nepheline.

Rocks of groups (a) and (b) are subalkalic basalts that may be either tholeiitic basalts or calc–alkalic basalts; and the rocks of groups (d) and (e) are essentially alkalic basalts. Most of the MOR and ocean-floor basalts are olivine tholeiites, as are many of the mildly alkalic *transitional basalts* that are discussed in Chapter 7. It is proposed that transitional basalt is a satisfactory name for the basaltic rocks that carry both normative hypersthene and olivine.

When considering the positions occupied by the various basaltic rocks in the generalized simple basalt system, it is important to note that the empirical line on the alkali silica diagram, that is used to separate the alkalic from the subalkalic basalts, is approximately the trace of the critical plane of silica undersaturation (cf. De Long & Hoffman 1975). Experimental studies on simple silicate systems, such as Di–Ab and Di–Fo–An, indicate that there is a plane that is located near the critical plane of silica undersaturation in the basalt tetrahedron that cannot be crossed by a magma during fractional crystallization at low pressures. Presnall et al. (1978: 203), for example, state that below about 0.4 GPa, the join Di–Fo–An represents, in simplified form, a thermal divide between the alkalic and subalkalic basalts. In the generalized simple basalt system, the olivine–clinopyroxoene–plagioclase plane does not exactly coincide with the low-pressure thermal divide (cf. Miyashiro 1978: 91), but occurs at slightly higher silica values; as a result of this some of the basalts that contain a little normative hypersthene should be regarded as *transitional basalts* with possible alkalic affinities.

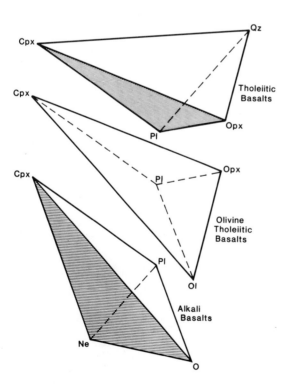

Fig. 5.4.2 The generalized simple basalt system 'exploded' along the plane of silica saturation and the critical plane of silica undersaturation (adapted from Yoder and Tilley 1962: Fig. 2).

5.5 Archaean basalts

Volcanic rocks make up more than half the supracrustal rocks in many of the Archaean areas of the Earth. The relative proportions of the different types of volcanic rocks vary from area to area. In a typical area containing rocks of this age, basaltic and ultramafic rocks would predominate in the lower stratigraphic units, whereas rocks of intermediate and silicic composition would predominate in the upper stratigraphic units. Well-documented sequences of Archaean volcanic rocks have, for example, been described from the Barberton Mountainland, South Africa, and the Abitibi Greenstone Belt of northern Canada (Viljoen & Viljoen 1969a; Goodwin 1977). In the latter area the volcanic succession has been estimated to consist of 1 per cent ultramafic rocks, 55 per cent basalt, 33 per cent andesite (sensu lato), 7 per cent dacite and 4 per cent rhyolite. These Archaean volcanic rocks are usually metamorphosed to the greenschist facies, or locally to the amphibolite facies; however, in many areas, they carry some primary igneous minerals. It is often difficult to classify these rocks as metamorphism has not only produced new mineral assemblages, but it has also redistributed some of the elements, particularly the large ion lithophile elements, such as K, Rb and Ba (cf. BVSP 1981: 5). Most of the Archaean volcanic rocks have Phanerozoic analogues; however, the rocks of the *komatiitic magmatic suite* are a notable exception (see Section 11.5). These lavas characteristically contain more than 18 wt% MgO (anhydrous basis), and many contain up to 33 wt% MgO. In some Archaean greenstone belts, komatiitic lavas make up as much as 10 per cent of the total volume of volcanic materials. Small volumes of komatiitic lava have been extruded in post-Archaean times, but such rocks are usually found to have evolved from magmas that were less magnesian that those produced in the Archaean. The Post-Cretaceous komatiitic rocks of Gorgona Island, Columbia, are an example of relatively young komatiitic materials.

For much of this century the possible existence of highly magnesian magmas has been debated. Bowen and Andersen (1914) demonstrated that such magmas could only be generated at high temperatures. In 1927, Bowen claimed that the field evidence, particularly the absence of known extrusive ultrabasic rocks, seemed to preclude the existence of such extremely hot magmas. Komatiites were first described in the early years of this century by field geologists working for the geological surveys in Zimbabwe, Canada and Australia. For example, the first bulletin of the Zimbabwe Geological Survey contains a description of komatiitic rocks with what are now called *spinifex textures*. Later in 1928, Macgregor described, figured and presented a chemical analysis of a Zimbabwean komatiite. In 1969 the Viljoen brothers described the komatiites of the Barberton Mountainland. This area is the most southerly extension of the well-developed African greenstone belts, and it contains the Komati Valley where these lavas are particularly well preserved.

Arndt and Nisbet (1982: 25) have defined komatiites as lavas, or volcaniclastic rocks, that contain more than 18 per cent MgO on an anhydrous basis. They also note that this rock type is usually recognized because: (a) either its mineral assemblage or chemical composition indicates that it has an ultramafic composition; and (b) its structures and/or textures indicate an extrusive origin. Detailed studies of Archaean lavas have revealed that the komatiites (sensu stricto) form the ultramafic portion of a magmatic rock series that includes *komatiitic basalts* (see Table 5.3.1). The komatiitic basalts are high-MgO basalts that occur in association with komatiites, and are considered to belong to the *komatiitic magmatic suite*. Many of the rocks of the komatiitic magmatic suite have the distinctive spinifex texture. Experimental studies by Lofgren (1980) have demonstrated that this texture can be generated by cooling a high-Mg melt that is essentially free of nuclei. The *peridotitic komatiites* are discussed in Section 11.5.

5.6 Mid-ocean ridge (MOR) basalts

MOR basalts are extruded from, or intruded into, fissures within the rift that bisect the 65 000 km long interconnecting mid-ocean ridge system. This volcanic activity thus supplies the materials that generate the oceanic crust. Circulating sea-water cools this new basaltic crust and assists in changing it into *ocean-floor metabasalt*. The latter rocks are essentially MOR basalts enriched in volatiles and elements such as Na, K and U. Most fresh MOR basalts are strongly depleted in K and the incompatible elements, as compared to all the other major types of basalt from the Earth, with the notable exception of the komatiitic basalts (see Table 5.3.2). The MOR basalts are not all of uniform chemical composition, and they can be divided into three main groups: (a) the *normal*, or depleted, *MOR basalts*; (b) the *enriched*, or plume-type, *MOR basalts*; and (c) the *transitional MOR basalts* (cf. Sun et al. 1979: 119). Normal MOR basalts, such as are found in most areas along the mid-ocean ridges, are as we have already noted, relatively depleted in the incompatible elements, and have relatively low $^{87}Sr/^{86}Sr$ ratios. Enriched MOR basalts contain more of the incompatible elements (P, K, Rb, Nb, Cs, Ba, light REE, Ta, Th and U) and the radiogenic isotopes of Sr and Pb. The enriched MOR basalts are usually found on topographic highs, or submarine platforms associated with islands that lie astride the ridge axis (for example Iceland, Azores, Galapagos, Bouvet and Reunion). Normal and enriched MOR basalts grade into one another, and the rocks of intermediate composition are called transitional MOR basalts. It is often suggested that the enriched MOR basalts are generated in areas where mantle plumes are active, thus they are also known as plume-type MOR basalts. Another minor type of MOR basalt with a distinct modal and chemical composition is the *highly-phyric plagioclase basalt*. It usually contains more than 18 per cent Al_2O_3, and is thus a high-alumina basalt (cf. Hekinian 1982: 32).

The FAMOUS (French–American Mid-Ocean Undersea Survey) project on the Mid-Atlantic Ridge near 36 °N has provided valuable information on the composition and structure of the volcanic rocks; and also on the nature of the magmatic processes that operate on active mid-ocean ridges. In the FAMOUS area, the African and American plates are diverging at a rate of approximately 22 mm/a. This is a moderate spreading rate as compared to a segment of the East Pacific Rise which is spreading at approximately 160 mm/a. The plate boundary in the FAMOUS area lies within a rift valley with walls that are between 1.2 and 1.5 km high, and a floor that is between 1.5 and 3 km wide. A discontinuous medial ridge, or line of volcanic edifices, dominates the topography of the inner floor of the rift valley. Another series of small volcanic edifices occur along the sides of the rift valley adjacent to the boundary escarpments. Detailed studies of the rift valley, using submersibles, have revealed that many fissures and faults are present. The fissures range in width from a few centimetres up to 8 m. According to Ballard and Van Andel (1977), the faults along the axial zone usually have throws of less than

1 m, and they tend to strike in a direction that is parallel to the axis of the rift valley. Whereas the volcanism in the rift valley is episodic, the faulting and fissuring is apparently continuous.

Five different types of MOR basalts have been mapped in the FAMOUS area (cf. Hekinian 1982: 73). The rocks from the volcanic edifices in the axial zone are usually picritic or olivine–phyric basalts; whereas the rocks from the peripheral areas are usually moderately phyric–plagioclase basalts, highly phyric–plagioclase basalts and plagioclase–olivine–pyroxene basalts. Generally the basalts of the axial zone have lower FeO/MgO ratios and lower TiO_2 contents than the basalts of the peripheral areas. The former basalts are usually regarded as being more primitive, and less differentiated, than the latter.

Thermal models of the Mid-Atlantic Ridge near 36 °N support the concept that persistent, high-level magma chambers exist beneath the axial zone of active mid-ocean ridges (cf. Hekinian 1982: 83, 356–9). Steady-state refilling and mixing of this magma with batches of fresh magma generated by upwelling and partial melting of mantle material would ensure that the magma remained close to saturation in olivine, clinopyroxene and plagioclase for long periods of time (cf. O'Hara 1977).

Mid-ocean ridges mark the position of mantle upwelling, magma production and extensive volcanic activity. It is proposed that in the axial zones of most segments of the mid-ocean ridge system, crustal distention is continually generating fractures. Some of these fractures encounter magma, and fissure eruptions of limited volume are likely to occur. At any particular time, such eruptions are taking place along some segments of the mid-ocean ridge system. An eruption is usually followed by a relatively long period of dormancy during which time the rocks of the medial ridge constructed by the eruption cool, fracture and subside. Eventually, new fractures encounter high-level magma, and a new cycle of ocean-floor spreading begins. It is thus suggested that divergent plate boundaries are continually fracturing, but only periodically being healed by a combination of magmatic and volcanic activity. Normal ocean floor is considered to consist of an upper layer that is mainly composed of pillowed lava, and in which resides most of the remnant magnetization characteristic of the ocean floor; and a lower layer that essentially consists of a dyke-sill complex.

The *ocean-floor metabasalts* are often called

spilites. According to Streckeisen (1980: 201) and the IUGS subcommission on the systematics of igneous rocks, spilites are 'basaltic rocks with eruptive features (texture, fabric) and characterized by the assemblage albite–chlorite, which may be due to metasomatic or metamorphic changes. Rich in alkalis (sodium, rarely potassium) and usually poor in calcium. Spilites often occur as submarine lava flows, commonly with pillow structure.'

5.7 Continental flood basalts

Large areas of the continents of Earth are covered by flood basalts (cf. Tyrrell 1937: BVSP 1981: 30–107). These lavas were extruded through fissures, and they form broad, flat, low-viscosity flows of large volume. According to the BVSP (1981: xxxiv), the average thickness of these accumulations of flood basalt is about 1 km, although they may be locally thicker. In most flood basalt provinces the lavas originally covered areas of the order of 2×10^6 km^2. Most of these basalts are considered to have been erupted in zones of tectonic tension and rifting, and they thus tend to fill broad subsiding basins. Both the Karroo (southern Africa) and Parana (South America) flood basalt provinces are interpreted as having evolved in tensional environments that developed during the break-up of Gondwanaland. In recent times the only large fissure eruption was the Laki, or Lakagigar, eruption that took place in Iceland in 1783 (see Section 1.9). This eruption was, however, many orders of magnitude smaller than a normal continental flood basalt eruption.

The age of continental flood basalts ranges from at least the Late Proterozoic (1.10–1.14 Ga) for the lavas of the *Lake Superior Basin* to the Miocene (6–17 Ma) for lavas of the *Columbia River Flood Basalt Province* of north-western USA. Other examples of continental flood basalts include: (a) the *North Australian Flood Basalt Province* of Late Proterozoic to Early Cambrian age (560–90 Ma; cf. Bultitude 1976); (b) the *Siberian Platform Flood Basalt Province* of the Tunguska Basin east of the Yenesei River in the USSR which is Late Permian to Middle Triassic in age (216–48 Ma; cf. Makarenko 1977; BVSP 1981: 32–3); (c) the *Karroo Flood Basalt Province* of southern Africa which is Late Triassic to Middle Jurassic in age (160–200 Ma; cf. Bristow & Saggerson, 1983; Cox & Hornung 1966; Walker & Poldervaart 1949); (d) the *Parana Basin Flood Basalt Province* of Argentina, Brazil, Paraguay and Uruguay which is also known as the Serra Geral Group, and is of Late Jurassic to Early Cretaceous age (119–49 Ma; cf. Rüegg 1975; BVSP 1981: 34–5); (e) *Deccan Flood Basalt Province* of India which is of Tertiary age (50–65 Ma; cf. Wadia 1975: 275–86; BVSP 1981: 98–9); and (f) the *Thulean Flood Basalt Province* which is scattered across the North Atlantic with fragments being located in the northern parts of the British Isles, Faeroe Islands, Greenland, Baffin Island and possibly Iceland; this is also of Tertiary age (52–66 Ma; cf. BVSP 1981: 88–98).

A feature of many of the continental flood basalt provinces, such as the Karroo Province, is the close association of the lavas with large numbers of basaltic dykes and sills (that is, the dolerites). This observation has led to the proposal that some extensive Proterozoic dyke swarms may be all that now remain of former continental flood basalt provinces.

Columbia river flood basalt province

The lavas of this province are a good example of the rocks found in a young continental flood basalt province. They cover an area of approximately 2×10^5 km^2, and have an estimated volume of 2×10^5 km^3 (Waters 1962). They were erupted between 6 and 17 Ma ago; however, approximately 99 per cent of the lava was erupted in a 3 Ma period shortly after the beginning of this eruptive event. The lavas were extruded into a basin-like structure that developed between the Cascade Range in the west and the Idaho Batholith in the east; and at present they crop out in northern Oregon, western Idaho and central and eastern Washington state. Individual flows may vary between 10 and 45 m in thickness, and a typical flow has a volume of between 10 and 20 km^3; some flows, such as the Roza and Pomona, contain several hundred km^3 of rock. Most of the lavas were erupted from a system of aligned fissures. These systems of fissures are usually between 10 and 100 km in length and up to several kilometres in width. Extrusion rates for the huge Roza and Pomona flows may have been as high as 1 km³/day, but the long-term production rate was probably of the order of 12 m³/s which is approximately 1000 times less productive.

At present the lavas of the Columbia River Flood Basalt Province are divided into five formations, and many members, on the basis of stratigraphy, geochemistry, magnetic polarity and radiogenic dating (cf. BVSP 1981: 79). The *Grande Ronde Basalt Formation* (14–16.5 Ma) contains about 80 per cent of the volume of eruptive materials in the Columbia River Flood Basalt Province. *Quartz-normative tholeiitic basalt* is the dominant rock type, and it occurs in association with *icelandite* and *olivine tholeiitic basalt*. The lavas of the Grande Ronde Basalt Formation include both high-Mg ($\bar{x}$ MgO = 5.3 per cent) and low-Mg ($\bar{x}$ MgO = 3.4 per cent) varieties. A particularly distinctive feature of these rocks is their relatively high silica content (51–6 wt%; that is, tholeiitic basalt to icelandite).

Strontium and neodymium isotopic studies of the rocks of this province have revealed a large range in values. The early lavas, such as the Imnaha Basalt Formation, have the most primitive values (initial $^{87}Sr/^{86}Sr$ 0.703 to 0.704: ϵ Nd greater than five), and there is an irregular trend towards increasing $^{87}Sr/^{86}Sr$ and decreasing $^{143}Nd/^{144}Nd$ with time. The isotopic data for the Grande Ronde Basalt Formation are usually interpreted as indicating that most of the rocks of this huge body of lava have been contaminated by continental crustal materials, even though there is little petrographic evidence of assimilation. With regard to the origin of continental flood basalts in general, the main debate at the present time is whether their parental magma was a primary tholeiitic basaltic magma or whether it was derived from a primary picritic magma. Some continental flood basalt provinces, such as the Karroo Province and the Thulean Province, contain significant volumes of picritic or picritic basaltic lava; and most of the other provinces contain at least some material of this composition (see Sections 5.15 and 11.4). A few areas within the Thulean Province also contain relatively large volumes of alkalic basalt and more differentiated alkalic rocks.

In the Nuanetsi–Lebombo province, that forms the eastern part of the Karroo super province, the earliest lavas are nephelinites, and they generally underlie a thick sequence of picritic basalts that are enriched in incompatible elements (cf. Bristow & Saggerson, 1983, 1046).

Some of these nephelinites overlie, or are associated with carbonatites (see Section 14.5).

5.8 Continental rift and palaeorift basalts

In the continental areas of the Earth, basaltic volcanism is often found in areas of tectonic tension and rifting. Extensional tectonic activity may, as has already been noted in Section 5.7, result in the eruption of continental flood basalts; however, the rifting of continental crust is associated with the emplacement and eruption of a very wide range of different igneous rocks. Such rifting is often linked to the incipient, or abortive, break-up of continental plates. Structural basins and rifts may also develop within a continent as the result of continent–continent collision, such as the *Baikal Rift* in the USSR. Other well-known rift systems include the *East African Rift System*, the *Rhinegraben* and the *Oslo Palaeorift* of Norway. Some rifts, such as the Oslo Palaeorift, are dominated by alkalic rocks; whereas others, such as the *Rio Grande Rift* of New Mexico and Colorado, contain mainly tholeiitic basalts (cf. BVSP 1981: 109–31). In Chapters 12 and 14 we will discuss the *alkaline rocks* found in the continental rifts and palaeorifts.

5.9 Oceanic intraplate basalts

The oceanic intraplate basalts are typically found on oceanic islands and seamounts. Some of the better-known localities of intraplate volcanism in the presentday ocean basins include Jan Mayen, Madeira, Canary Islands, Cape Verde Islands, St Helena, Tristan da Cunha and Gough Island in the Atlantic Ocean; Reunion, Mauritius and the Comoro Islands in the Indian Ocean; and Tahiti, the Hawaiian Islands and Guadeloupe in the Pacific Ocean. In the western Pacific there are large numbers of islands and seamounts that represent extinct intraplate volcanoes that have risen from the floor of the ocean. The very productive Hawaiian Islands contain rocks that belong to the tholeiitic, the alkalic and the nephelinitic rock series. On many oceanic islands and seamounts it is at present difficult to estimate the relative proportions in which the rocks of these various rock series occur. Tholeiitic basalts are considered to be the most abundant rock types on the Hawaiian Islands and Reunion; however, on many of the other islands, such as the Canary Islands and Tahiti, alkalic basalt is the dominant rock type.

Most of the alkalic basalt rocks found on the oceanic islands and seamounts are *sodic basalts* and they usually occur together with rocks of the hawaiite–mugearite–benmoreite–sodic trachyte association (see Ch. 7). Typical sodic basalts have been described from both the Hawaiian and Canary Islands (cf. Macdonald 1968; Fuster, Arana et al. 1968). *Potassic basalts* are much less abundant in the oceanic intraplate environment. Examples of rocks of this type occur, together with rocks of the trachybasalt (sensu stricto)–tristanite–potassic trachyte association, on the Tristan da Cunha Group and Gough Island in the South Atlantic (cf. Mitchell-Thomé 1970: 224–305).

It is often proposed that much of presentday oceanic intraplate volcanism is directly related to local areas of partial melting (that is, hot spots) within the upper mantle beneath the oceanic lithosphere. For example, the Hawaiian Ridge and the contiguous Emperor Seamount chain form a dogleg-shaped pattern across the north-western Pacific Ocean. Wilson (1963) and others have proposed that all the volcanoes in this long bent chain were produced by the same stationary magma generating system that was active beneath a mobile lithospheric plate. Before approximately 42.5 Ma the motion of the Pacific plate relative to the sublithospheric magma generating system was N 10 °W with a mean velocity of 60 mm/a; however, after this date the direction of movement changed N 70 °W and the velocity remained essentially constant to about 1.3 Ma when it speeded up to a mean velocity of 178 mm/a (BVSP 1981: 162)

In section 4.2 it was noted that sea-floor spreading is not exclusively confined to mid-oceanic ridges but may also occur in back-arc basins, or marginal basins, such as the Lau Basin to the west of Tonga in the south-western Pacific. Some petrologists claim that the basaltic rocks of the back-arc basin-spreading centres, which are sometimes called *marginal basin basalts*, are essentially identical to the rocks extruded at mid-oceanic ridge-spreading centres; whereas others maintain that some of the marginal basin basalts are transitional in composition between the MOR basalts and the basalts of the island-arc tholeiitic association as described in Section 5.10 (cf. Hawkins 1977).

5.10 Orogenic basalts

These basalts typically occur near convergent plate boundaries on *island arcs* and *seismically-active continental margins*. At present, the volume of magmatic rocks produced in this tectonic environment is huge: it is second in volume only to the materials produced on the mid-ocean ridges. There is also a great diversity in the types of magmatic rocks that evolve in this tectonic environment. The orogenic basalts make up only about 20 per cent of the total volume of volcanic rocks found in this tectonic setting; and there is not one, but at least five different types of basalt found in this environment. These basalts belong to: (a) the *boninite association*; (b) the *island-arc tholeiitic association*; (c) the *calc–alkalic association*; (d) the *high-K association*; and (e) the *shoshonitic association*. These rock associations are all discussed in more detail in Chapter 6. The *calc–alkalic basalts* are the principal type of basalt associated with the *orogenic andesites*; and they are also the most abundant type of orogenic basalt.

Subduction is the unifying tectonic feature that is characteristic of magmas generated along convergent plate boundaries. During the early stages in the evolution of island-arcs, most of the extrusive rocks are likely to belong to the boninite and/or island-arc tholeiite association; but during the main phase in the evolution of active continental margins, andesites and other rocks of the calc–alkalic association are usually extruded and/or intruded. The overall pattern of volcanic and magmatic activity at convergent plate margins is complex because: (a) the rate of plate convergence may vary; (b) the modal and chemical composition of the materials being subducted may vary; (c) the thickness and composition of the buoyant plate margin may vary; and (d) the wedge of upper mantle material that occurs above the Benioff seismic zone may change in physical properties and composition with the passage of time. In any particular area of plate convergence the magmas generated at different depths usually have different compositions. The Benioff seismic zone is usually regarded as marking the position of the subducted material; and the volatile components released by this material triggers magma genesis. As the Benioff seismic zone occurs at deeper levels away from the marginal trench, the site of melting and magma genesis probably also occurs at greater depths as one proceeds away from the marginal trench. In Fig. 4.2.1 it was shown that there is often a positive correlation of K_2O with distance from the marginal trench; thus the alkalic basalts of the high-K and shoshonitic associations that occur above active Benioff seismic zones usually occur at considerable distances from the marginal trenches. These relationships are well illustrated by the Sunda Arc in Java and Bali, Indonesia (cf. Whitford & Nicholls 1976). In many areas such as Japan and Argentina, the alkalic rocks occur in what are regarded as back arc regions (see Section 4.2).

5.11 Basaltic meteorites

The study of basaltic meteorites has greatly extended our knowledge of basaltic volcanism in the Solar System. *Eucrites* and *shergottites* consist entirely of basaltic materials, whereas the *howardites* and *mesosiderites* contain basaltic fragments variously mixed with other materials. The eucrites are the most common type of basaltic achondritic meteorite. They are extraordinary in that they crystallized some 4.54 ($\pm$ 0.02) Ga ago which is probably only 30 Ma after the earliest recorded event in the Solar System (the evolution of the refractory particles included in the Allende carbonaceous chrondritic meteorite). The eucrites are thus the oldest known basalts, and they probably formed as the result of the partial melting of the primitive condensed material from which the planets and asteroids evolved. Most eucrites are brecciated; some have textures that indicate that they cooled rapidly; whereas many others have coarser grain sizes and subophitic textures. Some planetologists have postulated that all, or at least some, of the eucrites are derived from the large (555 km in diameter) asteroid Vesta, because infrared sprctrophotometric observations have shown that it has basaltic rocks on its surface. The shergottites form a distinct group of non-brecciated basaltic meteorites; they are relatively young ($\approx$650 Ma), and their compositions indicate that they crystallized under more oxidizing, or Earth-like,

conditions than the eucrites. The chemical composition of representative examples of the basaltic meteorites are given in Table 5.11.1.

The essential minerals in the eucritic basalts are calcic plagioclase (35 per cent) and clinopyroxene (60 per cent). Pigeonite is the dominant primary pyroxene, but augite and orthopyroxene are present as exsolution and inversion products of the pigeonite. The plagioclase crystals usually range in composition between An_{80} and An_{90}, with some interstitial crystals being as sodic as An_{65}. Accessory minerals found in the eucritic basalts include cristobalite, tridymite, quartz, chromite, ilmenite, troilite and native iron. The shergottites usually contain more clinopyroxene (75 per cent) and less plagioclase (22 per cent). They usually contain two primary pyroxenes, pigeonite and augite. In the Shergotty Meteorite the plagioclase has been converted into maskelynite by high shock pressures. The maskelynite preserves the original feldspar forms and compositions; and in the Shergotty Meteorite the non-crystalline maskelynite ranges in composi-

Table 5.11.1 Chemical composition of selected basaltic meteorites

	1(%)	*2(%)*
SiO_2	49.34	50.1
TiO_2	0.64	0.92
Al_2O_3	13.00	6.68
Cr_2O_3	0.34	0.18
FeO	18.82	18.66*
MnO	0.56	0.50
MgO	7.27	9.40
CaO	10.38	10.03
Na_2O	0.47	1.28
K_2O	0.04	0.16
P_2O_5	0.09	0.71
	100.95	100.11
p.p.m.		
Sc	29	52.4
Rb	0.202	6.1
Sr	78	65
Y	16	—
Zr	46	—
Ba	31	90
Sm	1.70	1.25
Eu	0.62	0.49
Th	0.60	0.3

1. Juvinas Meteorite, an example of the most common type of eucrite (BVSP 1981: 221, 222).
2. Shergotty Meteorite, an example of the shergotite class of meteoritic basalts (BVSP 1981: 221, 222). *1.49 per cent Fe_2O_3 is included in the total of this analysis.

tion from $Or_1 Ab_{42} An_{57}$ to $Or_4 Ab_{60} An_{36}$ (cf. BVSP 1981: 226). Accessory amounts of the minerals cristobalite, titanomagnetite ($Mt_{37} Usp_{63}$), ilmenite ($Ilm_{95} Hm_5$), whitlockite and pyrrhotite also occur in the shergottitic basalts.

It has been proposed that the eucritic basalts are partial melts of a chemically-primitive source region in which the relative abundances, and probably also the absolute abundances, of the large ion lithophile elements were essentially chondritic, or similar to the mantle of the Earth. The eucrite parent body probably contained less alkalis and volatile components than the mantle. As the eucritic basalts are normally oversaturated in silica it is probable that their magma was generated at relatively low pressures. From these observations and the great age (4.54 Ga) of the eucritic basalts, it is concluded that they evolved from a magma generated within a small planetary body, or in a near-surface source region on a larger planetary body. This conclusion is consistent with evidence gleaned from the atmospheric entry trajectories of meteorites, as these data show that the meteorites may be samples of asteroids (cf. Wood 1979: 108) The shergottites are usually interpreted as being young, evolved, pyroxene-cumulate basalts. They may represent basalts that congealed from magma in the normal manner; or they may have evolved as the result of the impact melting of older basaltic materials. If the former petrogenetic model is correct, then the shergottities are direct proof that extraterrestrial basaltic volcanism has occurred at a late stage in the evolution of the Solar System. This is remarkable because at this late stage in the evolution of the Solar System, small planetary bodies, such as the asteroids, should lack the heat resources required to generate basaltic magma.

5.12 Mare basalts

As we noted in Section 1.9, Galileo divided the near-side of the moon into light-coloured, rugged, highland areas or *terra*; and smooth, dark-coloured areas. He called the latter seas or *maria*. We now know that the maria are seas of congealed basaltic lava, and that the Moon as a whole is remarkably free of water. These mare basalts are usually poor in SiO_2, Al_2O_3, Na_2O and K_2O relative to the common basalts of

Earth. They are also usually regarded as being akin to the tholeiitic basalts rather than the calc–alkalic or alkalic basalts of Earth (see Table 5.12.1). The mare basalts show extreme variations in their titanium contents (that is, 0.5–13 per cent TiO_2), and this oxide has been used to separate the mare basalts into high-Ti basalts (7–14 per cent TiO_2), low-Ti basalts (1.5–7 per cent TiO_2) and very low-Ti basalts (VLT basalts) that contain less than 1.5 per cent TiO_2. In Table 5.12.1 the high-Ti basalts are further divided into low-K and high-K basalts. Typical low-K, high-Ti basalts contain about 0.07 per cent K_2O; whereas typical high-K, high-Ti basalts contain approximately 0.34 per cent K_2O (cf. BVSP 1981: 239). The low-K mare basalts are usually fine- to medium-grained vesicular rocks with subophitic to ophitic textures. They tend to contain about 51 per cent pyroxene, 33 per cent plagioclase, 15 per cent Fe–Ti oxides and accessory amounts of olivine. Olivine and ilmenite abundances are usually lowest in the medium-grained specimens thus indicating that some local fractional crystallization occurred in these lavas. The high-K basalts are usually fine-grained vesicular rocks with a variety of different textures. These rocks usually contain more pyroxene (57 per cent) and Fe–Ti oxide minerals (21 per cent), but less plagioclase (22 per cent), than the low-K basalts (cf. BVSP 1981: 255).

Four groups of low-Ti basalts have been recognized: (a) olivine basalts; (b) pigeonite basalts; (c) ilmenite basalts; and (d) the feldspathic basalts (cf. BVSP 1981: 255). The olivine basalts are probably the most primitive of these; they range from olivine-bearing vitrophyric basalts to medium-grained rocks with cumulate textures; they contain approximately 58 per cent pyroxene, 22 per cent plagioclase, 14 per cent olivine and 6 per cent Fe–Ti oxides. Large, zoned pyroxene phenocrysts (pigeonite cores and augite rims) are generally found in the pigeonite basalts. These rocks contain approximately 66 per cent pyroxene, 28 per cent plagioclase and 6 per cent Fe–Ti oxides; and are usually considered to have evolved from the olivine basalts by olivine-dominated, near-surface fractional crystallization. The ilmenite basalts generally contain about 61 per cent pyroxene, 26 per cent plagioclase, 9 per cent Fe–Ti oxides and 4 per cent olivine. The feldspathic basalts will be discussed in Section 5.13.

Fragments of very low-Ti basalts were found in the Apollo 17 drill core and in the materials

Table 5.12.1 Chemical composition of selected basaltic rocks from the Moon

	1(%)	2(%)	3(%)	4(%)	5(%)	6(%)	7(%)	8(%)
SiO_2	39.76	41.00	43.56	46.68	46.7	45.2	47.2	50.83
TiO_2	10.50	11.30	2.6	3.53	0.92	2.6	1.24	2.23
Al_2O_3	10.43	9.5	7.87	10.78	10.0	11.1	20.1	14.77
Cr_2O_3	0.25	0.32	0.96	0.40	0.74	0.5	0.18	0.35
FeO	19.80	18.7	21.66	19.31	18.6	17.8	8.38	10.55
MnO	0.30	0.25	0.28	0.26	0.24	0.3	0.11	0.16
MgO	6.69	7.03	14.88	7.39	12.2	12.2	7.87	8.17
CaO	11.13	11.0	8.26	11.38	10.0	9.8	12.3	9.71
Na_2O	0.40	0.51	0.23	0.31	0.12	0.3	0.63	0.73
K_2O	0.06	0.36	0.05	0.07	<0.01*	0.08	0.49	0.67
	99.32	99.97	100.35	100.11	99.52	98.88	98.50	98.17
p.p.m.								
Sc	—	80.9	38.3	49.8	—	—	20	23.6
Ni	—	—	63.9	16	—	—	271	12.5
Cu	—	—	4.6	8.1	—	—	5	—
Zn	7.4	—	1.5	4.15	—	—	1.8	3.5
Rb	0.62	6.2	1.04	1.14	—	—	12.8	18.46
Sr	161	161	101	129	—	—	250	187.4
Y	112	—	39	50.5	—	—	174	—
Zr	309	—	106	123	—	—	842	970
Nb	—	—	8.5	14	—	—	52	—
Ba	108	330	67	71.1	—	—	630	837
La	15.5	28.8	6.02	—	1.2	6.76	56.4	83.5
Ce	47.2	82.8	17	19.8	—	17.9	144.0	211
Nd	40.0	62.8	12.3	14.4	—	13	87	131
Sm	14.4	22.3	4.24	4.84	1.0	3.93	24	37.5
Eu	1.81	2.29	0.84	1.12	0.30	0.88	2.15	2.72
Gd	19.5	29.3	5.65	6.59	—	4.2	28.1	45.4
Dy	12.9	33.4	6.34	7.86	2.0	6.0	32.7	46.3
Er	13.6	30.9	3.89	4.53	—	3.5	19.7	27.3
Yb	13.2	20.2	3.78	4.12	1.4	4.05	18.4	24.4
Lu	1.0	—	—	0.64	0.23	0.61	2.5	3.4
Hf	—	17.3	2.49	4.09	—	6.9	21	31.6
Th	1.1	4.03	0.75	0.93	—	—	10.42	10

1. Low-K, high-Ti mare basalt from Mare Tranquillitatis (10003). This pyroxene–phyric basalt contains approximately 50 per cent pyroxene, 32 per cent plagioclase, 16 per cent ilmenite, and minor amounts of troilite, cristobalite and apatite (BVSP 1981: 239).
2. High-K, high-Ti mare basalt from Mare Tranquillitatis (10049). This fine-grained intersertal basalt contains approximately 47 per cent pyroxene, 18 per cent plagioclase, 16 per cent Fe–Ti phases (mainly ilmenite), 1 per cent troilite and 18 per cent mesostasis (BVSP 1981: 239).
3. Low-Ti olivine mare basalt (12002). The exact location at which this sample was collected is not known. It was obtained during the Apollo 12 mission on the route between the lunar module landing site and Middle Crescent Crater. This porphyritic basalt contains approximately 54 per cent pyroxene, 22 per cent plagioclase, 15 per cent olivine, 6 per cent ilmenite, and minor amounts of chromite, troilite, cristobalite and spinels (BVSP 1981: 239).
4. Low-Ti pigeonite basalt from north of Head Crater, Apollo 12 site (12021). This pyroxene–phyric basalt contains approximately 60 per cent pyroxene, 28 per cent plagioclase, 7 per cent opaque phases (mainly ilmenite and spinel), 4 per cent tridymite and 1 per cent cristobalite (BVSP 1981: 239).
5. Very low-Ti basalt fragment from the Apollo 17 mission drill core (78526; BVSP 1981: 240).
6. Feldspathic basalt clast from ejecta, Cone Crater, Apollo 14 site (14072; McGee et al. 1977: 80–1). Rock also contains 0.08 per cent P_2O_5 and 0.12 per cent S.
7. Lunar highland basalt of the low-K Fra Mauro-type from the Apollo 14 site north of Fra Mauro (14310; BVSP 1981: 271).
8. Lunar highland basalt of the intermediate-K Fra Mauro-type from the foothills of the Apennine Mountains, Apollo 15 site (15386; BVSP 1981: 271).

* less than 0.01 per cent K_2O is presumed to be less than 0.005 per cent.

obtained from Mare Crisium on the Luna 24 mission. Many of the VLT basalts are glassy, but the phaneritic samples usually have subophitic textures, and contain approximately 62 per cent pyroxene, 32 per cent plagioclase, 5 per cent olivine and only 1 per cent Fe–Ti phases. A variety of different glassy basaltic rocks were obtained on the Apollo and Luna missions. It has been suggested that many of the glass spheres found on the lunar surface (that is, green glass spheres from Spur Crater on the Apennine Front and orange glass spheres from Taurus–Littrow) were produced by fire fountaining.

It is evident from the foregoing descriptions that the mare basalts are chiefly composed of clinopyroxene, plagioclase and Fe–Ti oxide minerals; olivine is often an important minor phase. The mineralogy of the mare basalts is thus essentially similar to that of the basalts of Earth. However, the mare basalts usually contain a more calcium-rich plagioclase, more Fe-Ti oxide minerals, particularly ilmenite; but they carry no hydrous minerals. The lack of water on the Moon has greatly reduced the number of minerals found on that planet as compared to the Earth. Pyroxene is the most abundant phase in the mare basalts, and individual crystals often show extreme compositional zoning. The pyroxenes that are usually present are pigeonite and augite; but a wide series of iron-rich pyroxenes and pyroxenoids also occur, including various ferropigeonites, ferro-augites, ferrohedenbergites and pyroxferroite (cf. BVSP 1981: 260). The compositions of the plagioclases in the mare basalts range from An_{73} to An_{98}; however, the plagioclases in most of these rocks fall within the more restricted range An_{85} to An_{95}. Exceptions include the VLT basalts that often contain more calcic plagioclase, and the high-K and feldspathic basalts that generally carry more sodic plagioclase. The modal abundance of the olivines in the mare basalts ranges from 0 to 36 per cent. Olivine usually crystallizes early, and is important in the fractional crystallization of these basalts; it ranges in composition from Fo_{80} to Fo_0. The fayalitic, or Fe-rich, olivines usually crystallize late, and they occur as rims in the zoned crystals, or in the groundmass where they are associated with minerals such as hedenbergite and cristobalite. Ilmenite is usually the most abundant Fe–Ti oxide mineral in the mare basalts. The morphology of the ilmenite crystals is extremely varied. Some of the 'blocky' euhedral crystals have cores of

armalcolite or chromian ulvöspinel; such crystals may have formed as a reaction between the included phases and the cooling basaltic magma. The lunar ilmenites are generally close to being stoichiometric phases but they may contain minor amounts of Cr, Al, Mn and Zr. Most of the mare basalts contain spinels of the chromite–ulvöspinel–hercynite series. The spinels often have cores of chromite coated by a rim of ulvöspinel, and there is a compositional discontinuity between the two phases. Armalcolite, (Fe, Mg) Ti_2O_5, is a mineral that was first described from the fine-grained basalts of Mare Tranquillitatis. Its name is derived from the first letters of the three astronauts, Armstrong, Aldrin and Collins, who collected the basalts that contained the mineral. It usually occurs as minute grains included in ilmenite crystals. The apparent stability of armalcolite with Mg-rich silicates indicates that it may be a stable phase in the lunar mantle, and it may also have helped in the concentration of Ti within the lunar mantle. Troilite, FeS, is the most abundant sulphide phase in the mare basalts; it occurs disseminated throughout the basalts as small, subrounded, interstitial grains. It forms under strongly reducing conditions, and some crystals contain grains of native iron.

The origin of both the mare basalts and the *highland basalts* will be discussed in the next section. This is because these two major types of lunar basalt seem to have complementary geochemical characteristics which probably means that the processes that generated the highland basalts, and other highland rocks, modified the composition of the source region where the mare basalts were later to be produced. The ages of the samples of mare basalts that have been determined range from 3.16 to 3.96 ga (BVSP, 1981, 752).

5.13 Lunar highland basalts and related rocks

The mare are surrounded and contained within older, higher and more densely-cratered areas knows as the *lunar highlands*. Most of the highland surface is older than 4.0 Ga, and it has been pulverized by the impact of large numbers of meteorites. The lunar highlands are thus only slightly younger than the meteorites, and they provide evidence as to the nature of the earliest stages in the evolution of a small planet. They probably also contain information that is crucial to a more complete understanding of the Early Archaean of the Earth and the other terrestrial planets. Taylor (1982: 180) has stated that 'the complexity of the highland samples constitutes a severe test for the scientific method of inductive reasoning, proceeding from the details to construct a general theory. Workers on these samples, which have endured countless meteorite impacts, must guard against the charms of the deductive approach, deriving the details from a general theory in the manner of medieval scholars . . .'

The study of rocks from the lunar highlands is complex because it is difficult to evaluate the extent to which the early period (4.0–4.6 Ga) of intense meteorite bombardment affected the chemical composition, modal composition and radiometric age of the surface materials. Over 60 per cent of the samples returned from the lunar highlands are *breccias*, and most of the remaining rocks are considered to have been generated by impact melting. The breccias may be classified into the following main groups: (a) the common *impact melt breccias* which usually consist of rock and mineral fragments set in a crystalline matrix with an igneous or pseudo-igneous texture; (b) the *granulitic breccias* which have been heated to near-melting temperatures and have been recrystallized; (c) the *monomict breccias* which are essentially composed of clasts of a single rock type; (d) *dimict breccias* which are essentially composed of clasts from two rock types; and (e) the *feldspathic fragmental breccias* which consist of several different types of clast set in a friable and porous feldspathic matrix (cf. Taylor 1982: 187–200).

Some of the breccias obtained from the lunar highlands contain clasts of basalt. These usually have higher Al_2O_3 (11–14 per cent), and lower total iron contents, than the normal mare basalts, and they are generally called *feldspathic basalts*. Their ages range from 3.9 to 4.0 Ga, and they were thus extruded at the time of the final great meteorite bombardment. As such basaltic clasts are rare in the highland breccias, this probably means that basalt volcanism was not particularly widespread there in the pre-3.8 Ga era. Table 5.12.1 (specimen 6) gives the chemical composition of one of these feldspathic basalts. This particular specimen (14072) contains 50 per cent clinopyroxene, 38 per cent plagioclase (An_{78}–

An_{96}), 2 per cent olivine (Fo_{64} – Fo_{71}), 2 per cent cristobalite and 8 per cent opaque phases that mainly consist of ilmenite and spinels (cf. McGee et al. 1977: 40–1).

The samples from the lunar highlands also contain a group of rocks with igneous, or pseudo-igneous textures, and distinctive chemical compositions. Taylor (1982: 201) has called these materials *melt rocks*, the BVSP (1981: 268–81) called them *lunar highland basalts*, whereas others have called them *impactites*. These highland basalts (sensu lato) are readily distinguished from the mare basalts because the Al_2O_3/CaO ratios of the former are twice as great as those of the latter (see Table 5.12.1). At present it is not clear whether these basaltic rocks are primary igneous rocks or pseudo-igneous rocks produced by impact melting. Specimen 14310 is an example of one of these rocks with a clast-free igneous texture. This rock contains 59.0 per cent plagioclase, 16.6 per cent clinopyroxene (pigeonite and augite), 16.3 per cent orthopyroxene, 1.8 per cent ilmenite, and a variety of minor phases such as ulvöspinel, native iron, troilite and a phosphate phase set in a very fine-grained mesostasis (BVSP 1981: 273).It also contains 20.1 per cent Al_2O_3, 8.4 per cent FeO, 12.3 per cent CaO, 0.63 per cent Na_2O and 0.49 per cent K_2O (see Table 5.12.1, No. 7). The trace element abundances characteristic of the highland basalts are also distinctly different from those usually found in the mare basalts. In the nomenclature used by the BVSP, specimen 14310 is called a *low-K Fra Mauro highland basalt*; the authors of this project also recognize a second type of highland basalt which they call the *intermediate-K Fra Mauro basalts*.

Specimen 15386 is a typical example of the intermediate-K Fra Mauro basalts. It was collected from the foothills of the Apennine Mountains on the eastern border of Mare Imbrium. This basalt (sensu lato) has an ophitic to intersertal texture and contains approximately 38 per cent plagioclase (An_{75}–An_{87}), 20 per cent orthopyroxene (En_{80}), 18 per cent clinopyroxene (augite, pigeonite and ferropigeonite), 4 per cent cristobalite, 3.5 per cent ilmenite, and minor amounts of native iron, troilite and other accessory phases set in a fine-grained mesostasis (BVSP 1981: 273). Table 5.12.1 (No. 8) shows that this rock is enriched in the incompatible elements and contains 0.67 per cent K_2O. An important characteristic of the intermediate-K Fra

Mauro basalts, and one that is not found in the low-K Fra Mauro basalts, is their lack of contaminants derived from impacting meteorites.

The authors of the BVSP have concluded that the intermediate-K Fra Mauro basalts are probably of volcanic origin. They also suggest that prior to their extrusion there was likely to have been some earlier volcanic activity on the Moon. Such activity would have been particularly likely at the time when the lunar crust was evolving. It is generally accepted that the low-K Fra Mauro basalts were extruded during the early stages in the history of the Moon. A persuasive argument in support of this concept is that these basalts, and even the mean chemical composition of the 'soil' (regolith) from the Apollo 14 site north of Fra Mauro, plot on the low-pressure olivine–anorthite–liquid cotectic. One would not normally expect crustal rocks that are mixed by meteorite impact to have this low-pressure, co-saturated magmatic composition.

It is postulated that there were two major periods of basalt volcanism on the Moon. During the *primordial stage* the extrusion of basalts was essentially incidental to the larger-scale magmatic processes that began with the melting of the outer layer of the Moon (4.5 Ga), and continued with the cooling and fractional crystallization of this 'magma ocean', and the evolution of a plagioclase-rich crustal layer (4.4 Ga). No pristine samples of the primordial basalts have been obtained, but the low-K Fra Mauro basalts are regarded as being chemically akin to the primordial basalts. During the second major period of basalt volcanism the mare basalts were extruded. Although these rocks cover large areas of the near-side of the Moon, they make up only a fraction of a per cent of the mass of the lunar crust. It is proposed that the magma from which these basalts evolved was generated by partial melting of ultramafic cumulate rocks at depths of between 150 and 450 km beneath the lunar surface (cf. Wood 1979: 124).

5.14 Basaltic eruptions on Earth

Both the continental flood basalts and the MOR basalts are extruded from fissures. At the present time Iceland, which lies astride the Mid-Atlantic ridge–rift system, is probably the best area in which to study this type of eruption. Non-flood type basaltic eruptions on land usually begin with an explosive opening of the vent, followed by the rapid discharge of a fluid-rich deposit of tephra. After this initial phase many basaltic volcanoes pass into a quiet phase with the eruption of freely-flowing lava. Such fluid lava often flows great distances from the active vent, and repeated eruptions may produce a broadly-rounded shield volcano. This quiet type of eruption is, as was noted in Section 1.9, known as an Hawaiian-type of eruption. The spatter, cinder and tuff cones that are often associated with such volcanoes are usually relatively small in size. Some basaltic volcanoes, particularly those that extrude calc-alkalic, or alkalic, basaltic materials, have higher volcanic explosivity indices, and produce more tephra and less lava than Hawaiian-type eruptions.

The basaltic lavas that flow on to dry land are usually described as being *pahoehoe, aa* or *block lavas*; and according to Macdonald (1967: 6),'pahoehoe is characterized by a smooth, billowy or rolling, and locally ropy surface, in contrast to the rough, jagged, spinose, and clinkery surface of aa, and the irregularly jumbled, rough, block-strewn surface of block lava'. Basaltic materials that are extruded in a subaqueous environment often occur as *pillow lavas*, or as *hyaloclasite*. Pillow lavas contain pillow structures, or discontinuous pillow-shaped masses that range in size from a few centimetres to a metre or more in their longest dimension. Individual pillows usually fit closely together; and the concavities in one pillow match the convexities in another (see Fig. 5.14.1). Grain sizes within the pillows tend to increase from exterior to interior. Pillow lavas have been observed forming beneath the sea (cf. Moore *et al.*, 1973). The *Leidenfrost effect* is the main reason why it is possible to extrude in a non-explosive manner incandescent lava (at a temperature of 1100 °C) into a body of water. In everyday life this effect is observed when a drop of water is deposited on a hot surface. Film boiling occurs, the drop is enveloped in a layer of water vapour, and it darts about freely on the hot surface. In a like manner, when hot lava is extruded into a body of water, it immediately becomes enclosed in a film of water vapour with a low thermal conductivity. This film acts as a thermal barrier between the hot lava and the relatively cold water (Mills, 1984). Hyaloclasite sometimes forms when ba-

Fig. 5.14.1 Pillow lavas in the Barranco de las Angustias, on the floor of the Caldera Taburiente, San Miguel de La Palma in the Canary archipelago.

saltic lava is extruded into water, ice or water-saturated sediment. In these environments the lava may congeal rapidly, shatter and form a deposit of small, angular, glassy rock fragments. Such deposits are known as aquagene tuffs of hyaloclasite.

5.15 Gabbros

The gabbros are medium- to coarse-grained intrusive rocks of basaltic composition. Their modal and chemical compositions vary greatly, as some grade into the *pyroxenites* and *peridotities*, whereas others grade into the *anorthosites* (see Ch. 10 and 11). The gabbroic rocks closely resemble the basalts in that their compositions range from alkalic to tholeiitic types, and they also include high-Al_2O_3 and high-MgO varieties. Many gabbros occur in dykes, sills and plugs; however, large volumes of gabbro are also found as major units within the great layered intrusions, such as the Muskox Intrusion of Canada and the Bushveld Intrusion of South Africa (see Section 2.3). *Alkalic gabbro*, for example, is found in the central complexes of the Gardar Petrographic Province of southern Greenland, and the Monteregian Hills, Quebec, Canada. Gabbros in which orthopyroxene is the dominant mafic mineral are called *norites*, and such rocks have also been described from many of the great layered intrusions. *Troctolites* are gabbroic rocks that are chiefly composed of calcic plagioclase and olivine, with little or no pyroxene. The well-known troctolites, or *allivalites*, of the Rhum central complex of the British Tertiary Province are generally interpreted as being plagioclase–olivine cumulates (cf. Wadsworth 1982: 417).

5.16 Primary basaltic magmas?

The basaltic rocks, and in particular the comparatively uniform and voluminous continental flood basalts, pose a petrogenetic conundrum. Did all of these rocks congeal directly from primary or near-primary basaltic magmas, or were the parental magmas more magnesium-rich, or picritic, in composition? According to Cox (1980: 630), both the West Greenland–Baffin Island segment of the Thulean continental flood basalt province, and the Nuanetsi-Lebombo province of the Karroo super province contain significant amounts of picritic or picritic basalt lava (see Section 11.4); and some of this picritic lava congealed from a completely, or very largely, liquid magma. With picritic magma being available during the evolution of these well-documented petrographic provinces, it is not surprising that it has been proposed (cf. Clarke 1970; Cox 1972) that the basaltic rocks of these provinces, and possibly many other provinces, are derived from primary picritic magmas. The Mg : Fe ratios of most basalts support this hypothesis, as they are usually too low to have been in equilibrium with the olivines that are considered typical of the upper mantle. It has, for example, been demonstrated by Gurney and Harte (1980) that the upper mantle olivines beneath the Karroo continental flood basalt province have Mg : Fe ratios that are suitable for the generation of primary picritic, but not primary basaltic, magmas. Is is also important to note that in convergent plate environments, the earliest and most primitive basalts are often the magnesium-rich basalts of the boninite association (see Ch. 6).

It is probable that most of the continental flood basalts, and possibly many other tholeiitic basalts, evolved as the result of the fractional crystallization of picritic magma. In this process olivine, clinopyroxene and plagioclase would be removed, and they would form cumulates. The minimum volume of such cumulates has been estimated to be approximately the same as the volume of comagmatic surface lavas. Cox (1980: 645) has proposed that the cumulates that are genetically related to the flood basalts are now probably located in sill-like bodies at, or near, the crust–mantle boundary. He has also proposed that when a batch of picritic magma is emplaced at the base of the crust, it tends to differentiate into a compositionally-zoned body with an upper basaltic layer and a lower ultra-mafic layer; and a new seismic Moho develops at the interface between these layers. Periodically, basaltic magma that is less dense than the overlying crust is released from the upper layer of the differentiating sill, and it moves up to the surface. It is suggested that relatively dense picritic magma only occasionally reaches the surface; this is likely to happen in areas where crustal thinning has occurred. The basaltic rocks of the Deccan, Karroo and Thulean continental flood basalt provinces all conform to a similar magmatic pattern that consists of early eruptions of picrite, or picritic basalt, followed by later eruptions of normal continental flood basalts. It is suggested that the rocks that occupy the subcrustal sill will, initially, have a gabbroic modal composition, but on cooling the phases will adjust and the rock will invert to a garnet–pyroxene–plagioclase granulite.

5.17 Petrogenesis of the basaltic rocks

Basaltic rocks have a wide distribution on the terrestrial planets. On Earth, their great temporal and spatial abundance has led to the development of the concept that basaltic magmas, and the more mafic primary magmas that are probably the precursors of some basaltic magmas, are all produced by a relatively simple, reproducible process that operates in the upper mantle. In Section 1.10 it was proposed that the upper mantle of the Earth is broadly layered with local modal and chemical heterogeneities. It was also suggested that at depths greater than approximately 60 km below the oceanic areas, and greater than approximately 120 km below the continental areas, the main rock types in the upper mantle are garnet lherzolites and garnet–clinopyroxene harzburgites; whereas at lesser depths the upper mantle rocks are mainly harzburgites and spinel lherzolites. From this it is concluded that the *simple mantle-rock system* (Fo–Di–Py) at 4.0 GPa which was discussed in Section 1.6 (see Fig. 1.6.1) is able to provide insights into the nature of the partial melting processes that normally generate the primary picritic and basaltic magmas of Earth; and it is also able to demonstrate how relatively large volumes of chemically homogeneous liquid can be produced by partial melting at an invariant point in this system. The *fractional melting* of natural multiphase upper mantle rocks may in fact proceed via a number of different invariant points (or quasi-invariant points), and the magmas produced at each of these points would have uniform major element compositions that would differ significantly from the melts produced at the other invariant points. Changes in pressure would not only change the phases present in the mantle rocks, but also change the positions of the invariant points in compositional space, and thus change the compositions of the liquids generated by partial melting.

If a rock formed from the congealation of a primary magma, the rock can be used to discover the identity of the solid phases that were in equilibrium with the magma in the source region. The rock is melted in the temperature and pressure range that is believed to correspond to the physical regime under which the primary magma was generated. It is then cooled, and the solid phases that are in equilibrium with the melt are regarded as the residual, or refractory, minerals that are normally left in the source region. This type of experimental study only produces unambiguous results for simple, anhydrous samples, such as those of primitive mare basalts. Experiments have, however, shown that these mare basalts are multiply saturated in olivine and various pyroxenes at pressures of between 0.6 and 1.5 GPa. This implies that the primary mare basalt magmas were generated in a source region that contained olivines and pyroxenes, and also that the source region was located between 150 and 300 km beneath the surface of the Moon. The interpretation of high-pressure melting experiments on the more chemically-complex basaltic rocks of Earth is more controversial (cf. BVSP 1981: 416). For example, in the many basalts studied, orthopyroxene is seldom on the liquidus at any pressure, yet harzburgite (ol. + opx) is regarded as the normal refractory, residual material left after the partial melting of fertile garnet lherzolite. Maaløe and Jakobsson (1980) have shown that there is a possible reaction relationship among olivine, orthopyroxene and liquid, and this might account for the anomalous absence of orthopyroxene from the liquidus of many basaltic melts at moderate and high pressures. Picritic liquids have, however, been found to have both olivine and orthopyroxene on their liquidus at moderate to high pressures (cf. Green et al. 1979). If a picritic magma was to form at high pressures (2.0–3.0 GPa) within the upper mantle it is likely that it would precipitate

and lose some of its liquidus phases while en route to the surface; and according to some petrologists (for example, O'Hara 1965), this is the usual way in which the basaltic magmas of Earth evolve.

Many partial melting experiments, using either natural or synthetic peridotites, have been performed over a broad range of pressures. For example, Mysen and Kushiro (1977) studied the partial melting of a mantle-derived garnet lherzoliote nodule obtained from the kimberlites of northern Lesotho. They found that at 2.0 GPa and 1475 °C, olivine, clinopyroxene, orthopyroxene and spinel coexisted with a tholeiitic basaltic melt; and also that a liquid of this composition was produced throughout the initial 25 per cent of the partial melting process. At higher temperatures, further melting produced liquids with compositions that moved along the olivine–orthopyroxene liquidus surface, thus generating picritic (25–40 per cent melting) and eventually komatiitic (over 40 per cent melting) liquids. At 3.5 GPa, melting began at a higher temperature (1625–30 °C), and the composition of the initial melt was that of an alkalic picrite, and it coexisted with garnet, olivine, clinopyroxene and orthopyroxene. Broadly similar experimental results have been obtained from the melting of depleted peridotites (that is, harzburgites). The main difference is that, when depleted peridotites are used, the pyroxene components are consumed relatively quickly and less initial melt is produced.

In Section 1.5 it was shown that the influx of volatile components, particularly water, into a body of anhydrous rock is likely to reduce its melting temperature; and if the rock is near its melting point temperature, this process is likely to promote partial melting. On Earth this type of hydrous partial melting is likely to occur in the mantle wedge that develops above slabs of subducted lithosphere. Before partial melting takes place, the aqueous fluid will react with the silicates and become enriched in silica (cf. Morse 1980: 414). The initial melt is likely to incorporate this fluid phase and thus become relatively enriched in silica even though it coexists with Mg-rich olivines. In his study of the simple garnet lherzolite system (Fo + Opx + Cpx + Gar) at high pressures, Kushiro (1972: 331) found that the liquid formed by 'extensive partial melting under vapour-present conditions' is relatively rich both in SiO_2 and MgO, and thus chemically akin to the rocks of the boninite association (see

Section 6.1). Rocks of this composition are known from island-arcs and some ophiolite sequences; and magma of this composition may be the primary magma that is generated during the initial stages in the evolution of island-arcs. Studies of the melting behaviour of lherzolitic materials under hydrous conditions have shown that with different amounts of melting, a variety of quartz-normative liquids can be produced at pressures of up to at least 2.5 GPa. At 2.0 GPa, for example, the initial melt produced under vapour-present conditions is enriched in both silica and alumina, and it is thus chemically akin to the intermediate rocks of the calc–alkalic association (see Section 6.1). The petrographic, geochemical and experimental evidence as to the primary, or derivative, nature of the calc–alkalic basalts is ambiguous. If these high-Al basalts are derived directly from a primary magma, such a magma would probably be generated in a hydrous source region at moderate pressures (0.5–0.8 GPa; cf. Wyllie 1979a: 508–9).

An examination of the extensive literature on the generation of basaltic magmas (cf. Morse 1980; Yoder 1976) reveals that most melting experiments using natural basalts, and most research into the synthetic systems relevant to the study of basalts and their magmas, indicate that the primary magmas from which the basaltic rocks evolved were essentially picritic, or komatiitic, in composition; however, experimental studies of the melting behaviour of peridotites in general, and garnet lherzolites in particular, under a wide range of physical conditions, indicate that a broad spectrum of different basaltic liquids can be produced. The authors of the BVSP (1981: 427) concluded that 'basalts may be both the direct products of mantle melting and the differentiates of more primitive melts'; they also claim that there are 'a wide range of primary magma compositions'. Such primary magmas would reflect the partial melting behaviour of depleted, fertile and even enriched mantle rocks under varying conditions of temperature, pressure, volatile content and oxygen fugacity.

The factors that determine the chemical composition of a particular basaltic magma are many and varied. It is evident that a single parental rock, such as a garnet lherzolite, could yield the various types of basaltic magma if there were appropriate changes in pressure and/or in the abundance and composition of the volatile components. Generally, 'high pressure and CO_2-rich volatiles produce alkali basalts, whereas low

pressures and H_2O-rich volatiles produce tholeiitic varieties' (Yoder 1976: 205). The variations in minor and trace elements found in the different basaltic rocks may generally be attributed to: (a) differing proportions of the major phases in the parental source rock; (b) the degree of partial melting; (c) the nature of melting process (batch melting, fractional melting, zone melting or disequilibrium melting); and (d) the abundance of various minor phases. In the partial melting of garnet lherzolite, the composition of the initial liquid essentially depends on the relative proportions in which clinopyroxene, or garnet, are consumed. At high pressures (2.0 GPa) clinopyroxene, which has a nepheline-normative chemical composition, tends to be the first major phase consumed; whereas at lower pressures garnet, which has a chemical composition that is both hypersthene and corundum-normative, is usually the first major phase consumed; thus alkalic basalt and basanite magmas tend to form at high pressures, and subalkalic basalt magmas are generated at lower pressures. With an increased amount of melting (30 per cent) at high pressure (2.5 GPa), normal garnet lherzolite is likely to produce a picritic liquid; whereas, if the amount of melting is low (5 per cent) at high pressures (3.0 GPa), the liquid is likely to be strongly nepheline-normative, possibly nephelinitic in composition (cf. Green 1970).

It is concluded that most of the primary subalkalic basaltic and picritic magmas generated on Earth resulted from the partial melting of normal upper mantle materials. The primary komatiitic magmas were probably generated by extensive partial melting of upper mantle materials at relatively high temperatures (1600–1850 °C), particularly when the upper mantle was hotter, and probably richer in volatile components; and the lithosphere and continental crust were likely to have been thinner, and the crust was possibly more dense (see Section 11.5). Sodic alkalic basalts usually contain more than 10 times the normal potassium content of the upper mantle, and the primary magmas that produced these rocks were probably generated by the partial melting of between 5 and 10 per cent of normal fertile mantle rock at pressures of the order of 1.0–1.5 GPa. One of the main reasons why the alkalic basalts are usually considered to have congealed from primary magmas is that they frequently contain mantle-derived, ultramafic xenoliths. This presages rapid ascent of the magma, and probably precludes significant fractional crystallization en route to the surface. The potassic alkalic basalts, however, contain approximately 25 times more potassium than normal fertile mantle rocks; and the genesis of such a magma probably requires one or more of the following: (a) a special melting process, such as zone melting; (b) a source region of exceptional composition such as garnet lherzolite veined with glimmerite; and/or (c) the operation of a rare process, such as local mantle degassing (see Ch. 12).

5.18 Selected references

Basaltic Volcanism Study Project (1981) *Basaltic Volcanism on the Terrestrial Planets*, Pergamon Press Inc., New York, USA.

Hess, H. H. & Poldervaart, A. (eds) (1967) *Basalts: The Poldervaart treatise on rocks of basaltic composition*, Vol. 1, Interscience Publishers, New York, USA.

Hess, H. H. & Poldervaart, A. (eds) (1968) *Basalts: The Poldervaart treatise on rocks of basaltic composition*, Vol. 2, Interscience Publishers, New York, USA.

Morse, S. A. (1980) *Basalts and Phase Diagrams*, Springer-Verlag, New York, USA.

Yoder, H. S. (1976) *Generation of Basaltic Magma*, US National Academy of Sciences, Washington, DC, USA.

CHAPTER 6

ANDESITES AND RELATED ROCKS

6.1 General statement

In 1835, Leopold von Buch used the term andesite to describe a group of rocks found in the Andes of Bolivia and Chile, and also in the Kamchatka peninsula of the USSR. He wished to separate these rocks from the *trachytic rocks* of Europe. Unfortunately, his definition was imprecise: it described the andesites as being essentially composed of 'albite mixed with a little hornblende'. A study of how the term andesite has been used in the past reveals that it 'has been applied at different times to various volcanic rocks of broadly intermediate composition' (Baker 1982: p. 12). The term has, however, usually been used to describe volcanic rocks that lack phenocrysts of either quartz or any of the feldspathoids, but contain plagioclase, both as a phenocryst and in the groundmass. In Chapter 3, it was demonstrated that andesites usually have SiO_2 contents that are intermediate between the basalts and the dacites. They also tend to have relatively high Al_2O_3 ($\bar{x} = 17$ per cent) contents and moderate $Na_2O + K_2O$ ($\bar{x} = 5$ per cent) contents. The term andesite has some merit, because the andesitic rocks of the Andes were extruded from a series of spectacular volcanoes that form an integral part of an extensive chain of fold-mountains and island-arcs that rim the Pacific Ocean; and it is in this tectonic environment that most modern andesites occur. Other rocks that commonly occur together with the andesites in this orogenic environment include the high-Al basalts (or calc – alkalic basalts), dacites and rhyolites. Rocks of this *orogenic andesite association* are also found in active con-

tinental collision zones, such as the one that extends from the Alps of southern Europe via Turkey and Iran to the Himalayas (cf. Thorpe 1982: 3).

Andesite is recorded as being an important rock type associated with 442 of the 721 volcanoes contained in Katsui's (1971) *List of the World's Active Volcanoes*. Most of these andesitic volcanoes occur above active Benioff seismic zones. The mean chemical composition of andesites (Table 6.1.1) is broadly similar to the estimated mean chemical composition of the continental crust of the Earth (Table 4.4.1); and this is one of the reasons why it is often suggested that andesitic magma has, and is, playing a significant role in the evolution of the continental crust. For example, Brown and Mussett (1981: 178) have proposed that the continental crust is at present growing at a rate of almost $0.5 \ km^3/a$, and that most of this new material is essentially andesitic in chemical composition.

Calc–alkalic rocks and magmas

Andesites of the orogenic association are often called calc–alkalic, calcalkaline or calc–alkali rocks; or they are said to belong to the calc–alkalic rock association, or the calc–alkalic rock, or magma, series. These terms were originally used in order to compare and contrast the *normal* calc–alkalic rocks that contained plagioclase feldspar, with the less abundant alkalic rocks. In 1920, Holmes (51) observed that the calc–alkalic rock association could not be 'strictly limited by definition'. At present, some petrologists use the term calc-alkalic rock series as a shorthand way of writing the subalkalic basalt–andesite–dacite–rhyolite suite and their intrusive equivalents (cf. Kuno 1968: 142); whereas others use the term calc–alkalic to describe any series of rocks, or magmas, that contains andesite (sensu stricto) or the intrusive equivalent of andesite (cf. Gill 1981: 7). It is often claimed that Peacock's (1931) *alkali–lime index* (that is, the SiO_2 value at which the CaO and the $Na_2O + K_2O$ curves in a suite of comagmatic rocks intercept) provides a suitable method for defining the calc–alkalic rocks (cf. Carmichael et al. 1974: 39); however, if one determines the alkali–lime index of a typical suite of rocks that contain orogenic andesites (see

Fig. 2.6.4), one discovers that they usually belong to what Peacock called the calcic series of igneous rocks. Rocks of the *tholeiitic basalt–icelandite suite* usually plot within the calc–alkalic field on Peacock's diagram. Since Nockolds and Allen (1953) published their estimate of the composition of the parental magma of the calc–alkalic rock series, many petrologists (cf. Wilkinson 1968; Rittman 1970; Nockolds & Le Bas 1977) have supported the concept that high-Al basalt is the principal type of basalt associated with orogenic andesites; and also that it is the typical basalt of the calc–alkalic rock association (see Table 5.3.2).

Kuno (1968: 143) proposed that the calc–alkalic rock series may be derived from tholeiitic basaltic magma, high-alumina basaltic magma or even from alkalic basaltic magma. Coulon and Thorpe (1981) claim that in nature there is no clear distinction between the tholeiitic and calc–alkalic rocks; and that the rocks of one series may grade into the other. Rocks of this gradational type are, for example, found on New Britain, and on the New Hebrides in the south-west Pacific. It has also been suggested that during the early and main stages in the magmatic differentiation of tholeiitic basaltic magmas there is normally a trend towards iron-enrichment (cf. Fenner 1929); whereas this trend is absent in calc–alkalic magmas (cf. Nockolds & Allen 1953): however, certain bodies of magmatic rocks, such as the Bushveld Layered Complex, contain some rocks that show the trend towards iron-enrichment, and others that do not (Walker & Poldervaart 1949: 661). If a single parental magma was able to produce both of these trends in magmatic differentiation, it would seem likely that subalkalic basaltic magmas can be set upon either of these trends in differentiation by local differences in, for example, the oxygen fugacity of the parental magma (Wager & Brown 1968: 244). From the foregoing discussion, it is evident that there is no generally accepted succinct definition of the calc–alkalic rock association. Most petrologists would, however, agree that the volcanic rocks of this association consist of a co-magmatic suite of subalkalic silica-oversaturated rocks; and that: (a) they tend to contain more Al_2O_3 than the normal rocks of the tholeiitic association; (b) their intermediate members do not normally develop any significant enrichment in iron; and (c) orogenic andesite is the most characteristic member of this association.

Boninite association

Little is known about the magmatic rocks that are produced during the early stages in the evolution of island-arcs. This is to be expected as such rocks would normally be deeply buried within the growing volcanic pile. Seaborne drilling and dredging, together with land-based studies, have, however, revealed that the youngest sequences of rocks, in several island-arcs of the western Pacific, contain rocks of the tholeiitic association, and lesser volumes of a group of high-Mg and low-Ti basalts, basaltic andesites and andesites. The latter group of rocks have been called *boninites* (Petersen 1891) after the Bonin island-arc where they were first described (Kikuchi 1890; Shiraki et al. 1977). Recently, similar rocks have been described from several submarine locations along the Mariana arc-trench slope (Dietrich et al. 1978) and in Papua New Guinea (Dallwitz 1968). Cameron et al. (1979) define boninite as being a highly magnesian, yet relatively siliceous, glassy rock that contains one or more types of pyroxene, some or all of which have a morphology that is characteristic of rapid growth, together with accessory amounts of magnesiochromite. Meijer (1980: 271) examined their chemistry, and he noted that they usually have: (a) high concentrations of the refractory elements Mg, Ni and Cr, combined with silica saturation or, more usually, silica oversaturation; (b) low concentrations of Ti, Zr, Y and the REE; and (c) relatively high volatile contents. Kikuchi's (1890) original boninite contained 54.44 per cent SiO_2 and 12.75 per cent MgO. If the mean chemical composition of the intermediate rocks of the boninite rock series (Table 6.1.1) are compared with the mean chemical composition of the andesites, they are found to have similar SiO_2 contents, but the andesites are richer in TiO_2, Al_2O_3, and Na_2O, and poorer in MgO and CaO. According to Cameron et al. (1979), the boninites are Phanerozoic equivalents of the komatiitic basalt; and they propose that they evolved from magma generated in the upper mantle during the initial stages in the subduction process.

Island-arc tholeiite series

In the foregoing sections on the orogenic andesite association and the boninite association, thol-

Table 6.1.1 Chemical compositions of andesitic rocks (%)

	1	2	3	4	5	6	7	8	9	10	11	12
SiO_2	58.2	57.9	57.6	57.6	57.4	56.0	61.7	57.3	54.4	54.2	55.0	61.3
TiO_2	0.82	0.87	0.77	0.32	1.25	1.43	0.98	2.00	1.10	0.70	0.80	0.81
Al_2O_3	17.2	17.0	17.3	14.3	15.6	15.7	14.4	14.3	14.8	15.5	16.3	16.0
Fe_2O_3	3.1	3.3	3.1	–	3.5	2.8	4.0	3.7	1.3	0.7	3.7	3.3
FeO	4.0	4.0	4.3	8.2*	5.01	7.2	4.3	6.3	8.9	9.0	3.7	2.1
MnO	0.15	0.14	0.15	0.13	–	–	0.20	0.18	0.2	0.18	0.14	0.09
MgO	3.2	3.3	3.6	6.0	3.4	2.4	1.04	2.4	7.2	6.3	4.3	2.2
CaO	6.8	6.8	7.2	9.9	6.1	5.7	4.3	5.8	9.0	9.3	7.7	4.3
Na_2O	3.3	3.5	3.2	2.1	4.2	3.9	4.4	4.5	2.1	1.6	3.3	3.7
K_2O	1.7	1.6	1.5	0.5	0.4	1.5	2.1	1.8	0.9	1.2	3.8	3.9
P_2O_5	0.23	0.21	0.21	0.1	0.44	0.54	0.34	0.58	0.10	0.06	0.39	0.33
H_2O^+	1.3	1.2	1.0	–	–	1.4	1.4	1.2	–	0.5	0.6	1.1
No. of analyses	2177	2600	2500	8	1	5	4	4	6	1	?	188

1. Mean chemical composition of Cenozoic andesites (after Chayes 1975: 548).
2. Mean chemical composition of andesites (after Le Maitre 1976a: 614).
3. Mean chemical composition of andesites (after Gill 1981: 3).
4. Mean chemical composition of the rocks of the *boninite* series (after Meijer 1980: 272 (FeO^* = total Fe as FeO)).
5. Typical *intermediate* rock of the *island-arc tholeiitic series* of Viti Levu, Fiji (after Jakeš & Gill 1970: 20).
6. Mean chemical composition of the *oceanic andesites* (after Thompson et al. 1973: 1020).
7. Mean chemical composition of *icelandites* from Thingmuli, Iceland (after Carmichael 1964: 422 (H_2O^- = 0.87 per cent and CO_2 = 0.12 per cent)).
8. Mean chemical composition of *icelandites* from the Galapagos Islands (after McBirney & Williams 1969: 146 (H_2O^- = 0.21 per cent)).
9. Mean chemical composition of *flood-icelandite* from the Karroo area of southern Africa (average Hangnest-type) (after Walker & Poldervaart 1949: 648).
10. Chemical composition of *flood-icelandite* lava from Barkly East, South Africa (after Walker & Poldervaart 1949: 695).
11. Average chemical composition *shoshonite latite* from the Aeolian Arc, southern Tyrrhenian Sea, Italy (after Barberi et al, 1974: 271).
12. Mean chemical composition of *latite* (after Le Maitre, 1976a: 616).

119

Table 6.1.2 Abundance of the low-K, calc–alkalic, high-K, and shoshonite series in intermediate volcanic rocks from four dissimilar, presentday, orogenic areas (data from Ewart 1982: 42–3).

Region	Relative abundance of volcanic rocks that contain between 52–60 % SiO_2 (%)	Relative abundance of volcanic rocks that contain between 56–63% SiO_2 (%)
Andean region of South America		
Shoshonite series	17.6	4.9
High-K series	21.6	61.8
Calc–alkalic series	50.0	32.6
Low-K series	10.8	0.7
South-western Pacific		
Shoshonite series	6.9	2.0
High-K series	21.8	25.6
Calc–alkalic series	43.7	57.8
Low-K series	27.5	14.6
Cascade–Alaska–Aleutian region		
Shoshonite series	0.0	0.0
High-K series	1.2	8.8
Calc–alkalic series	94.7	87.7
Low-K series	4.1	3.5
Mediterranean (Aeolian and Aegean Arcs		
Shoshonite series	26.0	21.4
High-K series	16.8	37.8
Calc–alkalic series	49.6	38.7
Low-K series	7.6	2.1
North-western Pacific margin		
Shoshonite series	1.2	1.6
High-K series	11.5	12.6
Calc–alkalic series	57.1	62.8
Low-K series	30.1	23.0

eiitic rocks have been mentioned; and it has been stated that the extrusion of such rocks is relatively common during the early stages in the evolution of island-arcs. Jakes and Gill (1970: 19) have studied these rocks, and they proposed that they should be called the *island-arc tholeiitic series*. Table 6.1.1 gives the chemical composition of a typical intermediate rock of the island-arc tholeiitic series. According to Gill (1981: 11), the characteristic features of this series are as follows: (a) they have low K_2O values; (b) they are tholeiitic according to Miyashiro's (1974) FeO^*/MgO versus SiO_2 diagram; and (c) they display rapid iron-enrichment. Gill also claims that these rocks are usually 'restricted to the volcanic front of plate boundaries characterized by convergence rates greater than 7 cm/year' (70 mm/a).

High-K and shoshonitic orogenic rocks

Peccerillo and Taylor (1976) used a K_2O versus SiO_2 diagram to divide the orogenic volcanic rocks into four rock series: that is, the *low-K series*, the *calc–alkalic series*, *high-K series* and the *shoshonite series*. The island-arc tholeiitic series and the boninite series are subsumed by the low-K series; and the normal orogenic andesites plot as intermediate members of the calc–alkalic series (see Fig. 6.1.1). Many presentday orogenic areas contain rocks that belong to the low-K, calc–alkalic, high-K and shoshonite series (cf. Ewart 1982: 42–3). This is illustrated by Table 6.1.2 which shows the relative proportions in which these various rock series occur in five dissimilar, presentday, orogenic regions. For example, most of the orogenic volcanic rocks of

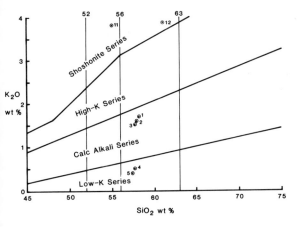

Fig. 6.1.1 A K_2O versus SiO_2 diagram similar to the one used by Peccerillo and Taylor (1976) to divide the orogenic volcanic rocks into the low-K, calc–alkalic, high-K and shoshonite series. The numbers refer to the rocks presented in Table 6.1.1 (that is, 1 to 3 are orogenic andesites, 4 is an intermediate boninitic rock, 5 is an intermediate tholeiitic rock, and 11 and 12 are latites).

the north-western Pacific margin Kuriles, Kamchatka, Japan, Izu-Bonin Islands, Marianas, Taiwan and the Philippines) belong to either the low-K series or the calc–alkalic series; whereas most of the orogenic volcanic rocks of the Mediterranean region (Aeolian and Aegean arcs) belong to either the high-K series or the shoshonite series. Table 6.1.2 only considers the abundance of the different orogenic volcanic rock series as they occur in the intermediate rocks, because: (a) Peccerillo and Taylor's (1976) classification is considered to be of limited value in determining the petrogenetic affinities of the rhyolitic rocks (that is, many rhyolites are at least partly produced by anatexis); and (b) the intermediate rocks make up over 50 per cent of all the orogenic volcanic rocks of the Earth (Ewart 1982: 43). Rocks of the high-K and shoshonite series characteristically occur in areas where the Benioff seismic zone is at its deepest (see Fig. 4.2.1), or in local areas where extentional tectonics occur.

Anorogenic andesites

As has already been noted, most Cenozoic andesitic rocks occur in association with convergent plate boundaries, and they have come to be known as the *orogenic andesites* (cf. Gill 1981); however, andesitic rocks are also found in ano-

rogenic tectonic environments. Such rocks are the *oceanic andesites* (Thompson et al. 1973: 1020), the *icelandites* (Carmichael 1964: 442) and the *flood-icelandites* (Middlemost 1975: 343). The oceanic andesites were first described from the aseismic Ninety–East Ridge in the Indian Ocean; and their average chemical composition is given in Table 6.1.1. According to Thompson et al. (1973: 1020), these rocks are compositionally similar to the icelandites of Iceland 'both in major element aspects and REE distributions', and they probably formed in 'shallow magma chambers' from a differentiating tholeiitic basaltic magma. The term icelandite was coined by Carmichael (1964: 442) in order to make a clear distinction between the andesites (sensu lato) found in the central-type volcanoes of Iceland and the orogenic andesites. He recorded that the icelandites of the type-area are often extremely fine-grained, and are chemically unlike orogenic andesites in that they are 'poorer in alumina and richer in iron'. Carmichael included intermediate rocks with silica contents of up to 65 per cent in his definition of icelandite. Table 6.1.1 gives the mean chemical composition of the icelandites from the type-area, Thingmuli, eastern Iceland. In the past, vast areas of the continents have been covered by flood basalts and flood-icelandites (see Section 5.7). The compositions of these two rock types grade into one another; and it is usually postulated that the flood-icelandites are either: (a) differentiated flood basalts; or (b) they evolved from flood-basaltic magmas that had been modified by the assimilation of sialic crustal materials. The *Hangnest-type* rocks of the Karroo flood basalt province of southern Africa (Walker & Poldervaart 1949: 648) are examples of flood-icelandites (see Table 6.1.1, No. 9). Anorogenic andesitic rocks with tholeiitic affinities, from the Tertiary volcanic district of western Scotland and Northern Ireland, are sometimes called *craignurites* and *leidleites*. Intuitively one might expect the term *tholeiitic andesite* to be a synonym for icelandite; however, Nockolds (1954: 1009) has used this term to describe basaltic rocks ($\bar{x} = SiO_2 = 51.4$ per cent) in which andesine is the dominant feldspar.

6.2 Textures and modal composition

Most andesitic volcanism is highly explosive. According to Rittmann (1962: 154–6), the *Ritt-*

man–Explosion Index (that is, percentage of pyroclastic material within a particular volcanic edifice) of volcanoes extruding andesite is usually greater than 90. This means that most orogenic andesites are pyroclastic rocks, with pyroclastic textures; thus andesites typically occur as *crystal tuffs, lithic tuffs, lapilli tuffs* and *agglomerates*. It is this predominance of pyroclastic materials that gives the composite cones of andesitic volcanoes their characteristic steep-sided (up to 33°) form. Steep slopes, together with large volumes of unconsolidated pyroclastic materials, may result in the development of *lahars*, or volcanic debris flows (see Section 1.9). The term lahar originated in Indonesia, where this type of activity is particularly common, and it has led to the loss of many lives and extensive damage to property (cf. Neal 1976). Van Bemmelen (1949: 191) described the lahars of Indonesia as mudflows that contained debris and angular blocks that were chiefly of volcanic origin.

Andesite lavas usually have porphyritic, or vitrophyric, textures; and the phenocrysts often provide a remarkable record of at least part of the evolutionary history of the rocks. Their colour indices (M) generally range from 20 to 40. Plagioclase and pyroxenes are the normal essential minerals; and *plagioclase* is usually the most abundant phenocryst. This abundance supports the observation that plagioclase is usually a liquidus phase in andesitic magma at eruption. Plagioclase is usually the only feldspar present as a phenocryst, but small sanidine laths have been reported in some K_2O-rich andesites (Jakes & Smith 1970). The plagioclase phenocrysts are usually complexly zoned. According to Gill (1981: 171), the complexly-zoned phenocrysts in andesites usually include one or more of the following features: 'a homogeneous internal region, frequently the core; patchy-zoned, inclusion rich (frittered) regions; regions of oscillatory zoning; abrupt, non-oscillatory changes in compositions of 10 to 30 mol.% An, often accompanied by resorption of the inner feldspar; a clear, normally zoned mantle; and a thin (<20 μm) rim, usually similar in composition to groundmass microlites'. Abrupt non-oscillatory changes, such as are often found as rims in many phenocrysts, probably indicate abrupt changes in the magmatic environment in which such crystals evolved. Reverse zoning in which calcic plagioclase surrounds a sodic core is found in many andesites; and this phenomenon is sometimes attributed to magma mixing or assimilation. According to Ewart (1976; 1979; 1982), the plagioclase pehnocrysts in andesites range in composition from An_{15} to An_{99}, and the average An content is in the labrodorite range. Plagioclase compositions may vary by up to 50 mol.% An in individual thin-sections, and up to 40 mol.% An in individual crystals (Gill 1981: 170). Small laths of plagioclase occur in the groundmass of some andesites; and they are usually more sodic than the bulk compositions of the associated phenocrysts. The compositions of the groundmass laths are often in the andesine range; however, some vitrophyric andesites contain small labradoritic laths.

Augite is the second most abundant type of phenocryst in andesites. According to Ewart (1976), it occurs in almost all porphyritic andesites. The cores of these augite phenocrysts usually have compositions that lie within the range Wo_{38-50} En_{40-55} Fs_{7-20}. Augite is also the most abundant groundmass pyroxene in the andesites. These small crystals either have compositions that are similar to the phenocrysts, or they are more Fe-rich, or Ca-poor, or both. Other clinophyroxenes that have been reported from andesites include subcalcic augite, pigeonite and clinoenstatite (cf. Gill 1981: 175). Most andesites do, however, also contain phenocrysts of primary *orthopyroxene*. In a suite of basaltic to andesitic rocks, the appearance of orthopyroxene usually heralds the disappearance of olivine. Orthopyroxene usually also appears to be antipathetic with the hydrous minerals hornblende and biotite. Phenocrysts of orthopyroxene generally have higher, and more variable, Fe/Mg ratios than coexisting augites; and they normally range in composition from En_{85} to En_{60} (that is, bronzite and hypersthene). Orthopyroxenes are also common in the groundmass of andesites, which is as one would expect because, as we have already noted, Kuno (1950: 993) claims that the volcanic rocks of the calc–alkalic series characteristically contain orthopyroxenes in the groundmass. These orthopyroxenes are often rimmed with pigeonite or subcalcic augite. There are thus at least five different types of pyroxenes that may be found in andesites. These pyroxenes are often zoned; and this zoning may be normal, with Fe/Mg increasing towards the rim, oscillatory or reverse.

Green to brown *hornblende* is the typical amphibole found in orogenic andesites. It normally does not occur in the groundmass, but it is found as a phenocryst. Some amphiboles show Fe/Mg zoning, which may be normal or reversed. Experimental studies indicate that andesitic magmas that precipitate hornblende should normally carry at least 3 per cent H_2O (cf. Burnham 1979); and such magmas are usually relatively rich in alkalis and have high (<0.5) Fe_2O_3/FeO ratios. Many hornblende phenocrysts show evidence of resorption, and in some the outer rim is replaced by a corona of plagioclase, pyroxene and magnetite. Many of these amphiboles are relatively deficient in silica (nepheline-normative). Such compositions are particularly common in amphiboles that crystallized from magmas that were generated in island-arc environments; whereas those found in rocks that evolved in continental environments are usually more silica-rich (Jakes & White 1972).

Olivine phenocrysts occur in minor (less than 1 vol.%) amounts in many SiO_2-poor andesites (Ewart 1976); however, this mineral has also been recorded in some SiO_2-rich andesites, such as the rocks of Paricutin Volcano in Mexico. As the modal olivine content generally correlates with the MgO content of the host rock, it is possible that much of this olivine is an accumulative phase. Kushiro (1975) has found that olivine is more stable in magmas with higher water and alkali contents, because these components tend to depolymerize their host magmas and decrease the activity of SiO_2. Groundmass olivines have been reported from a few andesites that do not contain orthopyroxenes. The compositions of most of the olivine phenocrysts lie in the range Fo_{85-65} (Ewart 1982). Zoning is found in some olivines, and it is usually normal.

Both *titanomagnetite* and *ilmenite* occur as primary minerals in andesites. The former mineral is the more abundant; and it occurs both as phenocrysts and in the groundmass. *Garnet* phenocrysts, and/or xenocrysts, occur in a number of andesites. The distribution of such rocks is normally restricted to continental margins that contain pelitic sediments (cf. Gill 1981: 188). The garnets occur as euhedral, or rounded, crystals; and they are usually between 1 and 2 mm in diameter. Some have coronas of plagioclase, magnetite or chlorite, that indicate reaction between the garnet and magma, followed by the precipitation of a rind of minerals that are stable at lower pressures. According to Gill (1981: 186), the garnets are normally almandine-rich (that is, iron-rich).

Other minerals found in andesites include *silica minerals, apatite, biotite, cordierite, anhy-drite* and *pyrrhotite* (cf. Gill 1981: 188–9). The silica minerals usually occur in the groundmass, and they generally consist of *tridymite* and/or *cristobalite*. In some andesites, *quartz* occurs, both in large crystals (megacrysts) and in the groundmass. The megacrysts are usually embayed, or surrounded by a thin corona of augite. Apatite is the characteristic accessory mineral in orogenic andesites.

Inclusions in andesites

Andesites generally contain a wide variety of different inclusions. Both *xenoliths* and *autoliths* occur; and they may occupy up to 5 per cent of the volume of the rock. A high proportion of the inclusions have glomerophyric, cumulate or pseudocumulate textures; and they are usually composed of plagioclase, clinopyroxene, orthopyroxene and magnetite (phases that are stable in a cooling andesitic magma). A few andesites contain ultramafic inclusions of lherzolite or pyroxenite. Some of those that were extruded on to the continental crust contain partly assimilated xenoliths that are enriched in SiO_2 and Al_2O_3; and these xenoliths are usually interpreted as being derived from rock fragments that were incorporated into the magma as it rose through the continental crust.

Icelandite petrography

The icelandites of Thingmuli in eastern Iceland (Carmichael 1964; 1967a) are usually porphyritic with a microcrystalline to glassy groundmass. Individual phenocrysts vary greatly in size. Plagioclase is the dominant phenocryst, and it is often zoned. The compositions of most of these phenocrysts fall within the range An_{40} to An_{45}. Microlites of plagioclase are common in the groundmass. A variety of different pyroxenes have been described from these rocks, and they include augites, ferroaugites, orthopyroxenes and pigeonites. Phenocrysts of olivine are rare and, according to Carmichael, they are generally Fe-rich fayalitic varieties. Magnetite is the dominant Fe–Ti oxide, and it is found both as a microphenocryst and as an interstitial phase in the groundmass. McBirney and Williams (1969: 145) found that the icelandites of the Galapagos Islands, in the eastern equatorial Pacific Ocean, carry abundant phenocrysts of plagioclase which are often normally zoned, with labradorite cores and andesine rims. Pigeonite occurs both as a phenocryst and in the groundmass; olivine is normally absent.

6.3 Geochemistry and normative composition

The andesites (sensu stricto), or orogenic andesites, are intermediate in their chemical composition between the subalkalic basalts and dacites. According to estimates by Chayes, LeMaitre and Gill (see Table 6.1.1), the average andesite contains approximately 58 per cent SiO_2, 17.2 per cent Al_2O_3, 3.3 per cent Na_2O and 1.6 per cent K_2O. The icelandites, or anorogenic andesites, normally contain similar amounts of SiO_2, Na_2O and K_2O, but less Al_2O_3 ($\bar{x} = 15$ per cent), and significantly more ($Fe_2O_3 + FeO$), MnO and TiO_2 (see Table 6.1.1). As has already been noted in Section 3.3, a simple empirical method of separating the andesites (sensu stricto) from the icelandites is to use the $Al_2O_3/ (Fe_2O_3 + FeO)$ ratio. If the ratio is more than 2, the rock is generally an andesite (sensu stricto); but if it is less than 2, the rock is generally an icelandite (sensu stricto). Figure 6.1.1 can be used to determine whether a particular orogenic andesitic rock belongs to the high-K or shoshonite rock series. Volcanic rocks that contain similar amounts of SiO_2 but more ($Na_2O + K_2O$) than the andesites and icelandites, are the *trachyandesites, trachytes* and *phonolites*; and they will be discussed in Chapters 7 and 12. The *latites*, which are included in Streckeisen's (1978) classification of the common volcanic rocks, usually have chemical compositions that are intermediate between the andesites and the trachyandesites. As can be seen in Table 6.1.1 and Fig. 6.1.1, the latites essentially differ from the andesites (sensu stricto) in that they contain significantly more K_2O ($\bar{x} = 3.87$ per cent), and thus belong to the *shoshonite rock series*.

It is instructive to examine the normative composition of andesites (Chayes 1969; Gill 1981: 112–16). Most andesites (sensu stricto) contain more than 12 per cent normative quartz, which is more than is permitted in andesites in the Streckeisen (1979) modal classification of volcanic rocks. Normative olivine is rare. According to Gill (1981: 113), the mean composition of the normative plagioclase in andesites

(sensu stricto) is An_{51}. This confirms the ineffectiveness of the traditional procedure of using normative plagioclase compositions as a method of separating the basalts ($>An_{50}$) from the andesites ($<An_{50}$). Approximately 15 per cent of the andesites contain small amounts (<4 per cent) of normative corundum. Le Maitre (1976a: 614) has calculated that the average andesite contains 65.1 per cent normative feldspar (essentially plagioclase), 12.4 per cent normative quartz, 9.5 per cent normative hypersthene, 4.8 per cent normative diopside, 4.7 per cent normative magnetite, 1.7 per cent normative ilmenite and 0.5 per cent normative apatite.

Trace element compositions of andesites

As compared to the MOR-basalts, the andesite (sensu stricto) usually contain more Rb, Sr, Cs, Ba, Pb, Th and U; and the abundance patterns of these elements in andesites generally mimic those of K and, to a lesser extent, Si. The R.E.E. group of elements usually have an abundance pattern that is similar to the MOR-basalts. Andesites are, however, generally depleted in Ti, Zr, Nb, Hf and Ta. Gill (1981: 138) claims that a Ba/Ta ratio greater than 450 is the single most diagnostic geochemical characteristic of island-arc magmas. The elements Sc, V, Cr, Co and Ni are usually preferentially concentrated in the ferromagnesian minerals rather than in a liquid phase; as these elements generally occur at low concentrations in andesites, it is often proposed that the andesites are derived from differentiated magmas, and not primary magmas that were in equilibrium with mantle peridotite. The chalcophile elements Cu, Zn and Mo generally occur in low, but variable, concentrations in andesites. These elements are of particular interest because they occur in high concentrations in the Cu–Pb–Zn–Mo–Ag–Au ore deposits that are associated both in space and time with some episodes of andesite volcanism (that is, the *porphyry copper* and *porphyry molybdenum* deposits).

Many studies have been made of the abundances of He, O, Sr, Nd, Pb and Th isotopes in andesites (cf. Gill 1981: 146–60). The main objective of these studies has been to determine the extent to which andesite magma is derived from 'normal' upper mantle materials, or from other sources, such as continental crustal rocks, or subducted metasomatised basaltic and sedimentary

rocks. Most Quaternary andesite samples obtained from near active convergent plate boundaries have $^{87}Sr/^{86}Sr$ ratios that range from 0.7030
to 0.7040. Such ratios lie within the range typical
of basalts from oceanic islands, but are higher
than the values normally found in MOR-basalts.
Andesites with $^{87}Sr/^{86}Sr$ ratios higher than 0.7040
are usually found extruded on to continental
crust that is more than 30 km thick and older
than 250 Ma. Such ratios are typical of New Zealand, the highlands of Papua New Guinea, Sumatra, central and south-western Japan, Ecuador,
Peru, Chile and Greece. The $^{143}Nd/^{144}Nd$ ratios
of most of the andesites that have been studied
are broadly similar to those of MOR-basalts;
however, those of northern Chile and Peru have
lower ratios that are akin to those characteristic
of older continental crustal rocks. Gill (1981:
160) has reviewed the isotopic data on andesites,
and he concluded that the Sr, Pb and perhaps the
Nd ratios found in most orogenic andesites indicate that their magmas were drawn from both
mantle and sialic crustal sources; whereas the O,
He and Th data are essentially indicative of a
mantle origin. He also proposes that the sialic
component may be added either from subducted
sedimentary rocks, or it may be obtained directly
by reaction with, and assimilation of, continental
crustal rocks.

6.4 Abundance and distribution

As we have already recorded, Cenozoic andesites (sensu stricto) are abundant in the island-
arcs and active continental margins that rim the
Pacific Ocean; and they are also abundant in the
Indonesian archipelago, the continental collision
zone that extends from the Alps to the Himalayas, and in the Antilles arc at the eastern edge
of the Caribbean plate. Andesitic rocks have also
been reported from the Archaean, Proterozoic,
Palaeozoic and Mesozoic. Condie (1976: 398)
studied the geochemistry of twelve *Archaean
greenstone belts* and claimed that approximately
20 per cent of the rocks they contained were
andesitic in composition. As the mineralogy and
possibly the chemical composition of many of
these rocks has been changed by metamorphism
and/or metasomatism, it would seem prudent to
regard these as andesites (sensu lato), and not
necessarily comparable to presentday orogenic

andesites. The same caution is probably justified
in all attempts at trying to determine the origin
of metamorphosed andesitic rocks.

Systematic variations in the chemical composition of andesites

In 1935, Tomita recorded a systematic change in
the mineralogy, and total alkali contents, of volcanic rocks across Japan. Since that time, many
similar observations have been made in other
areas of plate convergence (see Fig. 4.2.1). At
a constant silica value (for example, 58 per cent
SiO_2), the rocks from individual active plate margins usually show a systematic increase in K, Rb,
La, Th, U and H_2O, together with an increase
in their La/Yb and Rb/Sr ratios, and a decrease
in their K/Rb and Zr/Nb ratios, as one proceeds
across the active plate margin starting at the
oceanic trench (cf. Gill 1981: 212). These
changes in chemical composition are also reflected in the mineralogy of the rocks. It is also
claimed that the compositions of the ore deposits
associated with volcanic arcs vary in a systematic
way with increasing distance from a convergent
plate boundary (cf. Sillitoe 1976); and the normal sequence of the deposits is as follows: Fe
→ (Cu, Mo, Au) → (Cu, Pb, Zn, Ag) → (Sn,
W, Ag, Bi).

In a very few areas the simple spatial patterns
that have just been described are reversed. Such
reversals are believed to reflect local tectonic
and/or crustal complexities. In the past, some
petrologists have tried to relate the chemical
composition, particularly the K_2O content, of the
magmatic rocks of volcanic-arcs with the absolute depth to the Benioff seismic zone (Dickinson
& Hatherton 1967). Such attempts have proved
unsatisfactory because the realtionship between
K_2O content and depth to the Benioff seismic
zone differs in different volcanic-arcs (cf. Gill
1981: 212: and Fig. 4.2.1). The compositions
of the magmatic rocks of volcanic-arcs may
change significantly, but usually not systematically, as one proceeds along a volcanic-arc parallel to the convergent plate boundary. Such
variations are, for example, found in the Antilles
Arc in the eastern Caribbean Sea, where K_2O
values generally increase from north to south
which is along, and not across, this arc (cf.
Brown et al. 1977).

At convergent plate boundaries the compositions of the volcanic rocks that erupted on to the

margin of the buoyant plate generally change as one proceeds from areas of relatively thin continental crust to areas of normal thickness; that is, the volcanic rocks generally become enriched in SiO_2 and the large ion lithophile elements, their $^{87}Sr/^{86}Sr$ and $^{18}O/^{16}O$ ratios increase, but their $FeO*/MgO$ ratios (or tholeiitic tendency) decrease as the continental crust thickens. This observation supports the general assertion by Miyashiro (1974: 342) and others that the young island-arcs are mainly composed of basalts and basaltic andesites, and that a high proportion of these rocks belong to the tholeiitic rock series; whereas the volcanic rocks that are extruded on to thick continental crust usually carry a high proportion of silicic volcanic rocks, and most of these rocks belong to the calc–alkaline rock series. It is self-evident that the rate of plate convergence affects the temperature of the materials within and surrounding a slab of oceanic lithosphere that is being subducted, and it also affects the amount of volatiles released from the dehydrating slab per unit of time. According to Sugisaki (1972; 1976) and others, the abundance of the rocks of the tholeiitic rock series, relative to the abundance of the other rock series, usually increases as the rate of plate convergence increases.

6.5 Andesitic eruptions

Many andesite volcanoes have almost perfect conical forms. Such cones are produced by central crater eruptions of pyroclastic materials and lava. On Earth, the construction of these stratovolcanoes generally requires an explosivity index of approximately 2 (see Section 1.9); however, during an eruption the character, and violence, of the ejection of andesitic materials may change. What began as a Strombolian eruption (explosivity index 1 or 2) may eventually become an exceptionally powerful Plinean eruption explosivity index 5 or 6. Many eruptions of andesites are exclusively explosive, and thus produce only pyroclastic materials. Andesitic volcanoes may also produce nuée ardente and/or ignimbrite eruptions. The many andesitic volcanoes that contain ignimbrite deposits tend to have central caldera; and the ignimbrites are usually interpreted as having been extruded during a cataclysmic caldera-forming eruption, such as the

one that produced Crater Lake, Oregon, USA (Williams 1942). Many extensive andesitic ignimbrite deposits have been described from Japan. Some of these deposits are more silicic (dacitic) than the rest of the volcanic materials found in andesitic volcanic edifices. After the rare ignimbrite eruptions, the nuée ardente is probably the most dangerous type of andesitic eruption (for example, Mt Pelée, Martinique, Lesser Antilles, 1902). According to Walker (1982: 408), nuée ardente are usually the secondary consequence of a primary Strombolian, or Vulcanian, eruption that occurred on a high and steep-sided cone.

Andesitic lava is usually extruded at the end of a period of explosive eruptive activity, such as occurred at Bezymianny Volcano in the far east of the USSR in 1956 (Gorschkov, 1959). The extrusion of lava is usually attributed to the arrival at the surface of a gas-poor magma, after the explosive ejection of an upper fraction of gas-charged magmatic material. Generally the more mafic andesitic lavas form extensive flows, whereas the more viscous silicic andesites produce lava domes or short stubby flows (that is, coulée). The remarkably diverse styles of eruptive activity found in andesitic volcanoes arise because, immediately prior to being extruded, andesitic magmas vary greatly in their viscosity, yield strength and gas content. It is usually difficult to determine whether the gases released during an andesitic eruption are primary, or derived from heated groundwaters that have penetrated the volcanic edifice (cf. Walker 1982: 403–5).

6.6 Petrogenesis of the andesites

When considering the origin of modern andesites (sensu stricto) it is important to consider the following observations: (a) the andesites are often found together with calc–alkaline basalts, dacites and rhyolites; (b) the rocks of this association are usually extruded above active Benioff seismic zones; (c) the rocks of this association exhibit a number of systematic variations in their chemical compositions; (d) the andesitic rocks congealed from magmas that contained enough volatiles to erupt explosively. Before *plate tectonics* had become a dominant hypothesis in the study of the Earth, andesitic magma was usually considered to have originated during periods of mountain-building, when deep-seated continental crustal materials were partially melted under hydrous conditions. Experimental studies (cf. Winkler 1960; Wyllie & Tuttle 1961) have, however, demonstrated that such melts are more likely to have rhyolitic, or dacitic, compositions. Seismic studies have also shown that andesites can be extruded on to island-arcs that have evolved on oceanic crust or relatively thin continental crust. Geochemical studies (cf. Taylor 1969) have shown that some andesites from island-arcs contain no evidence indicating that they evolved from magmas generated from, or contaminated by, old sialic crustal materials.

Experimental studies have demonstrated that plagioclase is the liquidus phase in andesitic magma at atmospheric pressure. In anhydrous melts it remains the liquidus phase until it is replaced by clinopyroxene at 1.5 GPa (15 kb). Water can, however, suppress the stability field of plagioclase relative to the ferromagnesian minerals (cf. Sekine et al. 1979). Andesites usually contain phenocrysts of both clinopyroxenes and orthopyroxenes, and this is often interpreted as indicating that before their extrusion, most andesitic magmas contain sufficient water to suppress, or partly suppress, the crystallization of plagioclase, thus enabling the pyroxenes to be on, or near, the liquidus. According to Gill (1981: 194), andesitic magmas that were saturated in plagioclase, clinopyroxene and orthopyroxene at near-surface pressures would probably carry approximately 2 per cent H_2O, and occur at temperatures of between 1000 and 1100 °C. The amphibole-bearing andesites probably carry more water and were erupted at lower temperatures (900 to 1000 °C).

An attempt will now be made to describe a petrogenetic model that is able to account for the origin of normal, presentday, orogenic andesites. It must be stated at the outset that there are many possible variations on, and deviations from, this standard model. Under normal circumstances one might anticipate the following sequence of tectonic, thermal, magmatic and volcanological events to occur at a developing convergent plate boundary. (a) Subduction begins with the breaking of an oceanic plate, possibly along an old transform fault. A plate, or slab, of oceanic lithosphere moves downwards. It consists of a 5–10 km layer of oceanic crust that overlies a layer of depleted peridotite; and the latter is not likely to melt during its descent into the deeper mantle as it has already yielded basaltic magma.

The slab can be considered to have an elastic core and a brittle outer layer that tends to fracture. These fractures trap some of the available pelagic and/or terrigenous sedimentary materials. (b) The subducted rocks are metamorphosed; and their mineralogy changes as a function of pressure, temperature, and the abundance and composition of the ambient vapour phase. With subduction, the metamorphism is prograde from zeolite and/or prehnite pumpellyite via greenschist (or blueschist), amphibolite to eclogite facies assemblages. (c) Some heat is generated by friction (that is, shear-strain heating) along the sides of the slab; however, this is usually only of local importance. (d) Most of the dehydration of the rocks within the slab is expected to occur at depth of between 75 and 250 km, and over a wide temperature range. (e) The aqueous phase (or tenuous magma) derived from the dehydrating slab usually also contains silica, and may contain significant amounts of the incompatible elements including K, Rb, Sr, Th and U. The composition of this tenuous magma would to a large extent depend on the amount, age, alteration and provenance of the sedimentary component; and the amount and degree of alteration sustained by the igneous component of the subducted oceanic crust. Upon rising into the overlying *mantle-wedge*, this tenuous magma would lower the melting point of the mantle rock, and also lower the density and viscosity of the materials it permeated. Buoyancy forces would gradually result in the evolution of diapirs within the mantle-wedge. The liquids within these diapirs would coalesce and form even more buoyant magmas, the compositions of which would probably range from Mg-rich tholeiitic basalt to basaltic andesite. (f) As these magmas rise they fractionate with the removal of olivine, spinel, pyroxene and, eventually, plagioclase. If such a magma is emplaced into continental crust, the density contrast between the magma and the surrounding rocks is relatively low; and the magma slows down, or stops, and forms a magma chamber within, or at the base of, the crust. Magmatic differentiation would continue within the magma chamber with the removal of spinel, olivine, and/or orthopyroxene, plagioclase, augite, Fe-Ti oxides and, possibly, amphibole. The magma chamber may become compositionally zoned, with the upper part being enriched in a more silica-rich and differentiated magma. Such differentiated magmas would be andesitic, or even dacitic, in composition. Blocks of plutonic aspect are found in the materials extruded from the basalt-andesite volcanoes of the Lesser Antilles. These blocks usually contain some, or all, or the minerals plagioclase (An_{89}–An_{96}), hastingsitic amphibole, olivine (Fo_{68}–Fo_{88}), titanomagnetite, Ca-rich clinopyroxene (Di_{68}–Di_{79}) and orthopyroxene (En_{63}–En_{72}), and they have cumulate-type textures. The association of these blocks of cumulate material with volcanic rocks that have a compositional range from basalt to andesite suggests a genetic link, with the andesites being derived from a basaltic magma by fractional crystallization of minerals similar to those found in the cumulate blocks. Field evidence in support of this relationship is, for example, found in the materials that have erupted from the stratovolcano Mount Misery on St Kitts (cf. Rea 1982: 179–80). Yanagi and Ishizaka (1978) have proposed a detailed model for the Myoko group of active volcanoes from central Japan. They postulate a large magma chamber located at the base of the crust. It is periodically supplied with new magma from below, but fractional crystallization operates continuously within the magma chamber. The magmas expelled from the magma chamber consist of a blend of new primary, and old more differentiated, magma. Yanagi and Ishizaka (1978) propose that during the early stages in the evolution of such magma chambers, anhydrous minerals are precipitated, and this results in the gradual enrichment of the magma in water, with a concomitant increase in the partial pressure of oxygen. Kennedy (1955) and Osborn (1959) have demonstrated that if the partial pressure of oxygen is sufficiently high, magnetite crystallizes and locks up the iron as an oxide, and the residual liquid becomes more silica-rich and generally calc–alkaline in character. Once large magma chambers form, two other magmatic differentiation processes are likely to operate, and they are the assimilation of country rocks and differentiation resulting from the escape of fluids. (g) At greater depths, the materials in the subducted slab that were formerly basaltic or gabbroic are transformed into quartz eclogite, and the serpentine minerals together with the other phases in the slab are transformed into phases stable at higher pressures. (h) If at these high pressures the temperature of quartz eclogite rises above approximately 750 °C, partial melting occurs, and the initial magma is silica-rich (Ringwood 1974). These magmas would also have relatively high K/Na ratios, high abundances of

incompatible elements, and strongly fractionated R.E.E. patterns. It is proposed that such magmas are seldom erupted at the surface without their compositions being strongly modified by reactions with the phases they encounter on their path to the surface; but such magmas might be able to produce the rocks of the high-K and shoshonitic association. Ringwood (1982) claims that part of the subducted slab sinks to depths of approximately 600–650 km; and that the materials in this deeply-subducted slab are mainly composed of what was formerly metabasalt, gabbro and harzburgite. Below 650 km the former basaltic crust is still denser than the surrounding mantle rocks, but the former harzburgite becomes relatively buoyant.

In the preceding model, an attempt was made to trace the subduction of a slab of oceanic lithosphere in a relatively simple area of active plate convergence. In areas of greater structural complexity and thicker crust, other processes, such as partial melting and the assimilation of crustal rocks, may be more important. The amount of crustal assimilation is also likely to increase progressively as the country rocks heat up during a magmatic cycle. It has been proposed that some andesites evolved as the result of a subalkalic basaltic magma assimilating young, silica-rich volcanic materials (cf. Eichelberger 1974). Sakuyama (1981: 581) has shown that some of the calc–alkalic rocks (that is, the rocks of the hypersthenic series) of central Japan contain reversely-zoned mafic phenocrysts, and assemblages of phenocrysts that are not in chemical equilibrium with one another (Mg-rich olivines occur with more Fe-rich pyroxenes, and Mg-rich olivines occur with quartz). He interprets these data as indicating that some of the andesitic rocks of central Japan congealed from a magma produced by magma mixing. Other authors, such as Cawthorn and O'Hara (1976: 324–5), believe that the precipitation and removal of amphibole, either by itself or together with minor amounts of olivine and clinopyroxene, from a hydrous subalkalic basaltic magma may produce andesites over a large depth range in the continental crust and uppermost mantle. This differentiation mechanism would help explain how calc–alkalic magmas become enriched in silica yet not in iron, and also how some magmas become peraluminous (this is, contain normative corundum).

As was noted in Section 1.10, the modal and chemical composition of the upper mantle beneath the continents is likely to differ from that of the mantle beneath the oceans and island-arcs; therefore the composition of the mantle-wedge is likely to change from young island-arc to mature continental margin. Saunders et al. (1980: 356) proposed that the materials in the mantle-wedge beneath the continental areas are likely to be less dense and more refractory than those found beneath island-arcs; however, the rocks of the mantle-wedge beneath stable continental areas are also likely to contain veins of glimmerite, enriched in the incompatible elements. Such mantle material is a suitable source region for alkalic magmas enriched in the incompatible elements. In Chapter 12 it will be recorded that alkalic and hyperalkalic magmas may be generated in back-arc tectonic settings.

The Manicougan impact-melt-sheet in Quebec, Canada, has demonstrated that andesites can be produced by the impact melting of crustal materials (Floran et al. 1978); and it is postulated that this method of generating andesites may have been of more importance on Earth during the early Archaean when impact melting was more common. It is proposed that the icelandites, including the flood-icelandites, are generally produced by the fractional cyrstallization of tholeiitic basaltic magma, possibly assisted by the assimilation of crustal rocks.

6.7 Orogenic plutonic rocks

The modal and chemical composition of the andesite–dacite–rhyolite association is similar to that of the *quartz diorite–granodiorite–granite association* found in areas of plate convergence (cf. Thorpe 1982: 435). These similarities, and the close spatial and temporal links between these associations, show that they are all likely to have evolved under broadly similar conditions. In island-arcs, both the volcanic and intrusive rocks are likely to have evolved from mantle-derived magma; whereas in orogenic areas with thick continental crust, and in zones of continent–continent collision, the rocks, particularly the silicic rocks, are likely to contain chemical components derived from the partial melting and assimilation of crustal rocks. It has also been observed (cf. Brown 1982b: 457) that as one proceeds from island-arcs to mature continental margins, there is an increase in the ratio of intrusive rocks to extrusive rocks. Chapter 9 contains a more detailed description of the plutonic rocks that are characteristic of convergent plate boundaries.

6.8 Selected references

Gill, J. B. (1981) *Orogenic Andesites and Plate Tectonics*, Springer-Verlag, Berlin.

McBirney, A. R. (ed.) (1969) Proceedings of the Andesite Conference, *Oregon Dep. Geol. Mineral. Ind., Bull.*, **65**, 193.

Thorpe, R. S. (ed.) (1982) *Andesites: Orogenic Andesites and Related Rocks*, John Wiley & Sons, Chichester.

CHAPTER 7

THE TRACHYTE–SYENITE CLAN

7.1 General statement

The name trachyte is derived from the ancient Greek word *trachys* meaning rough; and it was originally claimed that trachytes tend to feel rough. Haüy (cf. Brongniart 1813: 43) introduced the term to describe rocks from a flow-banded volcanic dome known as *Drachenfels*. The dome is situated on the eastern bank of the Rhine between Rhondorf and Königswinter, south-east of Bonn in West Germany. It is approximately 450 m in diameter, Tertiary in age; and it forms part of the Siebengebirge Volcanic Complex (cf. Frechen 1976: 23–7). The rock from Drachenfels is a porphyritic quartz trachyte that carries large tabular phenocrysts of sanidine, smaller phenocrysts of oligoclase–andesine, and partly resorbed biotite, set in a fine-grained groundmass that is mainly composed of aligned laths of feldspar. A rock with this groundmass texture is usually said to have a *trachytic texture*. The type-rock contains 13 per cent normative quartz. Haüy originally described trachyte as being a porphyritic rock that contained glassy feldspars and small amounts of mica set in a grey to white feldspathic groundmass. Rosenbusch and Osann (1923: 373) used the term trachyte for young (neovolcanic) fresh rocks, whereas older, altered rocks of similar composition were called *quartz-free porphyries*, or *orthophyres*.

Leopold von Buch (1802) used the term *domite* to describe the trachyte that forms the Puy de Dome in the Auvergne district of central France. This older term is still used in France to describe trachytes, and in particular those of *la chaine des puys* to the west of Clemont-Ferrand (cf. Brousse 1961). *La chaine des puys* consists of over eighty discrete volcanic landforms in a 40 km long chain.

7.2 Textures and modal compositions

Trachytes occur as lavas or as pyroclastic rocks. The lavas usually have porphyritic textures; and both the lath-shaped phenocrysts and the rod-shaped microlites of the groundmass are generally arranged in subparallel fluidal patterns. Trachytic tuff, pumice-flows and ignimbrites with *eutaxitic structures* are relatively common. The term eutaxitic structure is applied to volcanic rocks that have a streaked, or blotched, appearance due to the alternation of bands, or elongate lenses, of different colour, composition or texture. Most of the phenocrysts in the lavas, and the megacrysts in the crystal tuffs and ignimbrites, are alkali feldspars, usually sanidine or anorthoclase. Other minerals that can usually be recognized in hand specimens of trachyte are plagioclase in the oligoclase–andesine range, and one or more of the dark-coloured ferromagnesian minerals. The common ferromagnesian minerals in normal trachytes are augite, ferroaugite, hornblende and biotite; however, the *peralkaline trachytes* usually contain soda-amphiboles of the riebeckite–arfvedsonite series, soda-pyroxenes such as aegirine–augite and aegirine, and/or aenigmatite ($Na_2Fe_5TiSi_6O_{20}$). Silica minerals, generally quartz and/or tridymite, are usually present as minute crystals within the groundmass. Common accessory minerals are Fe–Ti oxides, sphene, apatite and zircon. In some rare trachytes, Fe-Ti oxides are essential minerals, whereas phenocrysts of sphene are found in some trachytes from Kenya. *Foid-bearing trachytes* are a group of rocks that are intermediate in composition between the trachytes and phonolites; and according to Streckeisen (1978), the modes of these rocks may contain up to 10 per cent of minerals of the feldspathoid group (F) when A + P + F = 100 (see Ch. 3). According to Tröger (1935), the trachyte from the Siebengebirge, Rhineland, West Germany contains the following modal phases: sanidine (Or_{60} Ab_{36} An_{04}) 75 per cent, plagioclase (Ab_{74} An_{19} Or_{07}) 11 per cent, diopside 10 per cent, and sphene, apatite, Fe–Ti oxides and glass 4 per cent.

7.3 Geochemistry and normative composition

Trachytes generally contain more ($Na_2O + K_2O$) than the *trachyandesites* and *dacites*, less SiO_2 than the *rhyolites*, and more SiO_2 and less ($Na_2O + K_2O$) than the *phonolites*. These differences in chemical composition are shown in Fig. 3.3.2. Table 7.3.1 gives the mean major element composition of a number of trachytic rocks. These rocks generally contain between 56 and 66 per cent of SiO_2, 15 and 19 per cent Al_2O_3; and have high ($Na_2O + K_2O$) values (with a mean of approximately 10.5 per cent). If the mean chemical compositions of the trachytes are compared with those of the dacites, the trachytes are found to be relatively enriched in Al_2O_3, Na_2O and K_2O and depleted in MgO and CaO. The trachytes are usually divided into *normal* and *peralkaline* types; and both of these can be further subdivided into *sodic* or *potassic* varieties. Examples of the chemical composition of these different types are given in Table 7.3.1. The common *sodic trachytes* are usually part of the volcanic rock series *alkalic basalt → hawaiite → mugearite → benmoreite → sodic trachyte*; whereas the *potassic trachytes* tend to be the most differentiated members of the series *alkalic basalt → trachybasalt → tristanite → potassic trachyte*.

According to Le Maitre (1976a: 605), the average trachyte has the following normative composition: 46.3 per cent albite, 29.4 per cent othoclase, 7.1 per cent anorthite, 5.0 per cent quartz, 4.3 per cent magnetite, 2.1 per cent diopside, 2.1 per cent hypersthene, 1.3 per cent ilmenite and 0.49 per cent apatite. Nockolds (1954: 1016) has demonstrated that the average peralkaline trachyte is essentially an alkali feldspar rock that contains 85 per cent normative alkali feldspar; however, this rock also contains 1.5 per cent normative acmite (that is, aegirine) and 3.1 per cent normative nepheline. It is thus a *foid-bearing trachyte* as are many peralkaline trachytes.

7.4. Basalt–trachyte rock associations

As had already been noted, the trachytic rocks usually occur in association with other less

Table 7.3.1 Chemical compositions of trachytic rocks (%)

	1	2	3	4	5	6	7	8	9
SiO_2	62.76	58.28	63.02	61.21	65.93	62.14	61.65	61.7	60.0
TiO_2	1.05	0.86	0.70	0.70	0.61	0.72	0.52	0.5	0.9
Al_2O_3	15.69	18.28	16.48	16.96	17.07	16.77	17.22	18.0	20.2
Fe_2O_3	3.07	2.93	2.92	2.99	1.92	2.13	3.16	3.3	2.1
FeO	1.55	2.00	1.84	2.29	1.22	2.48	1.81	1.5	1.1
MnO	0.12	0.19	0.15	0.15	0.26	0.15	0.19	0.2	—
MgO	1.53	1.20	0.75	0.93	0.45	0.78	0.45	0.4	0.5
CaO	3.74	3.05	1.95	2.34	1.93	1.94	1.58	1.2	2.3
Na_2O	4.74	6.63	5.47	5.47	6.13	5.92	6.92	7.4	6.8
K_2O	4.10	4.82	4.75	4.98	4.32	5.35	5.80	4.2	6.1
P_2O_5	0.25	0.25	0.19	0.21	0.10	0.27	0.12	0.2	—
H_2O^+	0.34	1.47*	1.63*	1.15	0.32	0.52	0.58	—	—
H_2O^-	1.40			0.47	0.16	0.28	—	—	—
No. of analyses	1	264	332	534	5	3	12	5	4

1. Trachyte from the Drachenfels, Siebengebirge, West Germany (after Frechen 1976: 24) (CO_2 = 0.23 per cent, Cl = 0.10 per cent, SO_3 = 0.03 per cent and ZrO_2 = 0.02 per cent).
2. Mean chemical composition of Cenozoic trachytes with Q = 0 (after Chayes 1975: 548) (* H_2O+ and H_2O-).
3. Mean chemical composition of Cenozoic trachytes with Q greater than 0 (after Chayes 1975: 548) (* H_2O+ and H_2O-).
4. Mean chemical composition of trachytes (after Le Maitre 1976a: 605) (CO_2 = 0.09 per cent).
5. Mean chemical composition of domites from Puy de Dome, Auvergne, France (after Brousse 1961: 24–2, Nos. 128, 131, 133, 134 and 138).
6. Mean chemical composition of trachytes from the Isle of Mull, Scotland (after Beckinsale et al. 1978: 419).
7. Mean chemical composition of peralkaline trachyte (after Nockolds 1954: 1016, No. VII).
8. Mean chemical composition of sodic trachyte from Hawaii (after Macdonald 1968: 502).
9. Mean chemical composition of potassic trachyte from Tristan de Cunha, South Atlantic (after Baker et al. 1964: 531, No. 4).

differentiated rocks, that form the *sodic basalt–trachyte association* or the *potassic basalt–trachyte association*. The term *hawaiite* was introduced by Iddings (1913: 198) to describe basaltic rocks in which the 'normative plagioclase is andesine'; he also claimed that such rocks were 'well developed in the Hawaiian Islands'. The example of hawaiite that Iddings (1913: 220) quoted contained 7.1 per cent normative nepheline, 57.7 per cent feldspar (Or 11.1 per cent, Ab 28.3 per cent and An 13.3 per cent), 17.5 per cent normative diopside, 11.8 per cent normative magnetite and 9.1 per cent normative olivine (see Table 7.4.1, No. 1). This rock is now regarded as being atypical of the hawaiites of Hawaii (Table 7.4.1, No. 2), as they usually carry much less normative nepheline (mean = 0.3 per cent Ne) and more normative feldspar, particularly plagioclase (that is, mean normative feldspar composition, Or = 8.9 per cent, Ab = 35.1 per cent and An = 20.0 per cent). Hawaiites generally have Thornton and Tuttle differentiation indices of between 35 and 45, with a mean value of 42.5 (see Ch. 3).

Mugearite was first defined by Harker in 1904 (265) from near Mugeary on the island of Skye off the west coast of Scotland. He regarded it as being a special rock type because: (a) the main feldspar was oligoclase with subordinate orthoclase; (b) olivine and Fe-Ti oxides were more abundant than pyroxene; and (c) alkali feldspars made up approximately 70 per cent of the rock. In 1960, Macdonald proposed that the terms hawaiite and mugearite should be used to describe the alkalic intermediate rocks from oceanic islands. The andesine-bearing rocks would be hawaiites, whereas the oligoclase-bearing ones would be mugearites. He regarded the hawaiites as being intermediate in composition between alkalic basalt and mugearite. The chemical compositions of mugearites from both Scotland and Hawaii are given in Table 7.4.1. A typical mugearite contains neither normative quartz nor normative nepheline. It carries between 70 and 75 per cent normative feldspar (Or 14.6 per cent, Ab 40.1 per cent, An 17.1 per cent) and a small amount of normative hypersthene (mean = 2.2 per cent Hy). Mugearites usually have Thornton and Tuttle differentiation indices of between 45 and 65, with a mean value of 55.

Tilley and Muir (1964: 439) introduced the term *benmoreite* to describe alkalic rocks that are intermediate in composition between mugearite and trachyte. The name is derived from Ben More on the island of Mull off the west coast of Scotland, where rocks of this composition occur

Table 7.4.1 Chemical composition of hawaiites, mugearites and benmoreites (%)

	1	*2*	*3*	*4*	*5*	*6*	*7*	*8*	*9*
SiO_2	47.63	47.9	47.48	50.8	51.7	51.6	50.52	55.76	57.1
TiO_2	0.12	3.4	2.23	2.2	2.4	2.4	2.09	1.78	1.2
Al_2O_3	15.02	15.9	15.74	17.4	16.2	16.9	16.71	16.55	17.6
Fe_2O_3	8.15	4.9	4.94	3.5	6.0	4.2	4.88	3.10	4.8
FeO	10.40	7.6	7.36	9.2	6.6	6.1	5.86	6.02	3.0
MnO	0.80	0.2	0.19	—	—	0.2	0.26	0.22	0.2
MgO	3.50	4.8	5.58	2.9	3.6	3.3	3.20	1.08	1.6
CaO	6.87	8.0	7.91	5.6	6.2	6.1	6.14	3.23	3.5
Na_2O	4.92	4.2	3.97	5.9	4.6	5.4	4.73	6.28	5.9
K_2O	1.80	1.5	1.53	2.0	2.0	2.1	2.46	3.87	2.8
P_2O_5	0.08	0.7	0.74	0.5	0.7	1.1	0.75	0.40	0.7
H_2O^+	0.30	—	0.79	—	—	—	1.27	0.95	—
H_2O^-		—	0.55	—	—	—	0.87	0.80	—
No. of analyses	1	62	70	1	8	23	72	1	5

1. Chemical composition of hawaiite from the crater walls, Kilauea, Hawaii (after Iddings 1913: 220, No. 8).
2. Mean chemical composition of hawaiite from Hawaii (after Macdonald 1968: 502).
3. Mean chemical composition of hawaiites (after Le Maitre 1976a: 620).
4. Chemical composition of mugearite from Druim na Criche, near Mugeary, Skye, Scotland (after Muir & Tilley 1961: 188).
5. Mean chemical composition of mugearite from Scotland (after Walker 1952: 343).
6. Mean chemical composition of mugearite from Hawaii (after Macdonald 1968: 502).
7. Mean chemical composition of mugearite (after Le Maitre 1976a: 618) (CO_2 = 0.15 per cent).
8. Chemical composition of benmoreite from east of Kinlock Hotel, Mull (after Bailey et al. 1924: 27).
9. Mean chemical composition of benmoreite from Hawaii (after Macdonald 1968: 502).

(see Table 7.4.1, No. 8). This type-rock contains 3.4 per cent normative nepheline and 75.4 per cent feldspar (Or 22.8 per cent, Ab 47.3 per cent, An 5.3 per cent) and 3.7 per cent normative olivine. The benmoreites of the Hawaiian alkalic suite (Table 7.4.1, No. 9) contain neither normative quartz nor normative nepheline; but they do contain a small percentage of normative hypersthene (mean = 4.0 per cent Hy) and approximately 80 per cent normative feldspar (Or 16.7 per cent, Ab 49.8 per cent, An 12.8 per cent). Benmoreites usually have Thornton and Tuttle differentiation indices of between 65 and 75.

The term *trachybasalts* was originally used by Boricky (1874: 172) to describe nepheline- and nosean-bearing basaltic dyke rocks that had a rough appearance. Rosenbusch (1908: 1214) used the term to describe alkalic basalts that contained potassium feldspar, or anorthoclase, in addition to labradorite; and usually also contained small amounts of feldspathoids. In 1921 the Committee on British Petrographic Nomenclature suggested that the term trachybasalt should be used to describe 'intermediate potash-rich rocks containing basic plagioclase together with orthoclase' (that is, potassium feldspar). In the present study, trachybasalt (sensu lato) is regarded as a general term for alkalic basaltic rocks that are intermediate in composition between *alkalic basalts, tephrites* and *trachyandesites*; They include the *hawaiites, mugearites* and *trachybasalts* (sensu stricto). The trachybasalts (sensu stricto) are the potassic analogues of both hawaiite and mugearite. It is proposed that the ratio Na_2O/K_2O can be used to separate the trachybasalts (sensu stricto) from hawaiites and mugearites. If a trachybasalt (sensu lato) has a Na_2O/K_2O ratio that is less than 1.75, it is a trachybasalt (sensu stricto); if it is more, the rock is either a hawaiite or a mugearite. Rocks of the Tristan da Cuha group and Gough Island, in the South Atlantic, are usually regarded as being typical examples of the potassic series of the basalt–trachyte association (cf. Mitchell-Thomé 1970: 224–305). The average trachybasalt (sensu stricto) from Tristan da Cunha (see Table 7.4.2) contains 12.7 per cent of normative nepheline, 49 per cent normative feldspar (Or 17.7 per cent, Ab 11.2 per cent, An 20.0 per cent), 23 per cent normative diopside and 3.5 per cent normative olivine; it is thus chemically akin to the tephrites. According to Le Maitre (1976a: 619), the average trachybasalt (sensu stricto) contains only 2.3 per cent normative nepheline, 65 per cent normative feldspar (Or 15.1 per cent, Ab 29.4 per cent, An 20.1 per cent), 12 per cent diopside and 8 per cent olivine. Trachybasalts (sensu stricto) usually have Thornton and Tuttle differentiation indices of between 35 and 65, and a mean value of 47.

The term *tristanite* was introduced by Tilley and Muir (1964: 439) who regarded this rock type as a potassic analogue of benmoreite. Rocks

Table 7.4.2 Chemical composition of trachybasalts and tristanites (%)

	1	*2*	*3*	*4*	*5*
SiO_2	49.21	46.7	56.23	54.9	56.3
TiO_2	2.40	3.6	1.49	1.8	1.8
Al_2O_3	16.63	17.3	18.70	19.6	17.8
Fe_2O_3	3.69	3.8	2.81	2.8	2.9
FeO	6.18	7.1	3.09	2.9	4.7
MnO	0.16	—	0.12	—	—
MgO	5.17	4.7	1.66	1.5	2.3
CaO	7.90	9.7	4.82	5.7	4.7
Na_2O	3.96	4.1	5.04	5.9	4.8
K_2O	2.55	3.0	4.74	4.9	4.7
P_2O_5	0.59	—	0.41	—	—
H_2O^+	0.98	—	0.89	—	—
H_2O^-	0.49	—	—	—	—
No. of analyses	161	10	16	9	3

1. Mean chemical composition of trachybasalt (after Le Maitre 1976a: 619) (CO_2 = 0.10 per cent).
2. Mean chemical composition of trachybasalt from Tristan da Cunha (after Baker et al. 1964: 531).
3. Mean chemical composition of tristanite (after Nockolds et al. 1978: 78, No. 7).
4. Mean chemical composition of tristanite from Tristan da Cunha (after Baker et al. 1964: 531).
5. Mean chemical composition of tristanite from Gough Island (after Le Maitre 1962: 1328).

of this composition were considered to be typical of the potassic basalt–trachyte association of Tristan da Cunha. Table 7.4.2 gives the chemical composition of this rock type; and an examination of the chemical composition of this rock reveals that it differs from that of the *benmoreites* in that it usually has a Na_2O/K_2O ratio that is less than 1.5, whereas the benmoreites usually have a Na_2O/K_2O ratio that is grater than 1.5. Tristanites from the type area usually carry more than 5 per cent normative nepheline, and some of them carry over 10 per cent normative nepheline; and they are thus tephritic phonolites. The main normative mineral in the tristanites is alkali feldspar (cf. Baker et al. 1964: 520). According to Nockolds et al. (1978: 78), the average tristanite carries only 0.9 per cent normative nepheline. The Thornton and Tuttle differentiation indices of tristanites are generally between 65 and 75.

7.5 The Daly Gap

After studying the relative abundance of the different volcanic rocks on oceanic islands, Daly (1925) concluded that there was a paucity of intermediate rocks. This apparent lack of intermediate volcanic rocks in any suite of rocks on the continents, or on oceanic islands, is known as the *Daly Gap*, and it has been discussed by many petrologists including Baker (1968), Booth et al. (1978), Carmichael (1965), Chayes (1963; 1977), Harris (1963), Mukherjee (1967) and Presnall (1969). The magnitude of the Daly Gap has sometimes been exaggerated because of difficulties in identifying dark-coloured and/or pyroclastic intermediate rocks in the field (that is, the trachytic rocks are often light-coloured, and are thus readily observed to be different from all the other less differentiated rocks); however, the Daly Gap is considered to be real as demonstrated by Chayes' (1977) statistical study of the volcanic rocks of the Canary Islands, and the Booth et al. (1978) study of Sao Miguel Island in the Azores. The latter authors found that during the past 5000 years the proportions of basalt and trachyte that have erupted on this island are approximately equal. They state (313) that there is 'no doubt that rocks intermediate between basalt and trachyte constitute only a very small percentage of the total volume of erupted materials

on, or associated with, the island'. Presnall (1969) has tried to explain the Daly Gap by suggesting that the trachytic rocks are not all derived from the differentiation of basaltic rocks at relatively low pressures, and that some are generated by direct fractional melting within the upper mantle. Barth (1962a) and others have suggested that the abundance of trachyte relative to the intermediate rocks is due to a slowing down in the rate of crystallization at the trachytic stage of magmatic differentiation, due to a decrease in the rate of cooling and changes in the physical properties of the residual magma. For example, one would anticipate that the process of fractional crystallization would work relatively efficiently until the trachytic field was reached, then as the residual magma increased in viscosity, the process would first of all become inefficient, and then stop. In such circumstances, trachytic magma would be available for extrusion for a relatively longer time than the intermediate volcanic rocks.

It has also been proposed that the rocks of the basalt-trachyte association evolve in *compositionally-zoned magma chambers* (cf. Middlemost 1981), with the trachytic magma at the top and readily available for extrusion. Once a density-stratified magma chamber develops, the more dense mafic magmas are prevented from rising through it, and the lighter magma acts as a *density filter;* however, density filters can be bypassed.

7.6 Abundance and distribution

Trachytes of Cenozoic age generally have a low abundance, but a wide distribution, on both the continents and on oceanic islands and seamounts. They usually occur in close association with larger volumes of alkalic, or transitional, basalts; however, the largest known outcrops of trachyte are the *flood trachytes* that were extruded on to the floor of the southern Kenya Rift Valley. These flood trachytes occur in association with relatively small volumes of basaltic or intermediate rocks. Baker and Mitchell (1976: 482) have estimated that the volume of all the Plio-Pleistocene flood trachytes of the southern Kenya Rift Valley is approximately 1770 km³, whereas the volume of the associated basalts is only 670 km³. These flood trachytes are lavas that occur in association with ash-flow and air-fall pyroclastic deposits. According to Baker et al. (1977), the main reason why they formed flat-lying floods of lava, which is contrary to the normal behaviour of trachytic lavas that tend to form domes, plugs or coulée, is that they are peralkaline and have high Na, F and Cl contents that greatly reduce the viscosity of these lavas (see Section 1.4).

Webb and Weaver (1975) have described a group of trachytic volcanoes with a unique external form, from the northern part of the Kenya Rift Valley. These volcanoes are approximately 50 km in diameter; and they have a low-angle, shield-like shape that consists of stratiform flanks (composed of trachytic lavas, pumice beds and ignimbrites) encompassing a structurally-complex centralized system of vents, dykes and domes. A perusal of the literature on trachytes reveals that these rocks often occur in the structurally-complex central areas found in the eroded remains of volcanic edifices that were once probably similar to the low-angle, trachytic shield volcanoes of the northern part of the Kenya Rift Valley.

7.7 Trachytes and petrogeny's residua system

Trachytes appear to occupy a paradoxical position within the ternary system NaAlSiO^4 (Nepheline)–KAlSiO^4 (Kalsilite)– SiO$_2$ (Quartz) which Bowen (1937) has called *petrogeny's residua system*. On cooling, the compositions of many of the common residual magmas end up in this system, and fractional crystallization drives them towards the low-temperature trough, or *thermal valley* (see Fig 7.7.1). In detail, this low-temperature trough is found to contain a central ridge that splits the trough into two subsidiary troughs. One minor trough contains liquids of rhyolite–granite composition, whereas the other contains liquids of phonolite–nepheline syenite composition. In this simplified system, trachytic liquids occupy a composition field that is situated on the thermal ridge between the rhyolitic and phonolitic troughs; thus the evolution of trachytic liquids pose the problem of how can a liquid remain critically saturated with regards to silica during fractional crystallization, and finally congeal on a thermal ridge, and not move towards

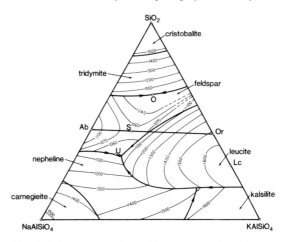

Fig. 7.7.1 Petrogeny's residua system (NaAlSiO$_4$-KAlSiO$_4$–SiO$_2$). O = the oversaturated minimum; S = the silica-saturated minimum, and U = the under-saturated minimum. The points O, S and U lie within what Bowen regarded as a *thermal valley* in the residua system (adapted from Bowen (1937) and Schairer (1950)).

either silica oversaturation (the rhyolites) or silica undersaturation (the phonolites).

It has been postulated that the shape of the low-temperature trough in petrogeny's residua system may change at higher pressures and/or at higher partial pressures of water vapour. Experimental studies (Bowen & Tuttle 1950; MacKenzie 1972; Morse 1969) have, however, shown that under hydrous conditions the general shape of the low-temperature trough is modified, but the rhyolite–granite and phonolite–nepheline syenite subsidiary troughs are preserved at pressures up to 1.0 GPa (10 kb). Such increases in pressure do, however, contract the field occupied by leucite; and this helps to explain why leucite is not normally found in plutonic rocks (Scarfe et al. 1966). It has also been proposed that petrogeny's residua system may be too simple in chemical composition to accurately simulate the fractional crystallization of magmas that enter the trachytic composition field (cf. Tilley 1957). An increase in the oxygen fugacity of a differentiating magma may, for example, result in the precipitation of magnetite and change the residual magma from being silica-saturated to being silica-oversaturated. In some comagmatic regions that contain both silica-oversaturated and silica-undersaturated rocks there is evidence that at least part of the fractional crystallization process took place at high pressures deep within the crust. Petrogeny's residua system also indicates that there is a *thermal barrier* (or ridge) that prevents the direct passage of a liquid by fractional crystallization, from the rhyolitic composition field to the phonolitic composition field, or vice versa. Petrological studies have, however, shown that the degree of silica saturation (oversaturation/undersaturation) of most trachytes is controlled by the initial composition of the parental basaltic magma (cf. Coombs & Wilkinson 1969; Miyashiro 1978).

Trachyte–comendite association and the Peralkaline tendency

The rocks of the basalt–trachyte association do not always terminate at trachyte. Some quartz-bearing, peralkaline trachytes differentiate beyond trachyte and terminate in the peralkaline rhyolite field of composition; whereas foid-bearing trachytes may occur in close association with phonolites. It is proposed that silica-saturated trachytic magmas usually congeal while astride the thermal ridge in petrogeny's residua system, because magmas of this composition are generally too viscous to differentiate further. Fractional crystallization, possibly assisted by volatile transfer, seems able to provide a feasible mechanism for generating comendites from peralkine trachytes. It is proposed that such comendites may evolve in long-lived, zoned magma chambers where they possibly represent but a thin buoyant boundary layer that rests at the top of a much more extensive density-stratified body of less differentiated magma.

In the basalt–trachyte association one normally finds that as fractional crystallization proceeds, the $Al_2O_3/(Na_2O + K_2O)$ ratio of the residual magma decreases. For example, in the Hawaiian alkalic suite (Macdonald 1968: 502) this ratio decreases from 3.7 in the alkali olivine basalts to 2.8 in the hawaiites, 2.3 in the mugearites, 2.0 in the benmoreites and 1.6 in the sodic trachytes. As magmatic rocks are said to be peralkaline when the molecular proportion of Al_2O_3 is less than the molecular proportion of $(Na_2O + K_2O)$, it is evident that the *peralkaline tendency* increases with increasing magmatic differentiation in the normal basalt–trachyte association. The main reason for this particular chemical trend is that the feldspars that precipitate from such an evolving series of magmas have consistently higher $Al_2O_3/(Na_2O + K_2O)$ ratios

than the magmas in which they occur. For example, during the early stages in the evolution of the magmas of the basalt–trachyte association, the magma is likely to precipitate plagioclase crystals that contain significant amounts of the anorthite component. If the composition of these early-formed plagioclase crystals was An_{50}, their chemical composition would be approximately 56.0 per cent SiO_2, 28.0 per cent Al_2O_3, 10.1 per cent CaO and 5.9 per cent Na_2O; and their $Al_2O_3/(Na_2O + K_2O)$ ratio would be 4.75. One can readily perceive how the separation of plagioclase of this composition from an evolving magma will lower the $Al_2O_3/(Na_2O + K_2O)$ ratio of the magma. During the cooling of the more differentiated benmoreite–trachyte magmas, sanidine is the most likely alkali feldspar to crystallize. As this mineral contains more K and Al than the host magma, the crystallization and removal of this phase will tend to produce a residual magma that is both sodic and peralkaline (cf. Bailey & Schairer 1964: 1198). Further fractional crystallization is likely to generate a peralkaline rhyolitic magma, because once a residual magma attains a silica content greater than 67 per cent, the crystallization and removal of any common rock-forming mineral other than the silica minerals (quartz, tridymite and cristobalite) would produce a residual liquid progressively enriched in silica (see Ch. 8).

7.8 Petrogenesis

According to Wright (1971), there is a whole *spectrum of trachytic rocks*, and they range in composition from rocks that grade into phonolites to those that grade into peralkaline rhyolites. Field evidence shows that not all of these trachytes evolved in the same way; but most trachytic magmas probably evolved at low pressures by the fractional crystallization of alkalic, or transitional, basaltic magmas. The degree of silica saturation (oversaturation/undersaturation) found in particular trachytic rocks is, as has been shown, essentially controlled by the silica saturation (oversaturation/undersaturation) of the parental basaltic magma. A few trachytic rocks, such as those from the Jos Plateau, Nigeria (Wright 1969), contain *lherzolitic xenoliths* that are believed to have been derived from the upper mantle. The evidence regarding the origin

Table 7.8.1 Average chemical composition of rocks of the hawaiite–trachyte association, from Canobolas Volcano, NSW, Australia (after Middlemost 1981)

	1	*2*	*3*	*4*
SiO^2	52.68	54.16	57.35	63.79
TiO$_2$	2.39	2.07	1.50	0.43
Al$_2$O$_3$	15.20	17.89	18.63	17.06
FeO*	11.32	9.30	7.52	5.27
MnO	0.17	0.20	0.11	0.14
MgO	4.85	2.88	1.43	0.43
CaO	7.49	6.28	4.58	1.44
Na$_2$O	4.15	4.39	5.24	5.90
K$_2$O	1.75	2.83	3.64	5.54

1. Average chemical composition of the hawaiites.
2. Average chemical composition of the mugearites.
3. Average chemical composition of the benmoreites.
4. Average chemical composition of the trachytes.
* FeO* = total Fe and FeO.

of these trachytes is, however, ambiguous. Some trachytes are found associated with *nephelinites* and *carbonatites* (see Ch. 14), and these rocks have been interpreted as fenites (that is syenites generated by strong alkali metasomatism) that have been locally mobilized and extruded (cf. King 1965).

A simple example of the evolution of a tra-chytic magma from a hawaiitic magma is given in Tables 7.8.1 and 7.8.2. The latter shows the proportions in which the various phases have been removed so that fractional crystallization can proceed from hawaiite via mugearite and benmoreite to trachyte. The rocks discussed in this example were obtained from the Middle to Late Miocene, Canobolas Volcano in central New South Wales, Australia (cf. Middlemost 1981). Table 7.8.2 demonstrates that it is arithmetically feasible to generate a mugearite from a hawaiite by removing approximately 12 per cent augite and lesser amounts of olivine (2 per cent) and Fe-Ti oxides (1.7 per cent). Benmoreite may be generated from the mugearite by the removal of 13.5 per cent labradorite, 7 per cent augite, 3.2 per cent Fe–Ti oxides and 2 per cent olivine; whereas the trachyte could be generated from a benmoreitic magma by the removal of 27.3 per cent labradorite, 4.7 per cent Fe–Ti oxides and 4.6 per cent augite.

7.9 Syenites

The syenites are a group of plutonic rocks that are essentially composed of alkali feldspars.

Table 7.8.2 Testing the feasibility of generating the various rocks on the hawaiite–trachyte association using mass balance mixing models (after Middlemost 1981)

Testing the feasibility of differentiating from hawaiite to mugearite: using the phases: magnetite, ilmenite, augite (En$_{40}$Fs$_{19}$Wo$_{41}$), olivine (Fo$_{78}$)

	Bulk comp. of added or substr. matl. (%)	*Obs. diff. between magmas*	*Calc. diff. between magmas*	*Obs.-calc. (residuals)*
SiO$_2$	42.41	1.480	1.852	–0.372
TiO$_2$	3.06	–0.320	–0.155	–0.165
Al$_2$O$_3$	2.42	2.690	2.439	0.251
FeO	21.07	–2.020	–1.855	–0.165
MnO	0.24	0.030	–0.006	0.036
MgO	15.63	–1.970	–2.010	0.040
CaO	14.87	–1.210	–1.355	0.145
Na$_2$O	0.30	0.240	0.645	–0.405
K$_2$O	0.01	1.080	0.445	0.635

Sum of the squares of the residuals = 0.8470

Phase name	*Amount as wt. % of init. magma*	*Amount of wt. % of added phases*	*Amount as wt. % as subtrd. phases*
Magnetite	–1.36	0.00	8.65
Ilmenite	–0.37	0.00	2.33
Augite	–12.01	0.00	76.19
Olivine	–2.02	0.00	12.83
Totals relative to initial magma =		0.00	15.77

Table 7.8.2 (*Cont'd*)

Testing the feasibility of differentiating from mugearite to benmoreite using the phases: labradorite, magnetite, ilmenite, augite ($En_{40}Fs_{19}Wo_{41}$), olivine (Fo_{78})

	Bulk comp. of added or substr. matl. (%)	Obs. diff. between magmas	Calc. diff. between magmas	Obs.-calc (*residuals*)
SiO_2	44.98	3.190	3.212	−0.022
TiO_2	3.65	−0.570	−0.558	−0.012
Al_2O_3	15.59	0.740	0.789	−0.049
FeO	14.33	−1.780	−1.768	−0.012
MnO	0.09	−0.090	0.005	−0.095
MgO	7.01	−1.450	−1.448	−0.002
CaO	11.16	−1.700	−1.708	0.008
Na_2O	2.92	0.850	0.602	0.248
K_2O	0.28	0.810	0.874	−0.064

Sum of square of the residuals = 0.0777.

Phase name	Amount as wt. % of init. magma	Amount as wt. % of added phases	Amount as wt. % as subtrd. phases
Labradorite	−13.64	0.00	52.53
Magnetite	−1.75	0.00	6.72
Ilmenite	−1.45	0.00	5.59
Augite	−7.03	0.00	27.06
Olivine	−2.10	0.00	8.10
Totals relative to initial magma =		0.00	25.97

Testing the feasibility of differentiating from benmoreite to trachyte using the phases: labradorite, magnetite, ilmenite, augite ($En_{29}Fs_{27}Wo_{44}$)

	Bulk comp. of added or substr. matl. (%)	Obs. diff. between magmas	Cal. diff. between magmas	Obs.-calc (*residuals*)
SiO_2	46.71	6.448	6.248	0.192
TiO_2	3.67	−1.070	−1.186	0.116
Al_2O_3	21.10	−1.578	−1.479	−0.091
FeO	11.74	−2.250	−2.366	0.116
MnO	0.07	0.030	0.026	0.004
MgO	1.30	−1.000	−0.318	−0.682
CaO	10.94	−3.140	−3.475	0.335
Na_2O	4.09	0.660	0.664	−0.004
K_2O	0.39	1.900	1.885	0.015

Sum of the squares of the residuals = 0.6494.

Phase name	Amount as wt. % of init. magma	Amount as wt. % of added phases	Amount as wt. % of subtrd. phases
Labradorite	−27.86	0.00	74.51
Magnetite	−2.27	0.00	6.21
Ilmenite	−2.45	0.00	6.69
Augite	−4.61	0.00	12.59
Totals relative to initial magma =		0.00	36.58

They generally also contain a small amount of plagioclase, one or more mafic minerals, and accessory amounts of quartz (that is, Q less than 5 per cent; 100P/(A + P) less than 35 per cent; when Q + A + P = 100). Foid-bearing syenites contain some feldspathoidal minerals but less than 10 per cent F, when A + P + F = 100.

Quartz syenites contain between 5 and 20 per cent quartz, when Q + A + P = 100. Syenites that contain little, or no, plagioclase are called alkali–feldspar syenites, that is, 100P/(A + P) less than 10 per cent. The syenitic rocks are thus regarded as the intrusive equivalents of trachytes.

The term syenite was used by the ancient Romans (*Pliny, the Elder*, for example) to describe the quartz-bearing or granitic rocks of Syene (now Asswan) in Egypt. Werner (1788: 824) applied the term 'sienit' to a hornblende-bearing plutonic rock from the Plauenscher Grund near Dresden in southern East Germany. The latter rock contained significantly less quartz than the granitic rock from Egypt. Rosenbusch (1877b: 113–14) defined syenite as being a plutonic rock that was essentially composed of alkali feldspar, and neither quartz, nor hornblende, were essential minerals.

Syenites are usually medium- to coarse-grained, with hypidiomorphic granular, or porphyritic, textures. In some rocks the alkali feldspars occur as tabular crystals, and if these crystals occur in a parallel or subparallel disposition, the rock is said to have a *trachytoid texture*. Most syenites contain a single perthitic or antiperthitic feldspar; however, others contain two feldspars, namely a nearly sodium-free microcline or orthoclase, and a sodium-rich plagioclase that is usually in the composition range between An_{20} and An_{40}. The syenites that contain only one feldspar (perthite or antiperthite) may be called *hypersolvus syenites*, as the presence of a single feldspar shows that the original feldspar crystallized at a temperature above the solvus in the system $NaAl_3O_8$–$KAlSi_3O_8$ (Tuttle 1955: 1629). Syenites that contain both potassium feldspar and a separate plagioclase phase are called *subsolvus syenites*. The mafic minerals that occur in normal syenites are hornblende, biotite, augite, ferroaugite, olivine and ferrohastingsite; whereas arfvedsonite, riebeckite, barkevikite, kaersutite, aegirine and aegirine–augite are characteristic of the peralkaline syenites. Fe–Ti oxides may exceed 5 per cent, but they usually occur as accessory constituents together with minerals such as quartz, apatite, zircon, sphene, nepheline and various sulphides. According to Tröger (1935), the Plauenscher Grund syenite contains 5 wt.% quartz, 51 per cent alkali feldspar, 20 per cent plagioclase (An_{25}), 19 per cent hornblende and accessory amounts of biotite, diopside, sphene, Fe–Ti oxides and apatite (see Table 7.9.1, No. 1).

A number of terms are used to describe different types of syenites. For example, in the Oslo palaeorift, Norway, the term *larvikite* is used to describe a particularly distinctive looking alkalic syenite–monzonite from Larvik (that is, the feldspars they contain display a 'change of colour' or labradorescence); and the term *nordmarkite* is

Table 7.9.1 Chemical compositions of syenitic rocks (%)

	1	2	3
SiO_2	58.70	58.58	57.84
TiO_2	0.95	0.84	1.30
Al_2O_3	17.09	16.64	18.43
Fe_2O_3	3.17	3.04	2.65
FeO	2.29	3.13	2.82
MnO	—	0.13	0.16
MgO	2.41	1.87	1.38
CaO	4.71	3.53	3.72
Na_2O	4.38	5.24	5.91
K_2O	4.35	4.95	4.21
P_2O_5	0.23	0.29	0.57
H_2O^+	0.89	0.99	0.78
H_2O^-	0.23	0.23	—
No. of analyses	1	517	24

1. Syenite from Plauenscher Grund, Dresden, southern East Germany (after Correns 1969; 435, No. 7).
2. Mean chemical composition of syenites (after Le Maitre 1976a: 604) (CO_2 = 0.28 per cent).
3. Mean chemical composition of larvikites from the Larvik ring-complex, Oslo Region, Norway (after Neumann 1980: 507–8).

used to describe a quartz-bearing alkalic syenite of the Nordmark area to the immediate north of Oslo. *Shonkinites* are syenites that contain more mafic minerals than is considered normal. The type-rocks from the Shonkin Sag Laccolith in Montana, USA (cf. Nash & Wilkinson 1970: 244–5) normally contain more than 12 per cent normative feldspathoids (leucite and nepheline), and are thus not syenites (sensu stricto). *Hypersthene syenites*, or orthopyroxene-bearing syenites, occur in association with many large bodies of anorthosite, such as those of the Adirondack Mountains of New York State, and the Laramie Range of Wyoming (Hargraves 1969; Klugman 1969). Barker et al. (1975) have discussed the origin of what they call the *gabbro–anorthosite–syenite–potassic granite suite* (see Ch. 10). *Fenites* are usually silicic country rocks that have been transformed into syenites by alkali metasomatism in the contact zones that surround carbonatite–ijolite intrusive complexes (see Ch. 14).

The mean major element compositions of the syenites are similar to those of the trachytes (see Tables 7.3.1 and 7.9.1); however, the syenites generally contain slightly less SiO_2, and more MgO, CaO and (Fe_2O_3 + FeO), than the trachytes. Syenites usually contain both normative quartz ($\bar{x}$ = 0.8 per cent) and hypersthene ($\bar{x}$ = 4.2 per cent), and over 80 per cent normative feldspar ($\bar{x}$ = Or 29.3 per cent, Ab 44.3 per cent, An 7.2 per cent). Le Maitre's (1976a: 604) average syenite has a Thornton and Tuttle differentiation index of 74.5.

The syenites and trachytes both have relatively low abundances and wide distributions. Syenites are even found on some oceanic islands. For example, the Rallier du Baty peninsula in the south-western corner of the Ile de Kerguelen in the southern Indian Ocean contains five ring complexes that are mainly composed of syenites and quartz syenites (Dosso et al. 1979). It is anticipated from the study of autoliths that syenitic rocks occur beneath the present volcanic edifices on many volcanic oceanic islands (as in Ascension Island in the South Atlantic Ocean).

Rocks associated with syenites

Syenites usually occur: (a) as relatively small independent subvolcanic intrusions; or (b) as local igneous facies, or satellite bodies, related to larger intrusions with different overall compositions. The Plauenscher Grund syenite is, for example, a local igneous facies within a larger body composed mainly of granitic rocks. In the younger granite province of northern Nigeria (Jacobson et al. 1958), the White Mountain igneous province of New Hampshire, USA (Chapman & Williams 1935), the Gardar alkaline igneous province of southern Greenland (Emeleus & Upton 1976), and the Fongen–Hyllingen layered basic complex of central Norway (Wilson et al. 1981), syenites occur in close association with other rock types. In the first two petrographic provinces, they are associated with much larger volumes of granitic rocks. The Gardar alkaline igneous province contains a wide range of plutonic rocks; one group of associated rocks is silica oversaturated, whereas the other group is silica undersaturated; and both groups contain syenites. In the Ilimaussaq complex, which is part of this province, peralkaline granites and silica-oversaturated syenites occur in close association with peralkaline foid syenites. Igneous layering is widely developed in the rocks of the Gardar alkaline igneous province; and it occurs in rocks that range in composition from gabbro to alkali feldspar granite. Such structures are particularly well displayed in the Nunarssuit and Klokken syenites (Parsons & Butterfield 1981). The large (160 km²) Fongen–Hyllingen layered basic complex of the Trondheim region of Nor-

way contains a 10 000 m thick sequence of rhythmically-layered rocks that range in composition from olivine–picotite (spinel) cumulates at the base to quartz-bearing ferrosyenites at the top. According to Wilson et al. (1981: 592), the syenites occupy less than 3 per cent of the exposed area of the complex, and they 'represent the uncontaminated final product of fractional crystallization of the entire complex'.

Syenite petrogenesis

In many areas, syenites are comagmatic with granites. As these syenites tend to form marginal igneous facies to much larger granitic bodies, the former are often interpreted as having evolved from the latter. This poses problems, because if a syenite is to evolve from a granite, significant amounts of SiO_2 have to be removed; and significant amounts of MgO, total Fe, MnO and TiO_2, and possibly CaO and Na_2O, have to be added. Such changes in chemical composition may be locally accomplished by the assimilation of mafic and/or carbonate rocks, and the escape of volatiles containing dissolved silica (Daly 1933: 447–8; Emmons 1953: 81). Toulmin (1960: 282) has proposed that the Beverly syenite of the Salem area of Massachusetts, USA formed as a local accumulation of alkali feldspar crystals in a magma that had a granitic bulk composition. The alkali feldspar crystals are considered to have accumulated in a relatively shallow peripheral part of a high-level magma chamber. An essentially similar model has been proposed for the origin of the Plauenscher Grund syenite (Shand 1950: 271). It does seem somewhat anomalous that it is often postulated that rhyolites, particularly alkali rhyolites, evolve from trachytes; yet syenites may evolve from granites.

Many syenites are, however, interpreted as being products of the fractional crystallization of basaltic magma. Examples of such syenites occur in the Fongen–Hyllingen layered basic complex and the Insch layered intrusion of Scotland. Read et al. (1961: 406) postulated that the syenites of the Insch gabbro-monzogabbro–monzonite–syenite intrusion crystallized from an extreme residual liquid that was concentrated by '*the gradual upward expulsion of the low temperature residue*' from a mush of settling crystals. In their study of the origin of the rocks of the White Mountain igneous province of New Hampshire, Chapman and

Williams (1935: 523) demonstrated that the removal of 53 per cent plagioclase, 10 per cent pyroxene, 10 per cent olivine and 4.5 per cent ilmenite from the parental basaltic magma would produce a monzonitic magma; and the removal of 17 per cent plagioclase, 16 per cent pyroxene and 2 per cent ilminite from the monzonitic magma would produce a syenitic magma. This fractional crystallization process is broadly similar to the one proposed for the generation of trachytic magmas. Both of these fractionation trends require the removal of a high proportion of plagioclase, and this may help explain the close association of many deep-seated hypersthene syenites with anorthosites (see Ch. 10). Barker et al. (1975: 97) have proposed that the syenites associated with anorthosites may form when alkalic basaltic magma of mantle origin reacts with, and partially melts, granulite facies rocks in the lower crust. They (152) propose that the lower crustal rocks would contain only a small volume of the 'low-melting fraction', and that 'reaction-melting' would produce 'iron-enriched gabbro first, then alkali diorite, and lastly quartz syenitic liquid'. Magmas of the latter composition would have a low density relative to the rocks of the lower crust, and they would readily move upwards into higher levels of the crust. Upton (1971: 112) claims that the evolution of the rocks of the Gardar alkaline igneous province was also associated with the large-scale production of anorthosites at depth. At pressures greater than 1.0 GPa (10 kb), clinopyroxene was the liquidus phase in the parental basaltic magma, and fractional crystallization resulted in the residual magma becoming enriched in Na_2O, K_2O and Al_2O_3. Upon being emplaced into a lower-pressure environment, plagioclase and olivine become the liquidus phases, and fractional crystallization resulted in the evolution of anorthosites, and a series of residual magmas that were hawaiitic, mugearitic, benmoreitic and trachytic in composition.

Trachytes and syenites are also found associated with *kimberlites* and/or *carbonatites* (see Chs 13 and 14). For example, kimberlitic, melilititic, trachytic and carbonatitic rocks are all found in close association at Saltpetre Kop near Sutherland, South Africa; and McIver and Ferguson (1979: 127) claim that the trachytes developed in a crustal environment as a result of the continued fractionation of what had originally been a kimberlitic magma. The chemical composition of the Saltpetre Kop trachyte is unusual in that it contains over 10 per cent K_2O (McIver & Ferguson 1979: 120, No. 22). King (1965: 97) has demonstrated that in the alkaline igneous centres of eastern Uganda some of the syenites 'have formed demonstrably as fenites by metasomatic processes', and that it is reasonable to infer that trachytes could have developed as 'mobilized fenites'.

7.10 Selected references

Baker, B. H., Gòles, G. G., Leman, W. P. & Lindstrom, M. M. (1977) Geochemistry and petrogenesis of a basalt–benmoreite–trachyte suite from the southern part of the Gregory Rift, Kenya, *Contrib. Mineral. Petrol.*, **65**, 303–32.

Emeleus, C. H. & Upton, B. G. J. (1976) The Gardar period in southern Greenland, pp. 152–81 in Escher A. & Watt, W. S. (eds), *Geology of Greenland*, Gronlands Geologiske Undersogelse, Copenhagen, Denmark.

Wright, J. B. (1971) The phonolite–trachyte spectrum, *Lithos*, **4**, 1–5.

CHAPTER 8

DACITE–RHYOLITE CLAN

8.1 General statement

The dacite–rhyolite clan is mainly composed of fine-grained, or glassy, silicic volcanic rocks. Their chemical compositions are essentially similar to the granites, granodiorites and quartz diorites; and they, like the granitic rocks, have extensive temporal and spatial distributions. Both the dacites and the rhyolites were originally described from the Vlădeasa Mountains (formerly the Siebenbürgen) in the Transylvanian region of Romania. The ancient Romans called this area *Dacia*. Ferdinand von Richthofen (1860) coined the term rhyolite, which he derived from the classical Greek word *rheo* meaning 'to stream', the name is an allusion to the *flow-banded* appearance of many rhyolites. Von Richthofen regarded the rhyolites as being alkali feldspar-bearing silicic extrusive rocks. In 1863, Guido Strache divided the silicic extrusive rocks of the Vlădeasa Mountains into: (a) dacites if they contained mainly plagioclase, quartz and hornblende; and (b) rhyolites if they were mainly composed of alkali feldspar, quartz and mica. The Streckeisen (1980: 196–7) classification of volcanic rocks regards the dacites as being modally similar to the granodiorites and quartz diorites (tonalites), and the rhyolites are regarded as being modally akin to the granites. In this classification the term *alkali rhyolite* is applied to rhyolites that contain alkali pyroxene and/or alkali amphibole in their mode or norm. The alkali rhyolites, and the silicic volcanic rocks that have a *peralkaline tendency*, are discussed in Section 7.7.

Most Cenozoic dacites and rhyolites were extruded in orogenic areas (for example the Andes of South America, Central America, western North America, Aleutian Arc, Kamchatka, Japan, Indonesia, Papua New Guinea, Fiji, Tonga-Kermadec, New Zealand, South Sandwich Islands and the island-arcs of the Mediterranean Sea); and they have broadly similar distribution patterns to the andesites that were discussed in Chapter 6. It is convenient to divide these *orogenic rhyolites and dacites* into low-K, calc–alkalic, high-K or shoshonitic suites, using Fig. 6.1.1. Ewart (1982: 42–3) has produced statistical data on the frequency distribution of the dacites and rhyolites that belong to these suites in various Cenozoic orogenic regions of the Earth. His table shows that these silicic rocks are mainly members of the high-K and shoshonite suites in the orogenic areas situated on continental crustal rocks (for example the Andes, much of western North America and the Mediterranean volcanic-arcs); whereas the silicic rocks tend to be members of the calc–alkalic and low-K suites in the orogenic areas that are at present evolving on oceanic crust (as in many of the island-arcs of the western Pacific). In some continental orogenic areas, such as the western USA, the rhyolitic rocks are more abundant than the dacitic rocks; and these proportions are contrary to what one would normally expect to occur with the fractional crystallization of basaltic, or andesitic, magmas.

According to Cameron et al. (1980), the largest continuous rhyolitic province on Earth is the Sierra Madre Occidental of western Mexico. In this province, ash-flow tuffs cover more than 250 000 km^2, and they attain a mean thickness of approximately 1 km. Lesser amounts of rhyolitic lava, and minor amounts of rock of intermediate composition, occur interbedded with these ash-flow tuffs. The most mafic rocks in this rock association are low-silica andesites, and they grade in chemical composition via normal andesites and dacites into the main body of rhyolites. Trace element data indicate that all of these rocks are genetically related. In Section 1.9 it was recorded that in 73 000 BC an ultraplinian eruption in the Toba volcanic–tectonic depression in northern Sumatra, Indonesia, produced a layer of rhyolitic tephra that now blankets an area in excess of 5 million km^2. This pyroclastic deposit is equivalent to more than 1000 km^3 of dense rhyolite.

Another vast pile of rhyolitic and dacitic rocks crop out in the Cenozoic Taupo Volcanic Zone of North Island, New Zealand (cf. Cole 1979).

These rocks, like so many other silicic extrusive rocks, are not only associated with seismically-active continental margins, but also with zones of block-faulting and extension in the continental crust. In many petrographic provinces, such as the Iceland Tholeiitic Province, the Yellowstone Province of north-western USA, and the Lebombo Province of Mozambique, there is what appears to be a *bimodal basalt–rhyolite rock association*; and the rocks of this association are usually extruded, in anorogenic tectonic environments, during periods of crustal extension and normal faulting (cf. Christiansen & Lipman 1972). Silicic rocks are also found associated with major continental rifts and palaeorifts (as the Ethiopian Rift), and in some areas of intraplate volcanic activity, such as that found in the Canary and Galapagos archipelagos, and in the Eastern Australian Tertiary Province.

Since the publication of the scientific results of the voyage of *HMS Challenger* in 1891, the ocean floor has been known to contain silicic rocks; and they have been variously described as dacites, rhyolites, aplites, tonalites, granodiorites, granites and quartz diorites. These silicic rocks usually have relatively low potassium contents, and some of the 'aplites' contain up to 78 per cent SiO_2 (cf. Hekinian 1982: 44). As was noted in Section 2.2, Dixon and Rutherford (1979) claim that these silicic rocks may have been derived from an immiscible liquid that evolved late in the crystallization history of a magma with a bulk composition similar to the MOR basalts. The fragments of rhyolitic glass that are found in the unconsolidated surface materials of the Moon are also believed to have been produced by liquid immiscibility (cf. Taylor 1982: 333). As many tholeiitic basaltic and komatiitic rocks of the Earth contain small blebs or ocelli of rhyolitic materials, it is evident that liquid immiscibility is a valid process in the generation of a relatively small amount of rhyolitic liquid at a late stage in the crystallization of many basic and ultrabasic silicate magmas (see Section 2.2). Liquid immiscibility may also assist in the evolution of compositionally-zoned magma chambers that contain an upper layer of rhyolitic liquid (cf. Hildreth 1981).

As it is usually easier to observe and interpret the structures, textures and phases that occur in the Cenozoic silicic rocks, petrologists tend to describe these younger rocks in more detail than the older ones. However, this must not be interpreted as indicating that most rhyolitic and dacitic rocks were extruded in the Cenozoic, because the geological record of the Earth shows that they were extruded in all eons, from the Archaean to the present. Dacites and rhyolites have, for example, often been described from the upper sections of the volcanic sequences in Archean greenstone belts (cf. Goodwin 1977).

8.2 Modal compositions and textures

Rocks of the dacite–rhyolite clan often congeal to form dark-coloured rocks with a conchoidal fracture and a vitreous lustre. If such rocks contain more than 80 per cent glass, they are called *obsidians* (cf. Streckeisen 1980 200). Many specimens of obsidian are colour-banded, and they may also contain microlites, crystallites, spherulites or perlitic cracks. When examined in thin section, under plane-polarized light, they are usually found to be pale brownish-yellow in colour. The refractive indices of glasses of rhyolite-dacite composition generally range from 1.48 to 1.52, and the highest values are found in the dacitic and peralkaline glasses. Highly vesicular varities of obsidian are called *pumice*; whereas glasses with a dull resinous or pitch-like lustre are called *pitchstones*. The latter usually contain crystallites and have a higher ($\approx$4 per cent) water content than the obsidians.

Most dacitic and rhyolitic lavas have porphyritic textures and display flow-banded structures; however, a high proportion of the Cenozoic silicic rocks of the Earth have pyroclastic textures and exhibit eutaxitic structures. Plagioclase is the most common type of phenocryst found in *dacites*; and it often displays strongly-developed normal oscillatory zoning. In the low-K dacites the plagioclases are usually labradorites, or bytownites; however, they become more sodic in the calc–alkalic dacites, and this soda-enrichment trend continues into the high-K dacites where the plagioclase is usually andesine with rims of oligoclase (cf. Ewart 1979: 56). Sanidine is also a significant phenocryst, in the high-K dacites; quartz is another common type of phenocryst, and it is particularly abundant in the dacites that contain more than 66 per cent SiO_2. Other phenocrysts found in dacites include clinopyroxene (diopside, augite and ferroaugite), orthopyroxene (bronzite and hypersthene), hornblende, biotite, Fe–Ti oxides, olivine and/or sphene.

Iron-rich pyroxenes and olivines are not usually found in dacites, however, well-known exceptions to this rule occur in the Asio and Sidara districts of Japan (cf. Kuno 1969).

According to Tröger (1935), the type dacite from Kis-Sebes (now Poeni) in Romania has the following modal composition: plagioclase 46 per cent, quartz 30 per cent, alkali feldspar 9 per cent, chlorite (pseudomorphed after pyroxene) 8 per cent, biotite plus hornblende 5 per cent, and Fe-Ti oxides plus apatite 2 per cent. Ewart (1979: 35) has produced the following mean modal composition of 101 selected orogenic dacites from the 'eastern belt' of the western USA: plagioclase 16.7 per cent, sanidine 2.7 per cent, biotite 2.6 per cent, hornblende 1.4 per cent, Fe-Ti oxides 1.1 per cent, clinopyroxene 0.66 per cent, quartz 0.62 per cent, orthopyroxene 0.35 per cent, sphene 0.03 per cent, olivine a trace, and groundmass 73.8 per cent. He has also produced the following mean modal composition of eighteen selected orogenic dacites from the Tonga-Kermadec Islands in the south-western Pacific: plagioclase 5.9 per cent, clinopyroxene 1.4 per cent, orthopyroxene 0.71 per cent, Fe-Ti oxides 0.34 per cent, olivine a trace, and groundmass 91.6 per cent.

Bryan (1979: 593) has described the dacitic rocks of Tonga as being 'among the most calcic of their kind in the world' ($\bar{x}$ CaO = 5.92 per cent). In these rocks, plagioclase is the most abundant phenocryst, and their compositions usually range between An_{80} and An_{85}; whereas the compositions of the groundmass plagioclases range from An_{45} to An_{65}; augite and hypersthene may also occur as phenocrysts. The groundmass pyroxenes tend to contain more iron, and they are usually ferroaugites and/or pigeonites. Quartz and alkali feldspars tend to be *occult minerals* (this is, they cannot be identified even in the groundmass). Lavas from the Tonga-Kermadec Petrographic Province, including the dacites, generally have distinctive chemical compositions that contain low concentrations of the incompatible elements. The silicic rocks of this province are of particular interest because they have evolved in an area far removed from continental crustal materials; and they probably resemble the initial materials used in the construction of new segments of continental crust.

The *rhyolites* are usually pyroclastic rocks, obsidians, or glassy rocks, and they tend to contain a significantly higher proportion of glass than associated rocks of basic, or intermediate, composition. They typically contain phenocrysts of feldspars, quartz and Fe–Ti oxides. Other minerals that are often recorded in normal rhyolites include clinopyroxene (augite, ferroaugite), orthopyroxene (hypersthene), biotite, amphibole (hornblende, cummingtonite), fayalitic olivine and sphene. Plagioclase (An_{20-40}) is the typical feldspar found in the low-K rhyolites, whereas sandine and anorthoclase are the characteristic feldspars in the high-K and alkali rhyolites. In many rhyolites the quartz phenocrysts display an embayed outline. The alkali rhyolites tend to contain a distinctive assemblage of mafic minerals that include arfvedsonite riebeckite, aegirine, hedenbergite and aenigmatite.

8.3 Geochemistry and normative composition

Tables 8.3.1 and 8.3.2 give the mean chemical compositions of a selection of dacites and rhyolites. As would be expected, the rhyolites are enriched in SiO_2 and usually, in K_2O; whereas the dacites tend to be strongly enriched in total Fe, MgO, CaO and TiO_2, and slightly enriched in Al_2O_3. These chemical differences are clearly illustrated by the normative compositions of these rocks. The rhyolites usually contain approximately 33 per cent normative quartz and 25 per cent normative orthoclase; whereas the dacites generally contain approximately 23 per cent normative quartz and 13 per cent normative orthoclase. According to Le Maitre (1976a: 607, 611), the average rhyolite has a Thornton and Tuttle differentiation index of 88.4, whereas that for the average dacite is only 67.6.

8.4 Eruptions of dacitic and rhyolitic materials

In Section 1.4 it was noted that silicic melts are usually more polymerized, and more viscous, than mafic or intermediate melts. High viscosity has a profound influence on the style of volcanic activity associated with the extrusion of silicic materials. Such materials are usually found in *coulée, volcanic domes* or *pyroclastic deposits*. The coulée and volcanic domes may be extruded

Table 8.3.1 Chemical composition of the dacites (%)

	1	2	3	4	5	6
SiO$_2$	65.01	65.33	66.21	65.60	65.36	65.57
TiO$_2$	0.58	0.62	0.63	0.65	0.63	0.60
Al$_2$O$_3$	15.91	15.58	16.34	16.04	16.22	14.15
Fe$_2$O$_3$	2.43	2.37	2.93	2.35	2.44	1.63
FeO	2.30	2.33	1.05	2.99	2.20	6.03
MnO	0.09	0.12	0.09	0.13	0.09	0.16
MgO	1.78	1.62	1.17	1.86	1.64	1.92
CaO	4.32	4.31	3.14	4.79	4.25	5.85
Na$_2$O	3.79	3.72	4.11	3.76	3.80	3.02
K$_2$O	2.17	2.27	4.11	1.66	3.15	0.91
P$_2$O$_5$	0.15	0.18	0.23	0.18	0.21	0.16
H$_2$O$^+$	0.91	1.54*				
No. of analyses	651	495	133	241	124	24
			p.p.m.	p.p.m.	p.p.m.	p.p.m.
Rb			113	61	109	13
Ba			1587	504	831	167
Sr			637	225	330	251
Zr			247	79	170	53
Zn			68	n.d.	64	106
La			92	10	23	40
Ce			283	28	55	10.4
Yb			2.7	3.8	1.5	2.8
Y			31	14	28	26
Cu			9	9	21	29
Ni			16	23	11	6
Co			8	15	10	14
Cr			16	12	13	16
V			63	37	72	96
Nb			17	n.d.	21	2.4
Li			n.d.	12	20	n.d.
Pb			34	9	7	3.6
Hf			n.d.	3.8	3.4	1.7

1. Mean chemical composition of the dacites (after Le Maitre 1976a: 611) (H$_2$O$^-$ = 0.28 and CO$_2$ = 0.06).
2. Mean chemical composition of Cenozoic dacites (after Chayes 1975: 548) (H$_2$O* = H$_2$O$^+$ and H$_2$O$^-$).
3. Mean chemical composition of orogenic dacites from the western USA (eastern belt) (after Ewart 1979: 34).
4. Mean chemical composition of orogenic dacites from Japan, Taiwan, Kuriles, Kamchatka, Saipan (after Ewart 1979: 34).
5. Mean chemical composition of orogenic dacites from the Mediterranean (after Ewart 1979: 34).
6. Mean chemical composition of dacites from the Tonga-Kermadec Islands (after Ewart 1979: 34).

as relatively quiet eruptive events; however, all of the large pyroclastic flow, surge and air-fall deposits were ejected during cataclysmic plinian, or ultraplinian, eruptions. As was noted in Section 1.9, most large silicic pyroclastic flow deposits are associated with large calderas, or with even larger volcano–tectonic depressions, such as the one associated with the Toba Volcanic Centre of northern Sumatra, Indonesia.

Silicic lavas may pile up and form steep-sided *domes* directly over the volcanic vents through which they erupt. Some domes result from the bodily upheaval of the materials that once filled volcanic vents, and such landforms are called *plug domes* (for example, Mt Pelee, Martinique, West Indies). Other domes form as the result of the extrusion of viscous lava through summit-vents, and they grow as the result of the piling up of a series of short thick flows. Such domes are known as *exogenous domes*, and possibly the best known of this type is the trachytic dome of Castello d'Ischia in the Bay of Napoli, Italy. Many silicic domes are *endogenous domes*, and they tend to grow by expansion from within, with a concomitant distention of the overlying layers. As there is but a limited amount of stretching that the cooling outer crust of a growing endogenous dome can sustain without rupturing,

Table 8.3.2 Chemical composition of the rhyolites (%)

	1	*2*	*3*	*4*	*5*	*6*	*7*
SiO$_2$	72.82	71.56	72.33	74.75	73.04	73.60	74.92
TiO$_2$	0.28	0.32	0.46	0.20	0.31	0.30	0.25
Al$_2$O$_3$	13.27	13.58	14.09	13.67	14.24	14.05	13.47
Fe$_2$O$_3$	1.48	1.58	1.80	0.95	1.44	1.32	1.01
FeO	1.11	1.10	1.75	0.61	0.54	0.50	0.89
MnO	0.06	0.07	0.10	0.05	0.07	0.06	0.06
MgO	0.39	0.47	0.78	0.29	0.47	0.54	0.32
CaO	1.14	1.41	3.35	1.14	1.36	1.59	1.57
Na$_2$O	3.55	3.80	4.07	3.63	3.76	3.70	4.18
K$_2$O	4.30	4.19	1.12	4.67	4.70	4.26	3.27
P$_2$O$_5$	0.07	0.12	0.18	0.05	0.08	0.08	0.05
H$_2$O$^+$	1.10	1.96*					
No. of analyses	670	547	33	200	143	45	83
			p.p.m.	p.p.m.	p.p.m.	p.p.m.	p.p.m.
Rb			n.d.	182	180	155	111
Ba			420	631	957	641	849
Sr			201	184	249	160	113
Zr			n.d.	142	217	222	159
Zn			85	39	n.d.	84	n.d.
La			6.7	66	76	n.d.	26
Ce			22	135	163	n.d.	43
Yb			4.9	4.3	2.0	n.d.	3.6
Y			11	32	29	n.d.	24
Cu			2	8	10	15	6
Ni			29	4	3	12	<2
Co			11	5	3	6	<2
Cr			16	6	3	n.d.	1
V			8	12	20	33	9
Nb			n.d.	19	27	n.d.	5.6
Li			7	40	n.d.	30	35
Pb			10	37	30	57	18
Hf			3.7	n.d.	n.d.	n.d.	4.5

1. Mean chemical composition of rhyolite (after Le Maitre 1976a: 607) (H$_2$O$^-$ = 0.31 and CO$_2$ = 0.08).
2. Mean chemical composition of Cenozoic rhyolites (after Chayes 1975: 548) (H$_2$O* = H$_2$O$^+$ and H$_2$O$^-$).
3. Mean chemical composition of low-K rhyolite, Japan–Kurile–Saipan region (after Ewart 1979: 44).
4. Mean chemical composition of rhyolites, western USA (western belt) (after Ewart 1979: 44).
5. Mean chemical composition of rhyolites, western USA (eastern belt) (after Ewart 1979: 44).
6. Mean chemical composition of rhyolites, western South America (after Ewart 1979: 44).
7. Mean chemical composition of rhyolites, Taupo Volcanic Zone, New Zealand (after Ewart 1979: 44).

the outer crust is often breached, and lava is found to have flowed down its sides. In the Tarawera Volcanic Complex in New Zealand, for example, there are eleven coalescing rhyolitic endogenous domes.

The first task that has to be performed, when studying pyroclastic rocks, is to identify the manner in which the pyroclastic material was transported from the vent to the place of deposition. Three main mechanisms for transporting pyroclastic materials are now recognized, and they are able to produce: (a) *pyroclastic fall deposits*; (b) *pyroclastic flow deposits*; and (c) *pyroclastic*

surge deposits. When air-fall deposits develop, the pyroclasts move through the air, after falling out of an eruptive plume. Lateral movements away from the vent are caused by a combination of factors, such as: (a) the initial lateral velocity imparted to the pyroclasts at the time of eruption; (b) the lateral expansion of the eruptive plume; and (c) the buffeting the pyroclasts receive from the prevailing wind. Pyroclastic flow deposits are produced when pyroclasts move over the ground as a hot and concentrated particulate flow in which there is a high particle : gas ratio; whereas surge deposits develop when pyroclasts are carried laterally in a ground-hugging dilute particulate flow that has a low particle : gas ratio (cf. Walker 1981b: 393).

Eruptions of rhyolitic materials are generally of a larger magnitude, but lower frequency, than those of materials of mafic or intermediate composition. Large diapirs of rhyolitic magma probably rise to high levels in the crust and then, if they rupture the surface layer, they eject extensive sheets of pyroclastic flow and air-fall materials: however, if a diapir becomes lodged at a high level in the crust, it may periodically release smaller batches of magma to the surface (cf. Walker 1981b: 395–6). Such a release of magma may be triggered by the emplacement of a more mafic magma at the base of the diapir. Many pyroclastic flow deposits are compositionally zoned, usually with the silicic material at the base, and more mafic material in the upper part of the deposit. Such rocks are probably ejected from compositionally-zoned magma chambers (see Section 2.2). For example, the tephra deposits that have been ejected from Hekla Volcano, Iceland are compositionally zoned; and studies of these materials have revealed that, after a period of being dormant, the silica content of the first material to be erupted tends to be related to the length of the preceding period of repose; that is, the longer the period of repose the more silica-rich, and differentiated, the tephra.

Tephrochronology

The pioneering work of Sigurdur Thorarinsson (1944) on the pyroclastic materials ejected by Hekla Volcano has led to the development of a new branch of volcanology called *tephrochronology*. Thorarinsson introduced the terms tephra and tephrochronology to modern volcanology; he introduced the word tephra because he 'needed a collective term for all pyroclasts', and he 'also wanted a term in linguistic harmony with magma and lava' (Thorarinsson 1981: 10). His studies revealed that individual layers of tephra could be correlated over large areas of Iceland; and each layer of tephra was an isochronous stratigraphic *marker band*. According to him (1981: 10), tephrochronology can be defined as 'a dating method based on the identification correlation and dating of tephra layers'. Tephrochronology is usually combined with studies of the distribution, thickness, grain size and the vari-

ations in composition found in tephra layers. These data enable volcanologists to determine the frequency, style and magnitude of volcanic eruptions from particular volcanoes or volcanic centres. This knowledge of the past behaviour of a volcano, or volcanic centre, enables volcanologists to make tentative predictions about their future behaviour (cf. Self & Sparks 1981). The compositional variations that are often found in tephra layers may provide insights into the processes operating in the magma chambers beneath volcanoes, or volcanic centres. Such data have, for example, shown that many silicic magmas evolve as the topmost layer in compositionally-zoned magma chambers (cf. Hildreth 1981).

Field mapping aided by tephrochronology has revealed that in the past 50 000 years there have been at least thirty-five rhyolitic plinian–ultraplinian eruptions from the Taupo and Okataina volcanic centres in the Taupo Volcanic Zone, New Zealand. Froggatt (1982: 301) has estimated that, during this period, the rhyolitic materials erupted from these centres have included 360 km^3 of air fall tuff, 350 km^3 of ignimbrite and 55 km^3 of lava: altogether, this is equivalent to 350 km^3 of rhyolitic magma. According to Cole (1981: 317), the Taupo Volcanic Zone is a 'volcanic arc and marginal basin of the Taupo–Hikurangi subduction system', and 97.4 per cent of the volcanic material is 'rhyolite and ignimbrite', 2.5 per cent is andesite, less than 0.1 per cent is high-Al basalt, and less than 0.1 per cent is dacite. There is thus a great preponderance of rhyolitic rocks in the Taupo Volcanic Zone. In order to account for the origin of these rhyolitic rocks, and also to account for the dominance of rhyolites relative to andesitic and basaltic rocks, Clark (1960) and later workers have proposed that the rhyolitic rocks were mainly derived from a magma that was generated in the crust by the partial melting of Mesozoioc greywackes and argillites. This mode of origin is supported by both trace element data and initial $^{87}Sr/^{86}Sr$ isotopic data (that is, the initial values for the rhyolites are usually approximately 0.706: cf. Cole 1981).

Another interesting group of silicic volcanic rocks are the Late Silurian dacites and rhyolites of the Canberra area of south eastern Australia. In the field these rocks appear to be normal silicic extrusive materials, yet many of them carry a relatively high proportion of megacrysts and xenoliths. A typical megacryst assemblage for one group of these rocks, the Hawkins Suite, is quartz, plagioclase, biotite, orthopyroxene, cordierite, garnet, ilmenite and magnetite. Wyborn et al. (1981) claim that most of these megacrysts are xenocrysts that have been carried up from the source region, where they were originally contained in the source rocks.

Many of the xenoliths obtained from these rocks are found to be composed of minerals that are essentially similar to the megacrysts. These dacites and rhyolites are notable because Wyborn et al. (1981) assert that: (a) they were mainly generated by the large-scale partial melting of metasedimentary source rocks; (b) these volcanic rocks occur in association with comagmatic granitic rocks; and (c) these silicic volcanic and plutonic rocks form a distinct petrographic province within the Palaeozoic Lachlan Fold Belt of south-eastern Australia (that is, the *S-types* of Chappell and White 1974). In general these S-type rocks carry paraluminous minerals such as biotite, muscovite and cordierite, contain more than 1 per cent normative corundum, have initial $^{87}Sr/^{86}Sr$ ratios of 0.708 or more, and as rock associations they tend to plot as irregular lines on variation diagrams.

Examples of silicic materials of the transitional rock association occur on Easter Island which lies approximately 500 km east of the crest of the East Pacific Rise. According to Baker et al. (1974: 86), these rocks have 'transitional tholeiitic affinities', and they range in composition via hawaiite, mugearite, benmoreite and trachyte to rhyolite. The basalts and basic hawaiites straddle the plane of silica saturation in the simple basalt system (Fo–Di–Ne–Qz); and on the alkali silica diagram they plot on either side of the boundary between the Hawaiian alkali and tholeiitic series, whereas the more differentiated rocks lie roughly midway between the mean values for these two Hawaiian series.

8.5 Petrogenesis

In Fig. 7.7.1 it was demonstrated that the rhyolitic rocks fall within a low-temperature trough in petrogeny's residua system; and in Chapters 5, 6 and 7 it was shown that many different parental magmas have liquid lines of descent that converge on the rhyolitic field in compositional space. For example, rhyolite is usually the most differentiated member of: (a) the tholeiitic rock association; (b) the calc–alkalic rock association; (c) the transitional rock association that is essentially intermediate between the alkalic and subalkalic rocks; and (d) the alkalic rock association. The dacites are the penultimate members of the first two subalkalic rock associations, but they do not belong to the more alkalic associations. This is because in the latter (see Section 7.7), the liquid line of descent traverses that part of compositional space that is occupied by the trachytes, and it thus avoids entering the dacitic field. Petrogeny's residua system can also be interpreted as indicating that rhyolitic melts are likely to be generated by the partial melting of a wide range of crustal materials.

The dacites and rhyolites of both the tholeiitic and calc–alkalic rock associations are usually considered to have been produced by the fractional crystallization of the more mafic members of these associations. However, the amount of silicic rock found in many individual suites of these subalkalic rocks is greater than the amount predicted by mass balance mixing models (see Section 2.6). This anomaly can be accounted for if one postulates that the assimilation of crustal rocks (possibly aided by selective fusion) produced a hybrid magma that was enriched in the lithophile elements, and with fractional crystallization the hybrid magma produced a larger volume of rhyolitic magma than the original magma would have been able to produce (see Section 2.5). The amount of rock assimilated by such a magma will depend on many variables, including (a) the amount of energy that is available to assist the assimilation process; and (b) the modal and chemical compositions of the crustal rocks encountered by the magma. It has already been noted that many silicic magmas evolve as the uppermost layer in compositionally-zoned magma chambers. Once a body of magma has developed a capping of low-density silicic magma, the low-density magma is the most likely material to be erupted when a new batch of denser parental magma arrives from depth. The movement of magma from a compositionally-zoned magma chamber is likely to produce some magma mixing; and evidence that this process occurs is found: (a) in compositionally-zoned pyroclastic deposits; and (b) in the *enclosures* of more mafic magmatic rock that are often found in rhyolitic granitic rocks.

In order to account for the almost bimodal basalt–rhyolite association found in some areas of the Thulean Petrographic Province, Walker

(1975) developed the following model. A picritic, or basaltic, magma is emplaced into the crust. Fractional crystallization, assisted by assimilation and the selective fusion of crustal rocks, yields a rhyolitic magma that gradually accumulates to form a diapir. The diapir rises through the denser superincumbent rocks. Batches of basaltic magma rise up below the diapir; however, because of their greater density, they are unable to pass through it. Gradually an elongate cylinder of more basic material develops beneath the diapir. As the slow-moving diapir of viscous material rises upwards, part of the more fluid basaltic magma is emplaced into the fractures that develop around the margins of the diapir. When the diapir comes close to the surface, some batches of basaltic magma are diverted into cone sheets; and swarms of nested cone sheets develop, with the intrusion of younger cone sheets inside older ones. Eventually the upper extremity of the diapir ruptures the surface layer, and silicic tephra is extruded explosively. The silicic magma that remains in the diapir is now at least partly degassed, and it rapidly loses heat to the surrounding rocks. Basaltic volcanism continues to recur, and as the upper levels of the diapir cool and contract, basaltic magma is injected to fill the potential voids. The silicic magma that remains in the diapir stays in contact with a pool of basaltic magma; and the relative movements of these two main magmas, together with the movements of any hybrid magmas that they may generate, produce the many intrusive and extrusive features characteristic of volcanic centres that contain rocks of the bimodal basalt–rhyolite association.

In other petrographic provinces, such as the Taupo Volcanic Zone in New Zealand, rhyolite is much more abundant than all the other associated rocks. The rhyolites of this rock association often contain evidence which confirms that they congealed from a magma generated by partial melting within the continental crust. If large-scale crustal melting does occur, one is faced with the dual problems: why does it occur, and how does it occur? It seems likely that large-scale crustal melting would occur in those crustal areas: (a) where suitable source materials (such as greywackes and argillites) are available; (b) where there has been a large input of heat (possibly obtained from magmas introduced from the mantle); and (c) where there has been an influx of volatile components (possibly derived from subducted materials; or from the movement and juxtaposing of crustal blocks that have different volatile contents, and are at different temperatures, such as might occur in continent–continent collisions). Once a segment of the crust begins to melt, or a large body of silicic magma forms within the crust, it becomes progressively more difficult for denser magmas derived from the mantle to penetrate this layer of lower-density, yet mobile, material. As soon as the mafic magmas cease to penetrate this layer, which now acts as a density filter, a runaway system of crustal melting is likely to develop; that is, heat-carrying mafic magmas are emplaced into the base of the growing pool of silicic magma, and this influx of heat enables selective anatexis to take place in the roof and wall rocks that enclose the silicic magma pool (see Section 2.5). The process of anatexis will be examined more fully in Chapter 9 because most of the evidence in support of this process is obtained from the study of the granitic rocks of the catazone.

8.6 Selected references

Barker, F. (ed.) (1979) *Trondhjemites, Dacites, and Related Rocks*, Elsevier Sci. Pub. Co., Amsterdam, The Netherlands.

Chapin, C. E. (ed.) (1979) Ash-flow tuffs, *Geol. Soc. Am., Spec. Pap.*, **80**, 1–212.

Hildreth, W. (1981) Gradients in silicic magma chambers: Implications for lithospheric magmatism, *J. Geophys. Res.*, **86 (B.11)**, 10153–92.

Self, S. & Sparks, R. S. J. (eds) (1981) *Tephra Studies*, D. Reidel Publ. Co., Dordrecht, The Netherlands.

CHAPTER 9

GRANITES AND GRANITIC ROCKS

9.1 General statement

Traditionally, the upper continental crust has been regarded as being composed of rocks that are rich in silica and alumina, and these *sialic* (an acronym for Si + Al) rocks are usually considered to be granitic at the top and gabbroic at the base. In field geology the term granite has often been applied to any holocrystalline, quartz-bearing plutonic rock; whereas in the early days of seismology it was given to any crustal rock in which the velocity of the compressional wave was between 5.5–6.2 km/s. Granite (sensu lato) has come to be regarded as the pre-eminent rock of the upper crust of the continents of the Earth. Any discussion of the development of ideas on the origin and evolution of the granitic rocks, and the related problem of the evolution of the continents, has to begin at least as far back as the eighteenth century, and the passionate debate between the *Vulcanists* and the *Neptunists* (see Section 1.2). According to the Neptunist, Abraham Werner (1786) in his *'Kurze Klassifikation'* as translated by Ospovat (1971: 48), 'granite is an aggregate rock which consists of feldspar, quartz and mica united with each other in a granular texture'. He believed that the original surface of the Earth was uneven and covered by a primeval ocean. The granites precipitated first, and they took their shape from the uneven configuration of the sea floor; and as the primeval ocean began to recede, gneiss, mica-schist and clay-slate were formed (Ospovat 1971: 20–1). Werner not only claimed that the granites formed by precipitation from water, but also that they were older than the metamorphic and sedimentary rocks.

John Playfair in his *Illustrations of the Huttonian Theory of the Earth* (1802: 82) states that granite is 'an aggregate stone, in which quartz, feldspar and mica are found distinct from one another and not disposed in layers'. He (84) proposed: (a) that granite had been 'melted by heat'; (b) that it was younger than the beds 'incumbent on it;' (c) that when emplaced it 'elevated the strata at the same time'. Hutton and Playfair thus regarded granite as being an igneous plutonic rock that may show intrusive contacts, such as those observed by Hutton and the members of the *Oyster Club* at Glen Tilt in Scotland in 1785 (Moore 1957: 99–100). Hutton's observations in a quiet Scottish valley to the southwest of Aberdeen did not, however, result in the immediate and universal acceptance of the concept that granites could be emplaced into older supracrustal rocks as hot bodies of magma.

Many European petrologists claimed that not all granites were necessarily of igneous origin. For example, many French petrologists believed that the granitic rocks were generated by *metamorphic processes*. In 1844, Virlet d'Aoust used the term *imbibition* to describe the hypothesis that fluids, particularly those of igneous origin, may soak into country rocks, such as shales, and transform then into granite; three years later he introduced the term *granitification* to describe this process. In 1869, Delesse proposed that some of the rocks formed by *granitization* may become so mobile that they can be squeezed towards the surface, and thus form intrusive granites at higher levels.

In 1877, Rosenbusch published his famous petrographic and chemical study of the contact metamorphism surrounding the Hohwald Granodiorite in the Vosges, France. He described the progressive sequence of phase changes found in the thermal aureole, and claimed that there was no significant change in the chemical composition of the country rocks of the aureole. From this observation he concluded that the granitic rocks are not produced by granitization. Rosenbusch was an extreme *magmatist*, and he even proposed that the gneisses were magmatic granitic rocks that had undergone dynamic metamorphism. The concept that some of the elements that make up the common rock-forming minerals are mobile in thermal aureoles was not generally accepted until 1921 when Goldschmidt demonstrated that both SiO_2 and Na_2O were introduced during the contact metamorphism of pelitic rocks in the Stavanger area of Norway. However, even when Rosenbusch's ideas on the origin of granite had become the orthodox view accepted by most, some petrologists, such as Alexander Henry Green (1882: 443), believed that there were 'granites and granites' . . . 'some formed in one way and some in another'.

In 1904, Termier developed and expanded the granitization hypothesis, and he proposed that *highly-energized emanations* were able to rise from unspecified depths and convert supracrustal rocks into granites. He believed that the evolution of granites, and regional metamorphism, were but two effects of the same cause. In 1907, Sederholm (88–9) introduced the term *migmatite* to describe the mixed, or composite, rocks (those composed of both igneous, or igneous-looking, and metamorphic materials) that occurred in association with the granitic rocks of southern Finland. He also 'fathered the view that batholiths were produced by partial fusion of the crust' (Wyllie 1977: 392). In 1909, Holmquist introduced the term *ultrametamorphism* to describe an extreme metamorphic process that resulted in the partial fusion of the country rocks. Later, as Sederholm's ideas on the origin of granite developed, he placed less emphasis on the emplacement of granitic magmas and attached more importance to the role played by volatile-rich fluids which he called *ichor*. The weakness in this hypothesis is that it implies that a relatively small quantity of ichor can contain sufficient energy to promote widespread granitization. Wegmann (1935) of Switzerland ascribed granitization to *stoffwanderung*, or the migration of ions. He also supported the concept of an advancing *migmatite front* that went ahead of the *granitization front*. By about this time the term granitization had come to mean a metamorphic/metasomatic process by which solid rocks are *transformed* into granitic rocks, by the entry and exit of materials, without passing through a magmatic stage. The major elements that were commonly supposed to be added during granitization were Na and K, while Fe, Mg and Ca were the elements that it was claimed were driven out, possibly to form what Reynolds (1947) called *basic fronts*. Reynolds (1947: 209) also introduced the term *transformist* to describe the petrologists who believed that only a small amount of magma was required to produce granitic bodies of batholithic proportions. The transformists claimed that granites are only incidentally magmatic, or igneous, rocks. One of the main proponents of what was called *wet transformism* was Read; and his book *The Granite Controversy* (1957) makes most enjoyable and informative reading. An example of one of his (373) thought-provoking remarks is that 'it is only by the grace of granitization that we have continents to live on'. The most extreme proponents of the granitization hypothesis were the *dry transformists* (for example: Perrin & Rouboult 1949: Perrin 1954; 1956) who claimed that granites formed as the result of the migration of ions through solids, and that magmas and fluids were usually superfluous.

Two of the staunchest supporters of the concept that granites normally form from the crystallization of magma were Niggli (1942) and Bowen (1948), and they were known as *magmatists*. In 1958, with the publication of Tuttle and Bowen's memoir on the 'Origin of granite in the light of experimental studies in the system $NaAlSi_3O_8 – KAlSi_3O_8 – SiO_2 – H_2O$', the tenor of the debate on the origin and evolution of the granitic rocks changed. This important publication introduced new concepts, but is also placed precise constraints on many of the more speculative older ideas on the origin of the granitic rocks. Tuttle and Bowen were not only concerned with the crystallization of granitic/rhyolitic magmas, they also developed an anatectic model for generating granitic/rhyolitic magmas. They (117) proposed that a number of crustal rocks, including sedimentary, metamorphic and igneous materials, had appropriate compositions for generating granitic/rhyolitic magmas; and that if such materials were hydrous, they could produce granitic melts at temperatures as low as 640 °C and pressures of the order of 0.4 GPa. Winkler and Von Platen (1957) confirmed this model in a series of melting experiments using supracrustal materials. In more recent times, detailed field and geochemical studies (cf. Pitcher & Berger 1972; Atherton & Tarney 1979) have demonstrated that the granitic rocks have formed in a number of different ways, and also that many different parental magmas have liquid lines of descent that converge on the granite/rhyolite field in compositional space (see Section 8.5 and Fig. 9.6.1). It is suggested that much of the controversy that once raged about the origin of the granitic rocks arose because of a *categorical error*; that is, all the granitic rocks were placed in one group, or category, and it was then implicitly, rather than explicitly, proposed that they all formed in the same manner.

In the Streckeisen (1973) classification of plutonic rocks, granite occupies a large area on the QAP triangular diagram; that is, granite (sensu stricto) contains between 20–60 per cent Q, and alkali feldspar makes up between 35–90 per cent of the total feldspar content. This definition of granite is not only in agreement with common usage over many years; but it has been found necessary to have a broad modal definition such as this because, as Tuttle and Bowen (1958: 127) have shown, it is possible for seven of the different types of granitic rocks found in Johannsen's (1917) modal classification to have the same chemical composition. This enigma is readily explained when one recalls that both sodium and potassium may be distributed in a number of different ways among the various phases found in the granitic rocks: for example, if much of the sodium is contained in what is regarded as a potassium feldspar (for example, a cryptoperthite), then Johannsen would call the rock a *kaligranite* (or orthogranite); whereas at the other extreme, if most of the sodium occurs together with calcium in plagioclase, and much of the potassium occurs in a mafic mineral such as biotite, the granitic rock would be called a granodiorite, or even a quartz diorite.

Tuttle and Bowen (1958: 79) studied the abundance of normative Ab–Or–Q in all the granitic rocks in Washington's (1917) compilation of chemical analyses of igneous rocks, and they found that the rocks that carry 80 per cent or more (Ab + Or + Q) form a coherent group with a limited range in compositions and a mean value of approximately $Ab_{32}Or_{32}Q_{36}$. They (128) also suggested that the granites, together with the other plutonic rocks that crystallize in *petrogeny's residua system* (that is, the syenites and nepheline syenites), can be classified by using the manner in which sodium is distributed between plagioclase and the alkali feldspars. In some granitic rocks all the sodium occurs as a component in perthite; and by analogy with the simple binary system $NaAlSi_3O_8$ (Ab)–$KAlSi_3O_8$ (Or) such *one-feldspar granites* have been called *hypersolvus granites* (that is, in the system Ab – Or a single feldspar crystallizes at temperatures that are above the solvus line for this system), whereas the *two-feldspar granites* are called *subsolvus granites* (cf. Tuttle & Bowen 1958: 129). In those granitic rocks that contain sodium feldspar in addition to potassium feldspar, the sodium content of the potassium phase is regarded as a measure of the temperature of final crystallization. Barth (1956; 1962b), for example, used this concept in his *two-feldspar geologic thermometer*. At relatively high temperatures the sodium content of the potassium feldspar is high (greater than 30 wt.%), whereas at lower temperatures it may fall to below 15 wt.%.

The Streckeisen (1973) definition of granite is regarded by some petrologists (cf. Barker 1981: 10131) as being too broad because it includes rocks that contain up to 90 per cent of minerals other than quartz and feldspar, whereas most normal granites contain less than 20 per cent of mafic and accessory minerals (that is, M). In the Streckeisen classification scheme, the proportions of the three defining end-members (QAP) are relative, and their absolute contents in a particular granite vary inversely with the total content of the other phases (that is, M); therefore a granite that is composed of only feldspar and quartz (alaskite) must contain at least 20 per cent quartz, whereas a rock containing 25 per cent M need contain only 15 per cent quartz to be classified as a granite. If rocks that vary in their M content, between 0 and 90, are all included within the definition of granite, this effectively precludes a concise chemical definition of granite; and granite thus defined occupies a much larger field in compositional space than the rhyolites which are usually defined using simple chemical criteria (see Ch. 8).

9.2 Modal composition and texture

The granitic rocks include: (a) the *alkali-feldspar granites*; (b) the *granites* (sensu stricto); (c) the *granodiorites*; and (d) the *tonalites* (see Fig. 3.2.1). Alkali feldspar is usually the only feldspar in the alkali-feldspar granites; however, according to Streckeisen (1974), up to 10 per cent of their total feldspar content may be plagioclase. In the granites (sensu stricto), between 10–65 per cent of the total feldspar is plagioclase; in the granodiorites, between 65–90 per cent; whereas in the tonalites, between 90–100 per cent. Streckeisen (1974: 781) regarded the *trondjemites* as leucotonalites in which M is less than 10. In these rocks the essential feldspar is normally oligoclase or andesine. The granitic rocks are usually regarded as leucocratic rocks (see Table 9.2.1), with the mafic mineral content being highest in the granodiorites and some of the tonalites.

Many granites do, however, contain occasional mesocratic to melanocratic enclosures, or 'black knots'. Some large bodies of granite display remarkable internal homogeneity, and Chayes (1952) showed that this was true of the fine-grained calc-alkali granites of New England, USA. He (237) demonstrated that the modes of 145 thin sections of these granites fall within the following limits: quartz 20–35 per cent, total feldspar 50–70 per cent, colour index 5–20 per cent, and that the ratio of the dominant to the subordinate feldspar is equal to, or less than, 2.5 (see Table 9.2.1). The accessory minerals found in these granites include Fe–Ti oxides, sphene, apatite, fluorite, carbonate minerals, zircon and tourmaline. Epidote occurs, but it is largely confined to the granites in which the plagioclase has been extensively altered.

Feldspars make up the greater part of most of the granitic rocks. The alkali feldspars in these rocks differ from those in the rhyolites (Section 8.2) in that the former normally contain orthoclase, orthoclase microperthite, microcline, microcline microperthite, or microcline perthite; whereas the latter usually contain sanidine, sanidine cryptoperthite, anorthoclase cryptoperthite, or anorthoclase. Most of the plagioclases found in the granitic rocks range in composition from oligoclase to andesine. The quartz content is usually between 20 and 40 per cent; and the common mafic minerals found in these rocks are biotite, muscovite and/or amphibole. A distinct group of granitic rocks are the orthopyroxene-bearing charnockitic rocks (see section 10.4). Tobi (1971: 202) has proposed that the charnockitic rocks, that are equivalent of the alkali-feldspar granites, granites, granodiorites and tonalites, should be called *alkali charnockites, charnockites, enderbites* and *quartz norites*, respectively. The term charnockite is derived from Job Charnock, the founder of Calcutta in India, because it was from his tombstone that the first specimen of this rock series was described (cf. Holland 1900: 134). Such orthopyroxene-bearing rocks are not typical of the granitic rocks, as the rocks of the charnockite series usually occur in granulite facies metamorphic terranes, and high-grade metamorphism is generally considered to be an essential factor in their evolution.

The accessory minerals that are usually found in the granitic rocks are apatite, zircon and the Fe–Ti oxides; others that occur in some granites include allanite, sphene, pyrite, tourmaline, fluorite, monazite and xenotime. The radioactive accessory minerals tend to occur within the mafic minerals, such as biotite, and they are often observed to be surrounded by distinctive 'haloes'. Almandine garnet, andalusite, cordierite and sillimanite have all been described from some granites. These 'metamorphic minerals' are usually regarded as being xenocrysts generated by the mechanical dismemberment, and partial assimilation, of crustal rocks. Such xenocrysts, for example, are found in the *S-type granitic rocks* of the Palaeozoic Lachlan Fold Belt of southeastern Australia (see Section 8.4).

The *alkali-feldspar granites* are essentially composed of alkali feldspar and quartz, and they generally also carry one, or more, mafic minerals such as biotite, muscovite, hornblende, alkali amphibole or alkali pyroxene. Extensive outcrops of riebeckite granite have, for example, been described from the Younger Granite Province of northern Nigeria. One of these peralkaline alkali-feldspar granites, the Liruei riebeckite–aegirine–granite, contains approximately 30.0 per cent quartz, 52.9 per cent orthoclase and microcline perthite, 8.3 per cent plagioclase (albite–oligoclase), 8.7 per cent riebeckite and aegirine, 0.1 per cent fluorite and a trace of zircon (Jacobson et al. 1958: 18; Table 9.3.1). These peralkaline granites may also carry accessory amounts of apatite, allanite, pyrochlore, cryolite, topaz, thorite and astrophyllite. According to Jacobson et al. (1958: 18–19), astrophyllite may be quite abundant near the margins of some of the riebeckite granites; whereas pyrochlore is typically found in the sodium-rich facies of these rocks. Other well-known peralkaline granites are the Quincy Granite of Massachusetts, USA, and the granites of the Oslo region of Norway.

The *calc–alkali granites* of New England, USA are good examples of granites (sensu stricto), and the mean modes of some of these rocks are given in Table 9.2.1. Tables 9.3.1 and 9.3.2 give the chemical composition of the Westerly Granite, Rhode Island, USA, which is possibly the most intensely-studied granite on Earth. Another well-known body of granite is the Rosses Complex of Donegal, north-western Ireland. It has been discovered that the main body of this complex consists of four units; and three of them are biotite granites, while the fourth is a muscovite granite. The mean modes of these granites (G_1 – G_4) are given in Table 9.2.2. In these rocks the plagioclase is generally zoned with a sericitized core (An_{18}), and such crystals tend to become progressively more sodic

Table 9.2.1 Selected modal analyses of granites from New England, USA (%)

	1	2	3	4	5	6
Quartz	27.4	26.9	31.0	27.2	28.8	27.5
Potassium feldspar	32.0	30.4	27.6	19.7	38.4	35.4
Plagioclase	33.4	35.2	30.4	35.4	25.2	31.4
Biotite	3.8	6.3	5.4	8.0	5.8	3.2
Muscovite	2.3	0.4	5.4	7.9	1.4	1.3
Opaque accessories	0.8	0.5	0.1	0.2	$\approx$0.1	0.8
Non-opaque accessories	0.4	0.3	0.2	1.6	0.3	0.4

1. Mean modal composition of thirteen specimens of the Westerly Granite, Rhode Island and Massachusetts (after Chayes 1952: 247).
2. Mean modal composition of thirteen specimens of the Milford Granite, New Hampshire (after Chayes 1952: 247).
3. Mean modal composition of fourteen specimens of the Fitzwilliam Granite, New Hampshire (after Chayes 1952: 248).
4. Mean modal composition of twenty-two specimens of the Barre Granite, Vermont (after Chayes 1952: 248).
5. Mean modal composition of fourteen specimens of the Pownal Granite, Maine (after Chayes 1952: 249).
6. Mean modal composition of twelve specimens of granite from the Smith Granite Co. of Westerly, Rhode Island (that is, US Geological Survey Standard Rock G-1) (after Chayes 1951: 61).

away from the core. The unaltered outer rims often have the composition of An_{11}. A particularly interesting textural feature of these rocks is the presence of aggregates of plagioclase that share a common outer zone. The potassium feldspar is usually microcline microperthite, and it has a mean composition of $Or_{87.9}Ab_{10.6}An_{1.5}$. It and the other essential minerals often enclose smaller grains of biotite. The muscovite-rich granites (that is, G_4) characteristically contain large irregular plates of muscovite. Pitcher and Berger (1972: 194) claim that 'it is clear from their textural relationships that both the microcline and muscovite in the Rosses Complex is of relatively late origin. Both minerals replace plagioclase, broken crystals of which may occur immediately adjacent to completely undeformed microcline and muscovite. Furthermore late veinlets of quartz and muscovite are common.'

Wedepohl (1969: 244) claimed that the *grano-diorites* make up approximately 34 per cent of the volume occupied by intrusive rocks in the

upper continental crust of the Earth. The term granodiorite was proposed by Becker, and used by Lindgren and others to describe a distinctive type of granitic rocks that they found to be abundant in the Sierra Nevada Batholith of California, USA (cf. Lindgren 1900). According to Johannsen (1932: 321), granodiorites are usually a little darker in colour than granites, and a little lighter than tonalites. Their appearance is usually like that of a granite; but the rock is generally greyer because of the smaller amount of orthoclase and the greater amount of plagioclase. Granodiorites from the type area in central California usually carry between 40–5 per cent plagioclase, 20–6 per cent quartz, 15–18 per cent potassium feldspar, 12–17 per cent biotite and hornblende, and accessory amounts ($\approx$2.5 per cent) of Fe–Ti oxides, sphene, apatite and zircon (Lindgren 1900: 275). Other accessory minerals that have been described, from the granodiorites of the *cordilleran-type batholiths* of the Americas, include allanite, andalusite, cassiterite, garnet, hypersthene, muscovite, olivine, pyrite, rutile and tourmaline. In the cordilleran-type batholiths, such as the Coast Range Batholith of Alaska and British Columbia, the Sierra Nevada Batholith of California, the Lower California Batholith of California and Baja California, Mexico, and the Coastal Batholith of Peru, the plutonic rocks can be divided into *superunits* which are major associations of consanguineous rocks. For example, the Santa Rosa Superunit of the Lima segment of the Coastal Batholith of Peru contains a complete suite of plutonic rocks that range in composition from quartz diorite to granite, and the most abundant rocks are tonal-

Table 9.2.2 Mean modal composition of granites from the Rosses Complex, Donegal, Ireland (after Pitcher and Berger 1972: 193) (%)

	G1	G2	G3	G4
Quartz	32.1	34.3	31.7	28.3
Plagioclase	40.9	37.2	40.3	38.7
Potassium feldspar	21.6	24.2	23.9	27.7
Biotite, Fe–Ti oxides and secondary minerals	5.1	4.1	2.7	1.3
Muscovite	0.3	0.2	1.4	4.0

ites and granodiorites (see Table 9.3.3). According to Nockolds et al. (1978: 24), the plagioclases found in the granodiorites have a mean composition of An_{28}, whereas the granites contain more sodic plagioclases, and the tonalites more calcic plagioclases. However, in all of these granitic rocks the hornblende-bearing rocks tend to contain more calcic plagioclases than the biotite-bearing rocks, which in turn contain more calcic plagioclase than the muscovite-bearing rocks.

The name *tonalite* was first used by Vom Rath (1864) to describe the rocks of Monte Tonale in northern Italy. He proposed that tonalites should be essentially composed of plagioclase and quartz, together with mafic minerals and only accessory amounts of potassium feldspar. The type-rock contained approximately 50–5 per cent normally-zoned plagioclase (An_{41-63}), 15–20 per cent quartz, 5 per cent alkali feldspar, 25 per cent mafic minerals, and accessory amounts of Fe–Ti oxides, sphene and apatite. If one excludes the trondhjemites, one finds that most tonalites contain a higher proportion of mafic minerals than the granodiorites and granites. The usual mafic minerals found in the tonalites are biotite and hornblende. Clinopyroxene (usually augite) may occur, and when it does it is usually mantled by either biotite or hornblende. The accessory minerals that are typically found in the tonalites include alkali feldspar, allanite, apatite, Fe – Ti oxides, garnet, muscovite pyrite, sphene and zircon. Tonalites are widely distributed in the cordilleran-type batholiths of the Americas; Larsen (1948) has, for example, described many from the Lower California Batholith. The Bonsall Tonalite is a typical example of these rocks, and a representative sample of this intrusive body, collected from 3 km northeast of San Luis Rey Mission, contains 50 per cent plagioclase (An_{41}), 25 per cent quartz, 14 per cent biotite, 6 per cent hornblende, 4 per cent alkali feldspar and 1 per cent accessory minerals.

The *trondhjemites* are leucotonalites; however, according to Barker (1979a: 2), the andesine-bearing leucotonalites should be called *calcic trondhjemites*, and the leuco alkali feldspar granites in which the predominant feldspar is albite and the oligoclase-bearing leucotonalites should both be considered to be trondhjemites (sensu stricto). Goldschmidt (1915) introduced the term trondhjemite to describe the leucocratic plagioclase-rich granitic rocks of an area to the south of Trondheim (or Trondhjem as he called it) in Norway. Unfortunately, the rocks of this area

have been metamorphosed to the greenschist facies; and their modal composition is as follows: 49 per cent plagioclase, 29 per cent quartz, 9 per cent muscovite, 9 per cent epidote, together with accessory amounts of microcline, sphene and apatite (cf. Barker & Millard 1979: 522). It is important to regard the trondhjemites as a discrete group of rocks that are separate from the tonalites, as these two groups have different distributions in space and time. The trondhjemites are particularly abundant in *Archaean grey gneiss complexes* which are among the oldest rocks known on Earth. According to McGregor (1979: 184), grey gneisses that have 'general trondhjemitic affinities' are the main component in the Archaean of Greenland, and these rocks include the 3.75 Ga old Amitsoq Gneisses of the Godthab region of West Greenland (see Section 4.2). Hunter (1979: 301) had demonstrated that rocks of trondhjemitic composition are particularly abundant in the pre-3.1 Ga old rock units in Swaziland and adjoining areas of South Africa.

Textures

The granitic rocks are medium- to coarse-grained, and they generally have a subhedral granular, or *granitoid texture*. Both the feldspars and the mafic minerals tend to occur in subhedral crystals, whereas the quartz usually occupies the intergranular spaces between these minerals. However, when the alkali feldspar has a low abundance, as in the tonalites, it usually occurs as anhedral crystals in close association with the interstitial quartz grains. Some granitic rocks are porphyritic, and they usually contain large subhedral to euhedral megacrysts of potassium feldspar; such megacrysts often enclose smaller crystals. Occasionally the potassium feldspars are ovoid in shape and surrounded by an overgrowth of plagioclase (usually oligoclase); and this is usually called *rapakivi texture* (see Section 10.4). Many of the epizonal granites have variable textures that include graphic, micrographic or granophyric, intergrowths of potassium feldspar and quartz. The cores of many granitic bodies show little or no preferred orientation of the constituent minerals; whereas near their margins there is often a tendency for the long axes of the more elongate minerals to be aligned, in a more or less parallel manner, so as to produce a distinct lineation. Many Precambrian granitic rocks are foliated and have banded or *gneissic textures*; such textures are usually interpreted as being of metamorphic origin.

Unlike the relatively simple textures of the basaltic rocks, the textural relationships between the minerals in the granitic rocks are seldom able to provide indisputable evidence of the magmatic origin of these rocks. Many of the textural features characteristic of these rocks are interpreted as having evolved at a late stage during their cooling history. According to Pitcher and Berger (1972: 333), these late-stage reactions and readjustments include: (a) the late growth of potassium or alkali feldspar: (b) exsolution in the alkali feldspars; (c) the evolution of albite rims and myrmekitic intergrowths on plagioclases adjoining the alkali fedspars; (d) the deformation twinning and alteration of plagioclase; (e) the chloritisation of biotite; and (f) the recrystallization and straining of quartz. Many petrologists have shown that the crystallization of the alkali feldspars is a complex process that involves exsolution, replacement and, frequently, inversion; and all of these processes occur at a late stage in the evolution of the granitic fabric. The widespread occurrence of undulatory and patchy extinction in the quartz grains clearly shows that they have had to respond to stress at a late stage in the evolution of the granitic fabric. It is postulated that in most two-feldspar granitic rocks, plagioclase and the mafic minerals crystallize early, and quartz and the alkali feldspars form late; and the crystallization–recrystallization of the latter mineral, assisted by the structural rearrangements attendant on its exsolution and inversion, the chloritization of the biotite, the homogenization and deformation twinning in the plagioclases, furnish a mechanism by which the whole, or part, of a granitic body can move while essentially solid. Luth (1976: 336) has summarized his views on the evolution of granitic textures by stating that 'most granitic rocks exhibit textural and mineralogic features which are less related to the ultimate magmatic origin and early history than to subsequent subsolidus recrystallization.'

9.3 Geochemistry and normative compositions

In Section 9.1 it was shown that the granitic rocks, as defined by Streckeisen (1973), may oc-cupy a large field in compositional space. A study of the modal and chemical compositions of the granitic rocks reveals that the overwhelming majority of these rocks occupy a much more limited field within compositional space. Most of the alkali-feldspar granites, and granites in which A > P, have chemical compositions that are broadly similar to the rhyolites; whereas most granodiorites, tonalites and granites in which P > A have chemical compositions that are broadly similar to the dacites (see Tables 8.3.1, 8.3.2 and 9.3.1). There is generally also a progressive decrease in TiO_2, Al_2O_2, MgO and CaO, and an increase in SiO_2 and K_2O in the series tonalite $\rightarrow$ granodiorite $\rightarrow$ granite $\rightarrow$ alkali-feldspar granite; however, there are many exceptions to this simple geochemical pattern, and they are usually mesocratic granites, or leucocratic granodiorites or tonalites. Table 9.3.3 shows the changes in chemical composition found in a series of rocks from the Coastal Batholith of Peru that grade from gabbros to granites; this table also contains selected trace element data for these rocks. Table 9.3.2 gives the complete trace element composition of the Westerly Granite of Rhode Island, USA.

The normative mineral compositions of the granitic rocks clearly illustrate their differences in major element composition. In the series tonalite $\rightarrow$ granodiorite $\rightarrow$ granite, there is usually a progressive increase in the amount of normative quartz ($\approx$16–30 per cent) and normative orthoclase ($\approx$12–24 per cent); a decrease in the amount of normative anorthite ($\approx$23–8 per cent), normative pyroxene ($\approx$11–3 per cent) and normative Fe–Ti oxides ($\approx$4–2 per cent); whereas the normative albite remains essentially constant ($\approx$30 per cent). These normative data also show that the mafic minerals produced by the C.I.P.W. normative system are not the minerals that are commonly found in the granitic rocks. This is well illustrated by specimen G-1 of the Westerly Granite, Rhode Island. This rock contains 27.2 per cent normative quartz which is similar to the modal value, 32.3 per cent normative orthoclase which is 3 per cent less than the modal value, 27.8 per cent normative albite and 7.0 per cent normative anorthite which is 3 per cent more than the modal plagioclase; and instead of 3.2 per cent modal biotite, 1.3 per cent muscovite, 0.8 per cent Fe–Ti oxides and 0.4 per cent non-opaque accessory minerals, it contains 1.7 per cent normative hypersthene, 1.4 per cent normative magnetite, 0.9 per cent norma-

Table 9.3.1 Chemical composition of selected granitic rocks (%)

	1	*2*	*3*	*4*	*5*	*6*	*7*
SiO_2	75.26	72.64	71.30	68.65	66.09	61.52	71.72
TiO_2	0.26	0.26	0.31	0.54	0.54	0.73	0.22
Al_2O_3	10.48	14.04	14.32	14.55	15.73	16.48	15.98
Fe_2O_3	2.42	0.87	1.21	1.23	1.38	1.83	0.49
FeO	1.32	0.96	1.64	2.70	2.73	3.82	0.88
MnO	0.10	0.03	0.05	0.08	0.08	0.08	0.03
MgO	0.35	0.38	0.71	1.14	1.74	2.80	0.53
CaO	0.57	1.39	1.84	2.68	3.83	5.42	2.83
Na_2O	4.04	3.32	3.68	3.47	3.75	3.63	5.56
K_2O	4.66	5.48	4.07	4.00	2.73	2.07	1.21
H_2O^+	0.48	0.34	0.64	0.59	0.85	1.04	0.53
H_2O^-	0.08	0.06	0.13	0.14	0.19	0.20	0.01
P_2O_5	0.08	0.09	0.12	0.19	0.18	0.25	0.06
CO_2	0.01	0.07	0.05	0.09	0.08	0.14	0.02
Total	100.11	99.93	100.07	100.05	99.90	100.01	100.07

1. Chemical composition of a riebeckite–aegirine granite from Liruei, Younger Granite Province of Northern Nigeria (after Jacobson et al. 1958: 17, No. 2). The rock also contains 0.18 per cent ZrO_2, 0.06 per cent Cl and 0.09 per cent F.
2. Chemical composition of US Geological Survey Standard G-1 granite from Westerly, Rhode Island, USA (after Fleischer 1969: 65, No. 3a).
3. Mean chemical composition of granite (after Le Maitre, 1976a: 606) (total number of analyses 2485).
4. Mean chemical composition of granite (variety adamellite) (after Le Maitre 1976a: 608) (total number of analyses 135; sample based towards rocks from Australasia).
5. Mean chemical composition of granodiorite (after Le Maitre 1976a: 609) (total number of analyses 885).
6. Mean chemical composition of tonalite (after Le Maitre 1976a: 612) (total number of analyses 97).
7. Chemical composition of trondhjemite from the type-area of Trondheim–Oppdal, Norway (after Barker & Millard 1979: 523, No. N–2); quarry 2 km east of Støren. Rock also contains 0.02 per cent F.

Table 9.3.2 Trace element composition of granite from Westerly, Rhode Island, USA: US Geological Survey Standard G-1 (after Fleischer 1965; 1969)

	p.p.m.		*p.p.m.*		*p.p.m.*
Li	24	Sr	250	Eu	1.3
Be	3	Y	13	Gd	5
B	1.5	Zr	210	Tb	0.6
N	8	Nb	20	Dy	2.5
F	700	Mo	7	Ho	0.5
Cl	≈70	Ru	<0.4	Er	2
Sc	3	Rh	<0.005	Tm	0.2
Ti	1500	Pd	0.0025	Y	1
V	16	Ag	0.04	Lu	0.2
Cr	22	Cd	0.06	Hf	6
Mn	230	In	0.025	Ta	1.6
Co	2.4	Sn	4	W	<0.8
Ni	1.5	Sb	0.4	Re	0.00056
Cu	13	Cs	1.5	Os	0.00006
Zn	45	Ba	1200	Pt	<0.01
Ga	18	La	100	Au	0.005
Ge	1	Ce	170	Hg	0.245
As	0.8	Pr	17	Tl	1.3
Br	0.13	Nd	55	Pb	49
Rb	220	Sm	9	Th	52
				U	4

Table 9.3.3 Chemical composition of selected rocks from the Coastal Batholith of Peru

	1(%)	2(%)	3(%)	4(%)	5(%)
SiO_2	48.29	58.53	69.45	71.35	75.34
TiO_2	0.62	0.99	0.36	0.32	0.18
Al_2O_3	19.07	16.25	14.88	14.32	12.87
Fe_2O_3	2.78	2.94	1.59	2.00	0.25
FeO	6.98	5.69	1.23	0.65	0.80
MnO	0.18	0.18	0.07	0.09	0.09
MgO	7.96	3.07	1.24	0.97	0.41
CaO	11.20	6.22	2.81	2.26	0.81
Na_2O	1.97	3.09	3.69	3.71	3.88
K_2O	0.24	1.57	3.29	3.13	4.38
P_2O_5	0.12	0.15	0.05	0.06	0.03
Total	99.41	98.68	98.66	98.86	99.04
	p.p.m.	p.p.m.	p.p.m.	p.p.m.	p.p.m.
Co	49	19	7	5	3
Cr	18	5	10	3	16
Ni	27	8	23	13	11
Rb	6	59	99	122	103
Sr	427	328	306	238	82
V	271	181	47	39	12
Y	8	43	11	14	14
Zr	27	129	111	96	87

1. Mean chemical composition of eight gabbroic rocks from the Coastal Batholith of Peru (after Atherton et al. 1979: 51, A).
2. Chemical composition of a tonalite from the Santa Rosa superunit, Lima segment of the Coastal Batholith of Peru (after Atherton et al. 1979: 51, K).
3. Chemical composition of a granodiorite from the Santa Rosa superunit, Lima segment of the Coastal Batholith of Peru (after Atherton et al. 1979: 51, L).
4. Chemical composition of a granite from the Puscao superunit, Lima segment of the Coastal Batholith of Peru (after Atherton et al. 1979: 51, M).
5. Chemical composition of a granite from the Pativilca pluton, Lima segment of the Coastal Batholith of Peru (after Atherton et al. 1979: 51, N).

tive corundum, 0.5 per cent normative apatite and 0.2 per cent normative calcite (see Table 9.2.1).

9.4 Abundance and distribution

The granitic rocks are very abundant, and have wide spatial and temporal distributions in the continental crust of the Earth. In Section 4.4 it was suggested that, in a normal section through the continental crust of the Earth, there are approximately 8 km of granitic rocks and migmatites. Brown (1979: 106) claims that 'tonalite is the dominant rock type in the continental crust and, despite near-surface metamorphic and sedimentary processes that bring about chemical segregation, the average composition of the continents is virtually tonalite'. The granitic rocks are particularly characteristic of Precambrian shield areas, but it is often difficult to establish the tectonic environment into which many of these rocks were emplaced. In the Phanerozoic, many of the largest bodies of granitic rocks, such as those that form the cordilleran-type batholiths, are associated with orogenic belts, seismically active continental margins and island-arcs. Other Phanerozoic granitic rocks are anorogenic, and usually have alkaline affinities; and they tend to be associated with rifts or palaeorifts, such as the Oslo Palaeorift and/or they occur in subvolcanic ring complexes that do not appear to be directly related to rifting, or subduction, but are often associated with subvolcanic or crustal doming (see Section 12.4). The cordilleran-type batholiths are usually composed of a large number of intrusive bodies that can be grouped into a limited number of superunits: for example, the Lima segment of the Coastal Batholith of Peru (see Table 9.3.3) is composed of nine such su-

Table 9.3.4 Chemical and modal composition of an anatectic alkali-feldspar granite (or leucogranite) from the Bhutan Himalaya (after Dietrich & Gansser 1981: 189, Specimen GH-471).

	%		p.p.m.		p.p.m.
SiO_2	73.16	Sc	3	Nd	16.6
TiO_2	0.11	V	<10	Sm	3.91
Al_2O_3	14.52	Co	17	Eu	0.41
Fe_2O_3	0.19	Zn	31	Tb	0.59
FeO	0.90	Ga	14	Yb	1.59
MnO	0.04	Rb	373	Lu	0.24
MgO	0.14	Sr	62	Pb	45
CaO	0.74	Y	14		
Na_2O	3.04	Zr	49		
K_2O	4.98	Nb	3		
K_2O	0.75	Ba	243		
P_2O_5	0.16	La	16.9		
Total	98.73	Ce	35.0		

			%
Mode:	Quartz		34
	Potassium feldspar		28
	Albite		28
	Muscovite		6
	Biotite		2
	Fe–Ti oxides		0.5
	Apatite		0.4
	Tourmaline		Tr

perunits. Such batholiths usually have the following characteristics: (a) elongate shapes that are aligned parallel to convergent plate boundaries; (b) bulk compositions that are usually in the granodiorite–tonalite range; (c) they tend to be associated with volcanic rocks that are often less silicic than the plutonic rocks; (d) regular geographic variations in the strontium and neodymium isotopes found in the various rocks; and these data are generally interpreted as indicating that the rocks contain various mixtures of components derived from both the upper mantle and the old continental crust (cf. De Paolo 1981); and (e) the major element compositions of the rocks within individual superunits generally follow a common calc-alkalic trend (see Section 6.1; cf. Atherton et al. 1979).

According to Brown (1979: 115), there are two main rock associations that contain large volumes of granitic rocks: (a) the calc-alkalic association; and (b) the alkaline association. The former association has predominated throughout most of the history of the Earth, including the Archaean; whereas magmas of the alkaline association only 'became important products of intraplate magmatism during mid-Proterozoic times' (1.5–2.0 Ga). He also claims that the chemical composition of the Late Proterozoic Pan-African, and Early Phanerozoic Caledonian granite, is essentially transitional between these two major rock associations; however, even in these rocks there is evidence of a bias towards 'subduction-related calc–alkaline magmatism'.

Archaean granites

Most Archaean terrains contain a variety of granitic bodies of various sizes and compositions; and at present many petrologists are trying to elucidate the relationship that is believed to exist between the emplacement of these rocks and the evolution of the continental crust (cf. Condie 1981). The earlier granitic rocks usually belong to the sodium-rich tonalite–trondhjemite association, and these rocks often contain gneissic structures. Many of them are intruded by large batholiths that contain medium- to coarse-grained granites (sensu stricto) that tend to contain megacrysts of potassium feldspar. In some areas, such as Swaziland and the Eastern Transvaal of South Africa, there is evidence of a third magmatic cycle during which a number of discrete bodies of granite were emplaced. It is instructive to make a closer examination of the granitic terrain that flanks the Barberton Greenstone Belt of the Eastern Transvaal and Swaziland, as it began evolving approximately 3.5 Ga ago with the emplacement of rocks of the tonalite–trondhjemite association. This event was accompanied by the evolution of large volumes of gneisses and migmatites. The second magmatic cycle began approximately 3.2 Ga ago with the emplacement of a number of huge granite batholiths, and after their emplacement the general area penetrated by these intrusions attained tectonic stability; that is, the area became a craton. In the Barberton area the third magmatic cycle began approximately 2.9 Ga ago with the intrusion of a number of discrete, potassium-rich bodies of granite and syenite. According to Anhaeusser and Robb (1981: 465), these late granitic rocks 'did not contribute significantly either to the construction or stabilization of the early continental crust but nevertheless represent the ultimate cycle in the formation of the granitic basement. Subsequently the stable platform that had formed was progressively denuded and a succession of cratonic-type volcano-sedimentary basins developed during the Proterozoic Era.'

Granites of convergent plate margins

The granitic rocks of the Himalayan area, and many other areas, such as the Palaeozoic Lachlan Fold Belt of south-eastern Australia, contain calc–alkalic granitic rocks that seem to belong to more than one rock association. Some of these associations are *compositionally restricted*, whereas others are *compositionally expanded*. According to Pitcher (1979b: 3), the former type of association usually contains approximately 2 per cent gabbro, 18 per cent tonalite + granodiorite and 80 per cent granite, whereas the compositionally-expanded association tend to contain approximately 18 per cent gabbro, 50 per cent tonalite + granodiotite and 35 per cent granite. Rocks of the compositionally-restricted association (or the aluminous association of Debon & Le Fort 1983; or the S-type of Chappell & White 1974) usually contain: (a) peraluminous modal compositions. (biotite and muscovite are the typical mafic minerals), and normative corundum; (b) high initial $^{87}Sr/^{86}Sr$ ratios, that are often greater than 0.708; (c) meta-supracrustal xenoliths and xenocrysts; (d) relatively low Na_2O contents; (e) irregular variation diagrams; and (f) thermally-harmoni-ous metamorphic contact rocks. The granitic rocks of the compositionally-restricted association are usually regarded as being mainly derived from the partial melting of continental crustal rocks. Although experimental studies have shown that rhyolitic/granitic melts can readily be produced by the partial melting of many continental crustal rocks, Pitcher (1979b: 2–3) has noted that during the Phanerozoic 'neither the temperatures nor the water-concentrations during ultrametamorphism in the deep crust are sufficiently high to permit remelting to occur, at least not without supplementation via the agency of mantle-derived magmas'.

The granitic rocks of the compositionally-expanded associations are essentially similar to the cafemic association of Debon and Le Fort (1983), and the I-type granitic rocks of Chappell and White (1974) and White and Chappell (1983). Pitcher (1982: 21) has refined the ideas of a number of petrologists on the tectonic settings characteristic of the various orogenic granitic rocks. He claims that these rocks can be separated into one of three types: (a) M-type; (b) I-(Cordilleran) type; and (c) I- (Caledonian) type. The M-type, or mantle-type, granitic rocks generally develop in oceanic island-arcs from mantle-derived parental magmas; and they are usually closely associated with island-arc volcanic activity (see Section 6.6). They characteristically belong to a suite of rocks that ranges in composition from gabbro to tonalite. These M-type plutonic rocks typically have initial $^{87}Sr/^{86}Sr$ ratios of less than 0.704, and they may contain porphyry Cu–Au mineralization and basic igneous enclosures. The most common group of granitic rocks are the I- (Cordilleran) type, and they are generally emplaced into seismically-active continental margins where they form huge, linear, composite batholiths. Their initial $^{87}Sr/^{86}Sr$ ratios are usually less than 0.706, and they tend to contain porphyry Cu–Mo mineralization; the dominant rock type in this expanded rock association is usually tonalite. In the I- (Caledonian) type of granitic rocks, emplacement is considered to be related to the uplift and decompression that occurs after the closure of an ocean basin. According to Pitcher (1982: 21), these rocks have initial $^{87}Sr/^{86}Sr$ ratios that are between 0.705 and 0.709. The dominant rock types are in the range granodiorite–granite, but these rocks are often associated with minor intrusive bodies of hornblende diorite, gabbro and ultramafic rocks of the Appinite-type (see Section 11.10).

Anorogenic granitic rocks

The anorogenic granitic rocks usually crop out in relatively small discrete bodies that are often part of subvolcanic intrusive complexes; they generally have alkaline affinities (see Ch. 12). A well-known group of anorogenic granitic rocks occur in the Tertiary Thulean Province, and they include the granophyres and epigranites (high-level granites) of the Hebridean segment of this province (see Section 8.5). Overall the Phanerozoic anorogenic granites are generally regarded as having evolved in local areas of the continental crust that have been subjected to sublithospheric heating and/or degassing; and in some provinces these rocks were emplaced into areas of intraplate doming, crustal extension and/or rifting (see section 12.4).

Granitic rocks of Venus

As yet there is no detailed data on the petrology of the rocks of Venus; however, some of the Venera Landers were capable of measuring the natural radioactivity in the surface rocks, and Venera 8 landed in an area where the surface rocks are estimated to contain 4 per cent K, 6.5 p.p.m. Th, and 3.6 p.p.m. U. Vinogradov et al. (1973: 259) demonstrated that this material was chemically akin to the silicic magmatic rocks of Earth (that is, the rhyolite/granitic rocks). They also suggested that it was likely that this granitic rock had been modified by the harsh conditions that are known to exist on the surface of Venus (see Section 1.9). Venera Landers 9 and 10 indicated the presence of basaltic rocks; and the presence of both mafic and silicic rocks is taken as indicating that the processes of magmatic differentiation have, and possibly still are, opcrating on Venus. The so-called lunar granites and the silicic rocks of the oceans are discussed in Section 8.1.

9.5 Aplites and pegmatites

The term *aplite* is derived from the classical Greek word *haploos* which means 'simple', and it has long been used to describe rocks of simple composition. For example, Von Leonhard (1823)

used it to describe fine-grained granitic rocks that were essentially composed of feldspar and quartz. Brögger (1898: 212) used the term, as it is usually used at present, to describe fine-grained dykes, or border facies rocks, that have a low colour index and a distinctive allotriomorphic granular texture. Such a texture is usually described as sacharoidal, or aplitic. Aplites may range in composition from granitic to dioritic, but the term aplite by itself is generally understood to mean a fine-grained, leucocratic alkali feldspar granite, or granite. However, the proportion of quartz within an aplite may vary, and some aplites pass into quartz veins, or bodies of quartzolite. Most aplites are restricted to the border zones, particularly the roof zones of epizonal, and particularly mesozonal, intrusive granites (cf. Buddington 1959). The marginal fissures that surround many granitic bodies are often partly, or completely, lined by aplites, or pegmatites. Many of these aplite veins, or dykes, are only a few cm thick. When examined in detail, some aplites are found to have cataclastic textures that are partly masked by recrystallization (cf. Emmons 1953: 73–4).

Pegmatites are holocrystalline rocks that are at least in part very coarse-grained; and they are generally recognized because they are appreciably coarser-grained than the plutonic rocks with which they are associated; that is, they are essentially *giant granites*. Although they are usually granitic in composition, they may have mafic or even ultramafic compositions. For example, the rocks at the base of the Merensky Reef in the Bushveld Layered Complex of South Africa are usually called pegmatitic pyroxenites (see Section 11.6). The term pegmatite is derived from the classical Greek word *pegma* which means 'something fastened together'; and according to Hess (1933: 447–8), the name was originally used to describe *graphic granites* 'in a fanciful allusion to the pegging or fastening together of the feldspar by rods of quartz'. Graphic granites are rocks characterized by intergrowths of quartz and alkali feldspar in which the quartz crystals have fairly regular geometric outline and orientations and the quartz intergrowths look like writing with wedge-shaped characters. Hess (1933: 447) described the pegmatites as being 'undoubtedly the most bizarre, the most contradictory, the most complex and altogether the most interesting group of rocks known. . . . They may be as simple in composition as a granite, or a list of the minerals from a complex pegmatite may look like a page from the index of Dana's System of Mineralogy'. Johannsen (1932: 74) has listed approximately 100 accessory minerals that are found in complex pegmatites. Many of these are rich in elements such a Li, B, F, Nb, R.E.E., Ta, Th and U; and this, is one of the main reasons why the pegmatites have been studied in detail (cf. Cameron et al. 1949; Fersman 1931; Uebel 1977).

In normal granitic pegmatites, the diameters of the crystals usually exceed 250 mm, and the alkali feldspar crystals often exceed 1 m in length; however, in some pegmatites, alkali feldspar, beryl, spondumene and mica crystals, that are over 10 m in length, have been described. Rickwood (1981) claims that the largest authenticated crystal of any type that has been discovered was a beryl from Malakialina, Malagasy; and it was 18 m in length, 3.5 m in diameter, and it had a mass of approximately 380 t. Pegmatites often have very irregular forms, and they may widen, narrow, branch and change direction abruptly. Their contacts with the country rocks are seldom sharp, and they often appear to merge into the rocks that surround them. Detailed mapping has shown that most pegmatites have an orderly arrangement of mineralogical and textural features. Cameron et al. (1949: 1), in their discussion of the internal structure of granite pegmatites, recognized three petrographic types: (a) fracture fillings which occupy fractures in previously consolidated pegmatites; (b) replacement bodies which are rock units that form by the replacement of pre-existing pegmatites; and (c) zones which are successive shells, complete or incomplete, that cluster around an inner core. Zoned pegmatites usually show a definite petrographic sequence as one proceeds from the border zones, via the wall and intermediate zones, to the core of the body. According to Cameron et al. (1949: 98), the dominant mineral assemblages in the various zones, from the walls inward to the cores, are as follows: (a) plagioclase + quartz + muscovite; (b) plagioclase + quartz; (c) quartz + plagioclase + perthite ± muscovite ± biotite; (d) perthite + quartz; (e) perthite + quartz + plagioclase + amblygonite + spodumene; (f) plagioclase + quartz + spodumene; (g) quartz + spondumene; (h) lepidolite + plagioclase + quartz; (i) quartz + microcline; (j) microcline + plagioclase + lithia micas + quartz; (k) quartz. They also note that, whereas no one pegmatite contains all members of this general sequence, the mineral assemblages that are present occur in the same order of succession as the various mineral assemblages in the general sequence. In some zoned pegmatites there is a systematic variation in the composition of the plagioclase from zone to zone, with an overall increase in sodium from walls to core (that is, andesine to albite).

Aplites and pegmatites are often found together in the border zones, and in the cupola protuberances, associated with mesozonal granitic bodies. It is perplexing to find this close association of rocks that represent the opposite extremes in the grain sizes found in plutonic rocks; particularly when aplite and pegmatite may occupy the same fissure. According to Varlamoff (1954), a cooling body of granitic magma may produce either aplites or pegmatites, depending mainly on the conditions of cooling and the rapidity with which the volatile components are released from the magma. The large crystals tend to crystallize from an aqueous fluid. However, the complex pegmatites often contain a large number of different mineral species, and it can thus be assumed they evolved from complex polyphase systems. According to Jahns and Burnham (1969: 843), the parental magma (sensu lato) of most granitic pegmatites crystallizes in three stages: (a) crystallization of essentially anhydrous minerals such as the feldspars and quartz; (b) the crystallization of minerals from both a silicate liquid, and a coexisting aqueous fluid of considerably lower viscosity; partitioning of the constituents between the silicate liquid and the aqueous fluid, rapid diffusion of constituents through the aqueous fluid, and the upward movement of the fluid phase, all contribute to the formation of pods and zones of different modal composition and texture: (c) crystallization and metasomatism by aqueous fluids after the crystallization of the silicate liquid. The crystallization of most granitic pegmatites is believed to occur in what is essentially a closed system. Complex zoning patterns may develop in some pegmatites because the space hosting the pegmatite continues to open while it is crystallizing, and this results in multiple injection, and a protracted period of crystallization and contact metasomatism. Both the aplites and pegmatites can be regarded as bearers of evidence concerning the nature of the late stage drainage systems that evolve in crystallizing batholiths.

9.6 Petrogenesis

In Section 8.5 it was shown that a number of different types of basaltic magmas (that is, tholeiitic, calc–alkalic, transitional and alkalic) evolve along liquid lines of descent that converge on the rhyolitic/granitic field in compositional space. It was also shown that rhyolitic/granitic magmas are readily generated by the partial melting of a wide range of crustal materials within the pressure interval characteristic of the continental crust (that is, anatexis). These two major processes (magmatic differentiation of mantle-derived magma and anatexis) merge. This is because the partial melting of crustal materials is often triggered by the introduction of magma from the upper mantle; whereas the assimilation of crustal materials by mantle-derived magma generates a hybrid magma that tends to be enriched in the lithophile elements and, with fractional crystallization, the hybrid magma is capable of producing larger volumes of rhyolitic/granitic magma than the original magma. These processes may converge completely when a segment of continental crust begins to melt, and fresh batches of magma continue to be injected into that segment. Once a large body of silicic magma forms, it becomes progressively more difficult for denser magmas that are derived from the mantle to penetrate this layer of lower-density mobile material. This is how a runaway system of crustal melting may develop. It is suggested that most granitic rocks are products of multi-stage processes, and that attempts to treat them as single-stage magmatic, or metamorphic processes, are subject to severe limitations; because as Luth (1976: 335) has observed, 'attempts to resolve questions bearing on the magnitude, and variability, of intensive thermodynamic parameters such as pressure, temperature, fugacity or partial pressure of various species, which ignore the multi-stage nature of the overall process are not likely to be successful'.

An important way in which some granitic rocks differ from the rhyolites is that they occur in thermal harmony with metamorphosed country rocks that surround them, and they thus appear to have formed in situ. Such rocks are called *autochthonous granites* and they are 'surrounded by great aureoles of migmatites and metamorphic rocks' (Read 1957: 364). The migmatites that surround these granites are usually composed of leucocratic layers of magmatic appearance (leucosomes) and darker layers of gneissic appearance (mesosomes) It is rewarding to examine the petrography of these migmatites, as it is usually found that with increasing metamorphic grade the leucosomes become broader, and more frequent, and they appear to form as the result of in situ partial melting and crystallization (cf. Johannes & Gupta 1982). In some areas one can find evidence that part of a body of autochthonous granite has been mobilized, and it has separated from the cocoon of migmatitic–metamorphic rocks that evolved at the site of partial melting. Read (1957: 365) has called these granitic rocks *parautochthonous granites*, and he claims that with further movement such materials may completely sever their genetic ties with the country rocks of the source area. Well-exposed examples of autochthonous and parautochthonous granitic rocks occur in the northern part of the Bhutan Himalaya. Gansser (1983: 99) has described these rocks; he states that 'within the more migmatitic gneisses occur fully mobilized medium to fine grained granites, which begin to intrude discordantly into the otherwise rather diffuse migmatites. Such locally developed granitic zones are frequent in the highly migmatized main body of the Masang Kang Peak'. Perera (1983: 17) claims that some of the pink granites of Sri Lanka occur as conformable layers within metasedimentary rock units, and that these granites evolved as the result of the essentially isochemical recrystallization of suitable sedimentary rocks. Other autochthonous granites contain only relict traces of earlier stratified rocks (that is, *ghost stratigraphy*).

The younger *leucogranites* of the Bhutan Himalaya are good examples of Tertiary granitic rocks that have been mainly, or completely, derived from anatexis of continental crust during continent–continent collision. In the simplest models such collisions result in crustal thickening, and the isostatic readjustments that are necessitated by this thickening result in a depression of the base of the continental block which is forced into a higher-temperature environment where crustal melting is likely to occur if the lower crustal rocks are of a suitable composition. The leucogranites intrude both the crystalline basement and the overlying sedimentary rocks of the High Himalayan Belt. According to Dietrich and Gansser (1981: 183), these leucogranites crop out in an area of approximately 2000 km², yet they have relatively homogeneous modal compositions; that is, their modes are usually within the range 30–4 per cent quartz, 23–30 per cent microcline, 32–7 per cent albite, 3–7 per cent muscovite, 1–3 per cent biotite, and accessory amounts of ilmenite, apatite, tourmaline and garnet. The chemical and modal composition of a typical specimen of these rocks is given in Table 9.3.4. These leucogranites have relatively low R.E.E. abundances and strong negative Eu-anomalies; they also have relatively high initial $^{87}Sr/^{86}Sr$ ratios (that is, 0.707). Such high values are characteristic of many of the other leucogranites of the High Himalayan Belt, and they probably evolved as the result of the melting of Palaeozoic, or older, continental crustal materials. Allègre and Othman (1980) have found low $^{143}Nd/^{144}Nd$ ratios (0.51183) for the Manaslu Leucogranite of the High Himalayan Belt, and they postulated that this leucogranite resulted from the partial melting of 1.1–2.3 Ga old crystalline basement rocks.

Most of the orogenic granitic rocks of the Phanerozoic belong to compositionally-expanded calc–alkalic associations, such as the rocks of the cordilleran-type batholiths of the Americas. It is postulated that the parental magmas responsible for the evolution of the various super-units in these compound batholiths were generated in the mantle-wedge above a zone of active subduction as described in Section 6.6. It is important to note that the overall chemical patterns found in these granitic rocks may mimic the patterns observed in orogenic volcanic rocks; that is, there are regional changes in composition across these elongate compound batholiths. For example, in 1927 Buddington showed that in the Coast Range Batholith of south-eastern Alaska, there is a progressive increase in silica and potassium as one proceeds east, or away from the location of the original marginal trench. Similar trends have been described from other cordilleran-type batholiths, such as the Sierra Nevada Batholith (cf. Bateman & Dodge 1970). Bateman (1983) has provided a detailed description of the central part of the Sierra Nevada Batholith, and he claims that quartz diorites, tonalites and gabbros predominate in the west, granodiorites and granites in the axial part of the batholith, and monzodiorites, monzonites, quartz monzonites and granites in the east. He (241–2) also claims that 'the most conspicuous chemical variation is an eastward increase in potassium',

and that this change is 'accompanied by eastward increases in uranium, thorium, beryllium, rubidium, the oxidation ratio, total rare earths, and initial $^{87}Sr/^{86}Sr$, and by decreases in specific gravity and calcium'.

Another particularly interesting batholith is the Inner Zone Batholith of south-western Japan. It is approximately the same size as the Sierra Nevada Batholith of California, and it is mainly composed of granites and granodiorites. These rocks do, however, show distinct regional variations in their chemical and modal compositions; for example, in the south the rocks are typically ilmenite-bearing, but as one proceeds northwards the Fe_2O_3/FeO ratio increases, and there is a concomitant increase in the abundance of magnetite. Ishihara (1977) has divided these granitic rocks into a *magnetite series* and an *ilmenite series*. Further research has shown that initial $^{87}Sr/^{86}Sr$ ratios decrease, and other geochemical changes occur, as one proceeds from south to north across the Inner Zone Batholith (cf. Czamanske et al. 1981). Uncontaminated magmas derived from the upper mantle generally crystallize as magnetite-free, ilmenite-bearing rocks; whereas magnetite-bearing rocks are generally derived from either hydrous magmas in which there has been a differential loss of H_2, or magmas that have assimilated oxidized supracrustal materials. Some magnetite-bearing granitic rocks contain early formed magnetite and sphene (that is, magnetite occurs as inclusions in the plagioclase), whereas in other rocks magnetite and sphene form at a late stage in their crystallization history (magnetite occurs as an interstitial phase). Attempts at linking the magnetite-series granites with the I-type granites, and the ilmenite-series granites with S-type granites (for example, Beckinsale 1979: 37), have not been successful, particularly as significant changes in oxygen fugacity can occur during the crystallization of a granitic magma. The relatively low oxygen fugacities of many S-type granitic rocks may indicate the presence of reducing materials, such as graphitic shales, in some segments of the continental crust.

Detailed studies of the Coastal Batholith of Peru have revealed that it is composed of approximately 1000 intrusive units; and according to Atherton et al. (1979: 48–50) the major plutonic components of the batholith consist of: (a) Gabbros and diorites of the Patap superunit which have had 'a long and complex history of crystallization involving crystal growth and accumulation, metamorphism, metasomatism, deformation and hybridization'. These basic rocks carry plagioclase ± olivine ± clinopyroxene ± orthopyroxene ± hornblende as primary phases, and the hornblende becomes a major phase at a late stage in their evolution. (b) An early group of granitic rocks also occurs, and they range in composition from quartz diorite to granites.

They are typified by the Santa Rosa superunit of the Lima segment (see Table 9.3.3). These superunits all tend to have a mafic marginal facies, and there is a crude increase in the silicic rocks towards the centre of the superunit. The essential phases that crystallized during the evolution of these superunits are pyroxene, hornblende, plagioclase, potassium–feldspar, biotite

Orogenic Granitic Rocks

Pacific-type	Cordilleran-type	Caledonian-type	Himalayan-type
Subduction beneath an oceanic island arc	Subduction of oceanic materials beneath a continental margin	Uplift and relaxation immediately after the closure of an ocean basin	Continent–continent collision
Small composite or zoned stocks	Huge composite batholiths	Discrete multiple intrusions	Large bodies of autochthonous granite, migmatites, and local stocks.
Essentially evolved from a mantle-derived magma that usually belongs to either the island arc tholeiite or the calc-alkaline series.	Calc-alkalic parental magmas, plus assimilation of continental crustal materials	Calc-alkalic parental magma plus anatexis of continental crustal materials	Large-scale anatexis of continental crustal materials
Tonalites	Tonalite, Granodiorites and Granites	Granodiorites and Granite	Leucogranites and Granites
Plutonism is generally short-lived	Plutonism is episodic and extends over a long period	Plutonism is generally short-lived	Plutonism of moderate duration.

Anorogenic Granitic Rocks

Barberton-type	Tholeiitic-type	Normal Alkalic-type	Hyperpotassic-type
Extensive melting and mobilisation of primitive proto-continental crust	Tholeiitic basalt magma emplaced into continental crust	Subvolcanic intrusions into continental areas of doming and rifting	Subvolcanic intrusions
Archaean grey gneiss complexes	Discrete stocks usually associated with a range of more mafic tholeiitic rocks	Composite stocks and ring dykes often associated with syenitic rocks	Composite stocks and ring dykes usually associated with quartz monzonites
Extensive anatexis and migmatite formation	Magmatic differentiation together with local assimilation of continental crustal materials	Magmatic differentiation of sodic alkalic basaltic magma, volume of silicic magma augmented by assimilation	Magmatic differentiation of hyperpotassic alkalic magma
Trondhjemites and Tonalites	Granodiorites and Granites	Alkali-Feldspar Granites and Granites	Alkali-feldspar Granites and Granites
Plutonism characteristic of the Archaean prior to the cratonization of the crust	Local intraplate plutonism	Intraplate doming and rifting	Local intraplate plutonism

Figure 9.6.1 Simplified model of the tectonic setting and nature of the granitic rocks of Earth

and quartz. Textural and structural evidence indicates that most of the crystallization took place within the crustal levels at which these rocks occur. However, the presence of calcium-rich cores in some of the plagioclase crystals, and the occurrence of mafic enclosures, demonstrate the importance of materials that crystallized at an earlier date in the evolution of these rocks. Such materials may have been derived from earlier comagmatic rocks, or they may represent xenocrysts and xenoliths. The zoning pattern found in the superunits is interpreted as showing that the front of crystallization moved in from the margins of the various units, and that separation of crystals from liquid was never complete. (c) A later group of superunits occur, and they form major ring complexes, such as the four of the Lima segment (cf. Pitcher 1978). These rocks are considered by some petrologists to represent a direct link between the intrusive units of the batholith and volcanic rocks of the same age. (d) Another group of intrusives occur as discrete bodies: these are generally granites, and they may contain a pegmatitic border facies. The Canas Pluton is an example of one of these intrusives, and it is a high-level cryptically-zoned body. According to Atherton et al. (1979: 52), the general high-level evolution of the superunits of the Coastal Batholith of Peru can be modelled in terms of plagioclase $\pm$ pyroxene $\pm$ hornblende fractionation. The Rb and K/Rb variations are compatible with plagioclase being a signifcant fractionating phase; whereas the Y and R.E.E. trends show that pyroxene was succeeded by hornblende at the tonalitic stage of magmatic differentiation is some superunits. Sphene and/or apatite were important fractionating phases in the late granites.

Two very different suites of orogenic granitic rocks, that is the leucogranites of the Bhutan Himalaya and the compositionally-expanded association of granitic rocks from the Coastal Batholith of Peru, have been examined. There are many other different types of orogenic belts, and the thermal characteristics of these areas can usually be categorized by determining the maximum grade of regional metamorphism associated with their development. Zwart (1967) has, for example, shown that granitic rocks are most abundant in orogenic belts, such as the Hercynian Belt of Europe, where there was low pressure/high temperature regional metamorphism, and they are rare in orogenic belts characterized by high pressure/low temperature regional

metamorphism. It has been proposed that low pressure/high temperature regional metamorphism, and possibly crustal melting and granite formation, is at present taking place beneath the north-western segment of the Japanese Arc and the Sea of Japan (cf. Takeuchi & Uyeda 1965).

The Caledonian granitic rocks of the British Isles are particularly interesting in that their genesis is usually associated with the closure of the Iapetus Ocean, yet there is little evidence that normal volumes of calc–alkalic materials were extruded and/or intruded during most of this period of subduction. Brown et al. (1981: 10512) have suggested that large volumes of basaltic andesite magma formed during this period, and in the northern segment of the Caledonian province this magma was trapped beneath crustal basement rocks, whereas in the southern segment it was trapped beneath the young accreting margin. After the closure of the Iapetus Ocean, the now adjacent continental margins entered 'a phase of postcollisional relaxation' and decompression, and large volumes of magma were emplaced into the upper crust where it differentiated to form the main group of Caledonian granitic rocks of the British Isles.

It is thus found that in the Phanerozoic Era on Earth, a broad spectrum of different granitic rocks have been generated in the tectonic environment that is associated with plate convergence (that is, oceanic island-arcs, oceanic plate –continental plate convergence and subduction, and continent–continent collisions). The compositions of these various granitic rocks are essentially determined by the composition and relative proportions of: (a) mantle source materials; (b) recycled (subducted) crustal materials; and (c) continental crustal materials, that they contain, and the extent of magmatic differentiation experienced by their parental magmas. It is, for example, claimed by some petrologists, such as White and Chappell (1983: 21), that the anatectic granites of an area can often be grouped into suites, and the differences between these suites essentially result from differences in the composition of continental source rocks; and that the 'first-order subdivision between suites is between those granitoids derived from sedimentary and from igneous source rocks, the S- and I-types'. The anorogenic granites of the Phanerozoic usually occur in relatively small outcrops associated with volcanic activity. They are generally considered to have formed from magma generated as the result of the upwelling of heat and/or volatiles beneath an area of continental lithosphere. This method of granite formation was probably more common in the Precambrian, and particularly in the Archaean. Detailed studies of the 'granitic rocks' of Venus should prove to be of great value, particularly if this planet has a global tectonic regime that is different from that presently found on Earth. Figure 9.6.1 gives a simplified model of the tectonic settings characteristic of the different types of granitic rocks found on Earth.

9.7 Selected references

Atherton, M. P. & Tarney, J. (eds) (1979) *Origin of Granite Batholiths; Geochemical Evidence*, Shiva Pub. Ltd, Orpington, Kent.

Luth, W. C. (1976) Granitic Rocks; pp. 335–417 in Bailey, D. K & MacDonald, R. (eds), *The Evolution of the Crystalline Rocks*, Academic Press Inc., London.

Pitcher, W. S. & Berger, A. R. (1972) *The Geology of Donegal: A study of granite emplacement and unroofing*, Wiley-Interscience, New York, USA.

Raguin, E. (1965) *Geology of Granite*, Interscience Pub., London.

Read, H. H. (1957) *The Granite Controversy*, Thomas Murby & Co., London.

Roddick, J. A. (ed.) (1983) Circum-Pacific Plutonic Terranes, *Geol. Soc. Am., Men.*, **159**, 1–316.

Tuttle, O. F. & Bowen, N. L. (1958) Origin of granite in the light of experimental studies in the system $NaAlSi_3O_8–KAlSi_3O_8–SiO_2–H_2O$, *Geol. Soc. Am., Mem.*, **74**, 1–153.

CHAPTER 10

THE ANORTHOSITES

10.1 General statement

The anorthosites are essentially plagioclase-rich rocks; and according to Streckeisen (1974: 780) they are gabbroic rocks that contain more than 90 per cent plagioclase (see Figs 3.2.2 and 3.2.3). In 1857, Hunt introduced the term anorthosite to describe the plagioclase-rich rocks of eastern Canada; and in 1863 he proposed that Labrador might be regarded as the type locality for these rocks. At this time the anorthosites of Labrador had already been described by workers such as Steinhauer (1814); and at an even earlier date, Werner (1780) described rocks composed of labradorite, or 'labradorstein', from this area. In 1823, Esmark described the plagioclase-rich rocks of the South Rogaland Igneous Complex of south-western Norway; however, he did not give these rocks a special name as he regarded them as being plagioclase-rich norites. In the past century, ideas concerning the origin of anorthosites have tended to mirror the hypotheses being proposed for the origin of the granitic rocks. For example, in the 1950s, Barth (1952: 229) suggested that one should 'remember that only anorthosites and granites (gneisses) form "intrusions" of batholithic dimensions'; and he then went on to propose that as many of the granitic rocks are produced by 'metasomatic granitization', then 'perhaps anorthosite exhibits a similar mode of origin, thus confronting us with the problem of a metasomatic anorthositization of batholithic dimensions'. In 1955, Michot wrote a paper entitled 'Anorthosites et anorthosites', and he thus echoed Read's (1948) concept that there are 'granites and granites'. Recently, considerable attention has been focused on the magmatic origin of both the granites and the anorthosites; however, it is widely recognized that in the catazone of the Earth, where many anorthosites form, there is a convergence of igneous, metamorphic and metasomatic processes.

Buddington (1939: 208; 1961: 422) grouped the anorthosites into two main classes: (a) the differentiated stratiform sheets, or lopoliths, that contained layers with strongly contrasted compositions, such as the Bushveld Layered Complex of South Africa (that is, the *stratiform-type*; see Section 11.6); and (b) large plutonic masses that are essentially non-stratiform and generally contain domical, or multidomical, structures, such as are found in the Adirondack Mountains of eastern North America (that is, the *massif-type*, or massive, anorthosites. Boulanger (1957) grouped the anorthosites of Malagasy into three classes; and his new class was called the *Sakeny-type*. The anorthosites of Sakeny, Malagasy, are of Archaean age, and they crop out as layers within gneisses. For example, the type-rock forms a band that is some 10 m thick, and it can be traced for approximately 6 km. Bridgwater and Harry (1968: 161) used this three-fold classification of the anorthosites in their study of the anorthosites of West Greenland. In marked contrast to the Sakeny-type of essentially Archaean anorthosites, layers of anorthosite have been described from a Cenozoic subvolcanic complex on the island of Fuerteventura in the Canary archipelago (cf. Fuster, Cendero et al. 1968). It is thus found that there is a broad spectrum of types of anorthosites, that range from bands within Archaean gneisses to cumulate layers that formed in either relatively small high-level magma chambers, huge lopoliths or batholiths.

10.2 Archaean anorthosites

Most of the anorthosites of the Earth were emplaced during the Precambrian, particularly in the mid-Proterozoic (1.2–1.8 Ga); however, there are also many extensive outcrops of Archaean age, such as the Fiskenaesset Complex of West Greenland (cf. Myers 1981). According to Windley (1973: 319), these Archaean anorthosites are usually of the *stratiform-type*. This means they formed as the result of the operation of the various magmatic differentiation processes (see Sections 2.2 and 2.3); however, most of these Archaean anorthosites have been deformed, and partially or completely recrystallized, during subsequent periods of orogenic activity. Not all petrologists agree with this igneous origin for the Archaean anorthosites; for example, Lacroix (1939) suggested that the Sakeny anorthosites of Malagasy were produced by the metamorphism of marly sediments. Similar conclusions were reached by Sørensen (1955) for the Buksefjord anorthosite of West Greenland, and by Naidu (1963) for the Sittampundi anorthosites of Madras State, India.

According to Windley (1973: 320), the Archaean anorthosites of the Earth crop out in two different environments: (a) within greenstone belts; and (b) in high-grade gneissic terrains. Many Archaean terrains are composed almost entirely of high-grade gneisses, whereas others contain both greenstone belts and high-grade gneisses. The gneisses generally contain amphibolite to granulite facies metamorphic mineral assemblages, and the age of this metamorphism is usually approximately 2.8 Ga. Anorthosite typically occurs in conformable layers and lenses within the gneisses; and such rocks have been described from West and East Greenland, north-west Scotland, Sierra Leone, Malagasy, the Limpopo Mobile Belt of Zimbabwe and South Africa, south India and Western Australia. According to Bridgwater et al. (1976: 43), 'metamorphosed calcic anorthosites and associated leucogabbroic and gabbroic rocks form one of the most distinctive rock units in the Archaean gneiss complex', where they occur as 'concordant layers and trains of inclusion throughout the complex in both West and South-East Greenland. They provide one of the best marker horizons for tracing out structures on a regional scale, for making lithostratigaphic correlations from one part of the complex to another'; and they are 'some of the oldest layered igneous rocks on Earth available for study'.
Primary igneous features are well preserved in the anorthositic and gabbroic rocks of the Fiskenaesset region of West Greenland.

The Fiskenaesset Complex is a layered sequence of metamorphosed anorthosite, leucogabbro and gabbro, with minor amounts of peridotite, dunite and chromitite. According to Windley (1973: 321), in the Fiskenaesset region

'there are 200 km (strike length) of anorthositic horizons'. The igneous stratigaphy, and primary structures and minerals are best preserved in the central part of the region (at Majorqap qâva), and in this area there are four main units: (a) the 50 m thick lower leucogabbro unit; (b) the 40 m thick gabbro unit; (c) the 60 m thick upper leucogabbro unit; and (d) the 200 m thick anorthosite unit. Most of the material in the anorthosite unit has been strongly deformed and thoroughly recrystallized, and it now usually consists of a mosaic of small ($\approx$ 1 mm) plagioclase grains together with minor amounts of hornblende and mica. Some specimens contain larger ($\approx$100 mm) crystals of plagioclase, and they probably indicate that the original anorthosite was coarse-grained. Bridgwater et al. (1976: 49) state that most igneous plagioclases from the Fiskenaesset Complex are zoned from cores of An_{86} to rims of An_{78}, and that except in the gabbro unit where plagioclase compositions are An_{90-98}, there is no major stratigraphic variation in plagioclase composition. It is also claimed that there has been little change in the bulk composition of the anorthositic rocks during metamorphism. A most important characteristic of these anorthosites, and anorthosites from other high-grade Archaean gneissic terrains, is that they contain highly calcic plagioclases.

Wiener (1981) has proposed that some of the Archaean anorthosites that occur in high-grade gneissic terrains, and (a) have tectonic rather than intrusive contacts, and (b) are associated with meta-basalts that contain pillow structures, may have originally evolved in magma chambers that developed beneath oceanic-spreading centres. He (1920) also claims that the Archaean gabbro–anorthosite complex of Tessiuyakh Bay, Labrador, and a nearby body of ultramafic rocks, may represent 'the lower crust and upper mantle section in an Archaean ophiolite' (see Section 11.8).

In the Archaean greenstone belts, the anorthosites may occur in association with the ultramafic rocks, but they are usually found in discrete bodies of layered igneous rocks. This type of stratiform anorthosite is, for example, found in at least two complexes within the Abitibi greenstone belt of the Canadian Shield. In the Dore Lake Complex at the north-eastern end of this greenstone belt, the layered igneous rocks have been folded, faulted and metamorphosed. Allard (1970: 481) claims that he has been able

Table 10.2.1 Chemical composition of selected anorthosites (%)

	1	2	3	4	5	6	7
SiO_2	50.28	45.87	44.35	44.1	55.9	55.1	47.41
TiO_2	0.64	0.22	0.05	0.02	0.24	0.15	0.16
Al_2O_3	25.86	28.62	31.34	35.5	27.2	27.1	29.84
Fe_2O_3	0.96	1.05	1.06	—	—	—	0.84
FeO	2.07	2.65	0.82	0.23	1.28*	1.97*	1.60
MnO	0.05	0.06	0.02	—	0.02	0.03	0.07
MgO	2.12	3.36	1.12	0.09	0.21	1.14	1.54
CaO	12.48	14.43	18.18	19.7	9.65	10.3	15.07
Na_2O	3.15	1.80	1.22	0.34	5.23	4.50	2.21
K_2O	0.65	0.39	0.05	—	1.10	0.43	0.36
H_2O^+	1.17	0.48	0.62	—	—	—	0.82
H_2O^-	0.14	0.05	0.10	—	—	—	—
P_2O_5	0.09	0.02	0.01	0.01	—	—	0.08
CO_2	0.14	—	0.20	—	—	—	—
	99.80	99.00	99.14	99.99	100.83	100.72	100.00
Total No. of analyses	104	3	3	1	1	1	21

1. Mean chemical composition of the anorthosites (after Le Maitre, 1976a: 631).
2. Mean chemical composition of Archaean anorthositic rocks from the Fiskenaesset Complex of West Greenland (after Windley 1973: 328).
3. Mean chemical composition of Archaean anorthosites from the Sittampundi Complex, Madras State, India (after Subramaniam 1956: 371). This rock contains 0.01 per cent Cr_2O_3.
4. Chemical composition of coarse-grained lunar anorthosite gathered from a poorly-consolidated breccia located on the rim of Spur Crater on the Apennine Front south-west of Mons Hadley (Sample 15415) (after Taylor, 1982: 206).
5. Chemical composition of massif-type anorthosite from roadcut 9 km north of Tahawas, Marcy Massif, Adirondack Mountains, NY, USA (after Simmons and Hanson 1978: 122). FeO* means total Fe as FeO.
6. Chemical composition of anorthosite which is the host rock of the Uighordlekh Block Structure, north eastern corner of Uighordlekh Island, Nain Complex, Labrador, Canada (after Simmons and Hanson 1978: 122). FeO* means total Fe as FeO.
7. Mean chemical composition of stratiform-type anorthosites (after Kempe 1965: 50).

to determine the original geometry of this complex which is over 40 km long, and contains a 3500 m thick anorthosite zone. He (481) regards the complex as a folded and metamorphosed stratiform-type layered intrusion; and he (489) has shown that the anorthosites of this complex are essentially composed of bytownite (An_{80}), together with minor amounts of zoisite and chlorite. The Bell River Complex of the Abitibi greenstone belt is also regarded as being a body of layered igneous rocks (cf. Windley 1973: 321).

Windley (1973: 326) has established that the Archaean anorthosites of Earth are: (a) usually enriched in CaO and Al_2O_3, and depleted in SiO_2, and Na_2O, relative to the Proterozoic massif-type anorthosites; (b) generally associated with chromitites or chromite-bearing rocks; and (c) usually contain highly calcic plagioclases. He (319) also claims that in many respects the Archaean anorthosites have 'more in common with lunar anorthosites than with other terrestrial anorthosites'; and (324) that these Archaean anorthosites 'constitute a new class of igneous rocks'.

10.3 Lunar anorthosites

The examination of lunar samples, and the data obtained from orbital studies of Al/Si concentration ratios (cf. Wood 1979: 119–21), has enabled petrologists to postulate that anorthosites, and anorthositic gabbros, are important rock types in the upper crust of the lunar highlands. Anorthosites are probably mainly responsible for the light colour of the surface in the highland areas, and also of the rays that cross the maria. These anorthosites are old (4.05–4.5 Ga), and they contain very calcium-rich plagioclase (An_{95-97}). They are thus akin to the Archaean anorthosites of Earth. Many of them carry low-calcium orthopyroxene (that is, hypersthene) and a little clinopyroxene (salite and/or augite), olivine, troilite and Fe–Ni metal. Sample 15415, which was collected from the Apennine Front south-west of Mons Hadley (see Table 10.2.1, No. 4), is a coarse-grained lunar anorthosite; it contains 97 per cent plagioclase (An_{95}) and 3 per cent pyroxene. The plagioclase grains are of many sizes, and they appear to have undergone repeated episodes of crushing and annealing (cf. McGee et al. 1977: 64–5). Most of the pyroxene occurs in small anhedral or rounded grains that are included in plagioclase grains, or occur at the central point of plagioclase triple junctions. The lunar anorthosites generally have low R.E.E. abundances, with a pronounced positive Eu anomaly. As the mare basalts tend to have a negative Eu anomaly, it is usually proposed that the Eu-depleted mare basalts were derived from source materials from which the feldspars making up the anorthosites had already been removed, possibly by flotation in a magma ocean (see Section 5.13). The $^{87}Sr/^{86}Sr$ ratios of the lunar anorthosites are very low, and according to Taylor (1982: 205) 'this constitutes primary evidence that they are relics of the early crust'.

10.4 Proterozoic anorthosites

In the Proterozoic, two remarkable belts of igneous rocks were emplaced into the crust of the Earth: one was situated in Laurasia and the other in Gondwanaland. The huge northern, or Laurasian Belt, extends from the Urals, or even further east, in the USSR to the western USA, and it contains most of the massif-type anorthosites. Herz (1969) has described the evolution of this extensive belt of igneous rocks as the *anorthosite event*. These anorthosites and associated rocks were emplaced between approximately 1.2 and 1.8 Ga ago, probably with most of them being emplaced between 1.4 and 1.5 Ga (Emslie 1978). According to Bridgwater and Windley (1973: 309), emplacement at the western end of the northern massif-type anorthosite belt was some 200–300 Ma later than that in the east. Field mapping has also shown that the major bodies of massif-type anorthosite are concentrated within belts of the crust affected by Proterozoic metamorphism and tectonic activity (that is, the Grenville and Dalslandian orogenies). The metamorphism that preceded the emplacement of these anorthosites was generally of the high-temperature/low-pressure type, and it was usually associated with the emplacement of large volumes of silicic rocks.

According to Isachsen (1969a: 435), the masif-type anorthosites, and the associated plagioclase-rich gabbros (78–90 per cent plagioclase), are 'by far the largest of the gabbroic plutonic complexes, having areal dimensions comparable to those of batholiths of granitic and intermediate rocks'. The massif-type anorthosites range in size from a few km² to tens of thousands of km², with most of them being in the range 100–1000 km² (cf. Anderson 1969: 51). Information about the thickness of massif-type anorthosites is usually lacking. Some appear to be funnel-shaped, whereas gravity data indicates that the main Adirondack anorthosite body is essentially a layered unit that is between 3–4.5 km thick, except for two local areas where it is thicker (Simmons 1964). Probably the largest massif-type anorthosite is the Dzhugdzhurskii Anorthosite Massif of eastern Siberia, USSR, which covers an area of approximately 30 000 km², and is believed to be 1.7 Ga old (cf. Lebedev & Pavlov 1957). Another characteristic of many of the massif-type anorthosites is that they occur in areas that have large negative gravity anomalies, which are usually interpreted as indicating that the anorthosites are not at present directly associated with any large masses of underlying mafic or ultramafic cumulates (for example, peridotites and pyroxenites).

The massif-type anorthosites do, however, usually occur in close temporal and spatial association with a series of plutonic rocks that have been called the *anorthosite kindred* (Hödal 1954: 139). She defined, and described, this kindred as being made up of *birkremites, charnockites, farsundites, enderbites, mangerite-syenites, mangerites, jotunites* and *norites*. These rocks are chemically akin to the alkali feldspar granites, granites, granodiorites, tonalites, alkali feldspar syenites, syenites, syenodiorites and gabbros; but they differ from these more frequently mentioned rocks in that they generally carry orthopyroxenes and dark feldspars. In many areas, such as in the Urals, Ukraine, Finland, Sweden, South Greenland, Labrador, Idaho, Nevada and California, the anorthosites crop out in close association with granites that have a *rapakivi texture*. This is a porphyritic texture in which rounded phenocrysts of potassium feldspar, (usually a few cm in diameter) are surrounded by a rim of sodium feldspar (usually oligoclose). It is thus evident that the Proterozoic *anorthosite event* produced a huge volume of plutonic, and volcanic, rocks. According to Bridgwater and Windley (1973: 313), the most satisfactory explanation for both the general thermal activity and specific magmatic events in the massif-type anorthosite belts is that they mark the location of 'a major rise of mantle material (for example the top of a convection cell) which remained active during the period 1000 to 2000 m.y. ago' (1.0–2.0 Ga). They also suggest that the concentration of anorthosites within this particular time-span probably indicates that 'conditions for their formation reached an optimum during one stage in the development of the crust which has not since been repeated on anything like the same scale'.

Massif-type anorthosites are found associated with the Jurassic Younger Granites of Niger and Nigeria (Black & Girod 1970). These rocks crop out in a linear belt that is approximately 1200 km long. A high proportion are high-level intrusive rocks that have been emplaced into ring-complexes; and they mainly consist of granites and syenites, together with less than 5 per cent of olivine gabbro and coarse-grained olivine-bearing anorthosite. In some of the complexes of the Air region of Niger, the anorthosites are regarded as the earliest member of the magmatic sequence.

The Proterozoic massif-type anorthosites of the disrupted southern belt have not been studied in the same detail as the rocks of the more extensive northern belt. Probably the largest body in the southern belt occurs in the huge Kunene Complex of southern Angola and northern Namibia (cf. Simpson 1970; Kostlin 1974). According to Simpson (89), the anorthosites of the Kunene Complex are exposed as a longitudinally elongated massif that is 300 km long and between 30 and 100 km wide. These rocks crop out over an area of 12 500 km^2, and a further 4000 km^2 of these rocks are believed to lie concealed beneath a cover of younger sediments. In the southern half of the complex, a 'pale massive anorthosite' is exposed; and Simpson (1970: 91) regards it as being very similar to the massif-type anorthosites of the Adirondack Mountains of New York State. The plagioclase is of intermediate composition (An$_{50-66}$), and it is occasionally associated with minor amounts of orthopyroxene and/or clinopyroxene. In the northern part of the complex, the rock is essentially a troctolitic anorthosite that normally contains between 70–95 per cent plagioclase (An$_{54-80}$), 1–30 per cent olivine (Fo$_{58-87}$), 0–12 per cent orthopyroxene, 0–5 per cent clinopyroxene, together with accessory amounts of titaniferous magnetite and biotite (Simpson 1970: 92). Kostlin (1974: 123) claims that the troctolitic anorthosite is intrusive into the 'pale massive anorthosite', and that the former has many of the petrographic and structural characteristics of a stratiform-type anorthosite.

Many of the large stratiform-type bodies of anorthosite are of Proterozoic age. For example, the Bushveld Layered Complex of South Africa covers an area of approximately 66 000 km^2, and it is approximately 19.5 Ga old. The anorthosite layers found in these stratiform bodies are generally considered to have evolved from basaltic, or picritic magmas, and the magmatic differentiation processes that generated them are discussed in Sections 2.2, 2.3 and 11.6.

10.5 Phanerozoic anorthosites

The Phanerozoic anorthosites, with the notable exception of the Jurassic massif-type anorthosites of Niger and Nigeria, are essentially of the stratiform-type. Well-known examples of these layered rocks crop out in the Thulean Igneous Province. This province, for example, contains the Skaergaard and Kap Edvard Holm layered complexes of East Greenland and the Rhum layered intrusion of Scotland (cf. Deer 1976; Emeleus 1982).

10.6 Petrogenesis

As De Waard (1969: 2) has clearly shown, many different petrogenetic models have been proposed for the origin of the anorthosites. These hypotheses range from: (a) the metamorphism and/or metasomatism of crustal materials; (b) partial, or complete, fusion of crustal rocks, producing either an anorthositic magma or an anorthositic residuum; (c) magmatic differentiation of a variety of picritic, basaltic or andesitic magmas to produce either anorthositic cumulates, or an anorthositic magma. There is general agreement that many of the Archaean anorthosites are of the stratiform-type; and also that anorthosites of this type range in age from the Archaean to the Cenozoic. This type of anorthosite is usually regarded as being a plagioclase cumulate rock that was generated by magmatic differentiation of a basaltic, or picritic, magma. Irvine (1975: 492) has also shown that the mixing of magmas may play a significant role in the origin of this type of anorthosite. His investigations have been primarily concerned with the system Fo–An–Or–Q, and he has shown that in this system it is 'possible to produce melts with only anorthite on the liquidus by mixing 'contaminated' basic liquid that has crystallized enough pyroxene to differentiate to the pyroxene-anorthite cotectic, with 'relatively fresh' liquid on the olivine–anorthite cotectic. Fractional crystallization of the intermediate liquid would then yield plagioclase precipitates comparable to anorthositic layers in the Muskox, Bushveld, Stillwater, and Rhum intrusions.' The petrogenetic models that have been proposed to account for the evolution of the massif-type anorthosites are much more diverse and controversial.

In his report on a detailed study of the evolution of anorthositic rocks of the Proterozoic Nain Complex on the coast of Labrador, Morse (1977: 1) states that he is convinced that 'many magmas were involved rather than a single one for the whole complex'. He estimates that the massif-type anorthosites of this area probably evolved at depths of between 13–22 km, in an essentially anorogenic cratonic environment. At least four chemically distinct magmas, of basic to intermediate composition, are postulated to explain the range of plagioclase compositions (An$_{34}$–An$_{90}$, with statistical modes at An$_{43}$, An$_{52}$ and An$_{58}$) observed in the anorthosites of Nain. He claims that one well-defined magma type that was important in the evolution of these rocks was a high-FeO, high-Al, low-K basaltic magma; and he also suggests that the granitic rocks associated with the anorthosites may have been generated by the partial melting of crustal rocks, with much of the heat being provided by the parental magmas of the anorthosites. It is also proposed that the anorthosites of Nain were emplaced into a continental rift environment. Morse (1977: 3) asserts that the 'massif anorthosites are the products of aborted cratonic rifts', and that they are restricted in space to such rift zones. He has also speculated that they are restricted in time because this particular style of rifting tectonics was essentially confined to the period between 1.2 and 1.8 Ga ago. Emslie (1978: 89) has suggested that the Proterozoic massif-type anorthosites of North America were emplaced at 'the beginning of activity in the mantle that eventually matured into continental rifting'. The Nain area is also

interesting in that it contains fine-grained leuconorite dykes (Colour Index or M = 15) that have chilled margins, and clearly cooled from a magma that was very rich in normative plagioclase (85 per cent). Dykes that contain rocks composed almost entirely of plagioclase (An$_{53–60}$) have also been described from Kanningen Island off the coast of Sweden (cf. Von Eckermann 1938: 279).

Experimental petrology has generated a number of concepts that are important in elucidating the origin and evolution of anorthosites. For example, Yoder and Tilley (1962: 461) found in their study of the melting behaviour of hydrous basaltic rocks (amphibolites) that, irrespective of the composition of the basaltic rock being investigated, 'the first phase to be consumed completely with increasing temperature above about 1,500 bars (0.15 GPa) was found to be plagioclase'; and also that 'if it were possible to separate the liquid from crystals at this stage (e.g. through filter pressing) and crystallize the liquid elsewhere, the product would be a plagioclase-rich rock, anorthosite'. They also noted that the plagioclases of natural amphibolites are oligoclase or andesine, and the anorthositic liquid resulting from partial melting would presumably have a similar relatively low An content. Their studies also reveal that the beginning of melting curve for amphibolites may be as low as 600 °C. Yoder and Tilley (1962: 462) conclude their discussion of the partial melting of amphibolites by stating that such a process 'may adequately describe the origin of some smaller anorthosite bodies where field work has uncovered the required ferromagnesium residuum'. Emslie (1970) and Kushiro (1974) have published phase diagrams for the systems plagioclase–diopside–enstatite and plagioclase–forsterite–H$_2$O, respectively, at 1.5 GPa, and they discovered that the minimum melt compositions in these systems contained between 75 and 80 per cent of the plagioclase component.

Yoder (1969: 13) has also proposed that some anorthosites, presumably those akin to the anorthosites found on Fuerteventura in the Canary archipelago, formed as cumulates during the fractional crystallization of alkalic basalt: that is, they accumulated during the process that led to the evolution of the rocks of the hawaiite–mugearite–benmoreite–trachyte association. Some of the anorthosites that are found associated with syenites may have also been produced in a similar manner. Yoder (1969: 21) concludes his paper on the origin of anorthosites by stating that it is tempting to consider the evolution of the massif-type anorthosites 'along with the vast volumes of amphibolites, migmatites, and granites, as evidence of a degassing phase in the Earth's history; a time when hydrous magmas and crystal mushes rose at moderate temperatures into the crust'.

Green (1969) has studied the anhydrous crystallization of high-Al basaltic and andesitic melts, at the pressures one would anticipate to find in the deep continental crust of the Earth. His experimental results support two models that have been proposed for the origin of the massif-type anorthosites. They first of all support the hypothesis that anorthosite may evolve as a crystalline residuum that remains after the partial melting, and removal of a silicic magma, from deep-seated crustal rocks of andesitic bulk compositions; and a corollary of this model is that the formation of granites by anatexis, and the evolution of massif-type anorthosites, may both be part of the same general process. If this process has been active, the crust beneath the many Precambrian granitic terrains may contain large bodies of anorthosite (cf. Ramberg 1948). In the second petrogenetic model, various processes of magmatic differentiation operate at depth within the crust, and generate plagioclase and ultramafic cumulates and complementary silicic liquids from an andesitic parental magma. Such magmatic differentiation process, may generate bodies of layered igneous rocks, and in this way the differences between the massif-type and stratiform-type anorthosites are likely to become blurred (cf. Romey 1968). It is also likely that most of the bodies of anorthosite, that form at depth within the crust, evolve within the catazone; and in this structural environment these rocks would be highly ductile, and thus would readily deform plastically or pseudoplastically (see Section 1.8). The large domical structures that are so typical of many massif-type anorthosites may form as the result of anorthositic layers becoming buoyant diapiric bodies that rise above the more dense comagmatic rocks with which they were originally associated. This concept is supported by the granulation and deformation of the plagioclase crystals found in many of these bodies of anorthosite (that is, protoclastic texture)

Philpotts (1981) has attempted to show how liquid immiscibility may be important in the generation of the massif-type anorthosites and the associated rocks of the anorthosite kindred. He (249) suggests that the cooling of an anhydrous andesite magma would result in the precipitation of a sodic labradorite to calcic andesine plagioclase cumulate. However, as the temperature falls further, pyroxene and/or olivine begin to crystallize and produce leuconorites and/or troctolites. This process enriches the residual magma in silica, alkalis and iron, and it should normally produce changes in the composition of the precipitating minerals. Contrary to this expectation, the compositions of the plagioclase in many large anorthosite bodies are relatively constant; and Philpotts (1981: 249) states that this occurs because the residual magma splits into two immiscible fractions (one silica-rich and the other iron-rich), and the alkalis and alumina preferentially enter the silica-rich liquid, and by so doing they buffer the composition of the plagioclase. Philpotts also claims that the compositions of the plagioclases can vary from one intrusion to another depending on the degree of fractionation of the magma at the time of unmixing. The formation of a layer of immiscible iron-rich liquid at the base of a magma chamber would also prevent the plagioclase crystals from sinking to the floor of the chamber, while the presence of the silica-rich liquid would prevent them from rising above the interface between the two immiscible liquids.

Simmons and Hanson (1978) have followed up the pioneering work of Buddington (1939) and others, and made a detailed study of the geochemistry of the Proterozoic massif-type anorthosites of eastern North America. They claim that their geochemical data, and mass balance mixing models, suggest that the parental magma from which these massif-type anorthosites evolved had the composition of an 'anorthositic gabbro', and contained 50–4 per cent SiO_2, > 20 per cent Al_2O_3, 1 per cent K_2O, atomic $Mg/(Mg + Fe^{2+})$ ratios of less than 0.4, 15–30 p.p.m. Rb, 400–600 p.p.m. Sr, 400–600 p.p.m. Ba, 40–50 times mean chondritic values for Ce, and 8–10 times mean chondritic values for Yb. It is proposed that a parental magma of this composition may be generated by the partial melting of tholeiitic basaltic material, or the fractional crystallization of a tholeiitic basaltic magma, at pressures of between 1.5–2.0 GPa, leaving a pyroxene-rich residuum (Simmons & Hanson 1978: 133). As this high-Al magma rises through the crust, it would become supersaturated with plagioclase. If the magma crystallizes at depth, orthopyroxene is a near liquidus phase, and this results in the evolution of 'noritic anorthosite'; however, if the magma crystallizes at shallower depths, olivine replaces hypersthene as a liquidus, or near liquidus, phase, and a 'troctolitic anorthosite' is formed. Simmons and Hanson (op. cit.) suggest that the source region for the parental magma of the massif-type anorthosites is in the uppermost mantle, or at the base of 'an orogenically thickened crust'. They also suggest that the initial water content of the parental magma is likely to determine the distance that such a magma is able to rise in the crust (cf. Harris et al. 1970). It is evident that a hydrous, and thus probably lower-temperature, magma will crystallize first, because as it rises to lower-pressure environments, water will come out of solution and if the magma is not superheated, crystallization will occur. It is thus suggested that the noritic anorthosites probably evolved from magmas that had higher initial water contents, and crystallized at greater depths, than the troctolitic anorthosites.

Wiebe (1980) has strongly defended the idea of anorthositic magmas. He claims that the Proterozoic massif-type anorthosites of North America have been generated by a series of magmas that range in composition from high-Al basalts to anorthositic magmas; and that these magmas (567) 'define an entirely new association which is clearly distinct from previously known basaltic and calc–alkaline series. This unique magma association implies that unique tectonic and thermal settings are responsible for the generation of the Proterozoic anorthosite massifs.'

It is concluded that anorthosites are likely to evolve in any body of basaltic magma (sensu lato) where the processes of crystal accumulation and sorting occur. The lunar anorthosites demonstrate that such processes were probably important during the early evolution of the crusts of the terrestrial planets; whereas the huge bodies of stratiform- and massif-type anorthosites of Earth indicate that whenever large bodies of basaltic magma are ponded within, or immediately beneath, the crust of a terrestrial-type planet, crystal accumulation and sorting is likely to generate ultramafic cumulates and complementary anorthosites. If these processes operate in an environment where the country rocks are highly ductile, and readily deform plastically, or pseudoplastically, it is likely that the dense ultramafic rocks, and the anorthosites, will tend to move away from one another.

10.7 Selected references

Isachsen, Y. W. (ed.) (1969) *Origin of anorthosite and related rocks*, New York State Museum and Science Service, **Mem. 18**, Albany, NY, USA.

Philpotts, A. R. (1981) A model for the generation of massif-type anorthosites, *Can. Mineral.*, **19**, 233–53.

Windley, B. F. (1973) Archaean Anorthosites: A Review: With the Fiskenaesset Complex, West Greenland as a model for interpretation, *Geol. Soc. S. Afr., Spec. Publ.*, **3**, 319–31.

CHAPTER 11

THE ULTRAMAFIC ROCKS

11.1 General statement

In Section 3.2, the *ultramafic rocks* were formally defined as those rocks that contain more than 90 per cent of the M-component in the QAFPM system. M consists of the mafic minerals (amphiboles, micas, olivines, pyroxenes and serpentines), apatite, primary carbonate minerals, Fe–Ti oxides, garnets, melilite, monticellite, spinels, troilite, native elements, sulphides, and accessory minerals such as zircon. Petrologists often modify this definition to include all rocks that have a colour index greater than 70 (cf. Wyllie 1967a: 1). With the notable exception of the *peridotitic komatiites* and some picrites, the ultramafic rocks are normally holocrystalline, and they are readily classified as being ultramafic rocks by using modal data. Most of the ultramafic rocks are essentially composed of olivine, orthopyroxene and clinopyroxene, and such rocks can be classified using Fig. 3.2.4. The pyroxenites at the base of this diagram (for example *orthopyroxenites*, *websterites* and *clinopyroxenites*) usually contain more than 44 per cent SiO_2, and they are thus ultramafic but not ultrabasic rocks; whereas the peridotites at the apex of the diagram (for example, *lherzolite*, *harzburgite*, *wehrlite* and *dunite*) normally contain less than 44 per cent SiO_2, and they are both ultramafic and ultrabasic. Most of the other ultramafic rocks, such as the *carbonatites, hornblendites, kimberlites, melitites, melilitolites, peridotitic komatiites* and *picrites*, are ultrabasic. Many of the 'alkaline rocks' (see Ch. 12) are ultrabasic but not ultramafic; the *jacupirangites* (nepheline-bearing pyroxenites), and the ultra-

mafic melilitic rocks, are notable exceptions. Another particularly interesting group of ultramafic rocks are the *eclogites*: their major element compositions are similar to the basalts, yet because they have crystallized at high pressures, their essential minerals are garnet (almandine–pyrope) and sodic pyroxene (omphacite).

The ultramafic rocks occur in a wide variety of rock associations. On Earth, rocks of this type are considered to be absolutely dominant in both the mantle and the core, and they also crop out in many different petrographic provinces within the crust. Most of the meteorites (that is, chondrites and irons), and probably most of the asteroids, have ultramafic compositions. In order to survey these rocks that vary so greatly in abundance, age, composition, distribution and origin, it has been found to be convenient to classify them into the following groups: (a) mantle rocks and xenoliths of these rocks; (b) core rocks and iron meteorites; (c) ultramafic stony meteorites and asteroids; (d) picrites; (e) peridotitic komatiites; (f) ultramafic zones in layered intrusions; (g) ultramafic rocks of the ocean floor; (h) orogenic (Alpine-type) ultramafic intrusions; (i) 'alkaline' ultramafic rocks; (j) kimberlites; (k) carbonatites; (l) zoned (Alaskan-type) ultramafic complexes; (m) ultramafic rocks (Appinite-type) associated with granitic batholiths; and (n) miscellaneous non-silicate ultramafic rocks. The rocks of group (a) have already been reviewed in Section 1.10, and the rocks of groups (i), (j) and (k) will be discussed in Chapters 12, 13 and 14, respectively.

11.2 Core rocks and iron meteorites

In Table 1.3.1 it was recorded that the Gutenberg seismic discontinuity, which lies at approximately 2900 km within the Earth, marks the core–mantle boundary. This seismic discontinuity represents a change from essentially solid lower mantle rock to a liquid outer core. At a depth of approximately 5150 km, the density of the core increases and the liquid outer core passes into a solid core of nickel–iron alloy. The mass of the core is approximately 32.5 per cent of the mass of the Earth. It has a mean density of approximately 11 000 kg/m^3, and it increases to over 13 000 kg/m^3 in the inner core. In the

Table 11.2.1 Chemical composition of the cores of the terrestrial planets (%) (after BVSP 1981: 638–43 and Mason and Moore 1982: 51–3)

	Mercury	*Venus*	*Earth*	*Mars*
Fe	92.4–94.5	78.7–94.4	68.9–89.2	59.8–88.1
Ni	5.4–7.6	4.8–6.6	4.8–7.4	5.8–9.3
S	0.0–0.35	0.0–10.0	1.0–26.1	3.5–34.3
O	—	0.0–9.8	0.0–8.0	0.0–18.7
Mass*	38.4–68.0	23.6–32.0	28.1–36.1	11.9–25.7

* Mass of core/total mass of planet × 100.

past, geophysical data, information from experimental studies at high pressures, and chemical data obtained from the study of meteorites, have all been used to construct models of the chemical composition of the core (cf. Washington 1925). Mason and Moore (1982: 51) have, for example, proposed that the core of the Earth has the following composition: 86.3 per cent Fe, 7.4 per cent Ni, 0.4 per cent Co and 5.9 per cent S. Other geochemists have proposed that the core, and in particular the much more massive molten outer core, contains 10–15 per cent of a light element such as S or Si. Shock compression studies at pressures appropriate for the outer core (Birch 1968) show that a 90 per cent Fe, 10 per cent Si alloy yields a satisfactory match of the density found in the outer core; whereas if sulphur is used, approximately 15 per cent is required. Brown and Mussett (1981: 105) have proposed the following bulk composition of the core at formation: 86 per cent Fe, 11 per cent S, 3 per cent Ni, and 'traces of other siderophilic and chalcophilic elements, possibly including up to 0.1 per cent potassium'. They (106) also suggest that at present the outer core probably contains 86 per cent Fe, 12 per cent S and 2 per cent Ni. Other elements that are believed to occur in significant quantities (that is, more than 0.05 per cent) are P, Co and K (cf. Morgan & Anders 1980). At present there is no consensus of opinion as to the amount of K stored in the outer core; however, if it contained approximately 0.1 per cent K, the radioactive decay of ^{40}K would probably provide enough heat to maintain convection currents within the outer core and thus keep the so-called *geomagnetic dynamo* operating. Alternatively, the geomagnetic dynamo may be partly, or wholly, powered by the release of latent heat during the gradual growth and solidification of the inner core.

All of the terrestrial planets probably possess iron-rich cores. Table 11.2.1 shows the sizes and chemical compositions that have been proposed for the cores of these planets. In various models the sulphur content of the core of the Earth is found to range from 1.0–26.1 per cent (cf. BVSP 1981: 641). The size and composition of the lunar core remains debatable; it is usually regarded as being small (that is, with a mass that is only 2 per cent of the mass of the whole planet) and essentially composed of Fe, Ni, S and Co.

Iron meteorites

Meteorites can be divided into differentiated and undifferentiated materials. In the chondritic meteorites, for example, the major elements are present in approximately the same proportions as they are in the solar atmosphere, and they may thus be regarded as samples of primitive, undifferentiated planetary material. The iron meteorites consist almost entirely of nickel–iron metal. Only melting, and the evolution of an immiscible iron-rich liquid, seems capable of producing materials of this composition. It is usually postulated that *irons* evolved on small planets, or asteroids, that were subsequently shattered by collisions in space. If this genetic model is correct, one is confronted with the problem of how such a small planet is able to generate sufficient heat to produce melting that results in the evolution of a body (or core) of nickel-iron. Possibly the required heat was obtained from short-lived radionuclides such as ^{26}Al, ^{244}Pu, ^{129}I (Wood 1968: 52), or electrical induction by a strong solar wind (Chapman et al. 1978: 72) (see Section 15.3).

The irons make up approximately 3.2 per cent of the observed meteorite falls (cf. Dodd 1981). They are essentially alloys of iron with between 4 and 20 per cent of nickel. Detailed studies reveal that they are usually composed of one or

Table 11.2.2 Chemical composition of the main classes of iron meteorites (after Keil 1969: 102)

	Fe	Ni	Co	Cu	P	S	C	Misc.	Total	No. of specimens
Hexahedrites*	92.62	6.07	0.61	0.29	0.25	0.06	0.15	0.18	100.23	78
Octahedrites†	90.67	8.22	0.59	0.03	0.18	0.09	0.08	0.30	100.16	126
Ataxites‡	79.63	18.85	1.01	0.05	0.12	0.08	0.10	0.19	100.03	38

* The nickel-poor ataxites are included in this class.
† Only the common medium-grained octahedrites.
‡ The nickel-rich ataxites.

two nickel–iron metallic phases (that is, kamacite with 5–7 per cent Ni, and taenite with 27–65 per cent Ni), with accessory amounts of troilite, schreibersite, and graphite. These accessory minerals are usually present as small rounded, or lamellar, grains scattered through the alloy. The nickel–iron metallic phases usually occur in lamellar intergrowths which show up as criss-cross, or triangular, patterns on polished and etched surfaces (Widmanstätten structures). These structures are characteristic of meteorites and enable one to distinguish between iron meteorites and pieces of scrap metal. There are three main types of irons: (a) *hexahedrites* in which the only essential phase is kamacite; (b) *octahedrites* which contain both kamacite and taenite; and (c) *ataxites* in which taenite is the only essential phase. The mean chemical compositions of the three types of irons are given in Table 11.2.2, and it is significant to note that they all contain small quantities of Co, Cu, P, S and C. It is anticipated that these elements are probably present in the cores of the terrestrial planets.

Stony-iron meteorites

The stony-iron meteorites, or *siderites*, are differentiated meteorites that are usually composed of approximately equal amounts of nickel–iron and silicate minerals; they consist of approximately 1.5 per cent of the observed falls. These meteorites are characterized by the coarseness of their mineral constituents, and this makes the sampling of these materials exceedingly difficult. They are usually grouped into two main classes, the *pallasites* and the *mesosiderites*. The pallasites consist of a continuous base of nickel–iron enclosing euhedral grains of olivine; whereas the mesosiderites are heterogeneous aggregates of silicate minerals, basaltic fragments and particles of nickel–iron alloy of irregular size (see Section 5.11).

11.3 Ultramafic stony meteorites and the asteroids

The stony meteorites are the most common type of meteorite, and they make up 95.7 per cent of the observed falls. They are divided into two main groups, the *chondrites* and the *achondrites*. The *basaltic meteorites* discussed in Section 5.11 belong to the achondritic group. Approximately 91 per cent of the stony meteorites are chondrites, and they can usually be separated from other igneous rocks by the presence of small spherical inclusions (1 mm in diameter) called *chondrules*. These chondrules generally consist of olivine and orthopyroxene, and they frequently have a radiating texture. According to Dodd (1981: 13),

'chondrites are agglomerate rocks whose chemical compositions closely approach the composition of the Sun, less most of its complement of hydrogen, helium, and other highly volatile elements. The agglomerate character of chondrites sets them apart from most other types of meteorites; their quasi-solar compositions distinguish them from all other meteorites and all known terrestrial and lunar rocks'.

Some chondrites consist almost entirely of chondrules, whereas others consist mainly, or entirely, of matrix. It is usually assumed that these variations, and the chemical differences that accompany them, developed before, or during, the aggregation of materials into the chondritic parent bodies, thus they are called primary variations. Chondrites with similar chemical compositions and primary texture often contain evidence that shows that they have experienced different degrees of thermal metamorphism within their parent bodies. Specimens that reveal no evidence of metamorphism are classified as belonging to petrologic type 1; as the metamorphic grade increases the petrologic type number is increased until it reaches a maximum of 7. The chondrites are now usually grouped into three main classes: (a) the *ordinary* (or common) *chondrites*; (b) the *carbonaceous chondrites*; and (c) the *enstatite chondrites*. Von Michaelis et al. (1969) showed that these three classes of chondrites have significantly different Mg/Si, Ca/Si, Ti/Si and Al/Si ratios (see Table 11.3.1). The enstatite chondrites are strongly reduced, and they contain mafic silicate minerals that are essentially iron-free; whereas the carbonaceous chondrites contain little or no metallic iron, and some of them contain significant amounts of ferric iron in the form of magnetite. High carbon values are not always characteristic of the carbonaceous chondrites (see Table 11.3.1).

Most of the meteorites that have been observed to fall on the Earth are *ordinary chondrites*. Their iron and siderophile element (for example Co, Ni, Ir and Au) contents are used to divide them into three groups: (a) the high-Fe (greater than 25 per cent) *H group*; (b) the intermediate-Fe, *L group*; and (c) the low-Fe (usually less than 21 per cent Fe) *LL group* (cf. Dodd 1981: 79). The ratio of oxidized to metallic iron also increases as one goes from the LL-group via the L-group to the H-group. Secondary (metamorphic) and tertiary (shock) features are particularly prominent in this class of chrondrites (that is, they are generally of petrologic types 3, 4, 5 and 6). A relatively simple method of determining the primary mineral assemblages

found in these anhydrous chondrites is to calculate their normative compositions, because their normative and modal mineral compositions tend to coincide, that is except for the feldspars. The normative feldspar is generally slightly more abundant, and more calcic than the modal feldspar. It is important to remember this, because feldspar is usually the only non-mafic mineral in the ordinary chondrites, and in these chondrites the feldspars have a normative abundance of approximately 10 per cent (see Table 11.3.2). It is proposed that most ordinary chondrites were originally ultramafic rocks (sensu stricto), that should be called *feldspathic harzburgites*. While on their parent planetary bodies they experienced thermal metamorphism in a dry, unstressed environment in a temperature range of approximately 400 to 950 °C, and at pressures that increased with temperature but did not exceed 0.1 GPa.

The *enstatite chondrites* differ from the ordinary chondrites in that they have lower Mg/Si and (Ca, Al, Ti)/Si rations, and they are highly reduced (see Table 11.3.1). Their modes are dominated by nearly iron-free, low-calcium pyroxenes (enstatite) that usually make up between 60–80 per cent of their volume. Other essential phases are nickel–iron alloy (20 per cent) and troilite, thus this class of stony meteorites is ultramafic in modal composition. The accessory minerals usually found include sodic plagioclase

Table 11.3.1 The chemical composition of the chondrite meteorites (after Dodd 1981: 19) (%)

Class	Enstatite		Ordinary		Carbonaceous			
Group	High-Fe	Low-Fe	H	L(LL)	I	M	0	V
Si	16.47	20.48	17.08	18.67	10.40	12.96	15.75	15.46
Ti	0.03	0.04	0.06	0.07	0.04	0.06	0.10	0.09
Al	0.77	1.06	1.22	1.27	0.84	1.17	1.41	1.44
Cr	0.24	0.23	0.29	0.31	0.23	0.29	0.36	0.35
Fe	33.15	22.17	27.81	21.64	18.67	21.56	25.82	24.28
Mn	0.19	0.12	0.26	0.27	0.17	0.16	0.16	0.16
Mg	10.40	13.84	14.10	15.01	9.60	11.72	14.52	14.13
Ca	1.19	0.96	1.26	1.36	1.01	1.32	1.57	1.57
Na	0.75	0.67	0.64	0.70	0.55	0.42	0.46	0.38
K	0.09	0.05	0.08	0.09	0.05	0.06	0.10	0.03
P	0.30	0.15	0.15	0.15	0.14	0.13	0.11	0.13
Ni	1.83	1.29	1.64	1.10	1.03	1.25	0.41	1.33
Co	0.08	0.09	0.09	0.06	0.05	0.06	0.08	0.08
S	5.78	3.19	1.91	2.19	5.92	3.38	2.01	2.14
H	0.13	trace	trace	trace	2.08	1.42	0.09	0.38
C	0.43	0.84	trace	trace	3.61	2.30	0.31	1.08
No. of samples	1	1	36	68	3	10	5	7

Table 11.3.2 Normative compositions of average H-and L-group ordinary chondrites (after Mason 1965) (%)

	H-group	L-group
Or	0.6	0.7
Ab	7.3	8.1
An	2.1	1.9
Di	4.0	4.6
Hy	24.5	22.7
Ol	36.2	47.0
Cm	0.6	0.6
Ilm	0.2	0.2
Ap	0.6	0.6
Troilite	5.3	6.1
Ni–Fe	18.6	7.5
	100.0	100.0

and one or more polymorphs of silica (cristobalite, tridymite and quartz). Other accessory minerals include oldhamite, daubreelite, graphite, schreibersite and djerfisherite $K_3(Na,Cu)(Fe,Ni)_{12}S_{14}$. Djerfisherite is particularly interesting as it is claimed that the presence of this mineral demonstrates that under highly reducing conditions potassium has a tendency to be chalcophile (that is, it tends to be partitioned into phases that contain sulphur). This observation has reinforced speculation concerning the concept that, during the evolution of the core of the Earth, significant quantities of both S and K were incorporated into the core (see Section 11.2). The strongly reduced nature of the enstatite chondrites is shown by their nearly iron-free silicate minerals, and the presence of lithophile elements, such as Ca, Mn, Mg and K, in sulphides. Textural and mineralogical data indicate that these chondrites were thermally metamorphosed to temperatures of between approximately 600–900 °C. Chemically and modally they are very similar to the enstatite achondrites; and it is probable that both groups of stony meteorites formed in the same region of the Solar nebula, possibly from the same parent body (cf. Dodd 1981: 146–52).

The *carbonaceous chondrites* are essentially unmetamorphosed (petrologic type 1), or weakly metamorphosed (petrologic types 2 and 3), collections of chondrules and unmelted aggregates, set in a fine-grained, volatile-rich matrix. These materials are both chemically and physically primitive. The unmetamorphosed specimens, and the matrices of the other specimens in this class, carry nearly undisturbed records of the preaccretionary, and accretionary, evolution of these meteorites. Detailed studies have enabled petrologists to divide the carbonaceous chondrites into four groups (I, M, O and V) on the basis of major element ratios and petrographic criteria (see Table 11.3.1). All the specimens of group-I material belong to petrologic type 1 and are physically and chemically the most primitive types of meteorites. The group-I carbonaceous chondrites (CI) are essentially microbreccias that do not contain chondrules or aggregates, but consist almost entirely of low-temperature phases. Such material also occurs in the matrices of the other carbonaceous chondrites. The O- and V-group carbonaceous chondrites are usually largely composed of chondrules and aggregates of unmelted solid particles, whereas specimens of the M-group usually contain about 50 per cent matrix, over 20 per cent isolated high-temperature mineral grains, less than 20 per cent of aggregates, and a small proportion ($\approx$ 2 per cent) of chondrules.

The CI chondrites are mainly composed of an extremely fine-grained aggregate of hydrous silicates (for example, septechlorite and montmorillonite) and subordinate amounts of magnetite, pyrrhotite and cubanite, thus these stony meteorites have ultramafic modal compositions. These chondrites usually also contain over 3 per cent C; and most of this C occurs as complex organic compounds, that include hydrocarbons, fatty acids and even amino acids. Anders et al. (1973) have shown that all of these organic compounds can be formed by abiogenic processes. The CI chondrites usually also contain approximately 1 per cent of isolated high-temperature mineral grains, such as olivines and pyroxenes. Many also contain veins that now contain minerals such as epsomite ($MgSO_4.7H_2O$) and Ca–Mg carbonates.

According to Dodd (1981: 55), the aggregates and chondrules that are found in most of the carbonaceous chondrites probably evolved at high temperatures from materials that separated out of the primordial Solar nebula; whereas the materials that now form the matrix of the chondrites are chemically unfractionated, and they probably evolved after the complete condensation of the Solar nebula. Table 1.10.1 gives the chemical composition of the Orgueil CI chondrite, which is probably some of the most primitive material presently available in the Solar System. Oxygen and magnesium isotopic studies of the various materials within the carbonaceous chondrites, particularly of the Allende meteorite, appear to show that the Solar nebula contained discrete components with different isotopic compositions (cf. Wasserburg et al. 1977). In order to explain this anomaly, it has been proposed that a supernova which was capable of creating a wide range of nuclides, including short-lived radionuclides such as [26]Al, exploded near the nascent Solar System just prior to its formation, thus providing the nuclides that are now recognized as isotopic anomalies.

Asteroids and the origin of meteorites

The asteroids consist of a great number of minor planets and smaller objects that orbit the Sun at distances that range from inside the orbit of the Earth to beyond the orbit of Saturn. Most of them (the *belt asteroids*) occur in a large torus between Mars and Jupiter; their total mass is at present less than that of the Moon. In recent years the spectra of sunlight reflected from the asteroids have been measured from the ultraviolet to the mid-infrared, and many of these reflectance spectra are found to exhibit absorption bands that are due to the presence of different minerals and hydrous compounds on the surfaces of the larger asteroids. It has thus been possible to classify these asteroids on the basis of their spectral curves (cf. Chapman 1976; Bowell et al. 1978); and this has led to the discovery that the spectra of many asteroids have strong similarities with the spectra of the various classes of meteorites. For example, Ceres, the largest asteroid, has a reflectance spectrum similar to that of an undifferentiated carbonaceous chondrite; whereas the slightly smaller asteroid Vesta (see Section 5.11) has a similar reflectance spectrum to the eucrites, and basaltic materials in general. It would thus seem, from these observations, that a relatively large mass is not all that is required to produce internal differentiation, and basaltic volcanism, on these minor planets. Detailed studies of the chemical and modal compositions and thermal histories of the irons, chondrites and eucrites suggest that they probably formed in parent planets with radii of between 100 and 500 km (cf. Dodd 1981: 309). It is now accepted that most of the meteorites, and particularly the carbonaceous chondrites, are fragments of asteroidal material. According to Chapman (1976: 701), 'the surfaces of most asteroids are like carbonaceous chondrites while a significant minority are of stony-iron composition', and 'other meteorite types' are also recognized. It is

suggested that the carbonaceous chondrites accreted at a late stage in the condensation and cooling of the Solar nebula, and that they initially occurred in a parental body rich in ices, and with the evaporation of these ices they developed their present petrographic characteristics.

11.4 Picrites and picritic basalts

Picrites were originally regarded as the extrusive, or high-level intrusive, equivalents of peridotites (cf. Johannsen 1938: 432–4). The term was first used by Gustav Tschermak (1866) to describe medium- to fine-grained melanocratic rocks from Silesia which is now on the border between modern Poland and Czechoslovakia. He derived the name from the classical Greek word *picros* meaning a bitter taste. According to Tröger (1935), a typical picrite contains approximately 51 per cent olivine, 37 per cent clinopyroxene, 8 per cent plagioclase (An_{88}), together with accessory amounts of minerals such as hornblende, biotite–phlogopite, Fe–Ti oxides, apatite, picotite and, possibly, analcite. At present the term picrite is used to describe olivine-rich melanocratic rocks that belong to either the alkalic, or the tholeiitic, rock associations. Such rocks are usually mainly composed of magnesian olivine and clinopyroxene, together with a lesser amount of feldspars (5–30 per cent), and a variety of accessory phases. Most of the rocks called 'picrites' contain more olivine (40–65 per cent) than normal basalts, but too little of the M-component (70–90 per cent) to be ultramafic rocks (sensu stricto).

Table 11.4.1 gives the chemical composition of five rocks that have been called 'picrites'. From the modal and normative data available it is concluded that these rocks contain between 41–60 per cent olivine, 9–27 per cent pyroxene and 18–26 per cent feldspar. They are thus olivine-rich basalts, and they should properly be called *picritic basalts*. When the chemical compositions of the picritic basalts are compared with those of the normal basaltic rocks (see Table 5.3.2), the picritic basalts are found to be significantly enriched in MgO and depleted in SiO_2, Al_2O_3, CaO and Na_2O. These picritic basalts contain between 21 and 31 per cent MgO, with a mean value of 24.8 per cent MgO. Their high-MgO contents are a chemical characteristic that they share with the rocks of the komatiitic magmatic suite (see section 11.5).

The picritic basalts cited in Table 11.4.1 are believed to have evolved in at least two different ways. For example, the picritic basalt from the base of the sill on Garbh Eilean, Shiant Isles, Scotland, is believed to be an olivine cumulate. It probably evolved from a mildly alkalic basaltic magma in which olivine had been concentrated prior to its emplacement. The mechanism that produced the concentration of olivine crystals was possibly *flowage-differentiation* (see Section 2.3). Drever and Johnston (1967a: 61) have examined the compositions of the minerals that are usually found in the picritic rocks associated with basaltic sills, and they have concluded that the olivine is usually magnesian (Fo_{70-85}) and the plagioclase is usually calcium-rich (An_{70-82}). The picritic basalts also occur as lava flows, and as small intrusions in which they are the dominant type of rock (cf. Drever & Johnston 1967b: 71–82). Such rocks probably congealed from primary magmas of picritic basalt composition (see Section 5.16). Contrary to the views expressed by Bowen (1928: 148–59), many of the picritic basalt intrusions of the British segment of the Thulean Igneous Province contain marginal selvages that have textures that demonstrate that they cooled quickly; and the bulk compositions of these chilled selvages are usually that of a picritic basalt.

A variety of different thermal metamorphic effects have been described in the country rocks that make contact with the minor intrusions of picritic composition. Wyllie (1961) has, for example, described the partial fusion of an arkosic sandstone by picritic magma in a sill on Soay in the Hebrides of Scotland. He claimed that 92 per cent of the original minerals in the rock were fused, and tridymite, cordierite and magnetite crystallized from the liquid produced by the partial melting process. This evidence clearly shows that some picritic magmas have been emplaced at high temperatures, probably greater than 1175 °C.

The finer-grained margins of the satellite dykes and sills that are associated with the Great Dyke of Zimbabwe, and the Bushveld Layered Complex of S. Africa, have picritic basaltic compositions (cf. Robertson & van Breemen

Table 11.4.1 Selected chemical analyses of 'picrites' (%)

	1	2	3	4	5
SiO_2	44.97	46.59	44.32	41.60	40.62
TiO_2	1.48	2.83	0.78	0.70	0.82
Al_2O_3	5.74	5.89	10.29	5.50	8.93
Fe_2O_3	3.45	3.54	1.88	3.20	0.57
FeO	10.18	8.31	8.93	8.00	12.61
MnO	0.18	0.16	0.11	0.17	0.39
MgO	24.15	21.00	22.07	30.60	26.31
CaO	6.26	5.79	8.06	5.10	5.64
Na_2O	0.91	1.37	0.94	0.60	1.32
K_2O	0.75	1.97	0.10	0.18	0.13
P_2O_5	0.23	0.46	0.12	0.09	0.15
H_2O^+	0.87	1.76	1.41	} 3.24	2.19
H_2O^-	0.29	0.10	0.92		0.61
CO_2	0.50	—	0.15		0.03
Total	99.96	99.77	100.08	98.98	100.32

1. Chemical composition of picrite from Shamandali Hills, Malibangwe District, Zimbabwe (Cox et al. 1965: 148). Modal composition 48.3 per cent olivine plus alteration products, 24.3 per cent augite, 2.8 per cent hypersthene, 19.5 per cent basic plagioclase, 1.1 per cent alkali feldspar and 2.3 per cent Fe–Ti oxides.
2. Chemical composition of alkalic picrite from 47 km east-south-east of Nuanetsi (Cox et al. 1965: 148). Rock also contains 0.19 per cent Cr_2O_3. Modal composition 41.0 per cent olivine plus alteration products, 25.9 per cent clinopyroxene, 24.2 per cent alkali feldspar, 3.8 per cent Fe–Ti oxides and 4.9 per cent micaceous groundmass.
3. Chemical composition of picrite collected 5–25 mm above the bottom contact of Igdlorssuit Intrusion, Sheet 2, Ubekendt Ejland, West Greenland (Drever & Johnston 1967b: 81).
4. Chemical composition of a picrite flow, Simiútap Kûa, Svartenhuk Halvø, West Greenland, (Clarke & Pedersen 1976: 370). This rock contains 54 per cent normative olivine and has a colour index of 81.
5. Chemical composition of picrite from the base of the sill on Garbh Eilean, Shiant Isles, Scotland (Walker 1930). This rock contains 4.1 per cent normative nepheline. Modal composition 60 per cent olivine, 26 per cent basic plagioclase, 9 per cent clinopyroxene, 2 per cent Fe–Ti oxides and 3 per cent zeolites (dominantly analcime).

1969). According to Cawthorn and Davies (1982: 91), the parental magma of the Great Dyke of Zimbabwe was picritic with 'komatiitic affinities'; and magma of this composition might be regarded as a link between the picritic basalts and the rocks of the komatiitic magmatic suite (see Section 11.5).

Excellent examples of subaqueous breccias, subaerial lavas and minor intrusions of picritic basalt composition crop out in the West Greenland segment of the more extensive Thulean Igneous Province; two examples of these rocks are cited in Table 11.4.1. According to Clarke and Pedersen (1976: 381), 'enormous volumes of picritic magma' were erupted during the early stages in the development of this subprovince; and they (382–3) have proposed the following petrogenetic model for the evolution of these picritic rocks: (a) the partial melting of garnet peridotite at a pressure of 3.0 GPa to produce large volumes of hypersthene normative picritic magma; (b) the rapid movement of much of this magma towards the surface; (c) part of the magma is extruded (subaqueously and subaerially) and the remainder is emplaced into a series of dykes, sills and magma chambers. The Tertiary volcanic rocks of West Greenland are remarkably similar to the rocks of the same age on Baffin Island, Canada; and it has been suggested that the rocks of the two areas are genetically related. According to this hypothesis, the massive outpourings of picritic materials occurred during the period of rifting that took place immediately prior to the start of the sea-floor spreading episode that separated West Greenland from Baffin Island (cf. Clarke & Upton 1971).

11.5 Peridotitic komatiites

The derivation of the term komatiite was discussed in Section 1.2, and Section 5.5 contains a description of the *basaltic komatiites*. This section contains a description of the *peridotitic komatiites*, or the komatiites (sensu stricto), and they are the ultramafic members of the *komatiitic magmatic suite*. According to Arndt and Nisbet (1982: 1), the 'komatiites are fascinating rocks, spectacular and varied in outcrop and in hand specimen, attractive in thin section, and of great geochemical, tectonic and economic signi-ficance'. Their most distinctive chemical characteristic is their high MgO content; and in the peridotitic komatiites it is normally greater than 20 per cent on an anhydrous basis (BVSP 1981: 6). The peridotitic komatiites have a wide temporal and spatial distribution, but most occur in Archaean terrains, such as the Barberton Mountain Land of S. Africa (3.5 Ga) and the younger Archaean rocks of: (a) Munro Township, Canada; (b) Belingwe, Zimbabwe; (c) the Pilbara and Yilgarn 'blocks' of Western Australia; and (d) the Finnish Greenstone Belts. Nickel sulphide ore deposits are found associated with peridotitic komatiites in the Kambalda area of Western Australia, several areas in Zimbabwe and in the Abitibi Greenstone Belt of Canada.

Viljoen and Viljoen (1982: 13) claim that, before they introduced the concept of komatiitic magmatic suite, they compared the chemical compositions of these rocks with 'those of well established classes of peridotites, picrites, basalts and allied rocks' and their study showed that the melanocratic extrusive rocks of the Komati Valley, S. Africa contained 'a number of unique chemical features' that were unlike 'any generally accepted rock type'. In Section 11.4 the picritic basalts were shown to contain more than 20 per cent MgO (anhydrous basis), thus it is not a high MgO content alone that defines the chemical characteristics of the komatiitic magmatic suite. According to Arndt et al. (1977), the komatiitic magmatic suite contains both cumulate and noncumulate rocks; and in the noncumulate rocks: (a) MgO ranges from >30 to <8 wt.%; (b) Mg/Mg + Fe ratios are generally high, especially when compared with rocks from other magma series having similar Al_2O_3 contents; (c) TiO_2 contents are low, in almost all cases <1 wt.%; (d) Ni and Cr are always high (usually in excess of 100 and 140 p.p.m., respectively); (e) the CaO/Al_2O_3 ratio usually ranges between 0.8 and 1.1, although in some samples it is as low as 0.6, and in other areas it may be as high as 2; and (f) skeletal crystals, including bladed (spinifex texture) or hollow (hopper) olivines, are developed in liquids containing >20 wt.% MgO; and hollow, needle-like pyroxene crystals (pyroxene spinifex texture) occur in liquids containing 12–20 wt.% MgO (see Table 11.5.1).

According to the BVSP (1981: 10), the peridotitic komatiites have the following petrographic characteristics:

Table 11.5.1 The chemical composition of selected peridotitic komatiites

	1(%)	*2(%)*	*3(%)*	*4(%)*
SiO_2	43.25	42.22	43.36	41.61
TiO_2	0.34	0.30	0.43	0.31
Al_2O_3	7.23	6.40	7.51	2.70
Fe_2O_3	1.40	2.78	2.22	5.63
FeO	8.77	6.94	7.67	4.35
MnO	0.18	0.15	0.17	0.17
MgO	24.06	26.35	23.16	30.58
CaO	6.92	5.94	6.33	4.29
Na_2O	0.77	0.52	0.68	0.15
K_2O	0.13	0.09	0.09	0.03
P_2O_5	0.03	0.02	0.04	0.02
H_2O^+	5.36	6.95	7.63	8.81
CO_2	0.14	0.14	0.07	—
Total	98.58	98.80	99.36	98.65*
p.p.m.				
Sc	25.3	23.1	24.7	—
Cr	2600	2530	2450	—
Ni	1150	1380	1250	—
Ga	8	8	10	—
Rb	2	1.9	1.3	—
Sr	5	25	12	—
Y	8.4	7.3	10	—
Cs	0.29	0.21	0.09	—
La	0.37	0.32	1.20	—
Ce	1.17	—	3.70	—
Sm	0.62	0.58	1.04	—
Eu	0.23	0.24	0.32	—
Tb	0.19	0.15	0.30	—
Yb	0.90	0.80	1.22	—
Lu	0.15	0.11	0.18	—
Hf	0.51	0.48	0.83	—
Pb	3	4	4	—
Th	—	0.11	—	—

1. Archaen peridotitic komatiite from Munro Township, Ontario, Canada (BVSP 1981: 14, ACH-2).
2. Archaean peridotitic komatiite from Munro Township, Ontario, Canada (BVSP 1981: 14, ACH-5).
3. Archaean peridotitic komatiite from Munro Township, Ontario, Canada (BVSP 1981: 15, ACH-17).
4. Mean chemical composition of eight peridotitic komatiites from the Komati Formation, Barberton Mountain Land, S. Africa (Viljoen & Viljoen 1969a: 72, Table 1, No. 5). *This chemical analysis also contains 0.22 per cent H_2O^-, 0.32 per cent Cr_2O_3 and 0.18 per cent NiO.

'all types are composed of olivine grains and minor chrome spinel in a matrix of fine-grained clinopyroxene and devitrified glass. In cumulates olivine grains are close-packed, solid, roughly equant and comprise 60–80 per cent of rock; in spinifex texture olivine forms large skeletal platy grains (35–60 per cent); and in spinifex-free, noncumulate rock, olivine may be equant or skeletal (45–70 per cent).'

Viljoen and Viljoen (1969: 91) state that the least altered specimens of peridotitic komatiite from the type area 'consist of closely packed, generally equidimensional but also tabular olivine crystals altered fairly extensively along partings and crystal boundaries to antigorite and magnetite'. Olivine also occurs in the groundmass that now mainly consists of 'tremolite, chlorite and magnetite. Chromite grains, invariably coated and partly replaced by magnetite, together with minor amounts of ilmenite and sulphides, constitute the remainder of the opaque minerals'. Viljoen and Viljoen (1969a: 100) have also calculated the normative mineral composition of their 'average peridotitic komatiite'; and it contains 54 per cent olivine, 24 per cent orthopyroxene, 11.6 per cent clinopyroxene, 9.4 per cent plagioclase (An_{84}) and 1.5 per cent Fe–Ti oxides.

The compositions of the olivines in the peridotitic komatiites usually range from Fo_{85}–Fo_{95}, with a mean value of Fo_{92}. Some of the spinifex-texture rocks contain normally-zoned crystals that range from Fo_{94} in the cores to Fo_{89} at the margins. The olivines in all the rocks of the komatiitic magmatic suite are remarkably rich in Cr_2O_3 (that is, 0.1–0.4 wt.%); and this is a chemical characteristic they share with the olivine inclusion found in some diamonds, and also with the olivines found in garnet lherzolite xenoliths from kimberlites. Most of the skeletal clinopyroxenes that occur in the peridotitic komatiites have compositions in the augite-salite range, with a mean value of $En_{42}Fs_{14}Wo_{44}$ (cf. BVSP 1981: 9–11); however, some acicular needles of pyroxene have cores of magnesium pigeonite and rims of augite. All of these pyroxenes have remarkably high Al_2O_3 contents (5–9 wt.%) that set them apart from most other pyroxenes from both the Earth and the Moon. The spinel group minerals are mainly chromites that have fairly low Al_2O_3 contents (12–15 wt.%), and moderately high MgO contents (11–14 wt.%). Chemical analyses of the glass in the mesostasis of some peridotitic komatiites reveal a range of compositions from peridotitic komatiite to basaltic komatiite (cf. Donaldson 1982: 233).

Most petrologists support the concept that the peridotitic komatiites congealed from a liquid that was generated in the mantle. However, there are still many ancillary questions that are being actively debated, including: (a) what proportion of the source materials has to be partially melted to generate a peridotitic komatiite liquid? The answer to this question depends on the composition of the source materials; that is, whether they were fertile garnet lherzolites, garnet harzburgites, or more refractory materials such as harzburgites, or even dunites (see Section 1.10). If the source rocks were fertile garnet lherzolites, approximately 65 per cent partial melting would be required; but the degree of partial melting would decrease to approximately 45 per cent if the more refractory materials were at the site of melting. (b) How abundant were the volatile components both in the source region and in the peridotitic komatiite magma? It is usually assumed that the source materials that melted to form peridotitic komatiite magma were essentially dry. However, some petrologists (for example, Allègre 1982: 495) claim that this type of magma is usually generated by the melting of hydrous source materials. Others have indirectly supported this concept by suggesting that there was significantly more mantle degassing during the Archaean Eon. If significant quantities of volatile components were available in the source region, they would lower the melting temperatures of the source materials, and thus promote magma generation at lower temperatures. (c) At what temperatures did the peridotitic komatiite magmas exist within the Earth? This question relates directly back to the previous question; and temperatures of between 1600 and 1850 °C are often mentioned. (d) Why did the partial melting that produced the peridotitic komatiite magma go beyond the stage at which nephelinitic, and then picritic, magma is formed? There seem to have been a number of contributory factors. For example, it is usually postulated that there was an abnormally large input of heat into the mantle during the Archaean (see Section 1.3), and that more of the mantle may have been partially melted than at present. It has also been found that komatiitic melts are relatively compressible, and the density of a peridotitic komatiite magma at pressures of the order of 2.0 GPa and temperatures of 1800 °C may exceed the density of some of the solid phases from which it was derived (for example, olivine). If these conditions prevailed, it is likely that continued heating would first of all generate a picritic liquid, and then a magmatic material that was essentially a mush of refractory crystals set in a komatiitic liquid; however, the latter 'magma' would be less dense than any overlying solid body of garnet lherzolite (cf. Nisbet 1982: 515), and thus capable of being intruded

upwards. If such a high-temperature (1600–1850 °C) dense liquid was to form in the mantle at the present time, it would probably be unable to rise through the lithosphere; however, in the Archaean, the lithosphere was probably much thinner, and the crustal segment of it was likely to have been more dense and less silicic than it is at present. It is thus proposed that primary peridotitic komatiite magmas may be generated within the Earth by a relatively high degree of partial melting (60 per cent) of lherzolitic–harzburgitic source rocks at depths of between 80–120 km. In the Archaean, such ultramafic magmas were readily able to penetrate the lithosphere; but in the Proterozoic and Phanerozoic, as the lithosphere grew thicker, the crust more silicic, and the mantle cooled, it would become progressively less common for peridotitic komatiite magmas to form and pierce the crust. However, if peridotitic komatiite magmas do still form in the upper mantle, and it seems likely that they do, they may form the *primary magmas* from which picritic and basaltic magmas may be derived in an orderly manner by polybaric fractional crystallization. Perhaps the Great Dyke of Zimbabwe evolved from a huge body of komatiitic magma that welled up and was trapped at the base of the crust; and there it formed a vast magma chamber that differentiated to form the komatiitic picrite magma that is now found congealed in the satellite dykes and sills of the Great Dyke (cf. Robertson & van Breemen 1969).

11.6 Ultramafic zones and major layered intrusions

Layered intrusions are intrusive bodies that contain layers with different modal compositions (see Sections 2.3 and 10.4). According to Wager and Brown (1968: 544), who wrote the book *Layered Igneous Rocks*, layering is an igneous phenomenon that depends for its origin 'largely upon the physical effects of gravity and the chemical effects of magmatic fractionation'. They (545) also suggest that *repetitive layering* is the main feature that distinguishes the major layered intrusions 'from sills which are in the simplest terms, equivalent to a single macro-unit of a major intrusion'. Repetitive layering is a remarkably common feature among gabbroic and ultramafic rocks. In most major layered intrusions the

ultramafic rocks (for example pyroxenites, dunites, peridotites and chromatites) occur within
the lower rock units; however, there are exceptions, such as the Rhum Complex of Scotland
which does not contain the thick layers of gabbroic rocks that are characteristic of most of the
major layered intrusions. The core of the Rhum
Complex is composed of layered cumulates that
essentially consist of 'varying amounts of magnesian olivine, diopsidic pyroxene, chrome spinel
and calcic plagioclase' (Emeleus 1982: 383).

According to Wager and Brown (1968: 540),
most major layered intrusions evolved from
parental magmas with '*tholeiitic affinities*'. Detailed studies of: (a) the chemical composition of
the chilled magmatic rocks that partially enclose
some layered intrusions; (b) the late differentiates that evolve in layered intrusions; and (c) the
fractionation trends observed in the minerals,
particularly in the pyroxenes, found in these
layered rocks, indicate that the parental magmas
from which most of the major layered intrusions
evolved were subalkalic basaltic, picritic basaltic
or komatiitic in composition; and the differentiation trends were essentially tholeiitic in character. Some of these intrusions, such as the
Skaergaard Layered Intrusion of East Greenland,
contain chilled margins that have relatively
high Al_2O_3 contents (cf. Wager & Brown 1968:
Table 7). The characteristic pyroxene fractionation trend found in the layered intrusions is
magnesian augite + bronzite $\rightarrow$ augite +
inverted pigeonite $\rightarrow$ augite + pigeonite $\rightarrow$
ferroaugite $\rightarrow$ ferrohedenbergite (Wager & Brown
1968: 550).

Bushveld layered complex

The Bushveld Complex of the north-central
Transvaal, S. Africa, is a good example of a major layered intrusion that contains ultramafic
rocks. Wager and Brown (1968: 407) have stated
that 'the Bushveld is the only discovered layered
intrusion in which the almost complete assemblage, ranging from ultrabasic to acid differentiates, can be observed directly and, by
comparison with certain fragmental patterns in
other layered intrusions, can safely be assumed to
have formed by crystallization differentiation in
place'. This Middle Proterozoic complex consists
of four lobes that give the complex a cruciform
shape; the whole complex covers an area of
approximately 66 000 km². At the present time,
most of the layered rocks dip at low angles (10–

25 °) towards the centres of the individual lobes
(cf. Hunter 1975; Willemse 1964), thus the various lobes are essentially basin-like in form. The
rocks of the main plutonic unit can be divided
into five zones, that is the lower, transition,
critical, main and upper zones (cf. Vermaak
1976: 1273, Fig. 2).

According to Vermaak (1976: 1271), the
Lower Zone can be divided into: (a) a marginal
norite suite; (b) a pyroxenite–norite suite; (c) a
harzburgite-pyroxenite suite; and (d) an upper
norite suite. In the western lobe the Lower Zone
is approximately 630 m thick, and in this area
the marginal norite suite consists of eight cyclic
units that vary in composition from leucocratic
to melanocratic norites; these rocks are essentially bronzite + plagioclase cumulates. The
pyroxenite–norite suite is transitional between
the marginal norites and overlying essentially
pyroxenitic rocks. In the western lobe, the harzburgite–pyroxenite suite is mainly composed of
orthopyroxenites that contain more than 85 per
cent bronzite (Coertze 1970: 7). The less common harzburgites are essentially olivine-
bronzite rocks that contain cumulus olivine. In
the upper norite suite, cumulus plagioclase
occurs in some of the anorthositic norites. Vermaak (1976: 1295) has proposed that the rocks
of the three upper suites of the Lower Zone
evolved from 'an early ultramafic magma of
komatiitic kinship'.

In the western lobe, the *Transition Zone* is
approximately 585 m thick and consists of: (a) a
lower pyroxenite suite; (b) a harzburgite-
pyroxenite suite; and (c) an upper pyroxenite
suite. The lower and upper pyroxenite suites are
essentially composed of monomineralic bronzite
rocks that usually carry less than 5 per cent post-
cumulus material, and show no systematic variation in their chemical composition. Between
these suites is the harzburgite–pyroxenite suite
which contains rhythmic layers of dunite, harzburgite and bronzitite. Vermaak (1976: 1277)
has proposed that the Transition Zone represents a fresh influx of magma.

The *Critical Zone* is approximately 1555 m
thick in the eastern lobe and 943 m thick in the
western lobe. According to Cameron (1970: 47),
the base of this zone is taken as 'the horizon
above which chromite appears intermittently as
an important cumulus mineral'. This zone is divided into: (a) a pyroxenite suite; (b) an inter-
mittently-developed noritic suite; and (c) an
anorthosite suite. The lower suite consists of a

layered sequence of feldspathic bronzitites that are separated by a number of chromitite seams, and two thin harzburgite layers. In the eastern lobe a 120 m thick layer of norite is developed above the pyroxenite suite. Plagioclase and bronzite are the essential cumulus minerals found in the rocks of the anorthosite suite; and the rocks of this suite range in composition from anorthosites to bronzitites. The composition of the cumulus plagioclase found in this suite varies irregularly between An_{70} and An_{80} (cf. Vermaak 1976: 1285); cumulus chromite is also found within the anorthosite suite. The anorthosite suite is capped by the platiniferous Merensky Reef: in the western lobe of the Bushveld Complex, this forms a rock unit that contains the following rock types: (a) a 0.51 m thick layer of pegmatititic pyroxenite that contains 64.3 per cent bronzite, 17.2 per cent clinopyroxene, 15.9 per cent bytownite (An_{73}), 2.6 per cent accessory phases, that include platinoid and associated sulphide minerals; (b) a 2.37 m thick layer of porphyritic pyroxenite that contains 73.0 per cent bronzite, 24.0 per cent bytownite, 2.0 per cent clinopyroxene, 1.0 per cent accessory phases; (c) a 0.31 m thick layer of pyroxenitic norite; (d) a 1.12 m thick layer of norite that contains 50.3 per cent bronzite, 48.5 per cent bytownite, 1.0 per cent clinopyroxene, 0.3 per cent accessory phases; (e) a 1.53 m thick layer of anorthositic norite; (f) a 3.45 m thick layer of spotted anorthosite; and (g) a 4.75 m thick layer of mottled anorthosite that contains 95.0 per cent bytownite, 3.0 per cent bronzite, 1.3 per cent clinopyroxene and 0.7 per cent accessory phases. The main discrete platinoid minerals in the Merensky Reef are braggite, cooperite and laurite, together with minor amounts of sperrylite (cf. Vermaak & Hendriks 1976: 1255); and the relative proportions of the various platinum group metals are 63 per cent platinum, 28 per cent palladium, 5 per cent ruthenium, 2.7 per cent rhodium, 0.7 per cent iridium and 0.6 per cent osmium.

In the eastern lobe, the *Main Zone* of the Bushveld Complex is approximately 3940 m thick (Von Gruenewaldt 1973: 208), and it contains rocks in which the only cumulus minerals are plagioclase, clinopyroxene and orthopyroxene. As the relative proportions of these phases vary from layer to layer, the rock types found range in composition from pyroxenites via norites and gabbros to anorthosites. Cryptic layering is an important feature of the Main

Zone; for example, the cumulus plagioclase at the base of this zone is bytownite (An_{76}), whereas that at the top is labradorite (An_{54}). The pyroxenes also change in composition, and in both the Ca-poor and Ca-rich pyroxenes there is an overall trend towards Fe enrichment (that is, $Ca_3 Mg_{78} Fe_{19} \rightarrow Ca_8 Mg_{41} Fe_{51}$, and $Ca_{43} Mg_{45} Fe_{12} \rightarrow Ca_{38} Mg_{33} Fe_{29}$; cf. Wager & Brown 1968: 351). In the Main Zone, the Ca-poor pyroxenes change from orthopyroxenes to pigeonites which are later inverted to hypersthene and exsolution lamellae of augite. Pigeonite–ferropigeonite continued to accumulate, together with a member of the augite–ferroaugite series, up to a level that is approximately 200 m below the top of the Upper Zone. When ferropigeonite ceases to crystallize, the pyroxene that continues to crystallize is a ferroaugite, and with further fractional crystallization this Ca-rich pyroxene becomes more Fe-rich, and ultimately ferrohedenbergite crystallizes in the uppermost rocks of the Upper Zone (cf. Atkins 1969: 228).

The *Upper Zone* varies in thickness and some of this variation is related to the amount of silicic rock that is included there. Most petrologists who have described the rocks of the eastern lobe quote thicknesses of the order of 2250 m. The base of this zone is usually taken as the first layer that contains cumulus magnetite. Such rocks are well exposed in the Magnet Heights area of the eastern Transvaal where the lower units in the Upper Zone consist of layers rich in cumulus magnetite (that is, the ultramafic rock magnetitite) that alternate with layers rich in cumulus plagioclase. The rocks of the Upper Zone are chiefly layered *ferrodiorites* composed of a cumulus assemblage of andesine, olivine (Fo_{0-45}), ferropigeonite, ferroaugite, titaniferous magnetite and apatite. In the uppermost suite, the rocks contain fayalite, ferrohedenbergite, sodic plagioclase (An_{30}), alkali feldspar and quartz, and they are usually described as *ferrosyenodiorites*. According to Hunter (1975: 5), the silicic rocks that overlie the ferrodiorites and ferrosyenodiorties usually exhibit a crude layering. A coarse-grained grey granite usually occurs at the base of the silicic rocks, and it grades upwards via medium-grained grey and red granites, red granophyric granites, to a granophyre.

The Bushveld Layered Complex deserves the appellation complex, because it appears to have evolved from a number of separate batches of magma which were emplaced into at least four discrete, yet interconnected, magma chambers.

Crystallization and magmatic differentiation (see Ch. 2) may have proceeded independently in each magma chamber, but in view of the lateral persistence of some distinctive layers, it is likely that the magmatic differentiation processes were interrupted periodically with magma moving laterally between the various magma chambers. Such flooding of the magma chambers is likely to have occurred with the introduction of new batches of parental magma. As Wager and Brown (1968: 405) have recorded, the distribution of minerals in the Bushveld Layered Complex essentially

'follows a precise pattern in relation to the stratigraphic sequence defined by the layering, from ultrabasic assemblages at the exposed base, through basic and then intermediate assemblages, to an acid assemblage near the exposed roof. The gradual compositional changes in the feldspars, olivines, pyroxenes and spinels, upwards, is from high-temperature to low-temperature members of their respective solid-solution series, and this cryptic layering, taken together with the graded character of many of the rythmically layered units, leaves little room for manoeuvre in outlining the crystallization sequence, from the floor upwards.'

It is proposed that multidiffusion convection, operating in a cluster of periodically-connected magma chambers, was the principle mechanism responsible for the differentiation of the magmas that mixed to form the huge Bushveld Layered Complex (see Section 2.3). This process provides a suitable mechanism for transmitting the effects of magma mixing, and assimilation, through the cooling bodies of magma. The assimilation of country rocks was probably important in augmenting the volume of silicic materials that developed during the late stages in the evolution of the complex (see Sections 8.5 and 9.6). Other processes, such as self-imposed filter pressing and infiltration metasomatism within an unconsolidated pile of cumulus minerals, are considered to have been particularly crucial in the evolution of the monomineralic rocks (for example, anorthosites, chromitites, dunites, magnetitites and pyroxenites). From the data presented by Vermaak (1976), it seems likely that the rocks of the Lower Zone, and possibly also those of the Transition and Critical Zones, were mainly derived from tholeiitic picrite, or komatiite, magmas; whereas the rocks of the Main and Upper Zones were mainly derived from tholeiitic basalt, or partially-differentiated tholeiitic picrite magmas. One might simplify the petrogenetic model for the evolution of the Bushveld Layered Complex by proposing that the batches of parental magma that generated the rocks below the Merensky Reef were essentially ultramafic in composition, whereas those above this layer were essentially subalkalic basaltic in composition; and postulate that the Merensky Reef formed as the result of the mixing of the two main magma types, and the consequent evolution of an immiscible platinum-bearing sulphide liquid (cf. Keith et al. 1982). It is tentatively suggested that most of the platinum-group elements were derived from the early ultramafic magmas, whereas the sulphur came from the later basaltic magma, and that prior to mixing the concentration of the platinum-group elements in the first magma was not limited by sulphide-saturation equilibrium (see Section 2.4).

11.7 Ultramafic rocks of the ocean floor

The ultramafic rocks found on the ocean floor are usually peridotites that have been partly or wholly serpentinized; that is, some or all of their olivines and pyroxenes have been changed by metamorphism into minerals of the serpentine group, such as antigorite (sometimes bastite after pyroxene), chrysotile and lizardite. Many of these serpentinized rocks have retained at least some of their original structures and textures. Detailed petrographic and geochemical studies have revealed that the oceanic crust contains a wide variety of metamorphosed ultramafic rocks that originally occurred as *harzburgites, lherzolites, dunites*, and less commonly *pyroxenites, wehrlites* and *websterites* (cf. Hekinian 1982). These rocks may contain relict primary minerals such as olivine (Fo_{90}), orthopyroxene (enstatite), clinopyroxene (diopsidic augites), Cr–Al spinels and/or plagioclase; and a variety of secondary minerals such as the serpentine group minerals, amphiboles, brucite, calcite, chlorite, haematite (and other Fe oxides), hydrogarnets, illite, prehnite and talc.

Samples of the ultramafic rocks of the ocean crust are usually dredged from fracture zones, or fault scarps. The latter are generally associated either with transform faults or with the boundary faults of the rift valleys that bisect the mid-ocean ridges. As was noted in Section 4.2, some of the freshest samples of peridotites from the ocean floor have been obtained from St Paul's Rocks which are islets located near the intersection of the St Paul Fractor Zone and the Mid-Atlantic Ridge. These rocks originally consisted of harzburgites that equilibrated at approximately 1100 °C and 1.5 GPa; and on their rapid ascent and emplacement into the crust, they became mixed with other mantle and crustal materials. According to Melson et. al. (1972: 267), St Paul's Rocks probably contain the youngest subaerially exposed peridotites. Some of the orogenic ultramafic intrusions that are to be discussed in Section 11.8 are regarded as having formed beneath mid-ocean ridges, and they were then carried passively along in the oceanic crust until they were obducted, or emplaced onto, or into, continental crust.

11.8 Orogenic (alpine-type) ultramafic rocks

This rock association includes many bodies of ultramafic rocks of various shapes and sizes that occur within orogenic belts and island-arcs. Many of these rocks have had complicated emplacement and post-emplacement histories, and much of the evidence regarding their origin has been obliterated by post-emplacement deformation and metamorphism. The most common group of orogenic ultramafic rocks consist of serpentinites and peridotites that crop out in strongly deformed, but generally low-grade, metamorphic terrains (for example, greenschist or blueschist facies). These rocks are often called the *ophiolites*, or the *ophiolite suite* (cf. Miyashiro 1975; Coleman 1977). The term ophiolite was introduced by Brongniart (1827) to describe serpentinites, or rocks consisting almost wholly of minerals of the serpentine group; and he derived the term from the classical Greek word *ophi* which means snake or serpent (the greenish, mottled and shiny appearance of many serpentinites was considered to be reminiscent of a snake). Steinmann (1906; 1927) introduced the concept of the ophiolite rock association, or suite. This rock association essentially consists of ultramafic rocks (for example, serpentinite and peridotite), gabbro, spilite and related rocks. He also observed that these rocks were frequently emplaced into, or associated with, pelagic sedi-

ments and cherts. In 1926, Benson (6) described the gabbros and ultramafic rocks, including the 'green rocks' and 'ophiolitic rocks' that are found in 'regions that have been intensely disturbed by overthrusting and alpine orogeny', as the *Alpine-type* igneous rocks. Thayer (1967: 222) emphasized that 'the ultramafic and gabbroic parts of ophiolite complexes 'are' identical with, and part of, the alpine igneous rock suite'.

In 1957, De Roever proposed that some Alpine-type peridotite bodies were tectonically-transported fragments of the upper mantle. Dietz (1963) suggested that the 'Alpine serpentinites' were fragments of the sea floor that had become tectonically caught up in an orogeny; and in the same year, Gass wrote a paper on the question of whether, or not, the Troodos Massif of Cyprus was a fragment of oceanic lithosphere of Mesozoic age. In 1966, Hess (5–6) acknowledged that although he had originally been a strong proponent of the hypothesis that 'ultramafic bodies in alpine mountain systems and island arcs represented intrusions of magma of the composition of serpentinized peridotite', his studies in the Caribbean region had forced him to change his mind. This was because detailed studies revealed: (a) 'the serpentines in Cretaceous sedimentary rocks along the southern flank of the Caribbean Mountains of Venezuela were exotic blocks rather than intrusions', (b) the serpentinized peridotites of the Greater Antilles were 'actually the basement complex beneath the islands and probably represented the equivalent of the oceanic crust'; and (c) that the peridotite intrusions with high-temperature contact-metamorphic aureoles such as the one at Tinaquillo in Venezuela, and those on the island of Margarita, were intruded as hot essentially solid bodies of crystals. In 1967, Gass described the geology and geophysics of the ultramafic rocks of the Troodos Massif of Cyprus. He (133–4) postulated that the volcanic rocks evolved in an oceanic setting, and that during the Alpine orogeny the African and Eurasian plates converged, and the African plate underthrust the area that was to become the Troodos Massif at such a depth 'that not only the volcanic pile, but also part of the upper mantle was uplifted above sea level'. The upper mantle materials now occur as the ultramafic rocks in what Gass called the Troodos Plutonic Complex. In the early 1970s, many petrologists found evidence in support of the proposal that Alpine-type ultramafic rocks, and rocks of the ophiolite rock association, were fragments of oceanic lithosphere that had been thrust over, or into, continental crust, at convergent plate boundaries. Studies of the oceanic lithosphere have generally supported the concept that the rocks found in ophiolite sequences are similar to those postulated for the oceanic lithosphere.

In September 1972, the Geological Society of America sponsored a field conference on ophiolites, during which it was agreed that the term ophiolite should refer to 'a distinctive assemblage of mafic to ultramafic rocks' (Anon. 1972: 24–5); and that in completely developed ophiolites the rock types occur in the following sequence, starting from the bottom: (a) 'ultramafic complex, consisting of variable proportions of harzburgite, lherzolite and dunite, usually with a metamorphic tectonic fabric (more or less serpentinized)'; (b) 'gabbroic complex, ordinarily with cumulus textures commonly containing cumulus peridotites and pyroxenites and usually less deformed than the ultramafic complex'; (c) 'mafic sheeted dyke complex'; and (d) 'mafic volcanic complex, commonly pillowed'. It was also stated that these rocks are commonly associated with: (a) 'an overlying sedimentary section typically including ribbon cherts, thin shale interbeds, and minor limestones'; (b) 'podiform bodies of chromite generally associated with dunite'; and (c) 'sodic felsic intrusive and extrusive rocks'. The conference participants also noted that 'faulted contacts between mappable units are common', and that whole sections of the ophiolite may be missing. They also recommend that incomplete, dismembered or metamorphosed ophiolites should be called 'partial, dismembered, or metamorphosed ophiolite'.

More recently, Coleman (1977: 17) has described a complete ophiolite rock association as consisting of the following sequence starting from the base: (a) metamorphic peridotites; (b) ultramafic cumulate rocks that grade upward into layered gabbros often containing trondhjemitic differentiates at the top; (c) sheeted dyke swarms of basic to intermediate composition; and (d) pillow lavas interlayered at the top with 'pelagic sediments and metalliferous precipitates'. He (18) also claims that 'the oldest rocks in the ophiolite sequence are the basal metamorphic peridotites which exhibit subsolidus recrystallization at temperatures and pressures attainable only within the mantle', and that 'direct igneous connections such as feeder dykes or transition zones between the metamorphic peridotites and

the overlying cumulates are unknown'. Detailed studies of the cumulate sequences usually reveal large sequences of olivine cumulates followed by clinopyroxene cumulates and plagioclase-rich gabbros. In ophiolites where the sheeted dyke swarms and overlying pillow lavas are well exposed, the structural relationships between these rocks suggest that they evolved in a tectonic environment that was frequently cut by rifts, and that basaltic magma was being intruded into these rifts, and also extruded on to a submarine surface that may contain unconsolidated pelagic sediments.

The basal metamorphic peridotite unit is usually composed of harzburgites and dunites. Generally, the harzburgites are dominant, and they have xenoblastic granular textures. They are essentially composed of forsteritic olivine and orthopyroxene (that is, enstatite–bronzite), together with accessory amounts of chromite and clinopyroxene. The clinopyroxenes occur as exsolution lamellae in large grains of orthopyroxene, and also as discrete accessory minerals; they are usually chromium diopsides. The dunites also tend to have xenoblastic granular textures, and they contain forsteritic olivine, together with accessory amounts of orhtopyroxene, clinopyroxene and chromite.

Many ophiolites contain an undeformed sequence of layered cumulates that grade upwards from olivine-rich ultramafic rocks, via gabbroic rocks, to small discontinuous bodies of trondhjemite (tonalite). The cumulus minerals are clinopyroxene, orthopyroxene, olivine, plagioclase and chromite; and the latter phase is generally found in the lower ultramafic cumulate layers that mainly consist of wehrlites, dunites, lherzolites and olivine websterites. Both the olivines and pyroxenes that occur in the ultramafic rocks are Mg-rich, and their compositions overlap those of the minerals found in the metamorphic peridotites.

As Coleman (1977: 140) has demonstrated, the ophiolites are typically exposed 'along belts of intense tectonism'. They generally occur along *geosutures* that mark the sites of earlier interactions between oceanic and continental lithosphere. A geosuture is a boundary zone between contrasting tectonic units of crustal materials. They are usually regarded as faults, or fault zones, that extend through the entire thickness of the crust. Some of the older ophiolite-bearing geosutures are now found within the interiors of the continents (for example, the 'Great Serpentine Belt' of eastern Australia; cf. Benson 1913). It is thus generally postulated that the crustal rocks of the ophiolite association are generated at accreting plate margins, and later a cooled slab of oceanic lithosphere containing these rocks is detached and emplaced onto, or into, a continental margin. This hypothesis is, for example, able to explain how high-temperature ultramafic and gabbroic rocks can come into contact with sedimentary materials without the latter being thermally metamorphosed. Many ophiolites have experienced repeated deformation and metamorphism which often transforms the regularly-layered ophiolites into *tectonic melanges*, or mixtures of blocks and fragments of all sizes embedded in a fragmented and generally sheared matrix. The ultramafic parts of such ophiolites are often transformed into serpentinites, which are: (a) less dense than the original rocks; and (b) can readily be deformed plastically. If a melange develops a serpentinite matrix, it will tend to respond to tectonism by moving, and such movement will make the structure of the melange more complex; and it may also result in the melange incorporating blocks of the country rocks through which it passes.

Papuan Ultramafic Belt

According to Davies (1971; 1976) and others, rocks of the ophiolite association crop out in many places along the length of the central mountain system of the Papua New Guinea mainland and eastward in the D'Entrecasteaux Islands. The largest of these bodies, and least disturbed tectonically, is the *Papuan Ultramafic Belt* that extends for 400 km along the northern front of the Owen Stanley Range. Davies (1976: 1) states that 'the Papuan ultramafic belt is made up of a simple layered sequence of peridotite (4 to 8 km thick), gabbro (4 km) and basalt (4 km) dipping at angles of 10 to 40° to east and northeast'. In the west and south-west the ophiolite has a faulted contact with a variety of meta-sediments and submarine basalts. The Papuan Ultramafic Belt is believed to mark the geosuture where a continent–island-arc collision occurred in the Tertiary. Jaques et al. (1983) have given a detailed description of Marum Ophiolite which is part of the Papuan Ultramafic Belt, and crops out to the north of the Bismarck Range. They (155) claim that the cumulate sequence in this ophiolite consists of a basal dunite

unit that is 'successively overlain by wehrlite, lherzolite, plagioclase lherzolite, pyroxenite, olivine norite-gabbro, and norite-gabbro and, finally, by minor anorthositic gabbro and ferronorite–gabbro near the top'. Well-preserved igneous layering and structures, and cumulus textures, have been interpreted by Jaques (1981: 35) as indicating 'an origin by magmatic crystallization in a large magma chamber by cumulus processes combined with in situ rhythmic crystallization from a mafic magma of evolving composition'; and also the 'cyclic units superimposed on the gross stratification suggest periodic influxes of fresh magma'.

According to Jaques (1981), the dunites contain cumulus olivine (Fo_{90-93}) and accessory amounts of chromian spinel (41–63 per cent Cr_2O_3). The wehrlites, olivine pyroxenites and

Table 11.8.1 The chemical composition of selected cumulus ultramafic rocks from the Marum Ophiolite, Papua New Guinea

	1(%)	2(%)	3(%)	4(%)
SiO_2	39.80	50.21	54.11	39.95
TiO_2	n.d.	0.03	0.05	0.02
Al_2O_3	0.04	1.77	0.80	4.08
Fe_2O_3	0.71	0.85	1.14	3.04
FeO	5.87	3.85	5.09	7.80
MnO	0.11	0.14	0.20	0.18
MgO	49.93	22.72	23.12	35.85
CaO	0.05	17.70	15.24	4.62
Na_2O	0.002	0.09	0.07	0.11
K_2O	n.d.	0.001	0.001	0.002
P_2O_3	n.d.	0.005	0.006	0.004
S	n.d.	0.02	0.01	0.02
Loss	2.52	2.06	0.73	4.33
Rest	0.94	0.54	0.36	0.65
Total	99.97	99.99	100.93	100.66
p.p.m.				
Sr	n.d.	6.6	5.6	21.0
Sc	2	50	49	13
V	5	85	70	37
Cr	4210	3130	2040	3120
Ni	2520	400	250	1560
Cu	4	5	1	31
Zn	40	26	34	73

1. Chemical composition of dunite from the Marum Ophiolite (after Jaques et al. 1983: 155, No. 567).
2. Chemical composition of wehrlite from the Marum Ophiolite (after Jaques et al. 1983: 155, No. 180).
3. Chemical composition of olivine pyroxenite from the Marum Ophiolite (after Jaques et al. 1983: 155, No. 51).
4. Chemical composition of lherzolite from the Marum Ophiolite (after Jaques et al. 1983: 155, No. 271).

lherzolites contain olivine (Fo_{86-90}), diopsidic clinopyroxene (Wo_{41-48} En_{48-52} Fs_{5-7}), chromian spinel (34–47 per cent Cr_2O_3) and bronzitic orthopyroxene (Wo_{1-3} En_{86-87} Fs_{10-13}); whereas the plagioclase lherzolites also contain interstitial Ca-rich plagioclase (An_{84-97}). In the websterites the orthopyroxene is generally in the range Wo_{2-3} En_{74-83} Fs_{14-24}, and the clinopyroxene Wo_{38-40} En_{46-50} Fs_{12-57}. Table 11.8.1 contains chemical analyses of selected samples of the ultramafic rocks from the cumulate rocks of this relatively unaltered ophiolite.

Jaques (1981: 35) has also estimated that the pyroxene-bearing cumulates crystallized at ≈ 1200 °C and ≈ 0.1–0.2 GPa pressure, under low oxygen fugacity conditions; whereas the underlying dunites and chromitites crystallized at higher temperatures (≈ 1300–50 °C). Subsequently the ophiolite has recrystallized under subsolidus conditions at ≈ 850–900 °C and pressures similar to the primary crystallization pressures. Both the petrological and geochemical data support the hypothesis that these cumulates evolved from a highly magnesian magma with low incompatible element abundances, and lower abundances of Ti, Zr and R.E.E. than normal MOR-basalts (cf. Jaques et al. 1983: 162).

Trinity Peridotite

Another Alpine-type ultramafic body, that differs from the Marum Ophiolite, is the Trinity Peridotite which crops out over an area that is approximately 50 km wide and 75 km long in the eastern Klamath Mountains of northern California, USA. It is regarded as being a diapir of upper mantle rocks. According to Quick (1981a: 11839), 'the main mass of the Trinity peridotite is composed of plagioclase lherzolite, plagioclase harzburgite, lherzolite, harzburgite, and dunite. Websterite and olivine websterite, wehrlite, olivine clinopyroxenite, clinopyroxenite and ariegite are less abundant and form dykes or cumulates at the base of gabbroic intrusions.' Ariegite is a rock rich in aluminous pyroxene. The abundant plagioclase lherzolites contain between 70–80 per cent olivine, 15–20 per cent orthopyroxene, 2–10 per cent clinopyroxene, 2–10 per cent plagioclase, 1–2 per cent spinel and trace amounts of amphibole. All the peridotitic rocks contain Mg-rich ferromagnesian minerals; that is, the olivines range from Fo_{88-93}, the orthopyroxenes from Wo_1 En_{91} Fs_8 to Wo_4 En_{87}

Fs_9, and the clinopyroxenes from Wo_{41} En_{54} Fs_5 to Wo_{48} En_{49} Fs_3. There is considerable overlap in the compositions of the ferromagnesian minerals among the various ultramafic rocks. The spinels are most Cr-rich in the dunites, and the Cr/Cr + Al ratio decreases in the series harzburgite, plagioclase lherzolite to lherzolite. Most of the plagioclases in the plagioclase lherzolites fall in the range An_{83-90}. Compositional variations within single thin sections, and crystals, suggest that most of the phases have undergone partial re-equilibration; for example, this process has resulted in a reduction in the alumina content of the pyroxenes, and the evolution of plagioclase and a little amphibole.

Quick (1981a: 11861) claims that the Trinity Peridotite ascended as a vast diapir that moved through the upper mantle from an initial depth of more than 30 km beneath oceanic crust. The diapir was initially mainly composed of spinel lherzolite that formed at relatively high temperatures and pressures. En route through the upper mantle, the materials within the diapir: (a) were continuously being deformed plastically; (b) reacted with 'transient magmas' generated at greater depths; and (c) were partially melted at a pressure of approximately 1.0 GPa (Quick 1981a: 11861). This melting event produced a tholeiitic basaltic magma; and that part of the magma trapped in the ascending diapir reacted with the solid phases present producing a crystal mush with a plagioclase lherzolite mineral assemblage. The kilometre-sized, tabular dunite bodies that occur within the Trinity Peridotite are interpreted by Quick (1981b) as marking the paths taken by ascending batches of picritic magma. It is claimed that parts of these dunites were produced by fractional crystallization and deposition of olivine from the picritic magma; whereas the margins of these bodies were formed by the extraction and removal of the basaltic components from plagioclase lherzolite wall-rocks (Quick 1981b: 413).

Lizard Complex

The Trinity Peridotite has much in common with the serpentinized peridotites of the Lizard Complex of southern Cornwall, UK (cf. Floyd 1982: 240–1). These peridotites are usually interpreted as having evolved from a high-temperature spinel-bearing lherzolite diapir that consisted of a central primary core (olivine + Al-orthopyroxene + Al-clinopyroxene + spinel) surrounded by a recrystallized anhydrous margin (olivine + orthopyroxene + clinopyroxene + spinel + plagioclase) that occasionally contains pargasitic amphibole (Green 1964). Relic textures, and the compositions of the minerals present, support the petrogenetic model that primary crystallization took place at moderate depth (50 km) in the mantle, followed by recrystallization and deformation, when the peridotites were emplaced tectonically at higher levels. Primary igneous textures are still discernible in the spinel–lherzolite core. These rocks resemble, but are not identical to, the crescumulates described from various layered ultramafic intrusions (cf. Rothstein 1981). Detailed studies of the distribution of Ca, Mg and Al in the clinopyroxenes has revealed that the primary assemblage equilibrated with the phases in the upper mantle at 1.5 GPa and at between 1250–1300 °C, and that some of the minerals re-equilibrated at 0.75 GPa and 1075 °C. On being emplaced into the crustal rocks, the peridotites produced a narrow high-temperature contact aureole (700–800 °C) in the adjacent hornblende schists. Some workers, however, regard the Lizard Complex as being an ophiolite.

Rhonda Peridotite

The Rhonda Peridotite Complex was emplaced into the Betic Cordilleras of southern Spain. It is a large (300 km²), high-temperature, alpine-type peridotite, that contains three main types of rocks, garnet lherzolite, spinel lherzolite and plagioclase lherzolite (cf. Obata 1980). The high-pressure pyropic garnets are considered to be particularly important in interpreting the petrogenesis of this complex. It is proposed that the different types of lherzolite evolved during the partial reequilibration and recrystallization of a body of hot (1000–1200 °C) quasi-solid peridotite that rose through the lithosphere. Obata (1980: 533) claims the initial equilibration occurred at pressures of between 2.0 and 2.5 GPa, and at temperatures of between 1100 and 1200 °C. Most of the re-equilibration took place in the temperature range 800–900 °C, at pressures that ranged from 1.2–1.5 GPa for the garnet lherzolites, to 0.5–0.7 GPa for the plagioclase lherzolites. Variation in pressure was thus the main reason for the evolution of the different types of lherzolites. When the peridotite in-

truded the crustal rocks, it produced a contact aureole in the surrounding sediments. According to Obata (1980: 569), the ascent through the crust was not diapiric, and 'some externally-induced, tectonic force must be sought for the cause of this movement'.

The preceding discussion has shown that the Alpine-type ultramafic rocks have equilibrated under a wide range of different physical conditions; and the main features that these rocks have in common is that they were emplaced, or tectonically assisted into their present positions, during 'orogenic events', and such orogenic events 'may reflect continent–island arc or continent–continent collisions, or abortive subduction of a continent' (Moores & MacGregor 1972: 221).

11.9 Zoned (Alaskan-type) ultramafic complexes

The zoned, Alaskan-type, ultramafic complexes also occur in orogenic belts, however, they contain a distinct rock association that sets them apart from the Alpine-type rocks (cf. Taylor 1967; Murray 1972). Most of these zoned complexes are relatively small (≈1 km in diameter), and they characteristically contain hornblende pyroxenites and hornblendites. Rocks of this association occur in south-eastern Alaska, USA, northern Venezuela, and in the Ural Mountains of the USSR. The well-developed complexes contain a core of dunite surrounded by successive shells of peridotite, olivine pyroxenite, magnetite pyroxenite and hornblende pyroxenite; and the whole complex is usually emplaced within a much larger body of gabbroic or dioritic rock. Taylor (1967: 120–1) proposed that these rocks form as the result of the intrusion of a series of different ultramafic magmas. Murray (1972: 313) proposed that these ultramafic complexes originated as the result of the 'fractional crystallization and flow differentiation of basaltic magma in the feeder pipes of volcanoes'. He claimed that the chemical composition of the parental magma was probably that of an olivine-rich tholeiitic basalt, and also that crystallization took place under hydrous conditions in the pressure range 0.2–1.1 GPa. Murray also suggested that the complementary magma, produced at the same time as the ultramafic cumulates, was probably a high-Al basalt or an andesite. Irvine (1973) produced a similar petrogenetic model to account for the Alaskan-type ultramafic complexes. He, however, proposed that the parental magma had the chemical composition of a water-rich alkalic picrite. Challis (1969) has proposed that many of the ultramafic bodies that are found in New Zealand were generated in magma chambers that once existed below basaltic and andesitic volcanoes. A particularly interesting group of zoned ultramafic cumulate rocks (for example, dunites and pyroxenites) are found in the relatively small (≈ 35 km^2) Gardiner Complex at Kangerdlugssuaq, East Greenland. The ultramafic rocks occur in association with a variety of silica-undersaturated alkalic rocks (for example, nepheline syenites, ijolites and melteigites) and carbonatites. Nielsen (1981: 71) claims that the ultramafic rocks evolved in a subvolcanic magma chamber when a series of batches of strongly alkaline magma, of olivine nephelinite to nepheline-bearing hawaiite composition, cooled and 'plastered' the walls of the chamber with cumulus ferromagnesian minerals.

11.10 Ultramafic rocks (appinite-type) associated with granitic batholiths

Many batholiths are composite intrusions that contain a variety of different rock types that include ultramafic rocks (cf. Wyllie 1969: 440). These ultramafic rocks are usually interpreted as being: (a) magmatic rocks; (b) cumulates from differentiating mafic or intermediate parental magmas; or (c) products of reaction between granitic magma and country rocks of suitable composition. In Scotland and Ireland, these rocks are usually considered to belong to the *appinite suite* (Bailey & Maufe 1916) (after Appin, Loch Linnhe, Scotland). The rocks of this suite are typically melanocratic hornblende-rich plutonic rocks, and they include hornblendites and olivine–hornblendites. According to Sabine and Sutherland (1982: 503), appinite is 'an extremely useful term for variable but readily recognizable rock-types, with the common hornblendic character that is undoubtedly of petrogenetic significance, and avoids names (which may be lengthy) that tend to split the suite into misleading subdivisions'. The type-rocks of the appinite suite generally occur as small, peripheral bod-

ies, associated with the Newer Granites of the Caledonide Orogen; and they are particularly common in composite intrusions that contain diorite, such as Garabal Hill, Glen Tilt, Glen Doll, Arrochar, and Glen Falloch (cf. Pankhurst & Sutherland 1982: 177). However, they also occur in association with more granitic composite intrusions such as the Ballachulish Granite of the Appin area, and the Ardara pluton of Donegal in Ireland (see Section 9.2). Pitcher and Berger (1972: 143–68) have written a whole chapter on the appinite suite in their book on *The Geology of Donegal*. In describing the appinite suite intrusions that occur in the Ardara cluster, they state (149) that they

'vary in outcrop size from 100 metres across to masses measuring about 1500 metres by 500 metres. The outcrops have a generally rounded outline with a tendency to be lenticular, due to the control exercised by the structural trend of the country rocks. In three dimensions, nearly all have the general form of steeply inclined pipes which either cut cleanly across the regional structures or force them aside'.

They also record that external to these intrusions, there is always a narrow contact metamorphic aureole that is up to 20 m wide. From their chemistry and mineralogy it seems probable that the ultramafic rocks of the appinite suite are cumulates from basaltic, or andesitic, magmas that were locally strongly enriched in water (Hall 1967); or they might have evolved from magmas that at higher levels within the crust formed lamprophyric dykes of vogesitic or spessartitic composition (see Section 12.6). Hall (1967: 156) also claims that the granitic rocks associated with the rocks of the appinite suite have 'distinctive compositions, indicative of formation under a high water pressure'.

11.11 Non-silicate ultramafic rocks

In Section 3.2 it was noted that the non-silicate ultramafic rocks are usually essentially composed of carbonate minerals, ore minerals (for example, magnetite and chromite), sulphur and apatite. The carbonate-rich magmatic rocks are discussed in Chapter 14; the sulphur-rich rocks are discussed in Section 1.9 which contains an examination of volcanism on Io; the Fe-rich core rocks and iron meteorites are discussed in Section 11.2; some of the magnetitite and chromitite rocks are considered in Section 11.6; and some of the apatite-rich magmatic rocks, that are usually associated with the intrusive carbonatites, are discussed in Chapter 14. A petrographically important, and interesting, group of non-silicate rocks are the El Laco magnetitite lava flows of the highlands of northern Chile.

Laco magnetitite flow

These magnetitite flows occur in association with, and are partly intruded into, other volcanic materials that are considered to be of Quaternary age. The flows are highly vesicular, display contorted flow banding and have ropy surfaces; and in the field they have the general appearance of basaltic lava flows (cf. Haggerty 1970; Parks 1961; Rogers 1968). In these flows the essential minerals are magnetite and hematite, and the accessory minerals are feldspar, calcic pyroxene, apatite, calcite and an iron-phosphate mineral. The rock contains up to 98 per cent iron oxide, and both the magnetite and hematite occur in euhedral crystals that may be several centimetres in diameter. Secondary hematite and maghemite develop extensively as oxidation products of the magnetite, and goethite occurs as a late-stage vesicle and veinlet infilling. According to Haggerty (1970: 330), if the Laco magnetitite flows were extruded as molten oxides, temperatures in excess of 1500 °C would be necessary; however, the porous nature of these flows indicates that 'large amounts of gas were present, thus suggesting that a process other than liquid extrusion was involved'.

Nelsonite

Another important group of non-silicate ultramafic rocks are the 'iron–titanium oxide and apatite rocks' (cf. Philpotts 1967). These rocks are also known as *nelsonites*, a name coined by Watson in 1907 to describe the iron-titanium oxide–apatite rocks of Nelson and Amherst counties, Virginia, USA (cf. Watson & Taber 1913). Nelsonite usually occurs in small intrusive bodies associated with anorthosites or 'alkaline', particularly carbonatitic, intrusive complexes. According to Philpotts (1967: 303), nelsonites have a consistent composition of two-thirds by volume Fe–Ti oxides and one-third apatite; and they 'invariably have dykes rich in ferromagnesian minerals and apatite associated with them'. After carrying out reconnaissance experiments in the system magnetite-fluorapatite, Philpotts (1967: 314) concluded that 'the iron–titanium oxide–apatite rocks commonly associated with anorthosites and alkaline complexes appear to be of igneous origin, not only because they form dykes, but because their composition, of approximately one-third apatite, two-thirds oxides by volume, corresponds to the eutectic between fluorapatite and magnetite'. The minimum temperatures of crystallization determined from the composition of the coexisting magnetite and ilmenite is in the range 850–1000 °C, and it also supports the concept that the nelsonites are igneous rocks. Philpotts (1967: 311) has demonstrated that nelsonites can evolve as immiscible liquids that separate from Fe–Ti oxide–apatite-rich dioritic magma such as would be expected to evolve during the formation of the anorthosite-mangerite (hypersthene-bearing alkalic monzonite) suite of rocks (see Ch. 10).

11.12 Selected references

Arndt, N. T. & Nisbet, E. G. (ed.) (1982) *Komatiites*, George Allen & Unwin, London.

Coleman, R. G. (1977) *Ophiolites: Ancient Oceanic Lithosphere?*, Springer-Verlag, Berlin.

Dodd, R. T. (1981) *Meteorites: A petrologic-chemical synthesis*, Cambridge Univ. Press, Cambridge.

Wager, L. R. & Brown, G. M. (1968) *Layered Igneous Rocks*, Oliver & Boyd, Edinburgh.

Wyllie, P. J. (ed.) (1967) *Ultramafic and related rocks*, John Wiley & Sons, New York, USA.

CHAPTER 12

THE ALKALINE ROCKS

12.1 General statement

The term alkalic is generally used in a broad sense to describe magmatic rocks that contain more of the alkali metals (particularly Na_2O and/or K_2O) than is considered normal for the group of rocks to which they belong (cf. Bailey 1976b: 419); and the term can generally be defined by using an alkali silica diagram (See Figs 3.3.2, 3.3.3 and 3.3.4). In petrology, the term alkaline is usually used either as a synonym for alkalic, or it is used in the expression *alkaline igneous rocks* to describe those rocks that contain essential amounts of foids (that is, minerals of the nepheline group, leucite, and sodalite group), and/or alkali-pyroxenes, and/or alkali-amphiboles, and/or melilite (cf. Sørensen 1974: 7). It is thus evident that the alkalic basalts, hawaiites, mugearites, trachybasalts and trachyandesites are usually alkalic, but not alkaline, igneous rocks. The trachytes and syenites are alkalic, and they may also be alkaline igneous rocks if they contain essential amounts of alkali–pyroxenes and/or alkali–amphiboles. Some of the rhyolites and granites are alkalic, and they may also be alkaline igneous rocks if they contain essential amounts of alkali–pyroxenes and/or alkali–amphiboles. The phonolites, foid–syenites, tephrites, foid–diorites, basanites, foid–gabbros, foid–bearing basalts and nephelinites are all examples of alkalic (or hyperalkalic) rocks that are also alkaline igneous rocks. The alkaline igneous rocks are of particular interest to petrologists because many of them appear to have evolved in special tectonic environments; and individual rocks are usually members of characteristic rock associations (cf. Sørensen 1974: 7).

These rocks can be divided into five major groups: (a) the *peralkaline silica-oversaturated rocks*; (b) the *peralkaline silica-saturated rocks*; (c) the *foid-bearing rocks* in which foids constitute less that 10 per cent of the felsic minerals; (d) the *feldspar–foid rocks* in which foids constitute between 10 and 60 per cent of the felsic minerals; and (e) the *foidites* and *foidolites* in which foids constitute over 60 per cent of the felsic minerals. Rocks in the first three major groups have been discussed in earlier chapters. This chapter will be mainly concerned with discussing the feldspar–foid rocks and the foidites–foidolites. The feldspar–foid rocks occupy a broad central band across the APF triangle of Streckeisen (1978; see Fig. 3.2.1). On the AF side of this band are the extrusive *phonolites* and intrusive *foid–syenites*; with increasing plagioclase relative to alkali feldspar these rocks grade into the *tephritic phonolites* and *foid–monzosyenites*, then the *phonolitic tephrites* and *foid–monzodiorites*, and finally the *tephrites* and *foid–gabbros* (see Figs 3.2.1 and 12.2.1). The *basanites* are regarded as being tephrites that contain significant amounts of olivine. This simple classification of the feldspar–foid rocks is not sufficient in itself to describe the many, and varied, rocks of this group. It is often useful to subdivide these major rock types using criteria such as colour index and Na/K ratio, as in Fig. 12.2.1.

The leucite-bearing rocks are a unique group of alkaline rocks that are found in widely scattered localities all over the Earth (cf. Gupta & Yagi 1980). Some of the well-known petrographic provinces that contain these rocks include: (a) the Toro-Ankole Province of western Uganda: (b) the Birunga Province that is situated in the border area between Rwanda, Uganda and Zaire; (c) the Massif Central region of France; (d) the Roman Province of Italy; (e) the Laacher See Province of West Germany; (f) the Mauricia and Almaria provinces of Spain; (g) the Leucite Hills of Wyoming, USA; (h) the West Kimberley region of Western Australia; (i) central New South Wales, Australia; and (j) Java and Sulawesi, Indonesia. Leucite-bearing rocks are seldom reported from oceanic islands, but there are a number of exceptions, such as the islands of the Tristan de Cunha group (cf. Gupta & Yagi, 1980: 48).

The Roman Province of Italy is probably the most studied ultrapotassic province. It is situated in central Italy and includes Sabatini, Vico and Vulsini volcanoes north of Rome, Alban Hills,

Ernici and Roccamonfina between Rome and Naples, and the Campanian area that contains the Phlegrean Fields and Somma-Vesuvio. The region where these volcanoes occur is a tectonically complex area of convergence between Africa and Europe, and it lies to the north of the active Aeolian Island Arc. At present, two main models have been proposed to account for the origin of these ultrapotassic rocks: (a) the ultrapotassic parental magma was generated beneath a continental rift system, similar to that found in the Birunga Province of central Africa (cf. Vollmer et al. 1981); or (b) the Roman Province lies above an active deep-seated Benioff seismic zone, as was proposed by Ninkovich and Hayes in 1972 (cf. Keller 1983).

12.2 Petrography

The *phonolites* are extrusive rocks that are essentially composed of alkali feldspar (for example, anorthoclase and/or sanidine), one, or more, mafic minerals (for example, the alkali pyroxenes, alkali amphiboles, augite, ferroaugite, biotite and fayalitic olivine), and one, or more, foids (for example, nepheline group, leucite and sodalite group). These rocks usually contain less than 15 per cent mafic minerals and more than 10 per cent foids. Streckeisen (1967: 186) proposed that the term phonolite should normally be preceded by the name of the dominant foid observed in the rock. The term itself was introduced by Klaproth in 1801 who derived it from the classical Greek word *phone* meaning sound, and he claimed that phonolites emitted a loud noise when struck by a hammer. The following is the mean mode of five phonolites from Homa Bay, Western Kenya (Le Bas 1977: 37): alkali feldspar 21.0 per cent, nepheline 13.4 per cent, analcite 2.0 per cent, nosean 0.8 per cent, aegirine–augite 16.5 per cent, alkali amphibole 4.2 per cent, Fe–Ti oxides 1.0 per cent, melanite garnet 0.4 per cent, sphene tr., and groundmass 40.7 per cent. These phonolites are characterized by the presence of euhedral phenocrysts of nepheline, some tabular alkali feldspar crystals, and zoned prismatic aegirine–augite crystals. The feldspars are often aligned and give the rock a trachytic texture. Phonolites also occur as: (a) pyroclastic rocks; (b) pumice deposits; (c) ash-flow deposits; and (d) glassy rocks. The latter

type of rock is well developed on Tenerife in the Canary Islands.

Leucite phonolites are typically found in potassium-rich alkaline petrographic provinces, such as the Roman Province of central Italy (cf. Washington 1906; Appleton 1972; Baldridge et al. 1981; Keller 1983). A leucite–phonolite from Roccamonfina Volcano in the Roman Province has the following modal composition: leucite 12.1 per cent, plagioclase 2.3 per cent, pyroxene 0.9 per cent, magnetite 0.4 per cent and groundmass 84.3 per cent (Baldridge et al. 1981: 322). The chemical composition of this rock is given in Table 12.3.1, and it is observed that it contains approximately twice as much K_2O and significantly less Na_2O than the average phonolite. Haüyne phonolites are typically found in the Canary Islands.

The *tephrites* are a group of extrusive rocks that are essentially composed of calcic plagioclase, clinopyroxene and a foid; and the foid normally constitutes more than 10 per cent of the felsic minerals. They differ from the basanites in that they do not contain essential amounts of olivine. The tephrites often contain minor amounts of alkali feldspar, and they thus grade with increasing alkali feldspar contents into the phonolitic tephrites and tephritic phonolites. Both sodium-rich and potassium-rich tephrites are found. Sodium-rich tephrites are, for example, known from the Canary Islands and Tahiti; whereas most of the lavas of Vesuvio, Italy, are potassium-rich leucite tephrites, phonolitic leucite tephrites and tephritic leucite foidite (cf. Pichler 1970: 166). The accessory minerals in tephrite are usually apatite and Fe–Ti oxides, perovskite, amphibole (usually alkali–amphibole), and biotite may also occur. In classical Greek the word tephra meant ash (see Section 8.4); according to Johannsen (1938: 230), Von Fritsch in 1865 was the first to use the term tephrite in approximately the modern sense; that is, for rocks that contains both feldspars and foids.

The *basanites* are a group of tephritic rocks that essentially contain calcic plagioclase, clinopyroxene, a foid, and olivine; and the foid normally constitutes more than 10 per cent of the felsic minerals. In most basanites the foid is nepheline, but it may also be leucite, sodalite, nosean, haüyne or analcite; thus basanites can be either sodium-rich or potassium-rich. Both types are found in the Cenozoic volcanic rocks of the Western Rift of central Africa (that is, South

Kivu, Virunga and Toro-Ankole areas). The plagioclase phenocrysts that are often found in these rocks usually range in composition from bytownite to labradorite, and many of them are normally-zoned. However, the plagioclase laths found in the groundmass are usually more sodium-rich. The clinopyroxene is generally titanaugite, and it occurs both as a phenocryst and in the groundmass. Some basanites contain alkali–amphibole, and/or biotite. The accessory minerals are usually apatite and Fe–Ti oxides; perovskite may also occur. The term basanite was used by the Greeks of classical times to describe rocks (or touchstones) used in testing the purity of alloys of gold and silver. These tests compared the streaks that appeared when alloys were rubbed over the touchstone. In sedimentary petrography, the term basanite is still used to describe dark-coloured, cryptocrystalline, or finely crystalline, quartz-rich rocks. Von Fritsch and Reiss (1868) were the first to use the term basanite in approximately the modern sense to describe foid-bearing extrusive rocks.

Somma-Vesuvio, Italy contains a remarkably extensive suite of volcanic rocks that range from leucite phonolite, via leucite tephritic phonolite, leucite-bearing latite, leucite phonolitic tephrite and leucite tephrite to leucite tephritic foidite (cf. Pichler 1970: 166). Leucite is such a typical mineral of the Somma-Vesuvio Volcanic Complex that it used to be called *Vesuvian garnet*. According to Pichler (1970: 131), as one proceeds from old Somma, via young Somma, to Vesuvio, the main differentiation trend is from leucite-bearing latite, via phonolitic tephrite, and tephrite, to tephritic foidite. The alkaline extrusive rocks that are essentially devoid of feldspar are called *foidites*, and they include the nephelinites, melanephelinites, leucitites and melilitites. Rocks of the carbonite–nephelinite–ijolite rock association are discussed in Chapter 14.

The *nephelinites* are usually fine-grained, porphyritic, extrusive or subvolcanic foidites that are essentially composed of nepheline and clinopyroxene (particularly titanaugite and/or diopside). They normally do not contain either olivine or feldspar. Similar extrusive rocks that contain 10 per cent or more olivine are called olivine nephelinites. Rocks in which there are more mafic minerals than foids are called *melanephelinites*. The plutonic equivalents of the nephelinites are the *urtites*, as are the *ijolites* that contain less than 50 per cent mafic minerals; whereas the plutonic

equivalents of the melanephelinites are the *meltiegites* and the *ijolites* that contain more than 50 per cent mafic minerals.

The remnants of Kisingiri Volcano in the Homa Bay district of western Kenya contain 600 m of nephelinitic lavas and agglomerates. According to Le Bas (1977: 89), these lavas are grey-green porphyritic rocks with phenocrysts of euhedral nepheline (up to 1 cm in diameter), clinopyroxene and Fe–Ti oxides. The pyroxene is usually diopside, and it is often zoned with the outer rim being composed of aegirine–augite. Similar minerals occur in the groundmass together with perovskite and rare crystals of poikilitic phlogopitic biotite. The melanephelinites are usually porphyritic dark green rocks with prominent pyroxene phenocrysts that are up to 1 cm long; Fe–Ti oxides, sphene and apatite also occur as phenocrysts. The groundmass usually contains clinopyroxene, analcite, nepheline, calcite, tiny perovskite granules, and brown glass. Some specimens contain poikilitic crystals of phlogopitic biotite.

The *leucitites* are a group of fine-grained, often porphyritic, extrusive to subvolcanic foidites that are essentially composed of leucite and clinopyroxene, particularly tinanaugite, diopside and/or aegirine–augite; feldspar is generally absent. Nepheline, Fe–Ti oxides and apatite are common accessory minerals; other less abundant accessory minerals include phlogopite, potassium richterite, haüyne, nosean, melilite, olivine, melanite, sphene and perovskite. When significant amounts of olivine are present, the rock is called an *olivine leucitite*; and examples of such rocks are found in the Leucite Hills, Wyoming, USA. If melilite is present in significant quantities, the rock is called a *melilite leucitite*; and examples of such rocks occur on the Villa Senni area of central Italy. Rosenbusch (1877b) appears to have been the first to use the term leucitite to describe rocks containing leucite and clinopyroxene in approximately equal amounts. A typical leucitite from Mt Jugo, Bolsena, central Italy contains 32 per cent leucite, 50 per cent clinopyroxene and lesser amounts of non-essential minerals such as Fe–Ti oxides, haüyne, zeolites, apatite and calcite (cf. Gupta & Yagi 1980: 10).

It is important to record that leucite is not usually found in Mesozoic, or older, rocks. This is probably mainly because it alters readily, and it is often found partly replaced by analcite. In some rocks, leucite is completely replaced by an intergrowth of potassium feldspar and nepheline, or it

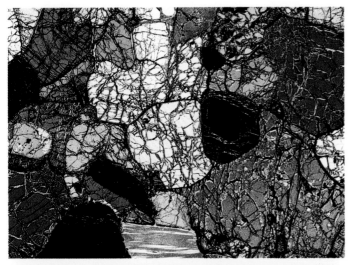

Photomicrographs reproduced from Mackenzie et al., (1982) *Atlas of Igneous Rocks and their Textures* (Numbers in brackets refer to photograph numbers of this work).

1 (113) A granular garnet *lherzolite xenolith* extracted from a kimberlite from Kimberley, South Africa. The minerals present are olivine, orthopyroxene, chrome diopside, garnet and phlogopite. See Section 1.10. Magnification ×7, XPL.

2 (121) *High-titanium mare basalt* obtained from the Taurus-Littrow Valley by the Apollo 17 mission (70017, 216). The rock is essentially composed of clinopyroxene, calcic plagioclase and ilmenite, with accessory amounts of cristobalite. See Section 5.12.
Magnification ×25, XPL.

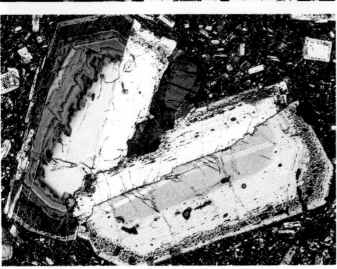

3 (97) Porphyritic *andesite* from Hakone Volcano, Japan. The plagioclase glomerocrysts show several types of zoning, that is, discontinuous, oscillatory and convolute zoning. Bands of inclusions are also observed near the margins of both of the large plagioclase crystals. Plagioclase is usually the most abundant phenocryst in andesites, and such phenocrysts are usually complexly zoned. This rock also contains pyroxenes and Fe-Ti oxides. See Section 6.2. Magnification ×24, XPL.

4 (64) A porphyritic *trachyte* with a trachytic groundmass texture from an unknown locality in Czechoslovakia. The small lath-shaped alkali feldspar crystals of the groundmass are aligned in a subparallel manner. Close study reveals that there are several domains within the photomicrograph, and each one has its own preferred direction of feldspar alignment. See Section 7.2. Magnification ×16, XPL.

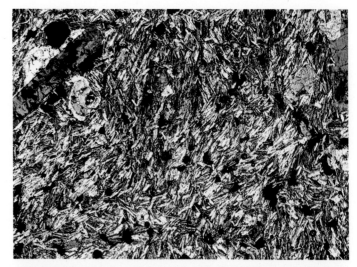

5 (8b) Glassy welded *crystal tuff* with an eutaxitic texture from the Tibchi Ring-Complex, Nigeria. See Sections 8.2 and 8.4. Magnification ×36, PPL.

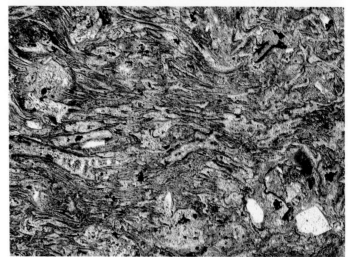

6 (74) A photograph of a polished hand specimen of *graphic granite* from an unknown locality. The dark mineral is smoky quartz, and the light mineral is alkali feldspar. See Sections 9.2 and 9.5. Magnification ×3.

7 (169) The Prairie Dog Creek *Chondrite* from Kansas, U.S.A., showing a variety of different types of chondrules. See Section 11.3. Magnification ×16, XPL.

8 (169) A view under higher magnification of the top left corner of photomicrograph 7. The *chondrule* at the left of the field of view consists of bladed twinned crystals of clinobronzite. This chondrule appears to be broken. The other large chondrule is also composed of pyroxene. An olivine crystal is visible at the bottom of the field of view. Magnification ×43, XPL.

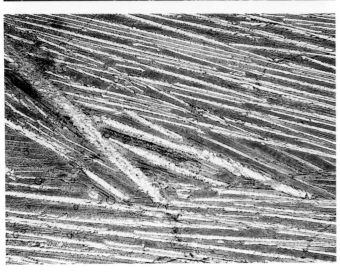

9 (115) *Komatiite* with a spinifex texture from Munro Township, Ontario, Canada. The pale phase originally consisted of olivine but it has been replaced by serpentine group minerals. The brown material was originally mainly composed of pyroxene and glass, but it has since been replaced by chlorite, tremolite and talc. See Section 11.5. Magnification ×3, PPL.

10 (129) Granular *norite* from the Bushveld Layered Complex, South Africa. Plagioclase, orthopyroxene and clinopyroxene are the essential phases. The clinopyroxenes show the highest interference colours, and some of them occur as lamellae within host crystals of orthopyroxene. See Section 11.6. Magnification ×12, XPL.

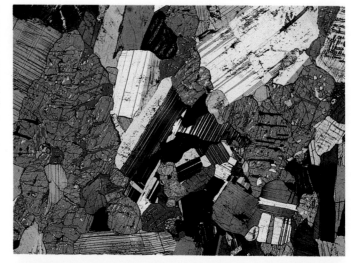

11 (148) *Nosean leucite phonolite* from Reiden, Eifel, W. Germany. This rock contains phenocrysts of clear leucite, light brown nosean with darker borders, and green pyroxene. See Section 12.2. Magnification ×11, PPL.

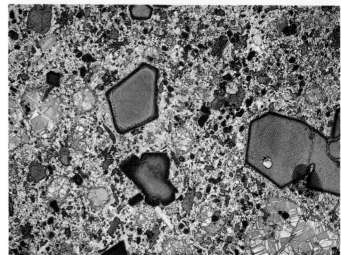

12 (148) This crossed polars view of the *nosean leucite phonolite* in photomicrograph 11, shows the isotropic nature of the nosean, the multiple twinning in the leucite, and the abundance of small sanidine laths in the groundmass. The mineral that occurs around the large nosean crystals, and has white of high order interference colours, is calcite. Magnification ×11, XPL.

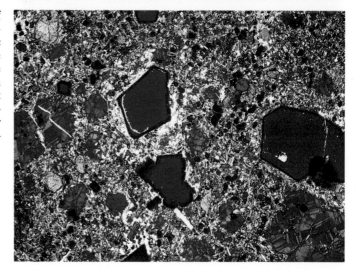

is surrounded by a rim consisting mainly of potassium feldspar and nepheline; such intergrowths are called *pseudoleucite*. Pseudoleucite is found in some plutonic rocks such as foid syenites and foid monzosyenites of the Loch Borralan area, north-west Scotland (cf. Woolley 1973). Leucite is not normally found in plutonic rocks because it is only stable at low pressures (cf. Scarfe et al. 1966).

The *melilitites* are a group of rare fine-grained, and usually porphyritic, extrusive, or subvolcanic, foidites. They are essentially composed of melilite and clinopyroxene, but they may also contain lesser amounts of foids, particularly nepheline or leucite. Rocks of this type have, for example, been described from Mt Nyiragongo north of Lake Kivu in eastern Zaire (cf. Sahama 1962); and Le Bas (1977: 100) has described a 100 m wide melilitite volcanic plug from Nyasumbe, on the north-eastern flanks of Kisingiri Volcano, western Kenya. This volcano also contains melilitite lavas (see Table 12.3.1). Melilitites that contain olivine are called *olivine melilitites*, and rocks of this type are, for example, found in the Sutherland district in the north-western Cape Province, S. Africa (cf. Taljaard 1936; McIver & Ferguson 1979). The mean mode of three of these olivine melilitites is olivine 30.8 per cent, augite 28.0 per cent, melilite 14.3 per cent, Fe–Ti oxides 13.0 per cent, perovskite 3.4 per cent, and 'irresolvable' phases 10.5 per cent (Shand 1950: 443). Other minerals that have been described from these rocks include phlogopite, apatite, zeolites, monticellite and nepheline. In the volcanic areas to the east and south-east of the Ruwenzori Mountains in western Uganda there are a variety of ultrabasic, potassic rocks that are essentially composed of various proportions of leucite, melilite kalsilite ($KAlSiO_4$), clinopyroxene and olivine (cf. Holmes 1942). These rocks have been called *katungites, ugandites* and *mafurites*, and they are of particular interest in that they contain the rare potassic mineral kalsilite. This mineral also occurs in some of the rocks extruded from Mt Nyiragongo, Zaire. Plutonic rocks that are mainly composed of melilite are called *melilitolites* (cf. Streckeisen 1967: 174). A well-known example of such a rock is found near Mt Uncompahgre, Gunnison Co., Colorado, USA. This rock contains between 63–67 per cent melilite, together with clinopyroxene, Fe-Ti oxides, perovskite, cancrinite, apatite, calcite, anatase, melanite, garnet and phlogopite (cf. Johannsen 1938: 321–2).

The *foid syenites* are medium- to coarse-grained intrusive rocks that essentially consist of alkali feldspar, more than 10 per cent foids (where A + P + F = 100), and one, or more, of the mafic minerals (for example, alkali-pyroxenes, alkali–amphiboles, augite, ferro-augite, biotite and fayalitic olivine). Accessory minerals may include sphene, apatite, zircon, Fe–Ti oxides, melanite garnet, sulphides, fluorite, carbonate minerals and a variety of rare accessory minerals such as eudialyte and astrophyllite. The foid–syenites usually have granitic, trachytoidal or porphyritic textures. Over the years, some thirty names have been given to various types of foid–syenite (cf. Sørensen 1974: 559–76). For example, some of the names that are used to describe *nepheline syenites* include *foyaite, juvite, kakortokite, khibinite, lakarpite, laurdalite, litchfieldite, lujavrite, mariupolite, nordsjoite, pulaskite, rischorrite, syenoide* and *toryhillite*; whereas names such as *assyntite, beloeilite, naujaite* and *sodalitite* have been used to describe the *sodalite syenites*. It is often convenient to divide the foid–syenites into four groups: (a) hypersolvus rocks that carry perthite or antiperthite; (b) rocks with discrete crystals of potassium feldspar and albitic plagioclase; (c) rocks with potassium feldspar only; and (d) rocks with albite only (cf. Allen & Charsley 1968: 10). Rocks of the first group crop out in the Oslo Petrographic Province of Norway (that is, the *laurdalites* of Laurdal, Norway). An example of a foid–syenite of the second group crops out in Ditró, or Ditrau, in Romania. These sodalite-bearing nepheline syenites are sometimes called *ditroites* (Zirkel 1866), and they generally contain both microcline and albite. The Fen Ring Complex of south-eastern Norway (see Section 14.1) contains a leucocratic nepheline syenite (*juvite* from this the type-area; Brögger 1921) in which the feldspar is exclusively potassium feldspar. Rocks of similar composition have been described from many other ijolite–carbonatite intrusive complexes (see Ch. 14). Examples of the fourth group crop out at Oktj'abr in the Ukraine, USSR; this area was formerly known as Mariupol and the albite-rich nepheline syenites of this area were called *mariupolites* (Morozewicz 1902). In Fig. 12.2.1 the mesocratic foid–syenites that contain between 30–60 per cent mafic minerals (M') are called *malignites*, and those that contain between 60–90 per cent mafic minerals (M') are called *shonkinites* (cf. Streckeisen 1974: Fig. 6b). According to Johannsen (1938: 116–18), malignite from the type-area of the Maligna

River, Ontario, Canada, has the following modal composition: 20.9 per cent potassium feldspar, 19.6 per cent nepheline, 48.2 per cent aegirine–augite, 5.8 per cent apatite, 2.0 per cent biotite, 1.0 per cent sphene, together with lesser amounts of Fe–Ti oxides and secondary minerals. The melanocratic foid–syenites are called shonkinites; and the term is derived from the American Indian name of Shonkin for the Highwood Mountains of Montana, USA. According to Johannsen (1938: 16), the type-shonkinite from Square Butte in the Highwood Mountains contains 46 per cent clinopyroxene, 20 per cent potassium feldspar, 10 per cent olivine, 8 per cent biotite, 6 per cent Fe–Ti oxides, 5 per cent nepheline, 4 per cent apatite and 1 per cent sodalite. Nash and Wilkinson (1970: 243) claim to have found up to 20 per cent pseudoleucite in the shonkinite specimens that they examined from the Shonkin Sag Laccolith in the north-eastern foothills of the Highwood Mountains.

The *foid–monzosyenites* (see Fig. 3.2.1) are the plutonic equivalents of the tephritic phonolites. They are rare rocks; and they can be separated into leuco–foid–monzosyenites, foid–

monzosyenites and mela–foid–monzosyenites as shown in Fig. 12.2.1. The *sommaites* are usually foid-bearing monzonites (*leucite monzonites*), but they grade into the foid–monzosyenites. These rocks were originally described by Lacroix (1905), and the type-rocks were blocks ejected by Somma Volcano, Italy. According to Tröger (1935) sommaite, from the type area near Napoli, contains 31 per cent sanidine, 28 per cent clinopyroxene, 25 per cent plagioclase (An_{60-70}), 9 per cent leucite, 4 per cent olivine, plus 3 per cent biotite, apatite and Fe–Ti oxides. The presence of leucite indicates that these 'plutonic' rocks crystallized at relatively shallow depths. The *miaskites* are transitional between the foid–monzosyenites and the foid–monzodiorites. They were originally described by Rose (1842) from Miask in the Ural Mountains of the USSR. According to Johannsen (1938: 165), these rocks contain approximately 34 per cent oligoclase, 33 per cent potassium feldspar, 13 per cent nepheline, 13 per cent biotite, 7 per cent sodalite, together with minor amounts of apatite, zircon, Fe–Ti oxides and cancrinite. The *husebyites*, from Huseby in the Oslo region of Norway (cf.

M'	P as a per cent of total feldspar content				F (Foids) = 60 to 100	
	F (Foids) = 10 to 60				*F (Foids) = 60 to 100*	
	0–10	10–50	50–90	90–100	Na > K	K > Na
30	Foid Syenite M' = 0–30	Leuco Foid Monzosyenite M' = 0–15	Leuco Foid Monzodiorite/ Monzogabbro M' = 0–20	Leuco Foid Diorite/Gabbro M' = 0–30	Urtite M' = 0–30	Italite M' = 0–10
		Foid Monzosyenite M' = 15–45	Foid Monzodiorite (An < 50) and Foid Monzogabbro (An > 50) M' = 20–60			Leuco Fergusite M' = 10–30
	Malignite M' = 30–60			Foid Diorite (An < 50) and Foid Gabbro (An > 50) M' = 30–70	Ijolite M' = 30–70	Fergusite M' = 30–50
60		Mela Foid Monzosyenite M' = 45–90	Mela Foid Monzodiorite/ Monzogabbro M' = 60–90			Mela Fergusite M' = 50–70
	Shonkinite M' = 60–90			Mela Foid Diorite/Gabbro M' = 70–90	Melteigite M' = 70–90	Missourite M' = 70–90

M' = the mafic and opaque minerals
P = plagioclase (An_{05-100})

Figure 12.2.1 Mafic mineral contents of the common alkaline plutonic rocks adapted from Streckeisen, 1974, Figure 6b).

Brögger 1933), are foid–monzosyenite; and according to Johannsen (1938: 165), they contain approximately 50 per cent potassium feldspar, 20 per cent andesine, 15 per cent nepheline, 12 per cent titanaugite, 3 per cent Fe–Ti oxides, together with minor amounts of apatite, biotite and barkevikite. Brögger (1933) regarded the husebyites as part of an essexite–foyaite rock association. Iddings and Morley (1915: 239) described a melanocratic foid–monzosyenite from Pic de Maros on Sulawesi, Indonesia, which they called a *marosite*.

The *foid-monzodiorites–monzogabbros* (see Fig. 12.2.1) appear to be slightly more abundant than the foid–monzosyenites. They include the *essexites*; this term was coined by Sears (1891) to describe the foid–monzodiorites from Salem Neck, Essex County, Massachusetts, USA. According to Tröger (1935), this neck contains approximately 39 per cent mafic minerals (hornblende, biotite, titanoaugite ± olivine), 30 per cent plagioclase, 12 per cent alkali feldspar, 10 per cent foids (mainly nepheline) and 9 per cent Fe–Ti oxides, sphene and apatite. Williams et al. (1982: 209) claim that the type-rock usually contains some 20 per cent nepheline. Lacroix (1922: 628–30) has described a number of essexites from Malagasy; in these rocks the nepheline is usually accompanied by sodalite and analcite. Unfortunately the term essexite has often been used very loosely to include rocks that contain a very low percentage, or even no foids; for example, the *Oslo essexites* (Brögger 1933) are essentially alkalic gabbros and monzodiorites. Barth (1945) gave the following range in modal composition for the Oslo essexites; plagioclase 25–57 per cent, alkali feldspar 5–22 per cent, biotite 3–14 per cent, olivine 3–11 per cent, hornblende 0–3 per cent, quartz 0–2 per cent, and the accessory minerals including Fe–Ti oxides and apatite 4–10 per cent. Such a rock is essentially a monzodiorite.

According to Streckeisen (1974: 781), the *foid-diorites* contain sodic plagioclase (An < 50) and the *foid–gabbros* contain a calcic plagioclase (An > 50). The relatively abundant nepheline gabbros are usually called *theralites*. This term was introduced by Rosenbusch (1887b: 247–8), and it was derived from the classical Greek word *thera* which means 'eagerly sought'; because Rosenbusch was at that time looking for a coarse-grained rock that was essentially composed of plagioclase and nepheline. He suggested that his eagerly sought rock might occur in the Crazy Mountains of Montana, USA. Wolff (1938: 1620)

has, however, subsequently shown that the 'theralites' of this area tend to carry more potassium feldspar than plagioclase. For example, the 'granular theralite' from the 100 m thick sill on Gordon Butte in the Crazy Mountains contains approximately 21 per cent orthoclase, 22 per cent nepheline, 11 per cent sodalite, 39 per cent clinopyroxene (zoned from augite cores to aegirine rims), 3 per cent biotite, 1 per cent Fe–Ti oxides, together with accessory amounts of apatite, sphene, analcite, cancrinite and secondary zeolites. According to the Streckeisen (1974) classification, this rock would be a mesocratic foidolite, or an ijolite, whereas some of the other 'theralites' from this area are malignites. Foid–gabbro, or theralite, consitutes part of the Lugar Sill of southern Strathclyde, Ayrshire, Scotland. Tyrrell (1912) gave the following mode for this rock: 35.9 per cent augite, 16.6 per cent nepheline, 16.4 per cent labradorite, 12.2 per cent amphibole, 8.7 per cent olivine, 6.7 per cent biotite, and 3.5 per cent accessory minerals that include Fe–Ti oxides and apatite. More recently, Sabine and Sutherland (1982: 519) have described this theralite as containing

'coarse idiomorphic titanaugite and finer granular pyroxene, large fresh olivine crystals, and plentiful biotite in a groundmass of allotriomorphic feldspar and turbid nepheline. The feldspar forms coarse allotriomorphic plates of sodic labradorite zoned to oligoclase, and was the last constituent to crystallize. Kaersutitic amphibole is sometimes present; abundant apatite needles, orthoclase, analcime, and iron ores (Fe-oxides) including ilmenite are accessory, and serpentine is an alteration product'.

Tyrrell (1912) has also described an olivine-rich foid–gabbro (or theralite) from the Kyle district of southern Strathclyde, Scotland. *Kylite* generally contains between 27–55 per cent olivine, 20–8 per cent titanaugite, set in a groundmass of labradorite (17–33 per cent), with subordinate amounts of nepheline ($\approx$ 5 per cent), analcime, Fe–Ti oxides, biotite, potassium feldspar and apatite (cf. Sabine & Sutherland 1982: 520). Haüyne-bearing foid–gabbros are sometimes called *mareugites* after Mareuge in the Auvergne of France where these rocks occur as inclusions in haüyne-bearing volcanic rocks (cf. Johannsen 1938: 222).

The *foidolites* are the coarser-grained, or plutonic, equivalents of the foidites; and in the system APF they contain more than 60 per cent F, or foids. In Fig. 12.2.1 they are first of all divided into Na-rich and K-rich rocks, and they are then subdivided using their mafic mineral content (M'). In the *urtites*, sodium exceeds potassium, and M' is less than 30. The term was introduced by Ramsay (1896) to describe rocks from Lujavr-Urt (now Lovozero) in the Kola Peninsula of the USSR. According to Gerasimovsky et al. (1974: 215–18), the Lovozero massif is a large (20 × 30 km) alkaline intrusive body that was emplaced during four separate intrusive events. The lower part of the massif is a concentrically-zoned body, whereas the upper part is a differentiated loccolith. Most of the massif is composed of foid–syenite; however, during the second intrusive phase a rhythmically-layered complex of alkaline rocks evolved, and it is within this layered complex that the urtites are found associated with nepheline syenites (that is, foyaites, aegirine lujavrites and amphibole (arfvedsonite) lujavites). According to Ramsay (1896), the urtites from the type-area contain between 82–86 per cent nepheline, between 12–16 per cent pyroxene and approximately 2 per cent apatite. The pyroxene is normally aegirine; and other minerals that have been described from these rocks include microcline, sodalite and sphene. In the Tuva region of the USSR, some ijolite–carbonatite intrusive complexes contain a rock that has been called *tuvinite*, or ultra-urtite, and it is composed of 95 per cent nepheline and calcite (cf. Heinrich 1966: 46).

Ijolite is a foidolite in which sodium exceeds potassium, and the mafic content (M') is between 30 and 70. The term was introduced by Ramsay and Berghell (1891), and they used it to describe mesocratic nepheline–pyroxene rocks from Iiwaara, Kuusamo, Finland. Rocks from the type-area contained between 49–55 per cent nepheline, 35–42 per cent clinopyroxene 1.7–2.5 per cent sphene, and one of the specimens examined by Ramsay and Berghell contained 2.2 per cent garnet. In the type-area the garnet is an andradite–melanite that is known as iivaarite. Other accessory minerals that are often described from the ijolites are wollastonite, perovskite and Fe–Ti oxides. Late-stage and/or secondary minerals include cancrinite, sodalite, analcite, pectolite and various zeolite and carbonate group minerals. In some ijolite–carbonatite intrusive complexes (see Ch. 14), the ijolitic rocks are found to grade into carbonatites (for example, pyroxene sovites). The clinopyroxenes found in ijolite tends to range in composition from titanaugites, via sodic hedenbergites, to aegirine; and the larger clinopyroxene crystals are often zoned with aegirine occurring in the outer margins.

Melteigite is a foidolite in which sodium exceeds potassium, and the mafic content (M') is between 70 and 90. The name was introduced by Brögger (1921) in his description of the Fen Ring Complex of south-eastern Norway (see Section 14.4); and the type-area is on Melteig farm. Brögger gave the following modal composition for the type-rock: 47.5 per cent clinopyroxene, 20.8 per cent nepheline, 6.1 per cent biotite, 5.5 per cent calcite, 4.8 per cent cancrinite, 4.5 per cent apatite, 4.4 per cent garnet, 4.2 per cent sphene, 1.2 per cent muscovite, 0.9 per cent pyrochlore and 0.6 per cent Fe–Ti oxides. The clinopyroxene tends to vary in composition from diopside via aegirine–augite to aegirine, and the garnet is usually a melanite. A biotite–melteigite (that is, *algarvite*) has been described from Navete, Caldas de Monchique, Algarve, Portugal (cf. Lacroix 1922: 646).

The much less abundant potassium-rich foidolites that have similar colour indices to the urtites, ijolites and melteigites, are *italites, fergusites* and *missourites*, respectively (see Fig. 12.2.1). In all of these rocks the predominant feldspathoid is leucite. Washington (1920) called the leucite-rich leucocratic foidolites italites because the only rock of this composition then known came from blocks within an agglomerate from the Albano Volcano, on the northern slope of the Alban Hills south-east of Rome, Italy. He (33) states that he named the rocks italite 'in honour of the country whose lavas are so famous for their abundance in leucite'. His blocks of italite were up to 30 cm in diameter and contained over 90 per cent leucite, together with minor amounts of other minerals, such as clinopyroxene, haüyne, melilite, melanite, apatite, biotite and Fe–Ti oxides. The chemical composition of these leucite–cumulate rocks is interesting as they usually contain more than 18 per cent K_2O. Pirsson (1905) defined fergusite as a granular intrusive rock essentially consisting of leucite (pseudoleucite) and subordinate augite. It crops out in a small circular stock-like body that is about 2 km in diameter, and it occurs at the head of Shonkin Creek, in the Highwood Mountains of Montana, USA. According to Johannsen (1938: 325), the name is derived from Fergus County in which the stock was supposed to be located; however 'the northern line of the county lies a little south of the place where the rock occurs'. The type-rock contains approximately 65 per cent pseudoleucite, 24 per cent clinopyroxene (augite to aegirine–augite), 8 per cent Fe–Ti oxides, and accessory amounts of apatite, biotite and olivine (Pirsson 1905: 86). The Highwood Mountains are also the type-area for missourites. Weed and Pirsson (1896) gave this name to the intrusive rock that forms the subvolcanic core of one of the extinct volcanoes of the Highwood Mountains. They (323) proposed the name missourite because the Missouri River is 'the most prominent and best known geographical object in the region where it [the missourite] occurs'. The rock from the type-area in Shonkin Creek contains approximately 50 per cent clinopyroxene (augite), 16 per cent leucite, 15 per cent olivine, 6 per cent biotite, 5 per cent Fe–Ti oxides, 4 per cent analcite, 4 per cent zeolites and a trace of apatite. In the material studied by Weed and Pirsson, the leucite was unaltered and it occurred in the form of anhedral crystals that filled the interstices between the mafic minerals.

12.3 Geochemistry and normative compositions

Table 12.3.1 gives the mean major element composition of the phonolites. If these values are compared with those of the mean trachyte (Table 7.3.1), the phonolites are found to be relatively enriched in Al_2O_3 (+2 per cent) and the alkali metals (+3 per cent), but depleted in SiO_2 (–5 per cent). The average phonolite is also found to contain 67.9 per cent normative alkali–feldspar and 16.5 per cent normative nepheline. The only other significant normative minerals are diopside 6.9 per cent magnetite 4.1 per cent and ilmenite 1.2 per cent. This rock has a Thornton and Tuttle differentiation index of 82.9, which is slightly higher than the average trachyte (80.7) but less than the average rhyolite (88.4). The voluminous flood-type phonolites (Table 12.3.1, No. 2) of the Eastern Rift of Kenya have a mean normative nepheline content of 25.5 per cent; and they are peralkaline in that they have a mean normative acmite (aegirine) content of 1.9 per cent. Some of the other phonolites from Kenya, such as the Kenya-type rocks (cf. Lippard 1973a: 227), are significantly more peralkaline.

Table 12.3.1 also gives the major element composition of nepheline–syenites, basanites, nephelinites, melanephelinites, tephrites, leucitites, leucite phonolites, phonolite leucite tephrites, olivine melilitites and melilitite lavas; whereas Tables 12.6.1, 12.6.2 and 12.6.3 give the major element compositions of the ordinary lamprophyres, alkaline lamprophyres, melilitic lamprophyres and the lamproites. Figures 3.3.3 and 3.3.4 show that the phonolitic, tephritic, basanitic and foiditic extrusive rocks normally occupy a distinct area on the alkali silica diagram; that is, they contain more ($Na_2O + K_2O$) than the normal alkalic rocks of similar SiO_2 content. It is thus useful to call these foid-rich rocks the *hyperalkalic rocks*. Such hyperalkalic rocks usually carry more than 10 per cent normative foids.

The data in Tables 9.3.1, 12.3.1, 12.3.2, 12.6.1, 12.6.2, 12.6.3, 13.3.1 and 13.3.2 demonstrate that there are many different types of alkaline rocks with diverse chemical compositions; however, most of these rocks are enriched in the incompatible elements, and are usually also enriched in one, or more, of the volatile components such as CO_2, H_2O and or/the halogens. Details of the trace element geochemistry of the kimberlites is given in Section 13.3 and that of the nephelinites in 12.3.2.

12.4 Diastrophism and the alkaline rocks

In Section 4.2 it was noted that the alkaline rocks of Earth usually occur in one of the following tectonic settings: (a) continental rifts and palaeorifts; (b) oceanic islands and seamounts; and (c) the outer magmatic zone of seismically-active continental margins and island-arcs; that is, in areas where the rocks of the high-K and shoshonite associations tend to occur (see Section 6.1). Many of the important alkaline provinces of Phanerozoic age are associated with faulting and rifting; and as Bailey (1974: 150) has noted, the alkaline rocks may not be exclusively restricted to rift zones; however, 'where continental rifting is known, alkaline magmatism is strongly in evidence'. It is also important to note that most Cenozoic rift zones are but the fractured crests of crustal arches, domes and upwarps that may be regarded as the primary tectonic feature. Some examples of continental rifts that contain alkaline magmatic rocks include: (a) the Baikal rift system of the USSR; (b) the East African and Ethiopian

Table 12.3.1 Chemical composition of selected alkaline igneous rocks (%)

	1	2	3	4	5	6	7	8	9	10	11	12	13
SiO_2	56.19	55.00	54.99	56.70	44.30	40.60	47.80	41.52	47.11	54.47	50.3	33.52	39.03
TiO_2	0.62	0.53	0.60	0.84	2.51	2.66	1.76	2.98	1.25	0.53	0.73	3.03	3.26
Al_2O_3	19.04	19.94	20.96	19.06	14.70	14.33	17.00	10.78	15.74	20.73	18.6	7.21	8.78
Fe_2O_3	2.79	2.41	2.25	2.71	3.94	5.48	4.12	7.95	4.54	2.28	2.9	1.74	7.73
FeO	2.03	2.27	2.05	1.70	7.50	6.17	5.22	6.11	4.54	1.46	3.9	9.56	6.65
MnO	0.17	0.27	0.15	0.21	0.16	0.26	0.15	0.23	0.27	0.19	0.12	0.23	0.26
MgO	1.07	0.51	0.77	1.04	8.54	6.39	4.70	7.53	5.24	0.74	4.9	19.55	8.45
CaO	2.72	1.42	2.31	2.62	10.19	11.89	9.18	13.74	11.01	3.24	8.9	16.76	16.49
Na_2O	7.79	8.34	8.23	7.55	3.55	4.79	3.69	3.28	2.02	4.37	2.2	1.86	0.96
K_2O	5.24	5.94	5.58	5.17	1.96	3.46	4.49	1.73	6.72	10.18	5.6	1.62	1.36
P_2O_5	0.18	0.07	0.13	0.22	0.74	1.07	0.63	0.73	0.44	0.13	0.63	1.29	0.73
H_2O^+	1.57	3.19	1.30	1.99*	1.20	0.54	1.03	2.71	0.87	0.43	0.29	—	4.64
No. of analyses	340	14	115	446	165	176	85	43	7	1	1	5	2

1. Mean chemical composition of phonolite (after Le Maitre 1976a: 602) (H_2O^- = 0.37 per cent and CO_2 = 0.08 per cent).
2. Mean chemical composition of the 'plateau type' phonolites of Kenya (after Lippard 1973a: 227) (H_2O^- = 0.66 per cent).
3. Mean chemical composition of nepheline syenite (after Le Maitre 1976a: 600) (H_2O^- = 0.17 per cent and CO_2 = 0.20 per cent).
4. Mean chemical composition of Cenozoic phonolite (after Chayes 1975: 548) (* = total H_2O).
5. Mean chemical composition of basanite (after Le Maitre 1976a: 627) (H_2O^- = 0.42 per cent and CO_2 = 0.18 per cent).
6. Mean chemical composition of nephelinite (after Le Maitre 1976a: 629) (H_2O^- = 0.54 per cent and CO_2 = 0.60 per cent).
7. Mean chemical composition of tephrite (after Le Maitre 1976a: 630) (H_2O^- = 0.22 per cent and CO_2 = 0.02 per cent).
8. Mean chemical composition of melanephelinite from East Africa (after Le Bas 1977: 299) (H_2O^- = 0.64 per cent and CO_2 = 0.28 per cent).
9. Mean chemical composition of leucitite (after Nockolds 1954: 1031).
10. Chemical composition of leucite–phonolite from Roccamonfina Volcano, Italy (after Baldridge et al. 1981: 322) (H_2O^- = 0.35 per cent, Cl = 0.18 per cent, SO_3 = 0.06 per cent, SrO = 0.24 per cent and BaO = 0.24 per cent).
11. Chemical composition of the AD 79 phonolitic leucite tephrite flow from Vesuvio, Italy (after Pichler 1970: 200) (Cl = 0.01 per cent, F = 0.1 per cent, SrO + BaO = 0.28 per cent, H_2O^- = 0.45 per cent).
12. Mean chemical composition of five olivine melilitites from Sutherland, north-western Cape, South Africa (after McIver & Ferguson 1979: 119) (H_2O^- = 0.35 per cent and loss on ignition = 2.76 per cent).
13. Mean chemical composition of two melilitite lavas from western Kenya (after Le Bas 1977: 301) (H_2O^- = 1.43 per cent).

Table 12.3.2 Mean chemical composition of nephelinite (after Wedepohl & Muramatsu 1979: 301–2)

p.p.m.		p.p.m.	
Li	16	Cd	0.052
C	205	In	0.034
Na	25 300	Ba	1 046
Mg	71 200	La	89
Al	61 600	Ce	171
Si	188 400	Pr	18
P	3 800	Nd	66
S	620	Sm	14.5
Cl	518	Eu	4.0
K	12 200	Gd	12.1
Ca	90 000	Tb	1.7
Sc	21	Dy	7.3
Ti	16 800	Ho	1.7
V	221	Er	3.3
Cr	344	Tm	0.88
Mn	1 500	Yb	2.3
Fe	91 080	Lu	0.39
Co	52	Hf	5
Ni	291	Ta	19
Cu	63	W	11
Zn	102	Hg	0.02
Ga	15	Tl	0.009
Ge	1.6	Pb	7.8
Rb	39	Bi	0.014
Sr	1 350	Th	11
Y	36	U	3.2
Zr	103		

rift systems; (c) the Gardar palaeorift of Greenland; (d) the Midland Valley palaeorift of Scotland; (e) the Oslo palaeorift of Norway; (f) the Rhine – Rhone rift system of western Europe; (g) the Rio Grande rift of New Mexico, USA; and (h) the St Lawrence palaeorift of eastern North America.

Le Bas (1980a, b) has followed the pioneering work of Bailey (1964; 1974) and others, and made a detailed study of the relationship between the uplift of continental crust, and the origin, evolution and emplacement of alkaline magmatic rocks. He has proposed that the doming associated with this type of magmatism may develop on three quite different scales: (a) *lithospheric doming*; (b) *crustal doming*; and (c) *subvolcanic doming*. A well-preserved example of a lithospheric dome is preserved in East Africa. The long axis of this dome extends for approximately 1500 km, as it extends from Lakes Albert and Turkana in the north to Lake Malawi in the south. This huge dome is centred on Lake Victoria, and it includes both the potassic western rift system and the sodic

eastern rift system of East Africa. It probably formed in a few tens of millions of years at the end of the Cretaceous period (65–80 Ma). Well-known crustal domes include the Kenya Dome of the Nairobi area, the Rhine Dome of West Germany and the Rungwe Dome of southern Tanzania. These crustal domes are generally about 200–500 km in diameter with a maximum uplift of approximately 1 km. Rifting is commonly developed along the crests of these domes. Alkaline igneous rocks such as foid-bearing basalts, phonolitic tephrites, tephritic phonolites, phonolites and olivine nephelinites are often extruded from these crustal domes. The extrusion of large volumes of alkalic trachyte and rhyolite tends to occur after the main graben-forming stage. Subvolcanic domes are relatively small, and they generally vary between 1 and 20 km in diameter. In many of the volcanic centres of East Africa, these subvolcanic domes lie buried under vast piles of volcanic materials; however, in some areas, such as Napak Volcano in eastern Uganda (see Ch. 14) and the Homa Mountains of western Kenya, the domes have been exhumed by erosion. According to Le Bas (1980: 37), the subvolcanic domes associated with carbonatitic ring complexes are in part generated by the metasomatism, or *fenitization* (see Section 14.1), produced by the emplacement of materials of the carbonatite–nephelinite–ijolite rock association. Subvolcanic domes may also be produced by the emplacement of confocal clusters of steeply-dipping cone sheets.

Seismic, thermal and geochemical evidence suggests that the lithosphere beneath East Africa is generally thick and gradually passes into a poorly-defined asthenosphere (see Section 1.10). According to Le Bas (1980a: 34), beneath old continental cratons some of the material that forms the asthenosphere 'adheres more to the overlying lithosphere than to the underlying mantle', and that the zone of decoupling within the asthenosphere is at a depth of about 400 km. It is thus proposed that the coherent lithospheric plate in the area of the Tanzanian Shield is approximately 400 km thick; and according to Le Bas, this would be an appropriate depth for the focus, or magmatic source, responsible for lithospheric doming. He (1980b: 119) claims that the thickening of the coherent continental plate under a large craton may bring the $\beta \rightarrow \alpha$ olivine inversion depth level to lie within the basal layer of the plate, and thus any expansion resulting from the inversion of the olivine would effect the overlying layers of the plate. It is thus postulated that rising heat, probably associated with the degassing of the deep mantle (see Sections 1.10 and 13.6), may result in the inversion of the olivine at the base of the plate, thus producing an expansion in this layer and doming in the overlying lithosphere. It is likely that the olivine inversion process takes place in garnet lherzolites that are at near-melting temperatures; and the introduction of a tenuous magma that is enriched in volatile components (mainly species in the subsystem H – C – O) and incompatible elements is likely to produce partial melting. This process will be enhanced by decompression melting as the individual rock units within the various layers of the lithosphere are flexed and arched upwards to form the evolving lithospheric dome. As the dome develops, magma streams towards the central decompressed region; and according to Le Bas (1980b: 120), this migration would result in the higher Rb/Sr ratios observed in the carbonatitic and nephelinitic rocks of the central zone, as compared with the lower values found in the peripheral Kenyan basalts.

The East African Lithospheric Dome is over 500 m high in the central region; and it encompasses most of Kenya, Uganda and Tanzania. It is not, however, a unique feature on the surfaces of the terrestrial planets, as there are larger lithospheric domes developed in both the Tharsis and Elysium volcanic provinces of Mars; and as was reported in Section 1.9, both of these domes are cut by an extensive system of radial fractures, and they are embellished with a variety of spectacular volcanic landforms. Large domes, and an associated system of rifts, have also been proposed for the Beta Regio and Phoebe Regio regions of Venus (cf. BVSP 1981: 882).

The Kenya Crustal Dome is approximately 700 km from north to south and 500 km from east to west, whereas the Rungwe and Western Rift domes are only 100 to 200 km across. It has been suggested that these differences in size may reflect the relative youth of the smaller domes. The fully-developed Kenya Dome has taken 10 Ma to evolve; and a variety of geophysical measurements have shown that it is underlain by a large 'pillow' of anomalous crust/mantle material that has a mean density of 3200 kg/m^3. This 'pillow' is situated between 15–25 km below the surface of the floor of the Kenya Rift, and it probably extends to a depth of 100 km. Geomagnetic deepsounding experiments by Banks and Beamish (1979) have demonstrated that the 'pillow' is a zone of high electrical conductivity, and that it is probably composed of partially molten (5–10 per cent) material. One might postulate that the 'pillows' at the base of the crustal domes of East Africa may represent vast diapirs of mobile mantle material that were originally part of the 'magma bolster' that evolved at the base of the even larger, and earlier, East African Lithospheric Dome. Many areas, such as the Kola Peninsula of the north-western USSR, contain alkaline rocks of different ages. Such resurgent alkaline magmatism may be related to the development of lithospheric domes; that is, if a 'magma bolster' developed beneath a region, it might be directly responsible for the first cycle of alkaline magmatic activity and indirectly responsible for the later cycles of broadly similar activity; as the latter rocks may have evolved from parental magmas generated by the partial melting of upper mantle materials enriched in incompatible elements derived from the 'magma bolster'. It is thus proposed that the cooling of a 'magma bolster' may generate widespread mantle metasomatism and the emplacement of glimmerite veins (see Section 1.10).

One of the most interesting problems associated with alkaline magmatism in East Africa is the occurrence of huge volumes of: (a) flood trachyte (see Section 7.6); (b) flood phonolite (see Section 12.5); and (c) nephelinites (see Section 14.4). Bailey (1974: 155–6) has proposed that in order to account for the widespread distribution and large volumes of these lavas, one has to postulate that the magmas, from which these lavas evolved, were generated by large-scale regional processes. Using concepts from Bailey (1974) and Le Bas (1980a, b), one might postulate that the initial magma released into the crust from the diapir that was to form the 'pillow' at the base of the Kenya Crustal Dome was essentially melanephelinitic in composition, and it resulted in the evolution of the nephelinites and associated rocks (see Section 14.5). As the diapir was forced into the crust, crustal doming occurred; and part of the magma within the diapir cooled, crystallized and differentiated to generate a phonolitic magma (see Section 12.5). With further cooling, and the removal of phonolitic magma from the diapir, rifting occurred in the overlying dome; and the magma draining into the apex of the diapir/pillow gradually changed in composition because: (a) it was now equilibrating with solid phases in a lower-pressure environment; and (b) the magma was gradually assimilating more crustal materials and becoming richer in elements such as silica. Fractional crystallization of these magmas led to the evolution of the flood trachytes. Once the pocket of magma at the apex of daipir/pillow had decreased in size, magmas, such as the melanephelinite derived from deeper levels within the upper mantle, were once again able to penetrate the crust in the area of the Kenya Crustal Dome.

Whereas many Phanerozoic continental alkaline provinces are directly associated with rifts, palaeorifts and possibly also with lithospheric and/or crustal domes, some large bodies of alkaline rocks cannot be directly related to tectonic features of this type. For example, the huge Khibina (1327 km^2) and Lovozero (650 km^2) alkaline massifs of the Kola Peninsula, in the north-west of the USSR, appear only to be associated with deep-seated fracture zones (cf. Gerasimovsky et al. 1974: 212), whereas other bodies of alkaline rocks are located in areas where there are changes in the orientation of monoclinal structures, such as occurs in the Nuanetsi-Lebombo Province of south-eastern Africa (cf. Sørensen 1974: 145). It has been proposed that the alkaline rocks in other continental petrographic provinces are associated with: (a) deep-seated fracture zones (see Section 13.4); (b) linear features of unknown tectonic significance; and (c) areas of block faulting.

12.5 Flood phonolites

Gregory (1921) was the first to recognize the vast volume of phonolitic lava that occurs in the Tertiary volcanic succession of the Kenya Rift. These rocks exceed 'the total volume of phonolitic lava found elsewhere in the world by several orders of magnitude' (Lippard 1973a: 217). The total volume of these phonolites is 25 000 km^3 which is about one-sixth of the total volume of Cenozoic volcanic rocks in this petrographic province. Lippard (1973a, b) has given a detailed description of the Miocene phonolites of the Uasin Gishu Plateau on the western side of the Kenya Rift. This plateau contains seven flows of flood phonolite that have a combined volume of 600 km^3. These lavas erupted in the area that is now the rift valley, and they then flowed westwards for distances of up to 60 km. Topographic irregularities impeded the westward movement of the three

lowest flows; however, the later flows wholly, or partly, buried these topographic barriers and flooded westwards. The voluminous fourth flow covered an area of 2400 km^2 to an average thickness of 100 m. These flood phonolites are of very uniform chemical composition (see Table 12.3.1), and they generally grade from being sparsely microporphyritic (3–5 per cent phenocrysts) to coarsely porphyritic (15–30 per cent phenocrysts). The phenocrysts are usually nepheline and sanidine-anorthoclase in roughly equal proportions, together with lesser amounts of Fe–Ti oxides, ferroaugite, biotite and apatite. Most of the abundant phenocrysts have corroded margins. The groundmass is generally a microcyrstalline mixture of alkali feldspar and interstitial alkali-pyroxene, amphibole and aenigmatite.

Most of the flood phonolites were extruded before the main phase of graben formation; and it is evident that a huge magma chamber, or 'pillow', would be required to produce these phonolites. If, as seems likely, the phonolitic magma was derived by fractional crystallization from a parental alkalic basaltic or nephelinitic magma, then the required magma chamber would have to be even larger. Goles (1976: 5) has noted that the area into which these phonolites erupted is approximately 400 km long and 70 km wide, and he has estimated that in the Miocene there was probably between 50 000 and 100 000 km^3 of phonolitic magma beneath what was to become the Kenya Rift, and further that this magma was probably derived from a parental magma that occupied a volume that was some five times as great as the phonolitic magma. It is suggested that once relatively low-density phonolitic magma formed at the top of the 'pillow' beneath the Kenya Crustal Dome it was able to prevent the eruption of more dense, and less differentiated, magmas.

12.6 Lamprophyres and lamproites

The term lamprophyre was introduced by Gümbel (1874) to describe a group of dark-coloured dyke rocks from the Fichtelgebirge of West Germany. He (36) derived the term from the classical Greek word *lampros* meaning 'bright' or 'glistening', as the rocks of the type-area contained prominent flakes of lustrous biotite. According to Streckeisen (1980: 202), the lamprophyres are 'not simply textural varieties of common plutonic or volcanic rocks', as they are 'more or less distinguished from plutonic and volcanic rocks by their mineral composition and texture, and, to varying degrees, also by their chemical composition'. He regards the following features as characteristic of the lamprophyres: (a) they are mesocratic to melanocratic, rarely ultramafic, porphyritic rocks; (b) they contain essential biotite-phlogopite and/or amphibole, together with clinopyroxene, olivine and occasionally melilite; (c) feldspars and/or feldspathoids (when present) are restricted to the groundmass; (d) hydrothermal alteration of olivine, pyroxene, biotite–phlogopite and plagioclase is common; (e) calcite, zeolites and other hydrothermal minerals are common; (f) they usually have comparatively high K_2O (or $K_2O + Na_2O$) contents at relatively low SiO_2 contents; and (g) their H_2O, CO_2, S, P_2O_5 and Ba contents are generally high as compared to rocks of similar SiO_2 content; and they consequently tend to have relatively high hydrous mineral, carbonate, sulphide, apatite and zeolite abundances. Another characteristic of the lamprophyres is that the minerals they contain, particularly the mafic phenocrysts, tend to be euhedral. Most lamprophyres and lamproites occur in dykes or diatremes, but some occur as lavas.

Streckeisen (1980: 194–5) recognizes three main types of lamprophyres: (a) the calc–alkaline lamprophyres; (b) the alkaline lamprophyres; and (c) the melilitic lamprophyres. The calc–alkaline lamprophyres are also known as the *lamprophyres* (*sensu stricto*), and the *shoshonitic lamprophyres* (cf. Wimmenauer 1973; Joplin 1966); and many petrologists regard these rocks as being the *ordinary lamprophyres*. These ordinary lamprophyres consist of the *minettes, vogesites, kersantites* and *spessartites*. Metais and Chayes (1963: 156–7) have made a detailed study of the chemical composition of the lamprophyres (see Table 12.6.1), and they concluded that 'in terms of average chemical composition minettes, vogesites, kersantites, and spessartites seem virtually indistinguishable. Except for potash, the observed averages for all major oxides in these four groups are so similar that significant differences would be difficult to establish.' If one compares the mean chemical composition of the *ordinary lamprophyres* with the chemical screen used to define the post-Archaean basalts of Earth Table 3.1.1), one discovers that the *ordinary lamprophyres* are all rejected by the screen because they contain too much (> 2.5 per cent) K_2O and

total H_2O. Whereas the spessartites are only just rejected, the minettes have an average K_2O content of 5.49 per cent, and are thus chemically quite distinct from the normal basaltic rocks. The minettes are more chemically akin to the leucite tephrites and leucite phonolitic tephrites than the alkalic basalts (see Table 12.3.1, No. 11). *Ordinary lamprophyres* are usually found associated with epizonal granitic, syenitic and monzonitic rocks, but they are also occasionally found associated with the rocks of alkaline carbonatite complexes (cf. Heinrich 1966: 55). It is the latter association that links the *ordinary lamprophyres* with the alkaline lamprophyres and melilitic lamprophyres, and enables most petrologists to agree with Metais and Chayes (1963: 156) that 'the rocks called lamprophyre, though exceedingly variable in composition, do form some kind of natural group'.

The four common ordinary lamprophyres are most readily classified using modal data; and the minerals that are characteristically present in these rocks include alkali feldspar (usually potassium feldspar), plagioclase (oligoclase and/or andesine), biotite–phlogopite, augite (usually diopsidic), amphibole (usually hornblende or kaersutite), olivine, quartz, apatite, Fe–Ti oxides and calcite. In minette, the essential minerals are alkali feldspar, biotite–phlogopite and augite; in kersantite they are plagioclase, biotite–phlogopite and augite; in vogesite they are alkali feldspar, hornblende and augite; and in spessartite they are plagioclase, hornblende and augite. The type-areas for the four ordinary lamprophyres are all in western Europe. Minette is an old term originally used by the miners of Framont in the Vosges in north-eastern France. Vogesite is derived from the word Vogesen which is the German name for the Vosges where these rocks crop out. The type-area for spessartite is the Spessart Mountains east of Aschaffenburg in West Germany. Kersantite was named after the village of Kersanton in France.

The alkaline lamprophyres and the melilitic lamprophyres will be considered together, because both groups contain alkaline rocks and are usually associated with alkaline complexes and the rocks of the carbonatite–nepheline–ijolite association. According to Streckeisen (1980: 203), the common alkaline lamprophyres are *camptonites, sannaites* and *monchiquites*; and they are chemically akin to the alkalic basalts, basanites and nephelinites. Camptonite is characteristically composed of amphibole (usually

Table 12.6.1 Chemical composition of the common lamprophyres (after Metais and Chayes 1963: 157) (%)

	Ordinary lamprophyres				Alkaline lamprophyres	
	Minette	*Vogesite*	*Kersantite*	*Spessartite*	*Camptonite*	*Monchiquite*
SiO_2	51.17	51.13	51.80	52.37	44.67	40.68
Al_2O_3	13.87	14.35	14.84	15.44	14.35	13.20
Fe_2O_3	3.27	3.63	3.03	3.27	4.50	4.87
FeO	4.16	4.74	5.32	5.35	7.19	6.47
MgO	6.91	6.84	6.29	6.27	7.02	9.17
CaO	6.58	7.05	6.24	7.36	9.45	11.02
Na_2O	2.12	3.00	2.98	3.30	2.99	3.06
K_2O	5.49	3.81	3.68	2.54	1.91	2.16
TiO_2	1.36	1.44	1.32	1.31	2.46	2.34
CO_2	1.30	0.74	1.14	0.41	1.58	1.38
H_2O (total)	2.42	2.62	2.56	2.36	3.12	3.52
No. of analyses	64	30	95	45	78	61

barkevikite and/or kaersutite), aluminous titanaugite, olivine and/or biotite–phlogopite (usually Ti-rich), set in a groundmass of plagioclase (usually labradorite), amphibole and pyroxene, together with subordinate amounts of alkali feldspar, feldspathoids, apatite, Fe–Ti oxides, zeolites and carbonate minerals. Sannaite is broadly similar to camptonite in modal composition, except that it contains alkali feldspar in place of plagioclase. Monchiquite characteristically contains aluminous titanaugite, amphibole (usually barkevikite and/or kaersutite), biotite–phlogopite, and often olivine set in a colourless isotropic groundmass of glass (potentially plagioclase + nepheline), analcite, or nepheline, and contining microlites of pyroxene, amphibole, Fe–Ti oxides, apatite, zeolites and carbonate minerals. *Alnöite* is an ultramafic melilitic lamprophyre that is generally composed of melilite and biotite–phlogopite, commonly with subordinate amounts of clinopyroxene, olivine, carbonate minerals, perovskite, apatite, nepheline, monticellite, Fe–Ti oxides and melanite garnet. *Polzenite* is a melilitic lamprophyre that usually contains between 10–30 per cent feldspathoids (mainly nepheline and haüyne), and it normally contains the same minerals as occur in alnöite; that is melilite, biotite-phlogopite and a feldspathoid mineral are the essential phases. It is interesting to note that the type-areas for alnöite (Alnö Island, Sweden) and sannaite (Sannavand, Fen Complex, southern Norway) are both well-known ijolite–carbonatite complexes (see Ch. 14). The type-area for camptonite is Campton, New Hampshire, USA; for monchiquite it is Sierra de Monchique in the Algarve of southern

Portugal; and for polzenite it is the Polzen area of the Bohemian Massif, Czechoslovakia. Some of the alkaline lamprophyres, such as the Tertiary lamprophyres of Wiedemanns Fjord, East Greenland, contain a variety of high-pressure xenoliths and megacrysts which indicate that these rocks probably evolved from parental magmas that were generated in a high-pressure environment.

Many good examples of both alkaline and melilitic lamprophyres crop out in the Monteregian Province of Canada; these rocks include camptonites, monchiquites and alnöites. The camptonites tend to occur to the east of Mount Royal, which is a park in the centre of the city of Montreal; the monchiquites occur between Mount Royal and St Dorothee, which lies some 17 km to the west at the southern end of Jesus Island; and the alnöites crop out to the west of St Dorothee. Most of the camptonites and monchiquites are fine-grained rocks that occur in dykes and sills; and approximately one-fifth of them carry ocelli that are composed of analcite- and/or nepheline-bearing trachytic materials. The ocelli are interpreted as being products of liquid immiscibility within a parental alkalic lamprophyric magma. Many of the Monteregian alnöites crop out in small plugs which are considered to have been emplaced explosively (cf. Philpotts 1974).

Niggli (1923) introduced the term *lamproite* to describe a group of lamprophyre-like subvolcanic, and extrusive, igneous rocks that are enriched in both potassium and magnesium. The high concentration of K_2O is usually reflected in an abundance of minerals such as leucite, phlogopite and potassium richterite. Typical lamproites include *cedricite, fitzroyite, mamilite, orendite, wolgidite* and *wyomingite*. The type-areas of all these rocks are either the West Kimberley region of Western Australia (Mt Cedric, Fitzroy Basin, Mamilu Hill and Wolgidee Hills; cf. Prider 1960) or the Leucite Hills is south-western Wyoming, USA (Orenda Butte and the state of Wyoming; cf. Carmichael 1967b). These rocks are essentially phonolitic leucitites or leucitites, but they generally have a distinctive chemical composition in that they are ultrapotassic (that is, $K_2O \approx 10$ per cent) and silica-saturated (that is, their normative quartz or leucite + nepheline contents do not exceed 5 per cent). The anomaly of leucite-rich rocks being saturated in silica is explained by: (a) the presence of a large amount of SiO_2 in the leucite (that is ideal leucite contains 55.0 per cent SiO_2, 23.4 per cent Al_2O_3 and 21.6 per cent K_2O), and (b) the presence of a quartz-normative interstitial glass in many of these rocks. These lamproites differ from most other leucitites in that they tend to be strongly peralkaline, and carry normative acmite (aegirine) and potassium metasilicate ($K_2O.Si_2O$). Many of these lamproites carry the unusual accessory mineral wadeite ($Zr_2K_4Si_6O_{18}$). The chemical compositions of a selection of these rocks is given in Table 12.6.2, which also reveals that the lamproites of Western Australia form a distinctive group of rocks that not only have high K_2O abundances, but also have remarkably high TiO_2 contents. In some areas, such as central West Greenland, the Ivory Coast and Western Australia, leucite lamproites are found associated with kimberlites (see Section 13.1).

Recently, diamond-bearing *olivine lamproites* have been described from the Prairie Creek diatreme of Arkansas, USA, and from a number of diatremes in the Ellendale and Argyle areas of north-western Australia (cf. Atkinson et al. 1984; Jaques et al. 1984; Smith and Skinner 1984). Field, petrographic and geochemical studies have shown that the olivine lamproites of the extensive Ellendale Petrographic Province grade via leucite-bearing olivine–diopside lamproites into the well-known leucite lamproites. According to Atkinson et al. (1984: 213), there are forty-five bodies of lamproite in this province, and twenty-seven of them are mainly composed of leucite lamproite, fourteen are olivine lamproites, and four are leucite–olivine lamproites. Four of the bodies that mainly contain olivine lamproites also contain minor amounts of leucite lamproite. The lamproites of the West Kimberley region are of Miocene (≈ 20 Ma) age, and most of them contain diamonds. The most diamondiferous of these rocks are the olivine lamproites, particularly the tuffaceous varieties. In the Halls Creek Mobile Zone, north-east of the Ellendale Petrographic Province, is the highly diamondiferous Argyle Diatreme. At the present level of exposure, the Argyle Diatreme is essentially composed of a variety of weakly-bedded crystal-lithic tuffs, cut by dyke-like bodies of olivine lamproite (Atkinson et al. 1984). The tuffs usually contain lamproite clasts set in a groundmass of olivine crystals comminuted lamproitic material and rounded quartz grains derived from the disaggregation of earlier sediments in the wall rocks surrounding the diatreme. According to Atkinson et al. (1984: 213), the intrusive olivine lamproites are essentially composed of altered phenocrysts of olivine (10–25 per cent) and phlogopite (15–30 per cent), set in a fine-grained potassium-rich groundmass. Minerals found in the groundmass include phlogopite, manganiferous ilmenite, titaniferous magnesiochromite, anatase, sphene, perovskite, apatite and sulphides. The Argyle Diatreme is remarkably rich in diamonds. In the period between late-1979 and mid-1982, sampling produced 47.56 kg (237 794 carats) of diamonds from 46 257 tonnes of olivine lamproite.

The lamprophyres range in composition from silica-oversaturated, via silica-saturated, to silica-undersaturated species, and their origin is controversial (cf. Joplin 1966; Rock 1977; Wimmenauer 1973; Yoder 1979b). Ordinary lamprophyres tend to occur in association with late orogenic, or anorogenic, granites, syenites, monzonites and other midly alkaline rocks. This group of lamprophyres is generally considered to have evolved from a hybrid magma that was produced by the mixing of an alkalic basaltic magma, particularly a potassium-rich basaltic magma, and the residual liquids in a partly crystallized body of plutonic rocks (see Section 9.5). Some of these ordinary lamprophyres appear to be directly related to ultramafic rocks of Appinite-type (see Section 11.10). The alkaline lamprophyres are generally interpreted as being derived from hydrous basanitic, or tephritic magmas that evolved in areas of crustal doming, and they may be emplaced during the early stages of continental rifting (cf. Brooks & Rucklidge 1973; Hansen 1980). Some of the alkaline lamprophyres, and most of the melilitic lamprophyres, occur in association with rocks of the carbonatite–nephelinitte–ijolite

Table 12.6.2 Chemical composition of selected lamproites (%)

	1	2	3	4	5	6	7
SiO_2	51.19	51.22	52.79	54.17	45.82	50.23	42.6
TiO_2	4.89	4.00	5.00	2.67	7.34	2.30	3.43
Al_2O_3	8.53	10.59	11.37	10.16	6.86	10.15	3.96
Fe_2O_3	6.12	6.91	5.41	3.34	6.07	3.65	*
FeO	1.38	1.33	1.83	0.65	1.98	1.21	8.43
MnO	0.06	0.05	0.07	0.06	0.10	0.09	0.14
MgO	7.15	6.67	4.84	6.62	10.90	7.48	25.0
CaO	5.82	2.34	2.21	4.19	4.70	6.12	5.05
Na_2O	0.58	0.07	0.45	1.21	0.84	1.29	0.52
K_2O	9.02	11.90	11.40	11.91	8.82	10.48	4.45
H_2O^+	1.99	2.04	1.49	1.01	2.40	2.34	4.96
H_2O^-	1.26	1.04	1.04	0.52	0.75	1.09	*
P_2O_3	0.79	1.33	1.03	1.59	1.83	1.81	1.27
CO_2	—	—	—	0.49	0.08	—	0.18
BaO	0.60	0.80	1.23	0.59	1.27	0.61	—
ZrO_2	—	—	—	0.22	—	0.25	—

1. Cedricite from Mt Gytha, Fitzroy Basin, Western Australia (after Wade & Prider 1940: 75).
2. Fitzroyite from Mamilu Hill, Fitzroy Basin, Western Australia (after Prider 1960: 84).
3. Mamilite from Mamilu Hill, Fitzroy Basin, Western Australia (after Prider 1960: 84).
4. Orendite from North Table Butte, Leucite Hills, Wyoming, USA (after Carmichael 1967b: 50).
5. Wolgidite from Mt North, Fitzroy Basin, Western Australia (after Wade & Prider 1940: 75).
6. Wyomingite drom a dyke margin, Boars Tusk, Leucite Hills, Wyoming, USA (after Carmichael 1967b: 50).
7. Mean chemical composition of twenty-one olivine lamproites from the Ellendale Petrographic Province, Western Australia (after Jaques et al 1984: 254) *Recalculated free of Fe_2O_3 and H_2O^-.

suite. The origin of this rock association is discussed in Section 14.5, and it is concluded that these rocks are usually derived from a melanephelinitic parental magma. Alnöite is often considered to have chemical, and possibly genetic, affinities, not only with the carbonatites, but also with the kimberlites (see Table 12.6.3).

The lamproites tend to occur in association with kimberlites; and they are often interpreted as having evolved from kimberlitic (sensu lato) parental magmas that differentiated, and were possibly contaminated by crustal materials, on their passage to the surface. For example, according to Scott (1979: 203), the lamproites of central West Greenland evolved during the relatively slow upward movement of batches of kimberlitic magma. Olivine and spinel crystallized first, and were removed at depth; and at higher levels the protolamproite magma was further modified by the crystallization of other phases such as diopside and phlogopite. Mitchell (1981: 250) has, however, demonstrated that the low-pressure compositional trends of the phlogopites from the leucite lamproites of Western Australia are very different from those found in the phlogopites characteristic of normal kimberlites; and he claims that the lamproites are 'unlikely to be low to moderate pressure

Table 12.6.3 Chemical composition of the melilitic lamprophyres (%)

	1	2
SiO_2	30.05	29.25
TiO_2	1.62	2.54
Al_2O_3	9.64	8.80
Fe_2O_3	2.12	3.92
FeO	9.10	5.42
MnO	0.99	—
MgO	16.15	17.66
CaO	17.65	17.86
Na_2O	2.91	0.77
K_2O	1.94	2.45
H_2O^+	3.72	2.61
P_2O_5	0.91	2.86
CO_2	3.58	—

1. Polzenite (variety vesecite) from the Polzen area of the Bohemian Massif, Czechoslovakia (after Wimmenauer 1974: 261).
2. Alnöite from Norrvik, Alnö Island (after von Eckermann 1948: chemical analysis numbers 73).

differentiates of kimberlite'. Jaques et al. (1984: 251) have recently proposed that the olivine lamproites of Western Australia were generated by a low degree of partial melting of an upper mantle harzburgite that had been strongly enriched in K and other incompatible elements.

12.7 Petrogenesis

It is evident that no single parental magma is able to produce all the alkaline rocks, because they occur in so many different tectonic settings, petrological associations and have such diverse chemical compositions. Their occurrence on oceanic islands and seamounts demonstrates that at least some of the parental magmas responsible for these rocks can be generated within the mantle; and also that these magmas can evolve in an environment far removed from any possible contamination by continental crustal materials. The *nephelinitic rock association* of the Hawaiian Islands is a striking example of oceanic intraplate alkaline volcanic activity.

During the first half of this century the alkaline rocks were generally considered to have evolved within the crust, and most petrogenetic models consisted of descriptions of processes that supposedly modified basaltic, or granitic, magmas and changed them into alkaline magmas (cf. Gittins 1979: 381). These models employed processes, such as: (a) gaseous transfer within a body of magma (see Section 2.2); (b) assimilation of crustal materials, particularly limestone (see Section 2.5); and (c) the fractional resorption of complex minerals, such as biotite/phlogopite or hornblende (cf. Wones 1979). In the past twenty years, concepts concerning the origin of the alkaline rocks have changed, and most petrologists now believe that the majority have evolved from parental magmas generated by partial melting within the mantle; and also that fractional crystallization, and other differentiation processes, are usually only able to accentuate an alkaline tendency that has already been imparted to the parental magma. It is thus proposed that the evolution of alkaline rocks is usually a two-stage process that consists of partial melting in an upper mantle source region, followed by magmatic differentiation at higher levels within the lithosphere. This model does not exclude the possibility that some alkaline rocks are generated by the partial melting of lower continental crustal materials. Such rocks may begin to melt as the result of: (a) the influx of volatile and incompatible elements from the underlying mantle; and/or (b) the relief of pressure resulting from crustal doming (cf. Bailey 1974).

It is now generally assumed that the alkalic picrites (Section 11.4), alkalic basalts (Section 5.17), basanites, melanephelinites, nephelinites (Ch. 14) and kimberlites (Ch. 13) all congealed from mantle-derived magmas; whereas the trachytes, phonolites and comendites are normally products of magmatic differentiation, possibly aided by the assimilation of crustal materials. As was noted in Section 7.7, the phonolites/nepheline syenites occupy one of the low-temperature troughs within the *thermal valley* in petrogeny's residua system. This means that silica-undersaturated alkalic basalt magmas, nephelinitic magmas and a variety of other silica-undersaturated magmas have liquid lines of descent that converge on the phonolite/nepheline syenite field in compositional space (see Fig. 7.7.1). The alkalic basaltic magmas probably pass through a trachytic stage in their fractional crystallization, whereas the basanitic and nephelinitic magmas follow more strongly undersaturated liquid lines of descent. Whereas petrogeny's residua system is useful in demonstrating how a variety of different silica-undersaturated alkaline magmas are able to produce phonolitic rocks, it is probably too simple a chemical system to accurately simulate the fractional crystallization of all magmas that enter the phonolitic composition field, particularly peralkaline magmas that are precipitating alkalic mafic phases, such as aegirine or aenigmatite.

The Erebus Volcanic Province, in the McMurdo Sound area of Antarctica, is an ideal area to study the evolution of phonolitic rocks, as it contains a full succession of rocks that range from basanites to phonolites; and at the present time, Mt Erebus Volcano contains a lava lake of phonolitic composition (see Section 2.6). These rocks range in age from the Late Miocene to the present, and they crop out in an area of crustal thinning and rifting. According to Kyle (1981: 495), the parental basanitic magma was generated by a small amount (1–7 per cent) of partial melting of garnet peridotite source materials at a depth of at least 80 km; and the tephritic and phonolitic rocks evolved as the result of the fractional crystallization of this magma; that is, with the crystallization and removal of olivine, clinopyroxene, plagioclase, Fe–Ti oxides, apatite and, occasionally, kaersutite.

As was noted in Section 12.4, most of the Phanerozoic alkaline rocks of the continental areas are associated with lithospheric doming, crustal doming and/or rifting. Some of the important characteristics of this type of magmatic activity include: (a) the occurrence of resurgent alkaline magmatism in some areas; (b) the presence of metasomatised, often glimmeritic, mantle xenoliths in the least differentiated of these alkaline rocks; (c) the extrusion and intrusion of rocks that are significantly enriched in volatile components, particularly species in the subsystem H–C–O, the halogens and the incompatible elements. According to Bailey (1983), alkaline magmatic activity is essentially controlled by the release of volatile-charged magmas from deep mantle sources. Fractures through the continental lithosphere act as channelways for these magmas, and the volatiles and incompatible elements from relatively large reservoirs within the mantle are drained through narrow fractures and rift zones. The latter process results in metasomatism, and/or partial melting and expansion in the mantle and crustal rocks bordering the channelways; and the composition of the ascending magma is to a large extent controlled by wall-rock reactions and polybaric fractional crystallization. Heat from the magma results in a gradual increase in the amount of partial melting and, depending on the composition of the materials being melted and the physical conditions prevailing in the area where the melting occurs, a wide variety of different magmas may be generated. They may possibly range from kimberlitic magmas, that move rapidly up deep-seated fracture zones and react very little with their wall rocks, to silicic alkaline rocks that evolve from magmas generated by the partial melting of strongly metasomatised (or fenitized) crustal rocks (see chs 13 and 14).

It is proposed that the highly silica-undersaturated alkaline magmas, such as the basanites, melanephelinites and various primitive potassium-rich magmas, are normally generated within the upper mantle at a depth of at least 80 km; and that the generation of these magmas tends to be triggered by the influx of low-viscosity fluids from the deep mantle (that is, mantle degassing). Such fluids tend to be enriched in both volatile components and incompatible elements; and

they may be products of zone melting (cf. Harris 1957). Once formed, the evolution of these magmas is mainly controlled by tectonic conditions. Some magmas remain trapped within the upper mantle, where they eventually crystallize and release some of their dissolved volatile components, and thus promote metasomatism; whereas others encounter fractures, and this may result in their rapid upward movement through the lithosphere as described in Section 13.6. The influx of low-viscosity fluids from the deep mantle is considered to do one, or more, of the following: (a) directly trigger the generation of primary alkaline magmas; (b) cause metasomatism in the upper mantle and/or lower crust, and thus produce materials, such as glimmerite, that may be suitable source rocks for the generation of alkaline magmas at a later date; and (c) become mixed into a larger mass of picritic, or basaltic, magma that it encounters on its way through the upper mantle, or lower crust. It is significant to note that Spera (1981: 62) has estimated that the amount of heat transported by low-viscosity fluids, fluxing through the upper mantle, is sufficient to generate all the alkaline magma that is believed to form on Earth at the present time (see Section 1.5).

12.8 Selected references

Gupta, A. K. & **Yagi, K.** (1980) *Petrology and genesis of leucite-bearing rocks*, Springer-Verlag Berlin.

Le Bas, M. J. (1977) *Carbonatite–Nephelinite Volcanism: An African Case History*, John Wiley & Sons, London.

Sørensen, H. (ed.) (1974) *The Alkaline Rocks*, John Wiley & Sons, London.

CHAPTER 13

KIMBERLITES

13.1 General statement

Kimberlites are rare alkalic (usually potassic) ultramafic rocks (see section 11.1). They are important because they contain a singular assemblage
of minerals and xenoliths that have been shown
by experimental petrology to have formed at
higher pressures, and presumably at greater
depths, than the solid phases found in any other
type of rocks known to occur at the surface of
the Earth; and kimberlites are also important
because they may contain diamonds in economic
quantities. The chemical and modal compositions of the mantle-derived xenoliths found in
kimberlites are given in section 1.10. According
to Dawson (1980: 2–3), the first kimberlites were
described by Vanuxem in 1837 from Ludlowville
near Ithaca, New York State. However, the term
kimberlite was introduced by Lewis (1887) to
describe the diamond-bearing, porphyritic mica
peridotites of the Kimberley area of S. Africa.
As originally defined, the term described an
idea, rather than a fixed composition in a systematic classification of igneous rocks; and the idea
was that kimberlites are rare ultramafic rocks
that contain diamonds, together with variable
amounts of xenocrysts and xenoliths. Diamond
is, however, only a rare accessory mineral in
kimberlites. For example, even in the very 'high-
grade' Mir diatreme in the Yakutia Kimberlite
Province of the USSR, the kimberlite contains
only one part diamond to every one and a half
million parts of kimberlite (cf. Sobolev 1977).

The petrography of kimberlites is both unusual, and complex, because: (a) they are hybrid
rocks that contain minerals, rock fragments and
congealed magmatic materials that formed in diverse physical and chemical environments; and
(b) they vary greatly in modal composition.
Olivine, serpentine group minerals, phlogopite,
garnet (usually pyrope), pyroxenes (diopside,
enstatite and/or bronzite), carbonate minerals
(usually calcite), monticellite, magnesian ilmenite, aluminous-magnesian chromite and perovskite are the minerals usually found in
kimberlites; however, the relative abundance of
these minerals in different rocks varies greatly,
and their bulk chemical compositions also vary
in response to these modal differences. There are
thus no simple modal, or chemical, criteria for
defining the term kimberlite; yet as they are rare
rocks, it would not be of much use to coin a series of terms to describe each kimberlitic rock
that differed in modal and/or chemical composition from the type-rock in Kimberley, S. Africa. In order to placate both the systematic
petrographers and the specialized kimberlite
petrologists, it is proposed that the term *kimberlite
kindred* should be used to describe this diverse
group of alkalic ultramafic rocks that contain a
unique assemblage of xenocrysts and/or xenoliths that equilibrated in a mantle environment
where diamond is stable. Mitchell (1970: 692)
defined kimberlite as

'a porphyritic, alkalic peridotite, containing
rounded and corroded phenocrysts of olivine
(serpentinized, carbonatized, or fresh) phlogopite (fresh or chloritized) magnesian ilmenite,
pyrope and chrome-rich pyrope set in a fine-
grained groundmass composed of second generation olivine and phlogopite together with calcite
(and/or dolomite), serpentine (and/or chlorite),
magnetite, perovskite, and apatite. Diamond
and garnet peridotite xenoliths may or may not
occur.'

More recently Clement *et al.* (1984: 223–4)
have reported on their study of several hundred
specimens of kimberlite from Africa, the Americas, China, Greenland, India and the USSR,
and they have concluded that the term kimberlite
(*sensu stricto*) can be defined as

'a volatile-rich, potassic, ultrabasic, igneous rock
which occurs as small volcanic pipes, dykes and
sills. It has a distinctively inequigranular texture
resulting from the presence of macrocrysts set in a
finer-grained matrix. This matrix contains, as
prominent primary phenocrystal and/or groundmass constituents, olivine and several of the
following minerals: phlogopite, carbonate

(commonly calcite, serpentine, clinopyroxene, diopside), monticellite, apatite, spinels, perovskite and ilmenite. The macrocryst are anhedral, mantle-derived, ferromagnesian minerals which include olivine, phlogopite, picroilmenite, chromian spinel, magnesian garnet, clinopyroxene (commonly chromian diopside), and orthopyroxene (commonly enstatite). Olivine is extremely abundant relative to the other macrocrysts, all of which are not necessarily present. The macrocrysts and relatively early-formed matrix minerals are commonly altered by deuteric processes, mainly serpentinization and carbonatization.'

Clement *et al.* (1984, p. 224) also note that kimberlites commonly contain ultramafic xenoliths derived from the upper mantle, and variable quantities of crustal xenoliths and xenocrysts.

Kimberlitic rocks are often difficult to recognize in the field. For example, Bardet (1973: 15–17) has described Precambrian *metakimberlites* from the Ivory Coast and Gabon. In the field, these rocks look like elongate bodies of schist; and they are particularly difficult to identify because they do not contain the usual indicator minerals (pyrope garnet and chrome diopside); however, they are diamond-bearing. At Seguela in the Ivory Coast the metakimberlites are associated with *leucite lamproites*. As we have already noted in Section 12.6, the lamproites of north-western Australia are often closely associated with kimberlites, and many of these lamproites are diamondiferous and contain mantle-derived xenoliths.

13.2 Modal composition and texture

In the previous section it was recorded that the modal compositions of the rocks of the kimberlite kindred vary greatly. Olivine is usually the most abundant mineral, but it may be partly, or completely, replaced by secondary minerals (for example, serpentine group minerals). Some kimberlitic rocks contain three generations of olivine: (a) large rounded olivine megacrysts (long axis greater than 3.5 mm) with compositions in the range Fo_{84-86}; (b) medium-sized megacrysts with compositions that are often more magnesium-rich than Fo_{90}; and (c) small groundmass olivines with compositions that are intermediate between the other two types. The megacrystal olivines generally have a low CaO content (that is, less than 0.1 per cent), and this is interpreted

as indicating that they crystallized in a 'deep-seated' environment (cf. Simkin & Smith 1970). The abundance of phlogopite and carbonate minerals is also highly variable; and according to some petrologists, kimberlites can be divided into three groups: (a) *kimberlites* (*sensu stricto*); (b) *micaceous kimberlites*; and (c) *calcareous kimberlites*, depending on the proportions of olivine, phlogopite and carbonate minerals that are present.

Kimberlitic rocks normally have porphyritic and/or pyroclastic textures, and the fragmental appearance of many of these rocks is enhanced by the occurrence of xenoliths. Most rocks contain megacrysts that are set in a finer-grained groundmass that tends to contain microphenocrysts. The megacrysts are both xenocrysts and phenocrysts, and they typically consist of olivine, phlogopite, magnesian ilmenite, garnet and pyroxene. They are usually set in a groundmass of serpentine group minerals and/or carbonate minerals, together with microphenocrysts of Fe–Ti oxides, micas, spinels, perovskite, pyroxenes, monticellite and apatite. Rocks from kimberlitic diatremes generally display fragmental and/or pyroclastic structures and textures; whereas the kimberlitic rocks that occur in dykes and sills usually have normal porhyritic textures, and they may even have chilled margins and flow structures. Except for Mwadui in Tanzania and Orapa in Botswana few of the Kimberlite diatremes are over a square kilometre in area, and many of them are less than a hectare in area. Some, such as the Mwadui, Catoca in Angola, and Zarnitsa in Siberia, have circular surface shapes; whereas others, such as Hololo in Lesotho, have elongated shapes. In three-dimensions, most diatremes form narrow inverted cones that taper gently with increasing depth (Hawthorne 1973: 163). At depth the diatremes usually pass into dykes, however, some have been found to intrude these dykes; Many show evidence that they evolved as the result of multiple intrusions. According to Wagner (1914), the kimberlitic diatreme, that became the Kimberley Mine in South Africa, consists of fifteen different intrusive units. Kimberlitic diatremes generally occur in clusters, and the dykes often occur in swarms. Not all of these dykes are linear in outcrop; for example, a kimberlitic ring-dyke has been reported from Yengema in Sierra Leone (cf. Dawson 1980: 7). Most kimberlitic dykes are narrow (<2 m) but long; for example, one has been traced for 65 km in the Winburg District of

S. Africa (cf. Dawson 1980: 33). Kimberlitic sills are rare, as are extrusive rocks of kimberlitic composition. A tuff-ring of kimberlitic composition has been described from near Kasma in Mali; and calcareous kimberlitic lava has been described from the Igwisi Hills of Tanzania (cf. Fozzard 1956). The 'meimechites' of Meimecha-Kotui in Siberia have also been called kimberlitic lavas; however, they are probably picrites (cf. Egorov 1970: 344).

13.3 Geochemistry

The major element compositions of most rocks of the kimberlite kindred are broadly similar to those of normal olivine-rich ultramafic rocks, except that the kimberlitic rocks are usually enriched in TiO_2, K_2O and P_2O_5 (see Table 13.3.1). While it is recognized that the concept of the

Table 13.3.1 Chemical composition of rocks of the kimberlite kindred (%)

	1	2	3	4	5
SiO_2	27.64	33.21	33.2	36.12	36.36
TiO_2	1.65	1.97	2.41	1.45	0.98
Al_2O_3	3.17	4.45	3.97	4.38	5.13
Fe_2O_3	5.40	6.78	9.36*	6.80	7.71*
FeO	2.75	3.43	—	2.68	—
MnO	0.13	0.17	0.16	0.22	0.16
MgO	24.31	22.78	23.56	22.82	17.43
CaO	14.13	9.36	9.82	8.33	11.16
Na_2O	0.23	0.19	0.48	0.29	0.42
K_2O	0.79	0.79	1.87	5.04	1.52
H_2O^+	7.89	8.04	—	4.89	—
H_2O^-	—	2.66	—	1.28	—
CO_2	10.84	4.58	5.16	3.80	—
P_2O_5	0.55	0.65	1.68	1.46	0.55

* Total iron as Fe_2O_3.

1. Average chemical composition of 623 Yakutian kimberlites (after Ilupin and Lutts 1971). This rock also contains 0.14 per cent Cr_2O_3 and 0.24 per cent S.
2. Average chemical composition of twenty-five Lesotho kimberlites (after Gurney and Ebrahim 1973: 283). This rock also contains 0.17 per cent Cr_2O_3 and 0.28 per cent S.
3. Average chemical composition of fourteen kimberlitic autoliths from the Wesselton Diamond Mine, S. Africa (after Danchin et al. 1975). This rock also contains 0.42 per cent Cr_2O_3 and 7.51 per cent 'loss on ignition minus CO_2'.
4. Chemical composition of a 'highly micaceous kimberlite' from the New Elands Diamond Mine, Boshof, S. Africa (after Dawson 1972: 302).
5. Average chemical composition of eighty South African kimberlites (after Gurney and Ebrahim 1973: 283). This rock also contains 0.22 per cent Cr_2O_3.

average chemical composition of the kimberlite kindred may be misleading, because individual kimberlitic rocks vary greatly in both their modal and chemical compositions, it is interesting to examine Wedepohl and Muramatsu's (1979: 301–2) data on the chemical composition of the 'average kimberlite' and the 'average ultramafic rock'. Their data shows that Li, F, P, K, Ti, Rb, Sr, Zr, Nb, Sn, Ba, Pr, Nd, Sm, Eu, Gd, Hf, Ta, Tl and Pb are enriched in the 'average kimberlite' by a factor of between 10 and 100; whereas C, Cs, La, Ce, Th and U are enriched in the 'average kimberlite' by a factor greater than 100 (see Table 13.3.2). The rocks of the kimberlite kindred thus have major element abundances that are essentially akin to the normal olivine-rich ultramafic rocks, but their incompatible element abundances are much higher than those of the 'average ultramafic rock'. Minor differences in chemical composition usually exist between the kimberlitic rocks that were emplaced as dykes; and those that were emplaced as diatremes. The dykes usually contain fewer xenoliths of crustal origin, and tend to have retained more of their primary volatile components; whereas the kimberlitic materials in the diatremes usually show evidence of having interacted with surface groundwaters while cooling.

13.4 Abundance and distribution

Rocks of the kimberlite kindred are widely distributed throughout south (S. Africa, Namibia, Botswana, Swaziland, Lesotho and Angola), central (Zaire, Central Africa Republic and Tanzania) and west (Ghana, Guinea, Ivory Coast, Liberia, Mali, Gabon and Sierra Leone) Africa; and at present Africa produces most of the gem and industrial diamonds that are sold on the world market. The kimberlitic rocks of Africa were mainly emplaced into old cratonic areas, such as the Kaapvaal Craton in the south, the Congo Craton in the centre and the West African Craton in the north-west. Another area that contains many outcrops of rocks of the kimberlite kindred is the Yakutian Province that lies within the East Siberian Platform in the USSR. Other important petrographic provinces that contain rocks of the kimberlite kindred include: (a) the Navajo-Hopi Province of south-western USA; (b) the Brazilian Province; (c) the South-

Table 13.3.2 The chemical composition of the 'average kimberlite' compared with the chemical composition of the 'average ultramafic rock' (after Wedepohl & Muramatsu 1979: 301–2)

Element in p.p.m.	Average kimberlite (K)	Average ultramafic rock (U)	$\frac{K}{U}$
Li	25	2	12.5
Be	≈1	≈0.4	≈2.5
B	36	7	5.1
C	16 200	100	162
F	1 900	97	19.6
Na	2 030	2 230	0.91
Mg	160 000	247 500	0.64
Al	18 900	14 300	1.3
Si	147 000	203 300	0.72
P	3 880	220	17.6
S	2 000	≈4 000	0.5
Cl	300	110	2.7
K	10 400	390	26.7
Ca	70 400	27 200	2.6
Sc	15	15	1.0
Ti	11 800	780	15.1
V	120	50	2.4
Cr	1 100	3 090	0.36
Mn	1 160	1 040	1.1
Fe	71 600	64 830	1.1
Co	77	110	0.7
Ni	1 050	1 450	0.72
Cu	80	47	1.7
Zn	80	56	1.4
Ga	≈10	2.5	≈4
Ge	≈0.5	1	≈0.5
Se	0.15	0.02	7.5
Rb	65	1.2	54.1
Sr	740	22	33.6
Y	22	2.88	7.6
Zr	250	16	15.6
Nb	110	1.3	84.6
Mo	≈0.5	0.2	≈2.5
Pd	0.053	0.01	5.3
Cd	0.07	0.06	1.2
Sn	15	0.52	28.8
Cs	2.3	0.006	383
Ba	1 000	20	50
La	150	0.92	163
Ce	200	1.93	104
Pr	22	0.32	68.8
Nd	85	1.44	59
Sm	13	0.40	32.5
Eu	3.0	0.16	18.8
Gd	8.0	0.74	10.8
Tb	1.0	0.12	8.3
Ho	0.55	0.16	3.4
Er	1.45	0.40	3.6
Tm	0.23	0.067	3.4
Yb	1.2	0.38	3.2
Lu	0.16	0.065	2.5
Hf	7	0.6	11.7
Ta	9	≤0.1	≥90
Pt	0.19	0.06	3.2
Au	0.004	0.007	0.57

Table 13.3.2 (*Cont'd*)

Element in p.p.m.	Average kimberlite (K)	Average ultramafic rock (u)	$\frac{K}{u}$
Hg	0.01	0.03	0.33
Tl	0.22	0.010	22
Pb	10	0.20	50
Bi	0.03	0.006	5.0
Th	16	0.07	229
U	3.1	0.025	124

ern and Central Indian Provinces; and (d) the North and East Kimberley provinces of western Australia. Isolated occurrences of kimberlites are found in other areas within the USA, Canada, Greenland, Finland, USSR, China, Argentina, Australia and Malaita in the Solomon Islands (cf. Dawson: 1980). Rocks of the kimberlite kindred vary greatly in age; that is from the Proterozoic to the Cenozoic. In some areas such as the Kaapvaal Craton, kimberlitic rocks of three different ages are known.

Most kimberlite-bearing diatremes are considered to lie on deep-seated fracture zones. For example, within the Kaapvaal Craton a single fracture system, called the *Lesotho trend*, controls the emplacement of kimberlitic materials in a zone that is approximately 600 km long and 280 km wide (Crockett & Mason 1968). The Kimberley area of southern Africa contains a high concentration of kimberlite-bearing diatremes, and it is located where the Lesotho trend fracture system intersects two other deep-seated fracture systems. A similar structural environment is believed to have controlled the emplacement of most of the kimberlitic rocks of the Yakutian Province in the USSR. The most consistent feature observed when considering the world-wide distribution of the rocks of the kimberlite kindred is their tendency to concentrate in old continental cratonic areas (cf. Daly 1933: 552). At present, old cratonic areas are characterized by low heat-flow values, and this characteristic was probably typical of similar cratonic areas in the past. It is thus likely that the magmas, from which the rocks of the kimberlite kindred evolved, were emplaced into a segment of the lithosphere that had low geothermal gradients. Such a segment of the lithosphere would probably provide a suitable location for the development of deep-seated fractures; and if the cooler rock of which it was composed did not contain zones of partial melting, this would also help promote the upward movement of magmas from deep within the mantle.

Petrographic studies have also revealed that the compositions of the rocks of the kimberlite kindred change in a regular manner within the Kaapvaal Craton of S. Africa and the Yakutian Province of the East Siberian Craton. At the centre of both of these cratons, the rocks of the kimberlite kindred contain significant quantities of both pyrope garnet and diamond. These rocks are surrounded by a zone in which the rocks of the kimberlite kindred are relatively depleted in both of these minerals. Beyond this zone the kimberlitic rocks do not normally carry either pyrope garnet or diamond, and in this outer zone they are characteristically found in association with other rocks, such as olivine leucitites, alkalic picrites, olivine melilitites, alnöites and carbonatites.

13.5 Emplacement

Kimberlitic magmas have to move rapidly through the lithosphere in order: (a) to transport the relatively high-density xenoliths of mantle origin that they usually contain (see Section 1.10); and (b) to prevent the resorption, or inversion, of the diamonds they contain. Experimental studies of the primary phases found in kimberlites, and some of their mantle-derived xenoliths, demonstrate that kimberlitic magmas are likely to have equilibrated with mantle materials at depths of at least 200 km. It is thus postulated that the parental magma of the kimberlite kindred is likely to be transported rapidly through the lithosphere (7–20 m/s) from depths of approximately 200 km (cf. Anderson 1979). The parental magma is only likely to be able to move rapidly when it encounters a deep-seated fracture. If this occurs, a low-viscosity fluid phase may separate from the magma and wedge open the fracture; and according to Anderson (1979), the speed at which the fracture is prised open is regulated by the velocity at which the magma moves into the fracture. There is no cogent reason to postulate that the first batch of magma moves up at a velocity in excess of 7 m/s, or that it comes from a depth of 200 km. It is more likely that a vent system develops gradually, and that the later batches come directly from greater depths and travel at higher velocities.

13.6 Petrogenesis

The rocks of the kimberlite kindred are a paradox, as they generally have major element compositions that are similar to primitive picrites; yet they are also enriched in the incompatible elements, and enrichment of this type is characteristically found in more differentiated rocks (see Table 13.3.2). Any hypothesis that attempts to account for the origin of kimberlitic magma has to be able to explain how such ultramafic magmas can come to contain significant concentrations of the incompatible elements. Wagner (1914), in his important book on *The Diamond Fields of Southern Africa*, and other more recent authors have proposed that kimberlitic magmas are generated in a source region that is relatively deep within the mantle, and the magmas are the products of a low degree of partial melting. This petrogenetic model is sometimes called the *incipient melting hypothesis*. The geochemical and experimental data that are at present available seem to indicate that this hypothesis would only work if the source materials had a special composition; that is, they were phlogopite-bearing garnet lherzolites, or garnet lherzolites veined with glimmerite (see Section 1.10; cf. Dawson 1980: 213). However, if one postulates source materials that are enriched in the incompatible elements, one is really shying away from the troublesome question of how these elements become concentrated.

Experimental studies by Wyllie and Huang (1975), and others, have shown that kimberlitic magmas are most likely to be generated by the partial melting of suitable peridotitic materials when CO_2 is present in the source region. Eggler and Wendlandt (1979) have confirmed this, and their experimental studies indicate that, at pressures of between 5.0–6.0 GPa, the initial partial melt, of a phlogopite-bearing garnet lherzolite

source rock in the presence of CO_2 and H_2O, is likely to be kimberlitic in composition. They (330) also suggest that at pressures greater than 5.0 GPa, kimberlitic liquids might be relatively common within the mantle and that 'the rarity of kimberlites as rocks may be attributed to the rarity of tectonic settings conducive to the ascent of appropriate magmas'.

Another hypothesis that has been proposed to account for the origin of kimberlitic magma is known as the *residual liquid hypothesis* (cf. Du Toit 1920; Verschure 1966; O'Hara & Yoder 1967). This petrogenetic model is usually linked with the concept that there is possibly a genetic connection between the extrusion of floods of tholeiitic basalt and the later emplacement of kimberlites. According to Verschure (1966: 1388), at the termination of a period of active mantle convection and the extrusion of flood basalts, pockets of tholeiitic basalt (or picrite) magma remained in the upper mantle. This magma cools under high-pressure conditions and pyrope and omphacite precipitate instead of plagioclase and augite (that is, eclogite assemblage). Fractional crystallization results in the settling of the garnets, and this yields a residual liquid enriched in alkalis. Under favourable conditions, a kimberlitic residual magma is eventually 'explosively ejected' from the deep-seated source region. A corollary to this hypothesis is that kimberlitic rocks, and their eclogitic enclosures, should be of the same age; however, this supposition is not supported by radiometric dating (cf. Allsopp et al. 1969). This residual liquid hypothesis is often presented in such a way that it implies that kimberlitic magmas are generated at lower pressures than is indicated by many of the megacrysts and xenoliths they contain. Gupta and Yagi (1979) have attempted to test the residual liquid hypothesis by studying the process of separating eclogitic phases from picritic magmas at high pressures. They conclude that this process usually produces a nephelinitic liquid, but if the source material is nepheline-normative it is likely to produce a liquid that is more kimberlitic in composition.

In order to explain why kimberlitic rocks contain high incompatible element abundances, and also why they normally contain megacrysts and xenoliths that equilibrated at high pressures, Harris and Middlemost (1970) proposed that kimberlitic magmas are generated in a two-stage process. In the first stage a tenuous magma, enriched in volatile components (mainly species in the subsystem H–C–O), and possibly generated by volatiles degassing from the deep mantle, rises by means of *zone melting* from a depth of approximately 600 km. As was noted in Section 1.6, the unique feature of zone melting is that it is able to concentrate the incompatible elements, from a large volume of essentially solid material, in a relatively small volume of magma. At higher levels in the upper mantle (260 km), the relatively hot, volatile and incompatible element-enriched tenuous magma induces partial melting to occur in the garnet Iherzolite mantle rock. The new magma, which is in equilibrium with the essential solid phases present at this depth in the upper mantle, is picritic in major element composition, but significantly enriched in the incompatible elements (cf. Wyllie 1980). Under ideal conditions, such a kimberlitic magma rises rapidly (12 m/s) towards the surface from a depth of at least 200 km. At 200 km, the kimberlite material is essentially a magma, but as it rises to higher levels it becomes a mechanical mixture of liquid magma, phenocrysts, xenocrysts, xenoliths, together with a large volume of a separate low-viscosity fluid phase. As this quasi-magma is propelled upwards through a variety of different physical and chemical environments, changes occur as the many phases of which it is composed attempt to adjust to the changing physical environment; and the phases also react with one another and the surrounding wall rocks. The first batch of quasi-magma that bursts explosively through to the surface is likely to produce a *maar*, or a low-relief coneless crater, that is surrounded by a *crater-ring* of kimberlitic pyroclastic materials. With the arrival of more batches of quasi-magma, the materials in the surface vents and contiguous feeder-dykes are entrained and mixed; and the solids are abraided in a vigorously-active fluidized system. Eventually the fluidized system collapses, and the different materials in the essentially degassed quasi-magma coalesce, and the typical rocks of the kimberlite kindred form as the result of this process, assisted by the crystallization and growth of a variety of low-temperature and low-pressure secondary minerals.

13.7 Selected references

Boyd, F. R & Meyer, H. O. A. (eds) (1979) *Kimberlites, Diatremes, and Diamonds: Their Geology, Petrology and Geochemistry*, Proc. 2nd Int. Kimberlite Conf., Am. Geophys. Union, Washington, DC, USA.

Dawson, J. B. (1980) *Kimberlites and their xenoliths*, Springer-Verlag, Berlin.

Nixon, P. H. (ed.) (1973) *Lesotho Kimberlites*, Lesotho Natl. Dev. Co., Maseru, Lesotho.

Sobolev, N. V. (1977) *Deep-seated inclusions in kimberlites and the problem of the composition of the Upper Mantle*, Am. Geophys. Union, Washington, DC, USA

Wagner, P. A. (1914) *The Diamond Fields of Southern Africa*, The Transvaal Leader, Johannesburg.

CHAPTER 14

CARBONATITES

14.1 General statement

Carbonatites are igneous rocks that contain more than 50 per cent of carbonate minerals (Streckeisen 1980). The term was introduced by Brögger (1921) who used it to describe a group of Early Cambrian carbonate-rich rocks from the Fen Ring Complex of south- eastern Norway. He proposed that the carbonatites, together with *ijolites*, and a variety of other associated silica-undersaturated 'alkaline rocks', were essentially of igneous origin. The outer boundary zone of the Fen Ring Complex consists of brecciated granitic country rocks that have been changed by metasomatic alteration into aegirine-bearing syenitic rocks that Brögger called *fenites*. Intense alkali metasomatism, or *fenitization*, is characteristic of most carbonatite complexes. The main products of this fenitization are usually orthoclase, together with a little limonite and/or hematite. In some carbonatite complexes, in which water-vapour pressures are believed to have been high, phlogopite is found instead of orthoclase; whereas in other complexes the fenites are sodic rather than potassic. Soda fenitization leads to the formation of *albitites*; such as those found associated with the carbonatites on Fuerteventura in the Canary archipelago. Some fenite aureoles contain both potassic and sodic fenites; for example, the principal carbonatite complexes of Malawi have outer sodic fenite aureoles that are replaced by inner potassic aureoles (cf. Woolley 1982: 14). Rubie and Gunter (1983: 165) claim that fenites show a progression from a high-temperature assemblage, consisting of sodium-rich alkali feldspar and a sodium-rich mafic mineral (for example, aegirine-augite) to an ex-treme potassic end-member assemblage consisting of pure potassium feldspar and iron oxide. They assert that the latter assemblage is only found in association with low-temperature carbonatites.

Both intrusive and extrusive carbonatites are found. Carbonatites may crop out as lava flows, deposits of tephra, dykes, sills, stocks or plugs; and carbonatite-like materials occur as ocelli, or as part of the groundmass, in some kimberlites and lamprophyric rocks. In Chapter 13 it was recorded that some kimberlites have a carbonate-rich groundmass (cf. Dawson & Hawthorne 1973). The intrusive carbonatites usually occur within ring-fracture intrusions, and are associated with alkalic pyroxenites, ijolites, syenites and fenites; whereas the extrusive carbonatites are characteristically found associated with *olivine-poor nephelinites* and *melanephelinites*. Nephelinites are extrusive rocks that contain more than 10 per cent modal nepheline, and little or no alkali feldspar. If there is more modal nepheline than mafic minerals, the rock is a nephelinite (sensu stricto); however, if the mafic minerals predominate, the rock is a *melanephelinite* (cf. Le Bas 1977: 34).

At present, most carbonatite volcanoes are found in eastern Uganda, western Kenya, northern Tanzania, and in the Registan Desert of Afghanistan. The active carbonatite volcano, *Oldoinyo Lengai*, is located approximately 16 km south of Lake Natron in the Eastern Rift of Tanzania (Dawson 1962). It is a steep-sided, cone-shaped volcano that rises approximately 2 km above the surrounding plains. The cone is mainly composed of nephelinitic and melanephelinitic tephra and flows, interbedded with carbonate tuffs, and partly covered by modern natro-carbonatite lavas and tephra. Vesicular calcite–carbonatite lava flows have been reported from the Fort Portal area of western Uganda (Von Knorring & Du Bois 1961); and calcite–carbonatite and magnesiocarbonatite lavas of Palaeozoic age have been reported from the Kola Peninsula of the USSR (Pyatenko & Saprykina 1976). Agglutinated calcite–carbonatite lapilli-tuffs, in which all the lapilli show forms acquired when droplets of a highly fluid liquid moved through the air, have been described from the Kaiserstuhl Complex of the Rhinegraben, W. Germany (Keller 1981).

Rocks of the carbonatite–ijolite–nephelinite association are more than mere petrological curiosities because: (a) they may contain minerals of economic importance; and (b) the detailed study of this association has provided new insights into the operation of some of the processes that generate the more abundant magmatic rocks. Carbonatite complexes have been found to contain economic deposits enriched in one, or more, of the following elements; Al, P, Ti, F, Fe, Cu, Zr, Nb, Ba, REE, Th and U; and research into the origin and evolution of the carbonatite–ijolite–nephelinite association has made petrologists reexamine their ideas concerning: (a) the nature of the transition from magmatic to metasomatic and hydrothermal processes; (b) the significance of carbon dioxide in volcanism, and in the generation of alkalic, silica-undersaturated rocks; (c) the role played by liquid immiscibility in magmatic differentiation; (d) the origin of peralkaline rocks; and (e) the relationship between the compositions of magmas and the tectonic environment in which they evolve.

Not all carbonate-rich rocks that occur in carbonatite complexes are interpreted as being entirely of magmatic origin. The large (20 km²) carbonatite at Sokli in northern Finland is considered to have a magmatic calcite–carbonatite core that is surrounded by a 1–2 km wide zone of impure carbonate-rich rock of metasomatic origin (cf. Vartiainen & Paarma 1979: 1296). Similar *metacarbonatites* have been described from other areas, such as the Wasaki Complex of western Kenya.

14.2 Modal composition and texture

Four main types of carbonatites are usually recognized: (a) *calcite–carbonatite*, which may be called *sövite* if coarse-grained and *alvikite* if finer-grained (b) *magnesiocarbonatite* which usually contains dolomite and/or ankerite; (c) *ferrocarbonatite* which is essentially composed of iron-rich carbonate minerals; and (d) *natrocarbonatite* which is essentially composed of Na–Ca–K carbonates (cf. Streckeisen 1979: 334; Woolley 1982: 16). Magmatic rocks that contain less than 10 per cent of primary carbonatite minerals are usually called calcite-, dolomite- or ankerite-bearing rocks (for example, calcite-bearing ijolite, dolomite-bearing alkalic peridotite etc.); whereas magmatic rocks that contain between 10 and 50 per cent carbonate minerals are usually called calcitic, dolomitic or ankeritic

rocks (for example, calcitic ijolite, dolomitic alkalic peridotite etc.). A group of high-level intrusive rocks that usually occur as explosion breccias or dykes in carbonatite complexes and have a broad range of compositions, that grade from phlogopite-bearing calcitic melanephelinites to phlogopite-bearing calcite carbonatites, are often grouped together and called *damkjernites* (cf. Kapustin 1981). The essential minerals in most carbonatites are calcite, dolomite or ankerite. They usually also contain at least some of the following minerals: apatite, phlogopite, magnetite, aegirine, aegirine-augite and pyrochlore $(Ca, Na)_2(Nb, Ta)_2O_6(O, OH, F)$. Less abundant accessory minerals include arfvedsonite, baddeleyite ZrO_2, baryte, bastnaesite $(Ce, La) CO_3 (F, OH)$, fluorite, melilite, monazite $Ce Po_4$, nepheline, olivine, orthoclase, parisite $(Ce, La)_2Ca(CO_3)_3F_2$, perovskite, pyrite, sphene and zircon (cf. Le Bas 1981: 134). The rare natrocarbonatites of Oldoinyo Lengai Volcano in northern Tanzania have quite different modal and chemical compositions (see Table 14.3.1). They are essentially composed of nyerereite $Na_2Ca (CO_3)_2$ with lesser amounts of fairchildite $K_2Ca (CO_3)_2$ in solid solution, and gregoryite which is approximately the anhydrous equivalent of nahcolite, together with a little calcite, and set in an interstitial glass phase (cf. McKie & Frankis 1977). According to Heinrich (1966: 163–4), the average calcite-carbonatite (sövite) from the Alnö carbonatite complex in Sweden contains approximately 76 per cent calcite, 7 per cent phologopite, 6 per cent apatite, 5 per cent sodic pyroxene and a wide variety of accessory phases. The high apatite content of these rocks is typical of most carbonatites, as are the large number of accessory phases. It has been estimated that at least 170 distinct mineral species occur in the carbonatites; and many of these minerals contain relatively rare elements such as F, Sr, Y, Nb, Ba, REE, Ta, Th and U. The modal compositions of the carbonatites are thus quite different from those of the normal silicate magmatic rocks that tend to contain relatively few phases, and the trace elements found in the silicate rocks tend to proxy for the major elements in the crystal structures of the common rock-forming minerals.

Many of the apatites found both in carbonatites and in associated rocks, such as ijolites, contain primary fluid inclusions (cf. Le Bas 1981: 137). These trapped fluids are usually enriched in Ca, Na, K, Cl, S, Ba and F (see Table 14.3.1, No. 6), and their bulk composition is essentially similar to that of the natrocarbonatites.

If such an alkali-rich magma was to evolve within the lithosphere, it would normally react with, and fenitize, the silicate country rocks and thus become less alkalic and more Ca- and Fe-rich than before. Fluid inclusion studies thus demonstrate that natrocarbonatite magmas may have been important in the evolution of many ijolite–carbonatite intrusive complexes that do not at present contain such materials.

14.3 Geochemistry

Woolley (1982: 16) has introduced a chemical method of classifying the common carbonatites excluding the natrocarbonatites. He uses a triangular diagram with CaO, MgO and (FeO + Fe_2O_3 + MnO) at the apices. Rocks that contain more than 80 wt.% of the CaO component are called calcite–carbonatites or sövites. The rest of the diagram is divided into two equal parts, the magnesiocarbonatites carry more MgO than (FeO + Fe_2O_3 + MnO), whereas the ferrocarbonatites carry more (FeO + Fe_2O_3 + MnO) than MgO. Table 14.3.1 gives a summary of the major element compositions of the various types of carbonatite. All these chemical analyses differ significantly from those of the main types of magmatic rocks that have been discussed in earlier chapters in that the carbonatites contain considerably less SiO_2 and more CO_2. Calcium, Fe, Mg, Mn, Na and K vary greatly between the different types of carbonatites; whereas Al and Ti usually occur at low abundance levels. When compared with crustal abundance data, and data obtained from sedimentary limestones, the carbonatites, as a group, are found to be strongly enriched in a variety of trace elements, such as F, P, S, Cl, Sr, Y, Zr, Nb, Mo, Ba, REE and Ta. Table 14.3.2 compares the abundances of some trace elements in carbonatites with those in an average limestone. This table also demon-

Table 14.3.1 Chemical composition of carbonatites (%)

	1	2	3	4	5	6	7	8
SiO_2	5.67	10.29	1.49	0.88	0.58	2.1	1.27	6.12
TiO_2	0.50	0.73	0.22	0.18	0.10	—	0.16	0.68
Al_2O_3	1.77	3.29	1.11	1.40	0.10	1.0	0.54	1.31
Fe_2O_3	8.00	3.46	6.97	3.81	0.29	—	2.24	7.09
FeO	—	3.60	—	0.36	—	0.9	—	—
MnO	0.78	0.68	1.58	0.65	0.14	—	0.32	0.75
MgO	6.10	5.79	1.62	0.38	1.17	—	0.58	12.75
CaO	37.06	36.10	46.29	50.83	15.54	19.8	52.36	29.03
Na_2O	1.09	0.42	0.34	0.48	29.56	26.3	0.12	0.14
K_2O	0.87	1.36	0.22	0.04	7.14	6.1	0.05	0.79
P_2O_5	1.73	2.09	1.63	1.02	0.95	—	1.47	2.66
H_2O^+	1.42	1.44	1.46	1.24	5.15	—	1.85	1.08
CO_2	32.16	28.52	33.97	37.57	31.7	29.2	37.4	37.03
F	0.38	0.81	—	—	2.26	1.4	—	0.09
Cl	0.31	—	—	—	2.90	6.9	—	—
SO_3	0.91	—	—	—	2.48	4.4	—	0.89
SrO	0.89	0.46	—	—	2.09	0.5	0.54	0.01
BaO	0.45	0.40	—	—	1.04	4.4	0.14	0.11

1. Mean chemical composition of 'some 200 complete and partial analyses' of carbonatites (Gold 1966: 84).
2. Mean chemical composition of the carbonatites (Heinrich 1966: 222) (S = 0.56 per cent).
3. Mean chemical composition of ten ferrocarbonatites from Western Kenya (Le Bas 1977: 318) (H_2O^- = 0.42).
4. Mean chemical composition of twelve medium- to fine-grained light-coloured calcite–carbonatites or alvikites from Western Kenya (Le Bas 1977: 317) (H_2O^- = 0.23).
5. Mean chemical composition of four natrocarbonatites, Oldoinyo Lengai Volcano, N. Tanzania (Le Bas 1981: 135).
6. Estimate of bulk composition of carbonatitic magma trapped in fluid inclusions in apatite crystals (Le Bas 1981: 135) (S = 0.2 per cent).
7. Chemical composition of calcite–carbonatitic lapilli from Henkenberg, Kaiserstuhl, Rhinegraben, W. Germany (Keller 1981: 429).
8. Chemical composition of magnesiocarbonatite (apatite-beforsite) dyke rock from Alnö, Sweden (Von Eckermann 1948: No. 99).

Table 14.3.2 Abundances of selected trace elements in carbonatites and an average limestone (after Le Bas 1981: 135)

	Carbonatite (p.p.m.)	Average limestone (p.p.m.)
Li	15–55	5
Sr	1000–7500	600
Y	10–130	9
Nb	50–1000	0.3
Ba	400–2900	90
La	160–1090	8
Ce	300–2320	12
Pb	10–150	9

strates how trace element data can be used to establish the magmatic nature of isolated bodies of carbonate-rich rock (cf. Crohn & Gellately 1968).

Detailed studies of the carbonatites of Malawi and western Kenya have demonstrated that the various carbonatitic rocks are usually emplaced in a definite sequence. This sequence begins with calcite–carbonatite, and proceeds via magnesio-carbonatite to ferrocarbonatite (cf. Le Bas 1977); and it corresponds to the fractional crystallization sequence determined experimentally for the system $CaCO_3 - MgCO_3 - FeCO_3$ (Wyllie 1965; Rosenberg 1967). Trace element data also support this differentiation model; for example, Sr decreases, and trace elements such as Ba and the REE increase, as one proceeds from the calcite–carbonatites to the ferrocarbonatites. The economic deposits of fluorite, REE, Th and U, that are found in some carbonatite complexes, are usually associated with the emplacement of the ferrocarbonatites. Oxygen and C stable isotope studies, and radiogenic isotope studies using Sr, Nd and Pb, all confirm that the carbonatites are normally derived from an upper mantle source region that is essentially similar to the one postulated for the generation of melanephelinite magma.

14.4 Abundance and distribution

The total volume of carbonatites in the crust of the Earth is believed to be very small, yet carbonatites are widely distributed on the continents, and they are also found on some oceanic islands, such as Fuerteventura in the Canary archipelago, and several of the islands in the Cape Verde Archipelago (cf. Silva et al. 1981). They usually occur within ring-complexes, or as extrusive rocks within volcanic edifices. The more common intrusive carbonatites tend to crop out as the cores of relatively small ($\bar{x}$ = 25 km²) elliptical, or circular, ring-complexes in which the carbonatites are normally intimately associated with rocks such as fenite, nepheline syenite, urtite, ijolite, melteigite and jacupirangite; whereas the extrusive carbonatites are usually associated with olivine-poor melanephelinite, olivine-poor nephelinites, phonolites and melilitites. Napak Volcano in Kenya provides indisputable evidence of a link between the extrusive and intrusive carbonatites (cf. King 1949). The central section of this volcano has been extensively eroded, and the eroded remnants now consist of two components: (a) a subvolcanic intrusive component that contains a nearly circular plug of carbonatite surrounded by ijolitic rocks; and (b) an extrusive component that mainly consists of nephelinitic tephra and lavas. Modern carbonatite lavas and tuffs are all natrocarbonatites, whereas the older carbonatitic materials are calcite–carbonatites, magnesiocarbonatites or ferrocarbonatites. The natrocarbonatites of Oldoinyo Lengai readily react with water, and their alkalis (Na and K) are leached away leaving a residue of $CaCO_3$. It thus seems likely that some carbonatite lavas and tuffs originally had a relatively high alkali content, and it was later depleted by leaching. Experimental studies support the concept that the natrocarbonatites are likely to be extrusive rocks, because materials of this composition are more readily erupted as fluid than materials of calcite–carbonatite composition (cf. Wyllie & Tuttle 1960). Hay and O'Neil (1983: 403) have examined the carbonatite and melilitite–carbonatite tuffs of the Laetolil Beds of Tanzania, and their detailed studies have revealed that these tuffs originally had an alkali composition similar to that of the natrocarbonatites of Oldoinyo Lengai, and that after being extruded the alkali components were dissolved, leaving a residuum of calcite–carbonatite. They also assert that the groundmass, of the calcite–carbonatite tuffs of the Kaiserstuhl Volcanic Complex of the Rhinegraben, may originally have been largely nyereite which has subsequently been replaced by calcite.

In both Africa and in the USSR there are many petrographic provinces that contain carbonatites, and in most of these they occur in close association with ijolites and/or nephelinites (sensu lato). The carbonatites are thus considered to belong to the carbonatite–nephelinite–ijolite rock association. This association, like may other 'alkaline' associations, is typically found in, or near, rift structures. There are, for example, notable concentrations in, or near, the East African Rift System, the Baikal Rift System of the USSR, the Rhinegraben, the St Lawrence Palaeorift, and along the rifted continental margins of the South Atlantic. Le Bas (1977: 280) has also shown that the rocks of the carbonatite–nephelinite–ijolite rock association are usually located on crustal swells. Rocks of this association range in age from the Early Proterozoic (for example, the Phalaborwa Carbonatite Complex of S. Africa) to the active, and recently active, nephelinite–carbonatite volcanoes of the Tanzanian sector of the East African Rift System (for example, Hanang, Kerimasi, Mosonik and Oldoinyo Lengai volcanoes).

14.5 Petrogenesis

Any account of the origin and evolution of the carbonatites must take into account the relative abundance and composition of all the associated magmatic and metasomatic rocks. If one examines the published descriptions of nephelinite–carbonatite volcanoes and ijolite–carbonatite intrusive complexes, one finds that the rocks they contain form a gradational series; and this enables one to construct a composite model of a typical carbonatite–nephelinite–ijolite volcanic complex (cf. Le Bas 1977: 288; Middlemost 1974: 277–8). A relatively simple composite model can be developed if one makes the following assumptions: (a) the *fenites* are produced by alkali-metasomatism, and the introduced alkalic components are mainly derived from carbonatite, and in particular natrocarbonatite, magmas, (b) the *syenitic rocks* are mainly mobilized fenites; (c) the *calcite–carbonatites, magnesiocarbonatites* and *ferrocarbonatites* may be produced in that order by the fractional crystallization of a parental *natrocarbonatitic magma*; (d) the *melanephelinites, nephelinites, ijolites, melilitites* and *phonolites* are all magmatic rocks

that congealed from magmas that evolved at depths below the volcanic complex; and (e) the *melteigites* and *jacupirangites* are essentially pyroxene and Fe–Ti oxide cumulative rocks, and the *urtites* are the complementary nepheline-rich rocks that evolved in a high-level magma chamber from a differentiating melanephelinitic–ijolitic magma. It is postulated that a number of magmas with different chemical compositions are introduced into the upper crust in areas where rocks of the carbonatite–nephelinite–ijolite association evolve. The silicate magmas cover a spectrum of compositions that range from melanephelinites to phonolites, whereas the carbonate magmas range from calcite–carbonatites to natrocarbonates. By studying the relative abundance of the various magmatic and metasomatic rocks that typically occur in carbonatite–nephelinite–ijolite associates, one can attempt to discern the proportions in which the various magmas were introduced into a typical, or ideal, volcanic complex; and from these data one is then able to estimate the chemical composition of the initial magma that gave rise to the rocks of the carbonatite–nephelinite–ijolite association.

Using data obtained from his study of the rocks of the carbonatite–nephelinite–ijolite association of western Kenya, Le Bas (1977: 288) has estimated that the initial magma was equivalent to the sum of 64 per cent melanephelinite, 19 per cent nephelinite, 6 per cent phonolite, 4 per cent melilitite, 4 per cent ijolite and 3 per cent natrocarbonatite. Such a magma would have melanephelinite composition that was intermediate between the average melanephelinite and the average ijolite; and it would contain approximately 24 per cent normative nepheline and have a colour index of approximately 55. The melilitites and some of the melanephelinites are regarded as being more primitive than the hypothetical initial magma; and it is proposed that a series of silicate magmas ranging from melilitites via melanephelinites to nephelinites (and possibly even to phonolites) evolved within the upper mantle. On moving up through the lithosphere, the decrease in confining pressure results in volatile-rich carbonatitic fluids separating from these silicate magmas (cf. Koster van Gross & Wyllie 1966); and depending upon the composition of the silicate magma, and the ambient pressure and temperature, the carbonatitic fluid varies in composition from an alkalic calcitic carbonatite to a natrocarbonatite. According to

Freestone and Hamilton (1980: 114), natrocarbonatitic liquids are likely to have been in equilibrium with silicate magmas of phonolitic composition, and the less evolved silicate magmas are likely to exsolve carbonatitic liquids that are richer in CaO.

The often discussed special relationship between kimberlites and carbonatites is considered to have been overstated. It is believed that carbonatites normally evolve from immiscible fluids that separate from alkalic, usually ultrabasic, primary magmas. These primary magmas are normally melanephelinites, nephelinites or phonolites, but they may be other less common alkalic magmas, such as melilitites or kimberlites.

14.6 Selected references

Heinrich, E. W. (1966) *The Geology of Carbonatites*, Rand McNally & Co., Chicago, USA.

Kapustin, Y. L. (1971) *The Mineralogy of Carbonatites*, Nauka Press, Moscow, USSR.

Le Bas, M. J. (1977) *Carbonatite–Nephelinite Volcanism*, John Wiley & Sons, London.

Tuttle, O. F. & Gittins, J. (1966) *Carbonatites*, Wiley, New York, USA.

Verwoerd, W. J. (1966) South African Carbonatites and their probable mode of origin, *Stellenbosch, Univ., Ann.*, **41A (2)**, 113–233.

CHAPTER 15

PATTERNS, PROCESSES AND PATHWAYS

15.1 Patterns of abundance

At the beginning of our enquiry into the nature and origin of the magmatic rocks, it was stated that rocks are essentially the solid stuff of which planets, natural satellites, and other broadly similar cosmic bodies are made; and it was also suggested that rocks can provide a key to a whole universe of ideas about the origin of the planets, the Solar System and the cosmos. In section 11.3 it was revealed that the chondrites have chemical compositions that are closely akin to that of the Sun, less most of its complement of H, He and other highly volatile elements. It was suggested that the meteorites, particularly the carbonaceous chondrites, are fragments of asteroidal material; and that such materials generally accreted at a late stage in the condensation and cooling of the Solar nebula. In section 1.10 it was shown that studies of the abundance of the chemical elements in the Sun, the chondrites and other bodies within the Solar System have enabled cosmochemists and geochemists to produce cosmic abundance tables. If one makes allowances for the planetary forming processes, one discovers that the abundance patterns of the chemical elements characteristic of such tables are clearly discernible in the total chemical compositions in the common primary magmas of the terrestrial planets (this is, the picritic basalts of Earth). This initial (or cosmic) control over the composition of the rocks that are found on the various planetary bodies is the main reason why, for example, silicon is considerably more abundant than germanium, and aluminium is much more abundant than gallium in normal magmatic rocks. It is interesting to attempt to discover how the elemental abundance patterns characteristic of the Solar System can be traced back to the processes responsible for the creation of the chemical elements.

Hypotheses concerning the origin of the chemical elements are an integral part of *cosmology*; and cosmology is the science of the space–time structure of the cosmos. In most modern systems of cosmology it is assumed: (a) that the local geometrical rules found in one part of the cosmos also apply in other local parts of space and time (the *principle of equivalence*); (b) that despite the clumping together of matter into stars, galaxies and clusters of galaxies, the cosmos looks much the same to an observer situated in any position within the cosmos, provided that it is studied on a large enough scale (*the cosmological principle*); and (c) that the cosmos contains an overwhelming predominance of matter over antimatter. The latter assumption probably means that the laws of physics were not entirely symmetrical under the extreme physical conditions (very high temperatures) that prevailed immediately after the cosmos came into being. Some cosmologists have considered the concept of the *perfect cosmological principle*; that is, one cannot observe any changes in the large-scale structure of the cosmos with respect to either space or time. Historically this hypothesis was important to our ideas concerning the creation of the chemical elements because it led to the evolution of the development of the *steady-state model of the cosmos*; and in this model *nucleosynthesis*, or the origin of the chemical elements, can no longer be relegated to a mysterious early epoch in the history of the cosmos when physical conditions were completely different. Nucleosynthesis has to be going on at present all over the cosmos.

Before examining current ideas on nucleosynthesis, it is apposite to note that at present most cosmologists support the hypothesis that is flippantly known as the *big-bang model*. According to a popular version of this hypothesis, the cosmos originated at a finite time (approximately 13.5 Ga) in the past. At the time of the big-bang, all energy and matter was condensed into a single, super-dense, and super-hot body that has been called the *cosmic egg*; and since that time the cosmos has continued to expand. It has also been suggested that the big-bang may have been a local phenomenon in a vastly larger cosmos. This concept is derived from the new *inflationary model of the cosmos* that postulates that the cosmos began with a very brief period of extraordinarily rapid expansion (or inflation). During this period of inflation, that continued for only 10^{-32}s, the diameter of the cosmos increased by a factor of at least 10^{50}. This inflationary model predicts that the observable cosmos is but one domain of expansion within a truly huge cosmos (cf. Guth & Steinhardt, 1984).

The big-bang is considered to have started a chain of reactions that eventually led to the synthesis of the first chemical elements. Weinberg (1977) has written a remarkable book on *the first three minutes* in the evolution of the cosmos. He begins his story one-hundredth of a second after the initial explosion, when the mean temperature of the cosmos was $\approx 10^{11}$ °C and the mean density of the matter contained within the cosmos was $\approx 3.8^9$ kg/l. Prior to this time super-dense particles had decayed to produce more baryons that antibaryons, and the cosmos was set on a pathway to become a cosmos of matter. As the matter in the cosmos rushed apart it became steadily cooler, and at the end of the first critical three minutes the cosmos was cool enough for protons and neutrons to begin to form into complex nuclei (that is, deuterium and helium); however, at this stage in its development the cosmos consisted mainly of light (photons), neutrinos and antineutrinos, together with a relatively small proportion of hydrogen and helium nuclei and electrons. The electrons were too energetic to be bound in atoms. According to Weinberg, after a few hundred thousand years (approximately 0.3 Ma) the cosmos was cool enough for the electrons to join with the nuclei to form atoms. These atoms essentially consisted of H (≈ 74 per cent) and He (≈ 26 per cent). Chemical process could now begin to operate, and the vast amounts of H, and much of the He, presently found in the cosmos, had been created. These gases would form aggregations of various sizes. Within the nascent galaxies, some of the clouds of these simple gases would experience gravitational collapse, and the interior temperatures of some of these protostars would rise until thermonuclear reactions began to occur, thus the first stars were born. Such stars would be stable if an equilibrium could be attained between gravitational collapse and the expansion resulting from fusion heating. The evolutionary pathways followed by the various stars are mainly determined by their masses.

In stars of approximately the same mass as the Sun, hydrogen fusion is likely to occur for ≈ 10 Ga; and then, when the hydrogen in the core of the star becomes exhausted, the zone of hydrogen fusion will migrate outwards and go on expanding until the temperature in this expanding shell drops below that required for fusion to take place. Meanwhile gravity will contract the helium-rich core of the star until the heating due to compression will trigger helium fusion. The outer shell of the stars will be heated and it will expand, and hydrogen fusion will recommence in the outer shell, while helium fusion occurs in the core. Such a star would be called a *red giant star*; and when the Sun reaches this stage ≈ 5 Ga from now. it will envelop Mercury, Venus and possibly Earth. According to Sagan (1981: 232), once most of the helium within the Sun has been used up, the Sun will 'slowly pulsate, expanding and contracting once every few millennia, eventually spewing its atmosphere into space in one or more concentric shells of gas'. The remains of the Sun will then collapse to become a *white dwarf star*, and it will ultimately cool to become a non-luminous *black dwarf star*. More massive stars of ≈ 10 Solar masses would evolve more rapidly, and eventually give rise to an enormous explosion, that would temporarily enable the star to shine as brightly as an entire galaxy of stars. If such a *supernova* leaves behind residual materials that are between 1.4–3.2 times the mass of the Sun, these materials will condense to form a *neutron star*. Stars of ≈ 50 Solar masses would have even shorter lives, and the residual materials of such stars would eventually contract with such force that even neutrons would collapse, and they would become *black holes*.

15.2 Processes of nucleosynthesis

At present our Milky Way Galaxy contains only ≈ 2 per cent of elements that are heavier than helium; and helium, together with all the nuclides heavier than it, can be created in a series of nuclear reactions that are known to operate within our galaxy. It is convenient to divide the processes responsible for the creation of the elements heavier than H into nine major groups (cf. Tayler 1966). When gravitational collapse heats up a protostar to a temperature of $\sim 1.7 \times 10^7$ °C *hydrogen fusion* occurs, and helium is the main nuclide synthesized (for example, the Sun). At higher temperatures ($\approx 2 \times 10^8$ °C) *helium fusion* occurs, and it synthesizes nuclides such as ^{12}C and ^{16}O; whereas at even higher temperatures ($\approx 5 \times 10^8$ °C) *carbon and oxygen fusion* results in the synthesis of nuclides such as ^{20}Ne, ^{23}Na, ^{24}Mg, ^{28}Si, ^{31}P and ^{32}S. During the latter process energy loss, particularly neutrino loss, is so great that this process can only be sustained for relatively short periods of time ($\approx 10^4$ a). At $\approx 10^9$ °C silicon fusion occurs, and alpha particles (helium nuclei) are successively added to nuclides such as ^{24}Mg, ^{28}Si, ^{32}S, ^{36}Ar and ^{40}Ca. This process is also known as the *alpha process*. At $\approx 4 \times 10^9$ °C the *equilibrium process* occurs, and it creates nuclides of the *iron peak* in the cosmic abundance curve. The elements created by this process include ^{51}V, ^{52}Cr, ^{55}Mn, ^{56}Fe, ^{59}Co and ^{62}Ni. Hoyle (1975: 324) has called the elements of the iron peak 'a pile of cosmic ashes that has resulted from the burning (fusion) of lighter nuclei'.

Quite different processes are required to generate the nuclides that are heavier than ^{62}Ni. The most important of these processes are: (a) the *s process*; and (b) the *r process*. Both create new nuclides by successive neutron capture. In the s process, neutron capture takes place relatively slowly, and the process is akin to the process that operates within a nuclear reactor; whereas in the r process, neutron capture takes place rapidly, and the process is akin to a nuclear explosion (that is, a high flux of neutrons for a relatively short time). The s process generally starts with Fe group nuclides, and it consists of the successive capture, by an individual nucleus of a large number of neutrons, and the emission of beta particles (that is, the decay of a neutron into a proton is said to produce an electron that is expelled as a beta particle). In the s process, the rate of neutron capture is so slow that the process tends to stop when it creates unstable nuclei with short half-lives, as such nuclides decay before there is further neutron capture; however, this process can account for creation of ≈ 150 nuclides. This process normally operates for a period of $\approx 10^5$ a in red giant stars that have exhausted the supply of H in their cores; and there is a steady supply of neutrons produced by reactions such as ^{13}C $+ ^4$He $\rightarrow ^{16}$O $+$ n (cf. Hoyle 1975: 378).

Is it postulated that the r (or rapid) process normally operates for a short time and may initially create nuclei with mass numbers of 280, before these huge nuclei undergo fission, thus generating new seed nuclei for the capture of more neutrons. The process probably operates for a period of ≈ 10 s during the explosion of a supernova, and after that the neutron flux decreases rapidly; however, such a vast explosion would also disseminate the new heavy elements so produced throughout vast volumes of space. Some nuclides that are rich in protons cannot be directly created by either the s or r processes, and they may result from either: (a) the addition of protons to suitable nuclei, followed by positron emission, or electron capture; or (b) photodisintegration reactions, whereby gamma rays eject neutrons from target nuclei. The abundance of some of the light elements is believed to be enhanced by high-energy interaction of cosmic rays on heavier atoms (that is, C, N and O) in interstellar space. As a result of such reactions the heavier atoms are split, thus creating lighter nuclei such as ^{6}Li, ^{7}Li, ^{9}Be, ^{10} and ^{11}B. The latter nuclides are readily destroyed in the interiors of normal stars, thus their overall low abundances.

Whereas the various processes of nucleosynthesis that have been discussed have contributed to the chemical composition of the Solar System, and most of the stars in the disk of our galaxy, there is a class of stars that emit spectra that reveal that they contain extremely low abundances of elements heavier than helium. Such stars are interpreted as being old stars (≈ 10 Ga) that formed relatively early in the history of our galaxy; and because of their great age they did not have much opportunity to inherit any significant quantity of heavy elements. These chemically-anomalous stars tend to follow eccentric, inclined orbits about the galactic centre; and they spend most of their time in the *galactic halo*, above or below the galactic disk. Planets associated with such stars are likely to have quite different bulk compositions as compared to those of the Solar System. Our galaxy is a rotating *spiral galaxy*, and it is like most other spiral galaxies in that it is well supplied with interstellar gas from which new stars, and probably planets, can form. The Milky Way Galaxy contains $\approx 10^{11}$ stars that generate about $\approx 10^{37}$W (J/s) of energy. Most of the galaxies in the cosmos are elliptical galaxies. The study of galaxies at a distance of ≈ 10 giga light-years away from the solar System has, however, not revealed any unequivocal evidence that there is an increase in young stars as one goes back in time.

Earlier in this chapter it was proposed that at approximately 13.5 Ga ago the big-bang triggered the initial process of *nucleogenesis* (that is, the cosmological production of H and He), and that since then nucleosynthesis has been creating the heavier elements within a variety of different stellar bodies. These bodies not only create elements, but also expel them into space, via *stellar winds*, or more violently when, for example, supernovae eject much of their mass into space. Such material may be later incorporated into a new generation of stars. Several supernovae explode in a typical galaxy each century; and such stars can create large quantities of the heavy elements, both prior to exploding and during the explosive phase. Data from radio astronomy, and other sources, indicate that explosions that probably dwarf the ones associated with supernovae may occasionally occur in the central regions of galaxies. With regard to the origin of the elemental abundance patterns found in the Solar System, it is of great interest to note that the elements that are created in greatest abundance by the various processes of nucleosynthesis are also more abundant in the materials of the Solar System.

When the Solar System came into being ≈ 4.55 Ga ago it probably evolved from a cloud, or nebula, of gases and dust that had a bulk chemical composition typical of that particular stage in the evolution of our galaxy; however, the nascent Solar System also received a small selection of elements that had just been created, and ejected, by a supernova. According to some *cosmogonists*, such as Sagan (1981: 234), the nearly simultaneous birth of the Solar System, and the explosion of a nearby supernova, are probably linked. The shock waves generated by the supernova may have compressed the interstellar gases and dust, and thus triggered the condensation of the Solar System. Some cosmochemists have interpreted the isotopic data from the CI carbonaceous chondrites as indicating that there were two supernoval explosions. The first one occurred $\approx 2^8$ a before the birth of the Solar System. It created nuclides such as ^{244}Pu, ^{129}I and a variety of other r process nuclides; whereas the later explosion triggered the condensation process in the Solar nebula, and injected nuclides such as ^{26}Al, ^{107}Ag and ^{16}O into the Solar nebula (cf. Taylor 1982: 413).

15.3 Planet-forming processes

The initial amount of angular momentum in the Solar nebula was mainly responsible for apportioning the matter in the Solar nebula into a single protosun, and a subsidiary disk of gas, dust and ice. As a result of self-gravitational effects, the protosun contracted and heated up until it was at a temperature high enough for hydrogen fusion to occur, thus the Sun was born. The matter in the subsidiary disk did not experience the high pressures and temperatures characteristic of the protosun; however, local self-gravitational effects would have caused some of the gas, dust and ice in the disk to gather into clumps, or planetesimals. Direct evidence of the processes that operated in the gaseous disk has apparently survived in the chondritic meteorites. They are 'generally held to be surviving samples of aggregated particulate matter from the nebula' (Wood 1979: 163). The chondritic meteorites tend to contain both high- and low-temperature phases, and the former are usually embedded in the latter. Isotopic studies have also demonstrated that these meteorites contain at least two populations of materials that were never completely mixed. The materials in the gaseous disk that did not aggregate into planetesimals, and were not captured by the Jovian planets, were probably blown away by an early, and more intense, solar wind.

It is usually postulated that the temperatures within the solar nebula, at the time of the evolution of the planetesimals, decreased outwards from the protosun, thus the planetesimals that developed near the protosun were enriched in high-temperature phases, whereas those that evolved in the outer Solar System contained a variety of carbonaceous compounds and ices. As the various planetesimals increased in mass, they had an increasing gravitational influence on the objects that passed near them, and they were perturbed into more eccentric orbits. The relative velocities between planetesimals on intersecting orbits increased. This produced higher impact velocities and more destructive collisions. Most of these high-velocity collisions would result in the dispersal of the materials within both planetesimals; however, the larger planetesimals, or protoplanets, would have enough mass to hold down most of the debris generated by impacts, and they would grow. Smaller planetesimals would be destroyed by the collisions, and most of the resulting debris would eventually be gathered up by the protoplanets.

At present, there are four main hypotheses that attempt to account for the difference in chemical composition between the planets of the

Solar System. According to the *equilibrium condensation model*, the temperature within the Solar nebula decreased systematically away from the protosun, and the minerals that were produced within the nebula tended to be in equilibrium with the gases that surrounded them; therefore their compositions were mainly dictated by a standard *condensation sequence* that graded from: (a) corundum, perovskite, melilite, spinel, diopside, forsterite enstatite and metallic iron at the temperatures predicted for the region that presently surrounds the orbit of Mercury; via (b) the plagioclases, and olivines and pyroxenes of intermediate Fe content, troilite and magnetite; to (c) the phyllosilicates carbonaceous compounds, sulphates and ices in the region that presently surrounds the belt asteriods. When the planetesimals began to form in the region of Mercury, the temperature was ≈ 1100 °C and the only minerals that were available to form the planetesimals were high-temperature phases, such as diopside, forsterite and metallic iron. According to this model the high density of Mercury is essentially due to its present high metallic iron content. The planetesimals that evolved in the region of Venus had a higher silicate/metallic iron ratio than Mercury, and they contained phases such as plagioclase. Earth formed in a cooler region of the nebula, where iron would have mainly occurred as grains of troilite and in silicates. All the iron in the region of Mars was probably present as sulphides, silicates or oxides. In the region of the belt asteroids, conditions were probably appropriate for the formation of carbonaceous chondrites. In the region of the Jovian planets, temperatures were low enough to permit the condensation, or survival, of ices of H_2O, NH_3 and CH_4. It is likely that the presence of this mass of icy material increased the efficiency of the planetary accretion process in the Jovian region of the Solar System. When Jupiter and Saturn attained a mass 20 times that of the Earth, they became gravitationally powerful enough to attract, and hold, uncondensed gases from the Solar nebula. Neptune and Uranus apparently did not grow large enough to capture gases from the Solar nebula.

In the *heterogeneous accretion model* the terrestrial planets are considered to have evolved from a hot Solar nebula: and as this body of gases cooled, the normal sequence of minerals condensed and immediately began to accrete, thus preventing reaction between the solid phases and the hot gases. In a simplified example of this model, a layered planet would evolve with the most refractory minerals accreting to form the core, and lower-temperature, highly-oxidized and hydrated minerals accreting near the surface. If accretion was rapid, a large proportion of the heat generated by the impacting planetesimals would be unable to dissipate into space and the temperature of the growing planet would rise, thus enabling much of the metallic iron and troilite to form a dense immiscible liquid that was eventually able to concentrate in the core of the accreting planet.

The single-stage *homogeneous accretion model* of planet formation is also known as the reduction during accretion model; and it is considered to occur in a low-temperature body of gases that contain planetesimals that have compositions similar to the CI carbonaceous chondrites (cf. Ringwood 1975: 569–85). It is postulated that when the mass of a protoplanet is low, the accreting planetesimals impact at low velocities, and the amount of heat that this process generates is small; however, as the mass of the planet increases, the velocities of the impacting planetesimals increases, and this promotes heating and, ultimately, melting of the surface materials. During the first stage of planet formation, a relatively cool, oxidized, volatile-rich planetary nucleus is formed. After this stage the surface temperature gradually rises and the accreting materials are degassed, and materials such as iron oxides are reduced to metal in a reducing atmosphere. Eventually this process produces a planet with abundant metallic iron at the surface, and a core that is rich in the components found in the CI carbonaceous chrondrites. The planet is thus gravitationally unstable; and after the metallic iron at the surface has segregated into relatively large bodies it sinks through the solid interior of the planet and concentrates in the core. This process generates much heat which causes the effective viscosity of the mantle to fall; and this drop in viscosity increases the rate of core formation, thereby enabling the generation of most of the core to occur within a relatively short time. The core-forming process would also produce strong convection currents within the mantle, and a mixing together of the early-formed carbonaceous chondritic material with the volatile-free reduced material of the initial mantle. It is also likely that, immediately after the core-forming process, the uppermost layer of the planet would be completely molten. In the model proposed by Ringwood (1975), the primitive atmospheres of the terrestrial planets are continuously washed back into the Solar nebula by a very strong solar wind, or even a T-Tauri type of 'solar hurricane'.

An examination of the phases present in the chondritic meteorites shows that they often contain a mixture of mineral grains that formed at different temperatures. It is thus feasible that the planets accreted from a mixture of planetesimals that had different compositions, and probably evolved in different parts and/or at different times within the Solar nebula. This hypothesis is usually called the *nonequilibrium accretion model* and, when developed, is able to incorporate concepts from all of the previously discussed models. For example, in order to account for the density differences between the terrestrial planets, one might postulate that most of the particulate matter accreted by these planets was generated by equilibrium condensation from the Solar nebula; and that as the planets grew in size and mass, heating, due to the increasing impact velocity of the planetesimals, assisted in the initial differentiation of the planets into cores, mantles and crusts. At about this stage in the evolution of the terrestrial planets, a veneer of hydrous, low-temperature material, that was chemically akin to the CI carbonaceous chondrites, was accreted. It is suggested that the planetesimals of CI carbonaceous chondritic composition accreted in the region now occupied by the belt asteroids; and, at the time of the rapid accretion of their giant neighbour Jupiter, they were perturbed into wildly eccentric orbits that projected them into the inner Solar System.

As we have already noted, the Jovian planets were eventually gravitationally powerful enough to attract and hold uncondensed gases from the Solar nebula. Once these massive bodies of gases, dust and ices had formed, they would experience a period of gravitational contraction and internal heating (that is, Helmholtz-Kelvin contraction) that was analogous to the processes followed by stars in the process of being born. During this contraction stage in their evolution both Jupiter and Saturn would have been hot and luminous. It has been estimated that the maximum internal temperature attained by Jupiter was approximately one-tenth of that required to initiate nuclear fusion (cf. Wood 1979: 181). The active star Luyten 726-8B is only 40 times more massive than Jupiter, whereas the Sun is over a 1000 times more massive.

Large amounts of heat were available during, and immediately after, the accretion of the terrestrial planets. Most of this heat came from: (a) short-lived radionuclides such as ^{26}Al; (b) electric currents induced in the planets by a strongly outward-flowing Solar wind; (c) planetesimal impact; and (d) the core-forming process. When viewed on a broad scale the subsequent evolution of these planets is essentially related to their cooling, and the thickening of their lithospheres. As the lithosphere grows thicker, most thermal activity is forced to retreat to greater depths within the planet, and eventually convection within the mantle is unable to initiate processes that are able to fracture the lithosphere and/or move lithospheric plates, thus, with the passing of time, internally-generated magmas find it increasingly difficult to penetrate the lithosphere.

The concept that the terrestrial planets have evolved through a series of broadly similar stages is a valuable unifying idea. It must, however, not be thought that rates of cooling are the only factors that influence the way in which the planets evolve. Dissimilar evolutionary behaviour would be expected in planets that have different chemical compositions and/or masses. Differences in mass and size would not only affect the rate at which a planet cooled, but they would also influence: (a) pressure gradients within a planet; and (b) the heat generated by the process of accretion. Planets that were large enough to hold an atmosphere and/or hydrosphere would experience distinctive types of volcanic activity and denudation. On planets, such as the Earth, which are tectonically active and also have a well-developed hydrosphere, the subduction of hydrous rocks would promote a special type of magma generation (see Ch. 6).

15.4 Pathways of change

Magmas are the agents of change within the interiors of evolving planets. Once they have become mobile they usually keep differentiating and changing their physical characteristics in response to the varying physical and chemical conditions they encounter. The magmatic rocks are a record of a small part of a far larger system, or series of systems, that partake in ceaseless creation, evolution and destruction. A particular time and place, within an evolving spiral galaxy, predestined the chemical composition of the nascent Solar System. The relatively small masses of the terrestrial planets, and the relatively high temperatures prevailing in the inner region of the Solar nebula at the time of their accretion, determined that these planets would not retain much of the H and He that was originally so abundant in the Solar nebula. Early core-forming processes heated the terrestrial planets and determined that they would be broadly layered, with accessible crusts that were chemically distinct from their bulk compositions. Detailed studies of the magmatic rocks of the Earth and Moon have provided a unified model of how the common magmas are generated, evolve and are emplaced, or extruded. Magmatic differentiation can be modified by a great many factors; however, when the common magmas differentiate they tend to follow remarkably stable pathways of change that are clearly revealed in their liquid lines of descent. Much further exploration of the Solar System is required to discover whether similar magmatic rocks, and differentiation trends, will be found in the materials making up the huge volcanoes of Venus and Mars, or in the surface materials of Titan the largest satellite of Saturn, and the Solar System.

The outer layers of the small planets, such as the Moon, cooled relatively quickly, and the magma-generating processes that aided in the transference of heat and volatile components from the interior of the planets to the surface soon slowed down, and eventually stopped. Because of their small masses, most of the volatile components that were liberated by volcanic activity escaped into space. On Earth, the largest terrestrial planet, the generation of magmas and the degassing of the mantle are still active processes; and both the atmosphere and hydrosphere are considered to represent accumulations of gases liberated by degassing. Molecular oxygen only became an important component in the atmosphere of the Earth after simple plant-life had evolved, and it started breaking down carbon dioxide by photosynthesis; thus simple microscopic blue-green algae were able to change the composition of the atmosphere of Earth; and in so doing change the processes of denudation, and the chemical composition of the supracrustal rocks. Since the Proterozoic, life-forms have played an important role in the formation of the sedimentary rocks, and in this way they have indirectly changed the compositions of some of the

materials that are subducted and recycled into the mantle.

We live at an interesting time, when much new information concerning the materials of the Solar System is being collected and discussed. As was noted in Section 1.9, one of the main reasons why the collecting of data from extraterrestrial sources has provided such a powerful stimulus in developing new, or refining old, petrological concepts is that on every known extraterrestrial planetary body, at least some of the paramaters that are significant in the generation of magmatic rock differ from those found on Earth, whereas others are essentially the same. This has meant that petrologists have not only had to construct a whole new range of petrogenetic models; but they have also been forced to re-examine some of the hypotheses that they had previously regarded as self-evident and true. Future studies of the petrology, and chemistry, of the huge volcanoes of Mars may, for example, show that some of the links that have been proposed to exist between magmatic and tectonic activity on Earth are fortuitous rather than essential.

I would like to end this discussion of magmas and magmatic rocks by asking all readers to support research related to the study of rocks of the terrestrial planets, the asteroids, and the rocky satellites of the Jovian planets. It is only by being challenged, and by being presented with new materials and processes, that petrologists will be able to expand their horizons, and come to regard the rocks of the Earth as materials that are an integral part of a series of larger systems that ultimately expand to include the whole cosmos. I believe that in the future the people of Earth will understand how all the rocks of the Solar System formed, even if the cosmos is found to be a more inscrutable place than we can at present imagine. This is because as Steven Weinberg (1977: 154–5) has stated,

'men and women are not content to comfort themselves with tales of gods and giants, or to confine their thoughts to the daily affairs of life; they also build telescopes and satellites and accelerators, and sit at their desks for endless hours working out the meaning of the data they gather. The effort to understand the universe is one of the very few things that lifts human life a little above the level of farce, and gives it some of the grace of tragedy'.

15.5 Selected references

Sagan, C. (1981) *Cosmos*, Macdonald Future Pub., London.

Tayler, R. J. (1972) *The origin of the chemical elements*, Wykeham Pub. (London) Ltd., London.

Taylor, S. R. (1982) *Planetary Science: A lunar perspective*, Lunar & Planetary Institute, Houston, Texas, USA.

Weinberg, S. (1977) *The first three minutes: A modern view of the origin of the universe*, Andre Deutsch, London.

Wood, J. A. (1979) *The Solar System*, Prentice-Hall, Inc., Englewood Cliffs, New Jersey, USA.

BIBLIOGRAPHY

Abich, H. (1841) Geologische Beobachtungen über die Vulkanischen Erscheinungen und Bildungen in Unterund Mittel – Italian, **1** (1), Ueber die Natur und Zusammenhang der Vulkanisehen Bildungen, Brunswick.

Ahrens, L. H. (1964) Element distribution in igneous rocks: VII: A reconnaissance survey of the distribution of SiO_2 in granitic and basaltic rocks, *Geochim. Cosmochim. Acta*, **28**, 271–90.

Ahrens, L. H. & Taylor, S. R. (1961) *Spectrochemical Analysis* (2nd edn), Addison-Wesley, Reading, Mass., USA.

Allard, G. O. (1970) The Dore Lake Complex, Chibougamau, Quebec – a metamorphosed Bushveld-type layered intrusion, *Geol. Soc. S. Afr., Spec. Publ.*, **1**, 477–91.

Allègre, C. J. (1982) Genesis of Archaean komatiites in a wet ultramafic subducted plate; Ch. 28, pp. 495–500 in Arndt, N. T. & Nisbet, E. G. (eds), *Komatiites*, George Allen & Unwin, London.

Allègre, C. J. & Othman, D. B. (1980) Nd–Sr isotopic relationship in granitoid rocks and continental crust development: a chemical approach to orogenesis, *Nature*, **286**, 335–46.

Allègre, C. J., Othman, D. B., Polve, M. & Richard, P. (1979) The Nd–Sr isotopic correlation in mantle materials and geodynamic consequences, *Phys. Earth Planet. Inter.*, **19**, 293–306.

Allen, J. B. & Charsley, T. J. (1968) *Nepheline–Syenite and Phonolite*, Inst. Geol. Sci. (UK), HMSO, London.

Allsopp, H. L., Nicholaysen, L. O. & Hahn-Weinheimer, P. (1969) Rb/K ratios and Sr-isotopic compositions of minerals in ecologitic and peridotitic rocks, *Earth Planet, Sci. Lett.*, **5**, 231–44.

Anders, E. & Ebihara, M. (1982) Solar-system abundances of the elements, *Geochim. Cosmochim. Acta*, **46**, 2363–80.

Anders, E., Hayatsu, R. & Studier, M. H. (1973) Organic compounds in meteorites, *Science*, **182**, 781–90.

Anderson, A. T. (1969) Massif-type anorthosite: A widespread Precambrian igneous rock; pp. 47–55 in Isachsen, Y. W. (ed.), *Origin of Anorthosite and Related Rocks*, New York State Museum and Science Service, Mem. 18, Albany, New York, USA.

Anderson, I. (1984) The restless volcanoes of Venus, *New Sci.*, 1398, 22.

Anderson, O. L. (1979) The role of fracture dynamics in kimberlite pipe formation: pp. 344–53 in Boyd, F. R. & Meyer, H. O. A. (eds), *Kimberlites, diatremes and diamonds: their geology, petrology and geochemistry*, Proc. 2nd Int. Kimerlite Conf., Am. Geophys. Union, Washington, DC, USA.

Anhaeusser, C. R. & Robb, L. J. (1981) Magmatic cycles and the evolution of the Archaean granitic crust in the eastern Transvaal and Swaziland, *Geol. Soc. Aust., Spec. Publ.*, **7**, 457–67.

Anonymous (1972) Penrose Field Conference: Ophiolites, *Geotimes*, **17(12)**, 24–5.

Appleton, J. D. (1972) Petrogenesis of potassium rich lavas from the Roccamonfina volcano, Roman Region, Italy, *J. Petrol.*, **13**, 425–56.

Argand, E. (1924) La tectonique de l'Asie, *13th Int. Geol. Congr.*, Liege, 169–371.

Arndt, N. T., Naldrett, A. J. & Pyke, D. R. (1977) Komatiitic and iron-rich tholeiitic lavas of Munro Township, northeast Ontario, *J. Petrol.*, **18**, 319–69.

Arndt, N. T. & Nisbet, E. G. (eds) (1982a) *Komatiites*, George Allen & Unwin, London.

Arndt, N. T. & Nisbet, E. G. (1982b) What is a komatiite?; Ch. 2, pp. 19–27 in Arndt, N. T. & Nisbet, E. G. (eds) *Komatiites*, George Allen & Unwin, London.

Arth. J. G. (1976) Behaviour of trace elements during magmatic processes: A summary of theoretical models and their applications, *US Geol. Surv., J. Res.*, **4**, 41–7.

Atherton, M. P., McCourt, W. J., Sanderson, L. M. & Taylor, W. P. (1979) The geochemical character of the segmented Peruvian Coastal Batholith and associated volcanics; pp. 45–64 in Atherton, M. P. & Tarney, J. (eds), *Origin of Granite Batholiths; Geochemical Evidence*, Shiva Pub. Ltd, Orpington, Kent.

Atherton, M. P. & Tarney, J. (eds) (1979) *Origin of Granite Batholiths; Geochemical Evidence*, Shiva Pub. Ltd, Orpington, Kent.

Atkins, F. B. (1969) Pyroxenes of the Bushveld Intrusion, South Africa, *J. Petrol.*, **10(2)**, 222–49.

Atkinson, W. J., Hughes, F. E. & Smith, C. B. (1984) A review of the kimberlite rocks of Western Australia; pp. 195–224 in Kornprobst, J. (ed.), *Kimberlites 1: Kimberlites and related rocks*, Elsevier, Amsterdam, The Netherlands.

Avias, J. V. (1977) About some features of allochtonous ophiolitic and volcanosedimentary suite units and their contact zones in New Caledonia, *International Symposium on Geodynamics in South-West Pacific*, Noumea (New Caledonia), Editions Technip, Paris, 245–64.

Bailey, D. K. (1964) Crustal warping – a possible tectonic control of alkaline magmatism, *J. Geophys. Res.*, **69**, 1103–11.

Bailey, D. K. (1974) Continental rifting and alkaline magmatism; Ch. 3.2, pp. 148–59 in Sørensen, H. (ed.), *The Alkaline Rocks*, John Wiley &Sons, London.

Bailey, D. K. (1976a) Experimental Methods and the Uses of Phase Diagrams; pp. 3–97 in Bailey, D. K. & Macdonald, R. (eds), *The Evolution of the Crystalline Rocks*, Academic Press, London.

Bailey, D. K. (1976b) Applications of Experiments to Alkaline Rocks; pp. 419–69 in Bailey, D. K. & Macdonald, R. (eds), *The Evolution of the Crystalline Rocks*, Academic Press, London.

Bailey, D. K. (1978) Continental rifting and mantle degassing; pp. 1–13 in Neumann, E. R. & Ramberg, I. B.

(eds), *Petrology and geochemistry of continental rifts*, D. Reidel Pub. Co., Dordrecht, The Netherlands.

Bailey, D. K. (1983) The chemical and thermal evolution of rifts, *Tectonophysics*, **94**, 585–97.

Bailey, D. K. & Schairer, J. F. (1964) Feldspar–liquid equilibria in peralkaline liquids – the orthoclase effect, *Am. J. Sci.*, **262**, 1198–1206.

Bailey, E. B., Clough, C. T., Wright, B. A., Richey, J. E. & Wilson, G. V. (1924) The Tertiary and Post-Tertiary geology of Mull, Loch Aline, and Oban, *Geol. Surv. Scot., Mem.*, Edinburgh.

Bailey, E. B. & Maufe, H. B. (1916) The geology of Ben Nevis and Glen Coe, *Geol. Surv. Scot., Mem.* **53**, Edinburgh.

Baker, B. H., Goles, G. G., Leman, W. P. & Lindstrom, M. M. (1977) Geochemistry and petrogenesis of a basalt–benmoreite–trachyte suite from the southern part of the Gregory Rift, Kenya, *Contrib. Mineral. Petrol.*, **65**, 303–32.

Baker, B. H. & Miller, J. A. (1963) Geology and geochronology of the Seychelles Islands and the structure of the floor of the Arabian Sea, *Nature*, **199**, 346–8.

Baker, B. H. & Mitchell, J. G. (1976) Volcanic stratigraphy and geochronology of the Kedony–Olorgesailie area and the evolution of the South Kenya rift valley, *Geol. Soc. Lond., J.*, **132**, 467–84.

Baker, I. (1968) Compositional variation of minor intrusions and the form of a volcano magma chamber, *Q. J. Geol. Soc. (Lond.)*, **124**, 67–79.

Baker, P. E. (1968) Comparative volcanology and petrology of the Atlantic island arcs, *Bull. Volc.*, **32(1)**, 189–206.

Baker, P. E. (1982) Evolution and classification of orogenic volcanic rocks; pp. 11–23 in Thorpe, R. S. (ed.), *Andesites: Orogenic Andesites and Related Rocks*, John Wiley & Sons, Chichester.

Baker, P. E., Buckley, F. & Holland, J. G. (1974) Petrology and Geochemistry of Easter Island, *Contrib. Mineral. Petrol.*, **44**, 85–100.

Baker, P. E., Gass, I. G., Harris, P. G. & Le Maitre, R. W. (1964) The volcanological report of the Royal Society expedition to Tristan da Cunha, 1962, *Phil. Trans. R. Soc. Lond.*, **256**, 439–578.

Baldridge, W. S., Carmichael, I. S. E. & Albee, A. L. (1981) Crystallization paths of leucite-bearing lavas: Examples from Italy, *Contrib. Mineral. Petrol.*, **76**, 321–35.

Balk, R. (1927) Die primare Struktur des Noritmassivs von Peekskill am Hudson, nordlich New York; geologische Beobachtungen zur Tektonik des Magmas und zu den Problemen der Differentiation und Palingenese, *Neues Jahrb. Mineral.*, Beilageband **57**, Abt. B, 249–303.

Ballard, R. D. & Van Andel, T. H. (1977) Morphology and tectonics of the inner rift valley at lat. 36° 50 ′N on the Mid-Atlantic Ridge, *Geol. Soc. Am., Bull.*, **88**, 507–30.

Banks, R. J. & Beamish, R. (1979) Melting in the crust and upper mantle beneath the Kenya Rift: evidence from Geomagnetic Deep Sounding experiments, *Geol. Soc. Lond., J.*, **136**, 225–33.

Baragar, W. R. A. (1960) Petrology of basaltic rocks in part of the Labrador Trough, *Geol. Soc. Am., Bull.*, **71**, 1589–644.

Barberi, F., Innocenti, F., Ferrara, G., Keller, J. & Villari, L. (1974) Evolution of Aeolian arc volcanism (southern Tyrrhenian Sea), *Earth Planet. Sci. Lett.*, **21**, 269–76.

Bardet, M. G. (1973) Metakimberlites; pp. 15–17 in Ahrens, L. H., Dawson, J. B., Duncan, A. R. & Erlank, A. J., *International Conference on Kimberlites*, Univ. Cape Town, Rondebosch, S. Africa.

Barker, F. (1979a) Trondhjemite: Definition, environment and hypotheses of origin; Ch. 1, pp.1–12 in Barker, F. (ed.), *Trondhjemites, dacites and related rocks*, Elsevier Sci. Pub., Amsterdam, The Netherlands.

Barker, F. (ed.) (1979b) *Trondhjemites, dacites and related rocks*, Elsevier Sci. Pub., Amsterdam, The Netherlands.

Barker, F. (1981) Introduction to Special Issue on Granites and Rhyolites: A Commentary for the Nonspecialist, *J. Geophys. Res.*, **86** (B.11), 10131–5.

Barker, F. & Millard, H. T. (1979) Geochemistry of the type Trondhjemite and three associated rocks, Norway; Ch. 17, pp 517–529 in Barker, F. (ed.), *Trondhjemites dacites and related rocks*, Elsevier Sci. Pub., Amsterdam, The Netherlands.

Barker, F., Wones, D. R., Sharp, W. N. & Desborough, G. A. (1975) The Pikes Peak Batholith, Colorado Front Range, and a model for the origin of the gabbro–anorthosite–syenite–potassic granite suite, *Precambrian Res.*, **2**, 97–160.

Barriere, M. (1976) Flowage differentiation: limitations of the 'Bagnold Effect' to the narrow intrusions, *Contrib. Mineral. Petrol.* **55**, 139–45.

Barth, T. F. W. (1931) Mineralogical petrography of Pacific lavas, *Am. J. Sci.*, ser. **5**, **xxi**, 377–405 and 491–530.

Barth, T. F. W. (1945) Studies of the igneous rock complex of the Oslo region, II, Systematic petrography of the plutonic rocks, *Norske Vid. Selsk. Skr. Math.-Naturv.*, Kl. 1944, No. **9**, 1 –104.

Barth, T. F. W. (1952) *Theoretical Petrology*: A textbook on the origin and the evolution of rocks, John Wiley & Sons, Inc., New York, USA.

Barth, T. F. W. (1956) Studies in gneiss and granite, 1; relations between temperature and the composition of the feldspars, *Nor. Vid.-Akad. Skr.*, **1**, 3–16.

Barth, T. F. W. (1962a) *Theoretical Petrology*: A textbook on the origin and the evolution of rocks (2nd edn), John Wiley & Sons, New York, USA.

Barth, T. F. W. (1962b) The feldspar geologic thermometers, *Nor. Geol. Tidsskr.*, **42(2)**, 330–9.

Barth, T. F. W., Correns, C. W. & Eskola, P. (1939) *Die Entstehung der Gesteine: Ein Lehrbuch der Petrogenese*, Berlin.

Basaltic Volcanism Study Project (1981) *Basaltic Volcanism on the Terrestrial Planets*, Pergamon Press, Inc., New York, USA.

Bateman, P. C. (1983) A summary of critical relations in the central part of the Sierra Nevada batholith, California, USA, *Geol. Soc. Am., Mem.*, **159**, 241–54.

Bateman, P. C., Clark, L. D., Hubber, N. K., Moore, J. G. & Rinehart, C. D. (1963) The Sierra Nevada Batholith, a synthesis of recent work across the central part, *US Geol. Surv., Prof. Pap.*, **414-D**, 1–46.

Bateman, P. C. & Dodge, F. C. W. (1970) Variations of major chemical constituents across the central Sierra Nevada Batholith, *Geol. Soc. Am., Bull.*, **81**, 409–20.

Beatty, J. K., O'Leary, B. & Chaikin, A. (eds) (1981) *The New Solar System*, Cambridge Univ. Press, Cambridge, UK, & Sky Pub. Corp., Cambridge, USA.

Beckinsale, R. D. (1979) Granitic magmatism in the tin-belt of south-east Asia; pp. 34–44 in Atherton, M. P. & Tarney, J. (eds), *Origin of Granite Batholiths; Geochemical Evidence*, Shiva Pub. Ltd, Orpington, Kent.

Beckinsale, R. D., Parkhurst, R. J., Skelhorn, R. R. & Walsh, J. N. (1978) Geochemistry and Petrogenesis of the Early Tertiary lava pile of the Isle of Mull, Scotland, *Contrib. Mineral. Petrol.*, **66**, 415–27.

Benson, W. N. (1913) The Geology and Petrology of the Great Serpentine Belt of New South Wales, Pt. 1, Introduction, *Linn. Soc. NSW (Australia), Proc.*, **38**, 490–517.

Benson, W. N. (1926) The tectonic conditions accompanying the intrusion of basic and ultrabasic igneous rocks, *Natl Acad. Sci. USA*, Mem., **1**, 1–90.

Best, M. G. (1975) Migration of hydrous fluids in the upper mantle and potassium variation in calc–alkalic rocks, *Geology*, **3**, 429–32.

Bhattacharji, S. & Smith, C. H. (1964) Flowage differentiation, *Science*, **145**, 150–3.

Birch, F. (1952) Elasticity and constitution of the Earth's interior, *J. Geophys. Res.*, **57**, 227–86.

Birch, F. (1968) On the possibility of large changes in the Earth's volume, *Phys. Earth Planet. Inter.*, **1**, 141–7.

Black, R. & Girod, M. (1970) Late Palaeozoic to Recent igneous activity in West Africa and its relationships to basement structure; Ch. 9, pp. 185–210 in Clifford, T. N. & Gass, I. G. (eds), *African Magmatism and Tectonics*, Oliver & Boyd, Edinburgh.

Blackburn, E. A., Wilson, L. & Sparks, R. S. J. (1976) Mechanisms and dynamics of Strombolian activity, *Geol. Soc. Lond., J.*, **132**, 429–40.

Blatt, H. & Jones, R. L. (1975) Proportion of exposed igneous, metamorphic and sedimentary rocks, *Geol. Soc. Am., Bull.*, **86**, 1085–8.

Block, S. & Bischoff, J. L. (1979) The effect of low temperature alteration of basalt on the oceanic budget of potassium, *Geology*, **7**, 193–6.

Boettcher, A. L. & O'Neil, J. R. (1980) Stable isotope chemical, and petrographic studies of high-pressure amphiboles and micas: evidence for metasomatism in the mantle source regions of alkali basalts and kimberlites, *Am. J. Sci.*, **280A**, 594–621.

Bohlen, S. R., Boettcher, A. L. & Wall, V. J. (1982) The system albite–H_2O–CO_2: a model for melting and activities of water at high pressure, *Am. Mineral.*, **67**, 451–62.

Boltwood, B. B. (1907) On the ultimate disintegration products of the radioactive elements, *Am. J. Sci.*, **4(23)**, 77–88.

Booth, B., Croasdale, R. & Walker, G. P. L. (1978) A quantitative study of five thousand years of volcanism on Sao Miguel, Azores, *Phil. Trans. R. Soc. Lond.*, **288**, 271–319.

Boricky, E. (1874) Petrographische studien en den basaltgesteinen Böhmens, *Archiv für die naturwissenschaftliche Landesdurchforschung von Böhmen, Prague*, **Abt. 2, Th. 2 (44)**, 172–8.

Borodin, L. S. & Paulenko, A. S. (1974) The role of metasomatic processes in the formation of alkaline rocks; Ch. 6.7, pp. 515–34 in Sörensen, H. (ed.), *The Alkaline Rocks*, John Wiley & Sons, London.

Bott, H. P. (1971) *The Interior of the Earth*, Edward Arnold, London.

Boulanger, J. (1957) Les anorthosites de Madagascar, *Comm. Tech. Coop. Africa S. Sahara*, **1**, 71–92.

Bowell, E., Chapman, C. R., Gradie, J. C., Morrison, D. & Zellner, B. (1978) Taxonomy of asteroids, *Icarus*, **35**, 313–35.

Bowen, N. L. (1915) Crystallization differentiation in silicate liquids, *Am. J. Sci.*, **4th Ser.**, **39**, 175–91.

Bowen, N. L. (1919) Crystallization-differentiation in igneous magmas, *J. Geol.*, **27**, 393–430.

Bowen, N. L. (1922) The reaction principle in petrogenesis, *J. Geol.*, **30**, 177–98.

Bowen, N. L. (1927) The origin of ultra-basic and related rocks, *Am. J. Sci.*, **Ser. 5, 14**, 89–108.

Bowen, N. L. (1928) *The Evolution of Igneous Rocks*, Princeton Univ. Press, Princeton, New Jersey, USA.

Bowen, N. L. (1937) Recent high-temperature research on silicates and its significance in igneous geology, *Am. J. Sci.*, **33**, 1–21.

Bowen, N. L. (1948) The granite problem and the method of multiple prejudices, *Geol. Soc. Am., Mem.*, **28**, 79–90.

Bowen, N. L. & Andersen, O. (1914) The binary system MgO–SiO_2, *Am. J. Sci.*, **4th series, 37**, 487–500.

Bowen, N. L. & Tuttle, O. F. (1950) The system Na-$AlSi_3O_8$–$KAlSi_3O_8$–H_2O, *J. Geol.*, **58**, 489–511.

Boyd, F. R. & Meyer, H. O. A. (eds) (1979) *Kimberlites, Diatremes and Diamonds: Their Geology, Petrology and Geochemistry*, Proc. 2nd Int. Kimberlite Conf., Am. Geophys. Union, Washington, DC, USA.

Bridgwater, D. & Harry, W. T. (1968) Anorthosite xenoliths and plagioclase megacrysts in Precambrian intrusions of south Greenland, *Medd. Grøenland*, **185**, 1–243.

Bridgwater, D., Keton, L., McGregor, V. R. & Myers, J. S. (1976) Archaean gneiss complex of Greenland; pp. 18–75 in Escher, A. & Watt, W. S. (eds), *Geology of Greenland*, (Greenland) Geol. Unders., Copenhagen, Denmark.

Bridgwater, D. & Windley, B. F. (1973) Anorthosites, post-orogenic granites, acid volcanic rocks and crustal development in the North Atlantic shield during the mid-Proterozoic, *Geol. Soc. S. Afr., Spec. Publ.*, **3**, 307–17.

Briggs, G. & Taylor, F. (1982) *The Cambridge Photographic Atlas of the Planets*, Cambridge Univ. Press, Cambridge.

Bristow, J. W. & Saggerson, E. P. (1983) A general account of Karroo Volcanicity in Southern Africa, *Geol. Rundsch.*, **72(3)**, 1015–59.

Brögger, W. C. (1894) Die Eruptivgesteine des Kristianiagebietes, I, Die Gesteine der Grorudit-Tinguait-Serie, *(Norske) Vid. Selsk. Skr., Kristiania, Math. Naturv.*, **4**.

Brögger, W. C. (1898) Die Eruptivgesteine des Kristianiagebietes, III. Das Ganggefolg des Laurdalits, *(Norske) Vid. Selsk. Skr., Kristinia, Math. Naturv.*, **6**.

Brögger, W. C. (1921) Die Eruptivgesteine des Kristianiagebietes, IV. Das Fengebiet in Telemark, Norwegen, *(Norske) Vid. Selsk. Skr., Kristiania, Math. Naturv.*, **9**.

Brögger, W. C. (1933) Die Eruptivgesteine des Oslogebietes, VII, Die chemische Zusammensetzung der Eruptivgesteine des Oslogebietes, *(Norske) Vid. Selsk. Skr., Oslo, Math. Naturv.*, K1. 1933, **1**.

Brongniart, A. (1813) Essai d'une classification minéralogique des roches mélangées, *Journal des Mines (Paris)*, **34**, 5–48.

Brongniart, A. (1827) *Classification et caracteres mineralogiques des roches homogénes et hétérogénes*, F. G. Levrault, Paris, France.

Brooks, C. K. & Rucklidge, J. C. (1973) A Tertiary lamprophyre dike with high pressure xenoliths and megacrysts from Wiedmanns Fjord, East Greenland, *Contrib. Mineral. Petrol.*, **42**, 197–212.

Brousse, R. (1961) Recucil des analyses chimiques des roches volcaniques Tertiaires et Quaternaires de la France, *Bull. Service de la Carte Geol. (France)*, **Tome 58, No. 263**, 1–140.

Brown, G. C. (1979) The changing pattern of batholith emplacement during Earth history; pp. 106–15 in Atherton, M. P. & Tarney, J. (eds), *Origin of Granite Batholiths; Geochemical Evidence*, Shiva Pub. Ltd., Orpington, Kent.

Brown, G. C. (1982a) The energy budget of the Earth; pp. 140–61 in Smith, D. G. (ed.) *The Cambridge Encyclopedia of Earth Sciences*, Cambridge Univ. Press, Cambridge.

Brown, G. C. (1982b) Calc–alkaline intrusive rocks: their diversity, evolution and relation to volcanic arcs; pp. 437–61 in Thorpe, R. S. (ed.), *Andesites: Orogenic Andesites and Related Rocks*, John Wiley & Sons, Chichester.

Brown, G. C., Cassidy, J., Locke, C. A., Plant, J. A. & Simpson, P. R. (1981) Caledonian Plutonism in Britain: A summary, *J. Geophys. Res.*, **86(B.11)**, 10502–14.

Brown, G. C. & Mussett, A. E. (1981) *The Inaccessible Earth*, George Allen & Unwin, London.

Brown, G. M. (1982) The British Tertiary Province: An appraisal of the igneous history; Ch. 27, pp. 345–50 in Sutherland, D. S. (ed.), *Igneous Rocks of the British Isles*, John Wiley & Sons, Chichester.

Brown, G. M., Holland, J. G., Sigurdsson, H., Tomblin, J. F. & Arculus, P. J. (1977) Geochemistry of the Lesser Antilles volcanic island arc, *Geochim. Cosmochim. Acta*, **41**, 785–801.

Bryan, W. G. (1979) Low-K_2O dacite from the Tonga-Kermadec Island Arc: Petrography, chemistry and petrogenesis; Ch. 20, pp. 581–600 in Barker, F. (ed.), *Trondjemites, Dacites and related rocks*, Elsevier Sci. Pub., Amsterdam, The Netherlands.

Buddington, A. F. (1927) Coast Range intrusives of southeastern Alaska, *J. Geol.*, **35(3)**, 224–46.

Buddington, A. F. (1939) Adirondack igneous rocks and their metamorphism, *Geol. Soc. Am.*, *Mem. 7*, 1–354.

Buddington, A. F. (1959) Granite emplacement with special reference to North America, *Geol. Soc. Am., Bull.*, **70**, 671–747.

Buddington, A. F. (1961) The origin of anorthosite re-evaluated, *India, Geol. Surv., Rec.*, **86**, 421–32.

Bullen, K. E. (1963) *An introduction to the theory of seismology* (3rd edn), Cambridge Univ. Press, Cambridge.

Bultitude, R. J. (1976) Flood basalts of probable early Cambrian age in northern Australia; pp. 1–20 in Johnson, R. W. (ed.), *Volcanism in Australasia*, Elsevier, Amsterdam, The Netherlands.

Bunsen, R. (1851) Ueber die Prozesse der vulkanischen Gesteinsbildungen Islands, *Annalen der Physik (Leipzig)*, 2nd series, ed. J. C. Poggendorff, **83**, 197–272.

Burke, K. (1976) Development of graben associated with the opening of the Atlantic, *Tectonophysics*, **36**, 93–111.

Burke, K. (1978) Evolution of continental rift systems in the light of plate tectonics; pp. 1–9 in Ramberg, I. B. & Neumann, E. R. (eds) *Tectonics and Geophysics of Continental Rifts*, D. Reidel Pub. Co., Dordrecht, The Netherlands.

Burnham, C. W. (1979) The importance of volatile constituents; Ch. 16, pp. 439–82 in Yoder, H. S. (ed.), *The Evolution of the Igneous Rocks: Fiftieth Anniversary Perspectives*, Princeton Univ. Press, Princeton, New Jersey, USA.

Burnham, C. W. & Davis, N. F. (1974) The role of H_2O in silicate melts: II: Thermodynamic and phase relations in the system $NaAlSi_3O_8$-H_2O to 10 kilobars, 700° to 1100 °C, *Am. J. Sci.*, **274**, 902–40.

Burri, C. (1964) *Petrochemical Calculations Based on Equivalents* (Methods of Paul Niggli), Israel Program for Scientific Translations, Jerusalem, Israel.

Cameron, A. G. W. (1982) Elementary and nuclidic abundances in the Solar System; in Barnes, C. A., Schramm, D. N. & Clayton, D. D. (eds), *Essays in Nuclear Astrophysics*, Cambridge Univ. Press, Cambridge.

Cameron, E. N. (1970) Compositions of certain coexisting phases in the eastern part of the Bushveld Complex, *Geol. Soc. S. Afr., Spec. Publ.*, **1**, 46–58

Cameron, E. N., Jahns, R. H., McNair, A. H. & Page, L. R. (1949) Internal Structure of Granitic Pegmatities, *Econ. Geol., Monogr.*, **2**, 1–115.

Cameron, M., Bagby, W. C. & Cameron, K. L. (1980) Petrogenesis of voluminous mid-Tertiary ignimbrites of the Sierra Madre Occidental, Mexico, *Contrib. Mineral. Petrol.*, **74**, 271–84.

Cameron, W. E., Nisbett, E. G. & Dietrich, V. J. (1979) Boninites, komatiites and ophiolitic rocks, *Nature*, **280**, 550–3.

Carmichael, I. S. E. (1964) The petrology of Thingmuli, a Tertiary Volcano in Eastern Iceland, *J. Petrol.*, **5(3)**, 435–60.

Carmichael, I. S. E. (1965) Trachytes and their feldspar phenocrysts, *Mineral. Mag.*, **34**, 107–25.

Carmichael, I. S. E. (1967a) The mineralogy of Thingmuli, a Tertiary volcano in Eastern Iceland, *Am. Mineral.*, **52**, 1815–41.

Carmichael, I. S. E. (1967b) The mineralogy and petrology of the volcanic rocks from the Leucite Hills, Wyoming, *Contrib. Mineral. Petrol.*, **15**, 24–66.

Carmichael, I. S. E., Turner, F. J. & Verhoogen, J. (1974) *Igneous Petrology*, McGraw-Hill Book Co., New York, USA.

Carr, M. H. & Greeley, R. (1980) Volcanic features of Hawaii: A basis for comparison with Mars, *NASA SP-403*, NASA, Washington, DC, USA.

Carswell, D. A. (1980) Mantle derived lherzolite nodules associated with kimberlite, carbonatite and basaltic magmatism: A review, *Lithos*, **13**, 121–38.

Cawthorn, R. G. & Davies, G. (1982) Possible komatiitic affinity of the Bushveld Complex, South Africa; Ch. 6, pp. 91–6 in Arndt, N. T. & Nisbet, E. G. (eds), *Komatiites*, George Allen & Unwin, London.

Cawthorn, R. G. & O'Hara, M. J. (1976) Amphibole fractionation in calcalkaline magma genesis, *Am. J. Sci.*, **276**, 309–29.

Cermak, V. & Hurtig, E. (1979) Heat flow map of Europe, enclosure; in Cermak, V. & Rybach, L., *Terrestrial heat flow in Europe*, Springer-Verlag, Berlin.

Challis, G. A. (1969) Discussion on the paper 'The origin of ultramafic and ultrabasic rocks' by P. J. Wyllie, *Tectonophysics*, **7**, 495–505.

Chapin, C. E. (ed). (1979) Ash-flow tuffs, *Geol. Soc. Am., Spec. Pap.*, **80**.

Chapman, C. P. (1976) Asteroids as meteorite parent-bodies; the astronomical perspective, *Geochim. Cosmochim. Acta*, **40**, 701–19.

Chapman, C. R., Williams, J. G. & Hartmann, W. K. (1978) The Asteroids, *Ann. Rev. Astron. Astrophys.*, **16**, 33–75.

Chapman, R. W. & Williams, C. R. (1935) Evolution of the White Mountain Magma Series, *Am. Mineral.*, **20**, 502–30.

Chappell, B. W. & White, A. J. R. (1974) Two contrasting granite types, *Pac. Geol.*, **8**, 173–4.

Chayes, F. (1951) Modal analyses of the granite and diabase test rocks; Part 5, pp. 59–68 in Fairbairn, H. W. (ed.), A cooperative investigation of precision and accuracy in chemical, spectrochemical and modal analysis of silicate rocks, *US Geol. Surv. Bull.*, **980**.

Chayes, F. (1952) The finer-grained calcalkaline granites of New England, *J. Geol.*, **60(3)**, 207–54.

Chayes, F. (1963) Relative abundance of intermediate members of the oceanic basalt–trachyte association, *J. Geophys. Res.*, **68**, 1519–34.

Chayes, F. (1966) Alkaline and Subalkaline Basalts, *Am. J. Sci.*, **264**, 128–45.

Chayes, F. (1969) The chemical composition of Cenozoic andesite; in McBirney, A. R. (ed.), Proceedings of the Andesite Conference, *Oregon Dept Mineral Ind., Bull.*, **65**, 43–63.

Chayes, F. (1975) Statistical Petrology, *Carnegie Inst. Wash., Yearb.*, **74**, 542–50.

Chayes, F. (1977) The oceanic basalt–trachyte relation in general and in the Canary Islands, *Am. Mineral.*, **62**, 666–71.

Chayes, F. (1979a) Partitioning by discriminant analysis: A measure of consistency in the nomenclature and classification of volcanic rocks; Ch. 18, pp. 521–32 in Yoder, H. S. (ed.), *The Evolution of the Igneous Rocks: Fiftieth Anniversary Perspectives*, Princeton Univ. Press, Princeton, New Jersey, USA.

Chayes, F. (1979b) Electronic computation and book-keeping in igneous petrology, *Episodes (IUGS, Newsl.)*, **1979(1)**, 16–19.

Chou, C. L. (1978) Fractionation of siderophile elements in the Earth's upper mantle, *Lunar Planet. Sci. Conf., Proc. 9th*, 219–30.

Christiansen, R. L. & Lipman, P. W. (1972) Cenozoic volcanism and plate tectonic evolution of the western United States, II, Late Cenozoic, *Phil. Trans. R. Soc. Lond.*, **A.271**, 249–84.

Church, B. N. (1975) Quantitative classification and chemical comparison of common volcanic rocks, *Geol. Soc. Am., Bull.*, **86**, 257–63.

Clark, R. H. (1960) Petrology of the volcanic rocks of Tongariro subdivision; Appendix 2 in Gregg, D. R. (ed.), The Geology of Tongariro Subdivision, *NZ Geol. Surv., Bull.*, **40**, 107–23.

Clarke, D. B. (1970) Tertiary Basalts of Baffin Bay: Possible primary magma from the mantle, *Contrib. Mineral. Petrol.*, **25**, 203–24.

Clarke, D. B. & Pedersen, A. K. (1976) Tertiary volcanic province of West Greenland; pp. 365–85 in Escher, A. & Watt, W. S. (eds), *Geology of Greenland, Grønlands (Greenland) Geol. Unders.*, Copenhagen, Denmark.

Clarke, D. B. & Upton, B. G. J. (1971) Tertiary basalts of Baffin Bay: field relations and tectonic setting, *Can. J. Earth Sci.*, **8**, 248–58.

Clarke, F. W. & Washington, H. S. (1924) The compo-sition of the Earth's crust, *US Geol. Surv., Prof. Pap.*, **127**.

Clement, C. R., Skinner, E. M. W. & Smith, B. H. S. (1984) Kimberlite redefined, *J. Geol.*, **92**, 223–8.

Cobbing, E. J. & Pitcher, W. S. (1972) The coastal batholith of central Peru, *Geol. Soc. Lond., J.*, **128**, 421–60.

Coertze, F. J. (1970) The geology of the western part of the Bushveld Igneous Complex, *Geol. Soc. S. Afr., Spec. Publ.*, **1**, 5–22.

Cole, J. W. (1979) Structure, petrology and genesis of Cenozoic volcanism; Taupo Volcanic Zone, New Zealand – a review, *NZ J. Geol. Geophys.*, **22**, 631–57.

Cole, J. W. (1981) Genesis of lavas of the Taupo Volcanic Zone, North Island, New Zealand, *J. Volcanol. Geotherm. Res.*, **10**, 317–37.

Coleman, R. G. (1971) Plate tectonic emplacement of upper mantle peridotites along continental edges, *J. Geophys, Res.*, **76(5)**, 1212–22.

Coleman, R. G (1977) *Ophiolites: Ancient Oceanic Lithosphere?*, Springer-Verlag, Berlin.

Condie, K. C. (1976) Trace-element geochemistry of Archean greenstone belts, *Earth-Sci. Rev.*, **12**, 393–417.

Condie, K. C. (1981) Geochemical and isotopic constraints on the origin and source of Archaean granites, *Geol. Soc. Aust., Spec. Publ.*, **7**, 469–79.

Consolmagno, G. J. (1979) Sulfur Volcanoes on Io, *Science*, **205**, 397–8.

Coombs, D. S. & Wilkinson, J. F. G. (1969) Lineages and fractionation trends in undersaturated volcanic rocks from the East Otago Volcanic Province (New Zealand) and related rocks, *J. Petrol.*, **10**, 440–501.

Correns, C. W. (1969) *Introduction to Mineralogy, Crystallography and Petrology* (trans. from the 2nd German edn by W. D. Johns), George Allen & Unwin Ltd., London, and Springer-Verlag, New York.

Coulon, C. & Thorpe, R. S. (1981) Role of continental crust in petrogenesis of orogenic volcanic associations, *Tectonophysics*, **77**, 79–93.

Cox, K. G. (1972) The Karroo volcanic cycle, *Geol. Soc. Lond., J.*, **128**, 311–36.

Cox, K. G. (1980) A model for flood basalt vulcanism, *J. Petrol.*, **21(4)**, 629–50.

Cox, K. G., Bell, J. D. & Pankhurst, R. J. (1979) *The interpretation of igneous rocks*, George Allen & Unwin, London.

Cox, K. G., Gurney, J. J. & Harte, D. (1973) Xenoliths from the Matsoku Pipe; pp. 76–92 in Nixon, P. H. (ed.), *Lesotho Kimberlites*, Lesotho Nat. Devel. Corp., Maseru, Lesotho.

Cox, K. G. & Hornung, G. (1966) Petrology of the Karroo basalts of Basutoland (Lesotho), *Am. Mineral.*, **51**, 1414–32.

Cox, K. G., Johnson, R. L., Monkman, L. J., Stillman, C. J., Vail, J. R. & Wood, D. N. (1965) The geology of the Nuanetsi Igneous Province, *Phil. Trans. R. Soc. Lond.*, **A.257**, 71–218.

Crockett, R. N & Mason, R. (1968) Foci of mantle disturbance in southern Africa and their economic significance, *Econ. Geol.*, **63**, 532–40.

Crohn, P. W. & Gellately, D. C. (1968) Probable carbonatites in the Strangways Range Area, Central Australia, *Aust. J. Sci.*, **31(9)**, 335–6.

Cross, W., Iddings, J. P, Pirsson, L. V. & Washington, H. S. (1902) A quantitative chemico-mineralogical classification and nomenclature of igneous rocks, *J. Geol.*, **10**, 555–690.

Cross, W., Iddings, J. P., Pirsson, L. V. & Washington, H. S. (1903) *Quantitative Classification of Igneous Rocks, based on Chemical and Mineral Characters, with a Systematic Nomenclature. With an Introductory Review of the Development of Systematic Petrography in the Nineteenth Century by Whitman Cross*, Chicago.

Curtis, G. H. (1968) The stratigraphy of the ejecta from the 1912 eruption of Mount Katmai and Novarupta, Alaska, *Geol. Soc. Am., Mem.*, **116**, 153–210.

Czamanske, G. K., Ishihara, S. & Atkin, S. A. (1981) Chemistry of rock-forming minerals of the Cretaceous – Paleocene Batholith in southwestern Japan and implications for magma genesis, *J. Geophys. Res.*, **86(B.11)**, 10431–69.

Dallwitz, W. B. (1968) Chemical composition and genesis of clinoenstatite bearing volcanic rocks from Cape Vogel, Papua: a discussion, *3rd Int. Geol. Congr.*, **2**, 229–42.

Daly, R. A. (1910) Origin of alkaline rocks, *Geol. Soc. Am., Bull.*, **21**, 87–118.

Daly, R. A. (1914) *Igneous Rocks and their Origin*, McGraw-Hill Book Co., Inc., New York, USA.

Daly, R. A. (1925) The geology of Ascension Island, *Am. Acad. Arts Sci., Proc. (Philadelphia)*, **60**, 3–124.

Daly, R. A. (1933) *Igneous Rocks and the depths of the Earth*, McGraw-Hill Book Co., Inc., New York, USA.

Dana, J. D. (1849) *United States Exploring Expedition during the Years 1838–1847 under the command of Charles Wilkes*, vol. **10**, Philadelphia, USA.

Danchin, R. V., Ferguson, J., McIver, J. R. & Nixon, P. H. (1975) The composition of late-stage kimberlite liquids as revealed by nucleated autholiths, *Phys, &Chem. Earth*, **9**, 235–45.

Darwin, C. R. (1844) *Geological Observations on the Volcanic Islands, visited during the Voyages of H.M.S. Beagle, with brief notices on the Geology of Australia and the Cape of Good Hope, being the Second Part of the Geology of the Voyage of the Beagle*, Smith Elder & Co., London.

Davies, H. L. (1971) Peridotite–gabbro–basalt complex in eastern Papua: an overthrust plate of oceanic mantle and crust, *Aust., Bur. Miner. Resour., Geol. Geophys., Bull.*, **128**, 1–48.

Davies, H. L. (1976) Papua New Guinea Ophiolites, *25th Int. Geol. Congr.*, Sydney, Excursion Guide **52A**, 1–13.

Davis, B. T. C. & Schairer, J. F. (1965) Melting relations in the join diopside–forsterite–pyrope at 40 kbars and one atmosphere, *Carnegie Inst. Wash., Yearb.*, **64**, 123–6.

Dawson, J. B. (1962) The geology of Oldoinyo Lengai, *Bull. Volc.*, **24**, 349–87.

Dawson, J. B. (1972) Kimberlites and their relation to the mantle, *Phil. Trans. R. Soc. Lond.*, A.**271**, 297–311.

Dawson, J. B. (1980) *Kimberlites and their xenoliths*, Springer-Verlag, Berlin.

Dawson, J. B. (1981) The nature of the upper mantle, *Mineral. Mag.*, **44(333)**, 1–18.

Dawson, J. B. & Hawthorne, J. B. (1973) Magmatic sedimentation and carbonatitic differentiation in kimberlite sills at Benfontein, South Africa, *Q. J. Geol. Soc. (Lond.)*, **129**, 61–85.

Dawson, J. B., Smith, J. V. & Hervig, R. L. (1980) Heterogeneity in upper mantle lherzolites and harzburgites, *Phil, Trans. R. Soc. Lond.*, A.**297**, 323–31.

Dawson, J. B. & Stephens, W. E. (1975) Statistical analysis of garnets from kimberlites and associated xenoliths, *J. Geol.*, **83**, 589–607.

Dawson, J. B. & Stephens, W. E. (1976) Statistical analysis of garnets from kimberlites and associated xenoliths: addendum, *J. Geol.*, **84**, 495–6.

De, A. (1974) Silicate liquid immiscibility in the Deccan traps and its petrogenetic significance, *Geol. Soc. Am. Bull.*, **85**, 471–4.

Debon, F. & Le Fort, P. (1983) A chemical–mineralogical classification of common plutonic rocks and associations, *R. Soc. Edinb., Trans.*, **73**, 135–49.

Debon, F., Le Fort, P. & Sonet, J. (1981) Granitoid Belts west and south of Tibet; about their geochemical trends and Rb–Sr isotopic studies; pp. 395–405 in *Geological and Ecological Studies of Qinghai-Xizang Plateau*, Vol. 1, Science Press, Beijing, China.

De Bono, E. (1977) *Lateral Thinking: A textbook of Creativity*, Penguin Books, Harmondswoth, Middlesex.

Decker, R. & Decker, B. (1981) *Volcanoes*, W. H. Freeman & Co., San Francisco, USA.

Deer, W. A. (1976) Tertiary igneous rocks between Scoresby Sund and Kap Gustav Holm, East Greenland; pp. 405–29 in Escher, A. & Watt, W. S. (eds), *Geology of Greenland*, Grønlands Geol. Unders., Copenhagen, Denmark.

Deer, W. A., Howie, R. A. & Zussman, J. (1966) An Introduction to the Rock-forming Minerals, Longman, London.

Delesse, A. E. O. J. (1869) *Etudes sur la Metamorphisme des Roches*, Acad. Sci. (Paris).

De Long, S. E. & Hoffman, M. A. (1975) Alkali/Silica distinction between Hawaiian tholeiites and alkali basalts, *Geol. Soc. Am., Bull.*, **86**, 1101–8.

De Paolo, D. J. (1981) A neodymium and strontium isotopic study of the Mesozoic calc–alkaline granitic batholiths of the Sierra Nevada and Peninsular Ranges, California, *J. Geophys. Res.*, **86 (B.11)**, 10470–88.

De Roever, W. P. (1957) Sind die Alpinotypen peridotitmassen vielleicht tektonisch verfrachtete Bruchstucke der Peridotitschale?, *Geol. Rundsch*, **46**, 137–46.

Desmarest, N. (1771) Sur l'origine et la nature du basalte a grandes colonnes polygones, determinees par l'histoire naturelle de cette pierre, observee en Auvergne, *Mem. Acad. Sci. Paris*, **87**, 705–75.

De Waard, D. (1969) Annotated bibliography of anorthosite petrogenesis; pp. 1–11 in Isachsen, Y. W. (ed.), *Origin of anorthosite and related rocks*, New York State Museum and Science Service, Mem **18**, Albany, New York, USA.

Dewey, J. F. (1980) Episodicity, sequence, and style at convergent plate boundaries, *Geol. Assoc. Can., Spec. Pap.*, **20**, 553–73.

Dickinson, W. R. & Hatherton, T. (1967) Andesite volcanism and seismicity around the Pacific, *Science*, **157**, 801–3.

Dietrich, V., Emmermann, R., Oberhansli, R. & Puchett, H. (1978) Geochemistry of basaltic and gabbroic rocks from the west Mariana basin and the Mariana trench, *Earth Planet Sci. Lett.*, **39**, 127–44.

Dietrich, V. & Gansser, A. (1981) The leucogranites of the Bhutan Himalaya (Crustal anatexis versus mantle melting), *Schweiz. Mineral. Petrogr. Mitt.*, **61**, 177–202.

Dietz, R. S. (1961) Continental and ocean basin evolution by spreading of the sea floor, *Nature*, **190**, 854–7.

Dietz, R. S. (1963) Alpine serpentinites as oceanic rind fragments, *Geol. Soc. Am., Bull.*, **74**, 947–52.

Dixon, S. I. & Rutherford, M. J. (1979) Plagiogranites as late-stage immiscible liquids in ophiolite and mid-ocean ridge suites: an experimental study, *Earth Planet. Sci. Lett.*, **45**, 45–60.

Dodd, R. T. (1981) *Meteorites: A petrologic-chemical synthesis*, Cambridge Univ. Press, Cambridge.

Donaldson, C. H. (1982) Spinifex-textured komatiites: a review of textures, compositions and layering; Ch. 16, pp. 213–344 in Arndt, N. T. & Nisbet, E. G. (eds), *Komatiites*, George Allen & Unwin, London.

Dosso, L., Vidal, P., Contagrel, J. M., Lameyre, J., Marot, A. & Zimine, S. (1979) Kerguelen: Continental fragment or oceanic island?': Petrology and isotopic geochemistry evidence, *Earth Planet. Sci. Lett.*, **43**, 46–60.

Dostal, J., Dupuy, C. & Leyreloup, A. (1980) Geochemistry and petrology of meta-igneous granulitic xenoliths in Neogene volcanic rocks of the Massif Central, France: Implications for the lower crust, *Earth Planet. Sci. Lett.*, **50**, 31–40.

Dostal, J. & Fratta, M. (1977) Trace element geochemistry of a Precambrian diabase dike from western Ontario, *Can. J. Earth Sci.*, **14**, 2941–4.

Dott, R. H. (1969) Hutton and the concept of a dynamic Earth; pp. 122–41 in Schneer, C. J. (ed.), *Towards a history of Geology*, M.I.T. Press, Cambridge, USA.

Drever, H. I. (1956) The geology of Ubekendt Ejland, west Greenland: pt. II, The picritic sheets and dykes of the east coast, *Medd. Grønland*, **137**, 1–41.

Drever, H. I. & Johnston, R. (1967a) The ultrabasic facies in some sills and sheets: Ch. 3.2, pp. 51–63 in Wyllie, P. J. (ed.), *Ultramafic and Related Rocks*, John Wiley & Sons, New York, USA.

Drever, H. I. & Johnston, R. (1967b) Picritic Minor Intrusions: Ch. 3.5, pp. 71–82 in Wyllie, P. J. (ed.), *Ultramafic and Related Rocks*, John Wiley & Sons, New York, USA.

Dunham, A. C. & Strasser-King, V. E. H. (1981) Petrology of the Great Whin Sill in the Throckley Borehole, Northumberland, *Rep. Inst. Geol. Sci. (UK)*, **81/4**, 1/32.

Durocher, J. (1857) Recherches sur les roches ignees, sur les phenomenes de leur emission et sur leur classification, *Acad. Sci. (Paris), C.R.*, **44**, 325–30, 459–65, 605–9, 776–80, 859–63.

Du Toit, A. L. (1920) The Karroo Dolerites of S. Africa; a study in hypabyssal injection, *Geol. Soc. S. Afr., Trans.*, **23**, 1–42.

Du Toit, A. L. (1927) A geological comparison of South America with South Africa, *Carnegie Inst. Wash., Publ.*, **381**.

Du Toit, A. L. (1937) *Our wandering continents*, Oliver & Boyd, Edinburgh.

Eggler, D. H. (1973) Role of CO_2 in melting processes in the mantle, *Carnegie Inst. Wash., Yearb.*, **72**, 457–67.

Eggler, D. H. & Wendlandt, R. F. (1979) Experimental studies on the relationship between kimberlite magmas and partial melting of peridotite; pp. 330–8 in Boyd, F. R. & Meyer, H. O. A. (eds), *Kimberlites, diatremes and diamonds: their geology, petrology and geochemistry*, Proc. 2nd Int. Kimberlite Conf., vol. 1, Am. Geophys. Union, Washington, DC, USA.

Egorov, L. S. (1970) Carbonatites and ultrabasic–alkaline rocks of the Maimecha–Kotui region, N. Siberia, *Lithos*, **3**, 341–59.

Eichelberger, J. C. (1974) Magma contamination within the volcanic pile: Origin of andesite and dacite, *Geology*, **2(1)**, 29–33.

Eichelberger, J. C. (1975) Origin of andesite and dacite: Evidence of mixing at Glass Mountain in California and at other circum-Pacific volcanoes, *Geol. Soc. Am., Bull.*, **86**, 1381–91.

Eichelberger, J. C. & Hayes, D. B. (1982) Magmatic model for the Mount St Helens blast of May 18, 1980, *J. Geophys. Res.*, **87(B9)**, 7727–38.

Einarsson, P. (1978) S-wave shadows in the Krafla Caldera in NE-Iceland, Evidence for a magma chamber in the crust, *Bull. Volc.*, **41(3)**, 187–95.

Einarsson, P. & Brandsdottir, B. (1980) Seismological evidence for lateral magma intrusion during the July 1978 deflation of the Krafla Volcano in NE-Iceland, *J. Geophys.*, **47**, 160–5.

Elders, W. A. & Rucklidge, J. C. (1969) Layering and net veining in hornblende lamprophyre intrusions from the coast of Labrador, *J. Geol.*, **77**, 721–9.

Emeleus, C. H. (1982) The central complexes; Ch. 29, pp. 369–414 in Sutherland, D. S. (ed.), *Igneous Rocks of the British Isles*, John Wiley & Sons Ltd., Chichester.

Emeleus, C. H. & Upton. B. G. J. (1976) The Gardar period in southern Greenland; pp. 152–81 in Escher, A. & Watt, W. S. (eds), *Geology of Greenland*, Grønlands (Greenland) Geol. Unders., Copenhagen, Denmark.

Emmons, R. C. (1953) Petrogeny of the syenites and nepheline syenites of Central Wisconsin, *Geol. Soc. Am., Mem.*, **52**, 71–87.

Emslie, R. F. (1970) Liquidus relations and subsolidus reactions in some plagioclase-bearing systems, *Carnegie Inst. Wash., Yearb.*, **69**, 148–55.

Emslie, R. F. (1978) Anorthosite massifs, rapakivi granites, and Late Proterozoic rifting of North America, *Precambrian Res.*, **7**, 61–98.

Escher, A. & Watt, S. (ed.) (1976), *Geology of Greenland*, Grønlands (Greenland) Geol. Unders., Copenhagen, Denmark.

Esmark, J. (1823) Om Norit-Formationen, *Mag. f. Naturvidensk*, **1**, 205–15.

Ewart, A. (1976) Mineralogy and chemistry of modern orogenic lavas – some statistics and implications, *Earth Planet. Sci. Lett.*, **31**, 417–32.

Ewart, A. (1979) A review of the mineralogy and chemistry of Tertiary–Recent dacitic, rhyolitic, and related sodic volcanic rocks; pp. 13–121 in Barker, F. (ed.), *Trondhjemites, Dacites and Related Rocks*, Elsevier Sci. Pub., Amsterdam, The Netherlands.

Ewart, A. (1982) The mineralogy and petrology of Tertiary–Recent orogenic volcanic rocks: with special reference to the andesite-basalt compositional range; pp. 25–87 in Thorpe, R. S. (ed.), *Andesites: Orogenic Andesites and Related Rocks*, John Wiley & Sons, Chichester.

Eyles, V. A. (1961) Sir James Hall, Bt, 1761-1832, *Endeavour*, **20**, 210–16.

Fenner, C. N. (1926) The Katmai magmatic province, *J. Geol.*, **34**, 675–772.

Fenner, C. N. (1929) The crystallization of basalt, *Am. J. Sci.*, **5th series**, **18**, 225–53.

Fenner, C. N. (1938) Contact relations between rhyolite

and basalt on Gardiner River, Yellowstone Park, Wyoming, *Geol. Soc. Am., Bull.*, **49**, 1441–84.

Fenner, C. N. (1944) Rhyolite–basalt complex on Gardiner River, Yellowstone Park, Wyoming: a discussion, *Geol. Soc. Am., Bull.*, **55**, 1081–96.

Fersman, A. E. (1931) Uber die geochemische-genetische Klassifikation der Granit-pegmatite, *Schweiz. Mineral. Petrogr. Mitt.*, **41**, 64–83.

Fleischer, M. (1965) Summary of new data on rock samples G-1 and W-1, 1962–1965, *Geochim. Cosmochim. Acta*, **29**, 1263–83.

Fleischer, M. (1969) U.S. Geological Survey standards – I; additional data on rocks G-1 and W-1, 1965–1967, *Geochim. Cosmochim. Acta*, **33**, 65–79.

Floran, R. J., Grieve, R. A. F., Phinney, W. C., Warner, J. L., Simonds, C. H., Blanchard, D. P. & Dence, M. R. (1978) Manicouagan Impact Melt, Quebec, 1, Stratigraphy, petrology, and chemistry, *J. Geophys. Res.*, **83**, 2737–59.

Floyd, P. A. (1982) The Hercynian trough: Devonian and Carboniferous volcanism in south-western Britain; Ch. 16, pp. 227–42 in Sutherland, D. S. (ed.), *Igneous Rocks of the British Isles*, John Wiley & Sons Ltd., Chichester.

Floyd, P. A. & Winchester, J. A. (1975) Magma type and tectonic setting discrimination using immobile elements, *Earth Planet. Sci. Lett.*, **27**, 211–18.

Fouque, A. F. & Michel-Levy, A. (1879) *Mineralogie micrographique: Roches eruptives francaises*, Mem. Carte Geol., France, 2 vols, Paris.

Fozzard, P. M. P. (1956) Further notes on the volcanic rocks from Igwisi, Tanganyika, *Tanganyika (Tanzania) Geol. Surv. Rec.*, **6**, 69–75.

Francis, P. (1976) *Volcanoes*, Penguin Books, Harmondsworth, Middlesex.

Francis, P. (1981) *The Planets: A decade of discovery*, Penguin Books, Harmondsworth, Middlesex.

Fratta, M. & Shaw, D. M. (1974) 'Residence' contamination of K, Rb, Li and Tl in diabase dikes, *Can. J. Earth Sci.*, **11**, 422–9.

Frechen, J. (1976) Siebengebirge am Rhein, Laacher Vulkangebiet, Maargebiet der Westeifel, *Sammlung Geol. Fuhrer*, **Bd. 56**, Gebruder Borntraeger, Berlin.

Freestone, I. C. & Hamilton, D. L. (1980) The role of liquid immiscibility in the genesis of carbonatites – an experimental study, *Contrib. Mineral. Petrol.*, **73**, 105–17.

Fridriksson, S. (1975) *Surtsey*, John Wiley & Sons, New York, USA.

Froggatt, P. C. (1982) Review of methods of estimating rhyolitic tephra volumes; applications to the Taupo Volcanic Zone, New Zealand, *J. Volcanol. Geotherm. Res.*, **14**, 301–18.

Fuster, J. M., Arana, V., Brandle, J. L., Navarro, M., Alonso, U. & Aparicio, A. (1968) *Tenerife: Geology and Volcanology of the Canary Islands*, Inst. 'Lucas Mallada', Madrid, Spain.

Fuster, J. M., Cendero, A., Gartesti, P., Ibarrola, E. & Lopez-Ruiz, J. (1968) *Futeventura: Geology and Volcanism of the Canary Islands*, Inst. 'Lucas Mallada', Madrid, Spain.

Fuster, J. M., Fernandez-Santin, S. & Sagredo, J. (1968) *Lanzarote: Geology and Volcanology of the Canary Islands*, Inst. 'Lucas Mallada', Madrid, Spain.

Fuster, J. M., Hernandez-Pacheco, A., Munoz, M., Rodriquez-Badiola, E. & Gardia Cacho, L. (1968) *Gran Canaria: Geology and Volcanology of the Canary Islands*, Inst. 'Lucas Mallada', Madrid, Spain.

Fyfe, W. S. (1980) Crust formation and destruction, *Geol. Assoc. Can., Spec. Pap.*, **20**, 77–88.

Gansser, A. (1983) *Geology of the Bhutan Himalaya*, Denkschriften der Schweizerischen Naturforschenden Gesellschaft, **Bd. 96**, Birkhäuser Verlag, Basel, Switzerland.

Gass, I. G. (1963) Is the Troodos Massif of Cyprus a fragment of Mesozoic ocean floor?, *Nature*, **220**, 39–42.

Gass, I. G. (1967) The ultrabasic volcanic assemblages of the Troodos Massif, Cyprus; pp. 121–34 in Wyllie, P. J. (ed.), *Ultramafic and Related Rocks*, John Wiley, New York, USA.

Gass, I. G. (1970) Tectonic and magmatic evolution of the Afro-Arabian Dome; pp. 285–300 in Clifford, T. N. & Gass, I. G. (eds), *African Magmatism and Tectonics*, Oliver & Boyd, Edinburgh.

Geikie, A. (1897) *The ancient volcanoes of Great Britain*, Macmillan, London.

Gerasimovsky, V. I., Volkov, V. P., Kogarko, L. N. & Polyakov, A. I. (1974) Kola Peninsula; Ch. 4.2, pp. 206–21 in Sörensen, H. (ed.), *The Alkaline Rocks*, John Wiley & Sons, London.

Gill, J. B. (1981) *Orogenic Andesites and Plate Tectonics*, Springer-Verlag, Berlin.

Gittins, J. (1979) The feldspathoidal alkaline rocks; Ch. 12, pp. 351–90 in Yoder, H. S. (ed.), *The evolution of the igneous rocks: Fiftieth Anniversary Perspectives*, Princeton Univ. Press, Princeton, New Jersey, USA.

Gold, D. P. (1966) The average and typical chemical composition of carbonatites, *Mineral. Soc. India*, **I.M.A. Vol.**, 83–91.

Goldschmidt, V. M. (1915) Geologisch-petrographische Studien im Hochgebirge des südlichen Norwegens, 3, Die Kalksilikatgneise und Kalksilikatglimmerschiefer des Trondhjem-Gebiets, *Norske Vid. Selsk. Skr. Math.-Naturv.*, **Kl, 10**.

Goldschmidt, V. M. (1916) Geologisch-petrographische Studien im Hochgebirge des südlichen Norwegens, 4; Ubersicht der eruptivgesteine im Kaledonischen Gebirge zwischen Stavanger und Trondhjem, *Norske Vid. Selsk. Skr. Math.-Naturv.*, **Kl, 2**, 75–112.

Goldschimdt, V. M (1921) Geologisch-petrographische Studien im Hochgebirge des südlichen Norwegens, 5, Die Injektions metamorphose im Stavanger-Gebiete, *Norske Vid. Selsk. Skr. Math Naturv.*, **Kl, 10**.

Goldschmidt, V. M. (1923) Geochemische Verteilungsgesetze der Elemente, *Norske Vid. Selsk. Skr. Math. Naturv.* **Kl, 3**.

Goles, G. G. (1976) Some constraints on the origin of phonolites from the Gregory Rift, Kenya, and inferences concerning basaltic magmas in the Rift System, *Lithos*, **9**, 1–8.

Goodwin, A. M. (1977a) Archaean basin-craton complexes and the growth of Precambrian Shields, *Can. J. Earth Sci.*, **14(12)**, 2737–59.

Goodwin, A. M. (1977b) Archaean volcanism in Superior Province, Canadian Shield, *Geol. Assoc. Can. Spec. Pap.*, **16**, 205–41.

Gorschkov, G. S. (1959) Gigantic eruption of the volcano Bezymianny (Kamchatka), *Bull. Volc.*, **20**, 77–109.

Green, A. H. (1882) *Geology: Part 1, Physical Geology*, Rivingtons, London.

Green, D. H. (1964) Petrogenesis of the high-temperature peridotite intrusion in the Lizard area, Cornwall, *J. Petrol.*, **5**, 134–88.

Green, D. H. (1970) The origin of basaltic and nephelinitic magmas, *Leicester Lit. & Philos. Soc., Trans.*, **64**, 26–54.

Green, D. H. (1975) Genesis of Archean peridotitic magmas and constraints on Archean geothermal gradients and tectonics, *Geology*, **3**(1), 15–18.

Green, D. H., Hibberson, W. O. & Jaques, A. L. (1979) Petrogenesis of mid-ocean basalts; pp. 265–99 in McElhinny, W. H. (ed.), *The Earth: Its Origin, Structure and Evolution*, Academic Press, London & New York.

Green, T. H. (1969) High-pressure experimental studies on the origin of anorthosite, *Can. J. Earth Sci.*, **6**, 427–40.

Greenberg, J. K. (1981) Characteristics and origin of Egyptian Younger Granites: Summary, *Geol. Soc. Am., Bull.*, **Pt. 1, 92**, 224–32.

Gregory, J. W. (1921) *Rift Valleys and Geology of East Africa*, Seeley, Service & Co. Ltd, London.

Greig, J. W. (1927) Immiscibility in silicate melts, *Am. J. Sci.*, **13**, 1–44, 133–54.

Groves, A. W. (1951) *Silicate Analysis: A manual for geologists and chemists with chapters on check calculations and geochemical data*, George Allen & Unwin Ltd, London.

Gümbel, C. W. von (1874) *Die paläolithischem Eruptivgesteine des Fichtelgebirges*, Gotha, München.

Gupta, A. K. & Yagi, K. (1979) Experimental study of two picrites with reference to the genesis of kimberlite; pp. 339–43 in Boyd, F. R. & Meyer, H. O. A. (eds), *Kimberlites, diatremes and diamonds: their geology, petrology and geochemistry*, Proc. 2nd Int. Kimberlite Conf., Am. Geophys. Union, Washington DC, USA.

Gupta, A. K. & Yagi, K. (1980) *Petrology and genesis of leucite-bearing rocks*, Springer-Verlag, Berlin.

Gurney, J. J. & Ebrahim, S. (1973) Chemical composition of Lesotho Kimberlites; pp. 280–93 in Nixon, P. H. (ed.), *Lesotho Kimberlites*, Lesotho Natl. Dev. Co., Meseru, Lesotho.

Gurney, J. J. & Harte, B. (1980) Chemical variations in upper mantle nodules from southern African kimberlites, *Phil. Trans. R. Soc. Lond.*, **A.297**, 273–93.

Guth, A. H. & Steinhardt, P. J. (1984) The inflationary universe, *Sci. Am.*, **250**(5), 90–102.

Haggerty, S. E. (1970) The Laco magnetite lava flow, Chile, *Carnegie Inst. Wash., Yearb.*, **68**, 329–30.

Hall, A. (1967) The chemistry of appinitic rocks associated with the Ardara Pluton, Donegal, Ireland, *Contrib. Mineral. Petrol.*, **16**, 156–71.

Hamilton, W. & Myers, W. B. (1967) The nature of batholiths, *US Geol. Surv., Prof. Pap.*, **554-C**.

Hansen, K. (1980) Lamprophyres and carbonatitic lamprophyres related to rifting in the Labrador Sea, *Lithos*, **13**, 145–52.

Hardee, H. C. (1982) Permeable convection above magma bodies, *Tectonophysics*, **84**, 179–95.

Hargraves, R. B. (1969) A contribution to the geology of the Diana syenite gneiss complex; in Isachsen, Y. W. (ed.), Origin of anorthosites and related rocks, *NY State Museum Sci. Serv., Mem.*, **18**, 343–56.

Hargraves, R. B. (1976) Precambrian geologic history, *Science*, **193**, 363–71.

Hargraves, R. B. (ed.) (1980) *Physics of magmatic processes*, Princeton Univ. Press, Princeton, New Jersey, USA.

Harker, A. (1895) *Petrology for students* (1st edn), Cambridge Univ. Press, Cambridge.

Harker, A. (1904) The Tertiary igneous rocks of Skye, *Geol. Surv. Scot., Mem.*, Edinburgh.

Harker, A. (1909) *The Natural History of Igneous Rocks*, Methuen & Co., London.

Harper, L. F. (1915) Geology and mineral resources of the Southern Coalfield, Part 1, The South Coast Portion, *NSW Geol. Surv., Mem.*, **7**, 1–410.

Harris, P. G. (1957) Zone refining and the origin of potassic basalts, *Geochim. Cosmoschim. Acta*, **12**, 195–208.

Harris, P. G. (1963) Comments on a paper by F. Chayes, 'Relative abundance of intermediate members of the oceanic basalt–trachyte association', *J. Geophys. Res.*, **68**(17), 5103–7.

Harris, P. G., Kennedy, W. Q. & Scarfe, C. M. (1970) Volcanism versus plutonism – the effect of chemical composition; in Newall, G. & Rast, N. (eds), Mechanism of Igneous Intrusion, *Geol. J., Spec. Issue*, **2**, 187–200.

Harris, P. G. & Middlemost, E. A. K. (1970) The evolution of kimberlites, *Lithos*, **3**, 79–88.

Hart, S. R. & Allégre, C. J. (1980) Trace-element constraints on magma genesis; Ch. 4, pp. 121–59 in Hargraves, R. B. (ed.), *Physics of Magmatic Processes*, Princeton Univ. Press, Princeton, New Jersey, USA.

Hatherton, T. & Dickinson, W. R. (1969) The relationship between andesitic volcanism and seismicity in Indonesia, the Lesser Antilles and other island arcs, *J. Geophys. Res.*, **74**, 5301–10.

Hawkins, J. W. (1977) Petrologic and geochemical characteristics of marginal basin basalts; pp. 355–65 in Talwani, M. & Pitman, W. C. (eds), *Island Arcs, Deep Sea Trenches and Back-Arc Basins*, Am. Geophys. Union, Washington, DC, USA.

Hawthorne, J. B. (1973) Model of a kimberlite pipe; pp. 163–6 in Ahrens, L. H., Dawson, J. B., Duncan, A. R. & Erlank, A. J. (eds), *International Conference on Kimberlites*, Univ. Cape Town, Rondebosch, South Africa.

Hay, R. L. & O'Neil, J. R. (1983) Carbonatite tuffs in the Laetolil Beds of Tanzania and the Kaiserstuhl in Germany, *Contrib. Mineral. Petrol.*, **82**, 403–6.

Heier, K. S. (1973) A model for the composition of the deep continental crust, *Fortschr. Mineral.* **50**, 174–87.

Heinrich, E. W. (1966) *The Geology of Carbonatites*, Rand McNally & Co., Chicago, USA.

Hekinian, R. (1982) *Petrology of the Ocean Floor*, Elsevier Sci. Pub. Co., Amsterdam, The Netherlands.

Helz, R. T. (1980) Crystallization history of Kilauea Iki Lava Lake as seen in drill core recovered in 1967–1979, *Bull. Volc.*, **43**(4), 675–701.

Henderson, P. (1982) *Inorganic Geochemistry*, Pergamon Press, Oxford.

Herz, N. (1969) Anorthosite belts, continental drift and the anorthosite event, *Science*, **164**, 944–7.

Hess, F. L. (1933) Pegmatites, *Econ. Geol.*, **28**, 447–62.

Hess, H. H. (1954) Geological hypotheses and the Earth's crust under the oceans, *R. Soc. Lond., Proc.*, **A.222**, 341–8.

Hess, H. H. (1960) Stillwater Igneous Complex, Montana, *Geol. Soc. Am., Mem.*, **80**.

Hess, H. H. (1962) History of ocean basis; pp. 599–620 in

Engel, A. E. J. et al. (eds), *Petrologic Studies: A volume in honour of A. F. Buddington*, Geol. Soc. Am., New York, USA.

Hess, H. H. (ed.) (1966) Caribbean geological investigations, *Geol. Soc. Am., Mem.*, **98**, 1–310.

Hess, H. H. & Poldevaart, A. (eds) (1968) *Basalts: The Poldervaart treatise on rocks of basaltic composition*, Vols 1 & 2, Interscience Pub., New York, USA.

Hess, P. C. (1980) Polymerization model for silicate melts; Ch. 1, pp. 3–48 in Hargraves, R. B. (ed.), *Physics of Magmatic Processes*, Princeton Univ. Press, Princeton, New Jersey, USA.

Hildreth, E. W. (1979) The Bishop Tuff: Evidence for the origin of compositional zonation in silicic magma chambers, *Geol. Soc. Am., Spec. Pap.*, **180**, 43–75.

Hildreth, W. (1981) Gradients in silicic magma chambers: Implications for lithospheric magmatism, *J. Geophys. Res.*, **86(B.11)**, 10153–92.

Hödal, J. (1954) Rocks of the anorthosite kindred in Vossestrand, Norway, *Nor. Geol. Tidsskr.*, **24**, 129–243.

Holland, T. H. (1900) Charnockite series, a group of Archaean hypersthenic rocks in peninsular India, *India, Geol. Surv., Mem.*, **28(2)**.

Holmes, A. (1913) *The age of the Earth*, Harper & Brothers, London & New York.

Holmes, A. (1920) *The Nomenclature of Petrology*, Allen & Unwin, London.

Holmes, A. (1929) A review of the continental drift hypothesis, *Mining Mag.*, **40**, 205–9.

Holmes, A. (1936) Transfusion of quartz xenoliths in alkali, basic and ultrabasic lavas, south-west Uganda, *Mineral. Mag.*, **24**, 408–21.

Holmes, A. (1942) A suite of volcanic rocks from south-west Uganda containing kalsilite (a polymorph of KAl SiO$_4$), *Mineral. Mag.*, **26**, 197–217.

Holmes. A. (1944) *Principles of Physical Geology*, Thomas Nelson & Sons Ltd, London.

Holmquist, P. J. (1909) Nagra Jamförelsepunktev emellan nordamerikarsk och fennoskardisk prekambrisk Geologi, *Geol. Fören.* Stockh. Förh., **31**, 25–31.

Hoyle, F. (1975) *Astronomy and cosmology: A modern course*, W. H. Freeman & Co., San Francisco, USA.

Hubbert, M. K (1937) Theory of scale models as applied to the study of geologic structures, *Geol. Soc. Am., Bull.*, **48**, 1459–1520.

Hunt, T. S. (1857) Report of progress for the years 1853, 1854, 1855, 1856, *Can. Geol. Surv., Mem.*, 373–83.

Hunt, T. S. (1862) Descriptive catalogue of a collection of the crystalline rocks of Canada: Descriptive catalogue of a collection of the economic minerals of Canada and of its crystalline rocks sent to the London International Exhibition, *Can. Geol. Surv.*, 1862, 61–83.

Hunt, T. S. (1863) On the chemical and mineralogical relations of metamorphic rocks, *Dublin Quart. J. Sci.*, **32**, 220–30.

Hunter, D. R. (1970) The ancient gneiss complex in Swaziland, *Geol. Soc. S. Afr., Trans.*, **73**, 107–50.

Hunter, D. R. (1975) *Provisional tectonic map of the Bushveld Complex, 1 : 500,000, and the regional geological setting of the Bushveld Complex*, Econ. Geol. Res. Unit, Univ. Witwatersrand, Johannesburg, S. Africa.

Hunter, D. R. (1979) The role of tonalitic and trondhjemitic rocks in the crustal development of Swaziland and the eastern Transvaal, South Africa; Ch. 9, 301–32 in

Barker, F. (ed.), *Trondhjemites, dacites and related rocks*, Elsevier Sci. Pub., Amsterdam, The Netherlands.

Hutton, J. (1795) *Theory of the Earth, with Proofs and Illustrations*, Vols. 1 & 2, Edinburgh.

Iddings, J. P. (1903) Chemical composition of igneous rocks expressed by means of diagrams with reference to rock classification on a quantitative chemico-mineralogical basis, *US Geol. Surv., Prof. Pap.*, **18**, 1–92.

Iddings, J. P. (1909) *Igneous rocks: Composition, texture and classification, description and occurrence*, 2 vols, New York & London.

Iddings, J. P. (1913) *Igneous rocks: Composition, Texture and Classification, Description and Occurrence*, 2 vols, John Wiley & Sons Inc., New York, USA.

Iddings, J. P. & Morley, E. W. (1915) Contributions to the petrography of Java and Celebes, *J. Geol.*, **23**, 231–45.

Ilupin, I. G. & Lutts, B. G. (1971) The chemical composition of kimberlite and questions on the origin of kimberlite magma (in Russian), *Soretskaya Geol.*, **6**, 61–73.

Innocenti, F., Manetti, P., Mazzuoli, R., Pasquaré, G. & Villari, L. (1982) Anatolia and north-west Iran; pp. 327–49 in Thorpe, R. S. (ed.), *Andesites, orogenic andesites and related rocks*, John Wiley & Sons, Chichester.

Irvine, T. N. (1963) Origin of the ultramafic complex at Duke Islánd, Southeastern Alaska, *Mineral. Soc. Am., Spec. Pap.*, **1**, 36–45.

Irvine, T. N. (1973) Bridget Cove Volcanics, Juneau area. Alaska: Possible parental magma of Alaskan-type ultramafic complexes, *Carnegie Inst. Wash., Yearb.*, **72**, 478–91.

Irvine, T. N. (1975) Olivine–pyroxene–plagioclase relations in the system Mg$_2$SiO$_4$–CaAl$_2$Si$_2$O$_8$–KAlSi$_3$O$_8$–SiO$_2$ and their bearing on the differentiation of stratiform intrusions, *Carnegie Inst. Wash., Yearb.*, **74**, 492–500.

Irvine, T. N. (1980a) Magmatic infiltration metasomatism, double-diffusive fractional crystallization, and adcumulus growth in the Muskox Intrusion and other layered intrusions; Ch. 8, pp. 325–83 in Hargraves, R. B. (ed.), *Physics of Magmatic Processes*, Princeton Univ. Press, Princeton, New Jersey, USA.

Irvine, T. N. (1980b) Magmatic density currents and cumulus processes, *Am. J. Sci.*, **280-A**, 1–58.

Irvine, T. N. (1981) A liquid-density controlled model for chromitite formation in the Muskox Intrusion, *Carnegie Inst. Wash., Yearb.*, **80**, 317–24.

Irvine, T. N. & Baragar, W. R. A. (1971) A guide to the chemical classification of the common volcanic rocks, *Can. J. Earth Sci.*, **8**, 523–48.

Irvine, T. N. & Smith, C. H. (1967) The ultramafic rocks of the Muskox Intrusion, Chapter 2.3, pp. 38–49 in Wyllie, P. J. (ed.) *Ultramafic and Related Rocks*, John Wiley & Sons, Inc. New York, USA.

Irving, E. (1956) Rock magmatism: a new approach to the problems of polar wandering and continental drift; pp. 24–61 in Carey, S. W. (ed.), *Symposium on the present status of the continental drift hypothesis*, Univ. Hobart, Tasmania, Australia.

Isachsen, Y. W. (1969a) Origin of anorthosite and related rocks – a summarization; pp. 435–45 in Isachsen, Y. W. (ed.), *Origin of anorthosite and related rocks*, New

York State Museum and Science Service, Mem. **18**, Albany, New York, USA.

Isachsen, Y. W. (ed.) (1969b) *Origin of anorthosite and related rocks*, New York State Museum and Science Service, Mem. **18**, Albany, New York, USA.

Isacks, B. & Molnar, P. (1969) Mantle earthquake mechanisms and the sinking of the lithosphere, *Nature*, **223**, 1121–4.

Ishihara, S. (1977) The magnetite-series and ilmenite-series granitic rocks, *Mineral. J. (Tokyo)*, **27**, 293–305.

Jackson, E. D. (1961) Primary textures and mineral associations in the ultramafic zone of the Stillwater Complex, Montana, *US Geol. Surv., Prof. Pap.*, **358**.

Jackson, E. D. (1967) Ultramafic cumulates in the Stillwater, Great Dyke and Bushveld Intrusions; Ch. 2.2, pp. 20–38 in Wyllie, P. J. (ed.), *Ultramafic and Related Rocks*, John Wiley & Sons Inc., New York, USA.

Jackson, E. D. & Schlanger, S. O. (1976) Regional synthesis, Line Island Chain, Tuamotu Island Chain, and Manihiki Plateau, Central Pacific Ocean, *Deep Sea Dril. Proj., Initial Rept.*, **33**, 915–27.

Jacobson, R. R. E., Macleod, W. N. & Black, R. (1958) Ring-complexes in the Younger Granite Province of Northern Nigeria, *Geol. Soc. Lond., Mem.*, **1**, 1–72.

Jahns, R. H. & Burnham, C. W. (1969) Experimental studies of pegmatite genesis: I, A model for the derivation and crystallization of granitic pegmatites, *Econ. Geol.*, **64(8)**, 843–64.

Jakes, P. & Gill, J. B. (1970) Rare earth elements and the island arc tholeiitic series, *Earth Planet. Sci. Lett.*, **9**, 17–28.

Jakes, P. & Smith, I. E. M. (1970) High potassium calc–alkaline rocks from Cape Nelson, Eastern Papua, *Contrib. Mineral. Petrol.*, **28**, 259–71.

Jakes, P. & White, A. J. R. (1972) Hornblendes from calc–alkaline volcânic rocks of island arcs and continental margins, *Am. Mineral.*, **57**, 887–902.

Jakobsson, S. P. (1980) Outline of the petrology of Iceland; Ch. 8, pp. 57–73 in *26th Int. Geol. Congr.*, Paris, Guide Book for excursions **163C & 164C**, Iceland.

Jaques, A. L. (1981) Petrology and petrogenesis of cumulate peridotites and gabbros from the Marum Ophiolite Complex, Northern Papua New Guinea, *J. Petrol.*, **22(1)**, 1–40.

Jaques, A. L., Chappell, B. W. & Taylor, S. R. (1983) Geochemistry of cumulus peridotites and gabbros from the Marum Ophiolite Complex, Northern Papua New Guinea, *Contrib. Mineral. Petrol.*, **82**, 154–64.

Jaques, A. L., Lewis, J. D., Smith, C. B., Gregory, G. P., Ferguson, J., Chappell, B. W. & McCulloch M. T. (1984) The diamond-bearing ultrapotassic (lamproitic) rocks of the West Kimberley Region, Western Australia; pp. 225–54 in Kornprobst, J. (ed.), *Kimberlites 1: Kimberlites and related rocks*, Elsevier, Amsterdam, The Netherlands.

Johannes, W. & Gupta, L. N. (1982) Origin and evolution of a migmatite, *Contrib. Mineral. Petrol.*, **79**, 114–23.

Johannsen, A. (1917) Suggestions for a quantitative mineralogical classification of igneous rocks, *J. Geol.*, **25**, 63–97.

Johannsen, A. (1931) *A descriptive petrography of the igneous rocks*, Vol. 1, Introduction, textures, classification and glossary, Univ. Chicago Press, Chicago, USA.

Johannsen, A. (1932) *A descriptive petrography of the igneous rocks,*, Vol. 2, The quartz-bearing rocks, Univ. Chicago Press, Chicago, USA.

Johannsen, A. (1937) *A descriptive petrography of the igneous rocks*, Vol. 3. The intermediate rocks, Univ. Chicago Press, Chicago, USA.

Johannsen, A. (1938) *A descriptive petrography of the igneous rocks*, Vol. 4, Part I, The feldspathoid rocks, Part II, The peridotites and Perknites, Univ. Chicago Press, Chicago, USA.

Joplin, G. A. (1966) On lamprophyres, *R. Soc. NSW, J. Proc.*, **99**, 37–44.

Jung, D. (1958) Untersuchungen om tholeyit von Tholey (Saar), *Beiträge zur Mineralogie und Petrographie*, **6**, 147–81.

Kalkowsky, E. (1886) *Elemente der Lithologie: Für Studirende bearbeitet*, C. Winter, Heidelberg, Germany.

Kapustin, Y. L. (1971) *The Mineralogy of Carbonatites*, Nauka Press, Moscow, USSR.

Kasputin, Y. L. (1981) Damkjernites – dyke equivalents of carbonatites, *Int. Geol. Rev.*, **23(11)**, 1326–34.

Katsui, Y. (ed.) (1971) *List of the World's Active Volcanoes (with map)*, Volcanological Society of Japan/International Association for Volcanology and Chemistry of the Earth's Interior. Naples, Bull. Volc. Eruptions Spec. Issue.

Keil, K. (1969) Meteorite composition; Ch. 4, pp. 78–115 in Wedepohl, K. H. (ed.), *Handbook of Geochemistry*, Vol. 1, Springer-Verlag, Berlin.

Keith, D. W., Todd, S. G. & Irvine, T. N. (1982) Settling and compositions of the J–M platinum–palladium reef and other sulfide zones in the banded series of the Stillwater Complex, *Carnegie Inst. Wash., Yearb.*, **81**, 281–6.

Keller, J. (1981) Carbonatitic volcanism in the Kaiserstuhl Alkaline Complex: Evidence for highly fluid carbonatitic melts at the Earth's surface, *J. Volcanol. Geotherm. Res.*, **9**, 423–31.

Keller, J. (1983) Potassic lavas in the orogenic volcanism of the Mediterranean area, *J. Volcanol. Geotherm. Res.*, **18**, 321–35.

Kempe, D. R. C. (1965) A meta-anorthositic rock from Kilwa district, *Geol. Surv. Tanganyika (Tanzania), Rec.*, **11**, 49–51.

Kennedy, G. C. (1955) Some aspects of the role of water in rock melts, *Geol. Soc. Am., Spec. Pap.*. **62**, 489–504.

Kennedy, W. Q. (1933) Trends of differentiation in basaltic magmas, *Am. J. Sci.*, **25**, 239–56.

Kikuchi, Y. (1890) On pyroxenic components in certain volcanic rocks from the Bonin Island, *J. College of Science, Imperial Univ. of Tokyo*, **3**, 67–89.

King, B. C. (1949) The Napak area of Karamoja, Uganda, *Uganda Geol. Surv., Mem.*, **5**.

King, B. C. (1965) Petrogenesis of the alkaline igneous rock suites of the volcanic and intrusive centres of eastern Uganda, *J. Petrol.*, **6**, 67–100.

Klaproth, M. H. (1801) *Abhandlungen der koniglich preussischen Akademie der Wissenschaften zu Berlin.*

Klugman, M. A. (1969) The geology and origin of the Laramie Anorthosite Mass, Albany Country, Wyoming; p. 369 (Abs.) in Isachsen, Y. W. (ed.), Origin of anorthosites and related rocks, *NY State Museum Sci. Serv., Mem.*, **18**,

Konnert, J. H. & Karle, J. (1972) Tridymite-like structure in silica glass, *Nature*, **236**, 92–4.

Koster van Groos, A. F. & Wyllie, P. J. (1966) Liquid immiscibility in the system $Na_2O–Al_2O_3–SiO_2–CO_2$ at pressures to 1 kilobar, *Am. J. Sci.*, **264**, 234–55.

Kostlin, E. C. (1974) The Kunene Basic Complex, Northern South West Africa; pp. 123–35 in Kroner, A. (ed.), *Contributions to the Precambrian geology of Southern Africa*, Dept. Geology, Univ. Cape Town, Rondebosch, S. Africa.

Kremenetskiy, A. A., Yushko, N. A. & Budyanskiy, D. D. (1980) Geochemistry of the rare alkalis in sediments and effusives, *Geochem. Int.*, **178(4)**, 54–72.

Kuno, H. (1950) Petrology of Hakone Volcano and the adjacent areas in Japan, *Geol. Soc. Am., Bull.*, **61**, 957–1020.

Kuno, H. (1960) High-alumina basalt, *J. Petrol.*, **1**, 121–45.

Kuno, H. (1968) Origin of andesite and its bearing on the island arc structure, *Bull. Volc.*, **32**, 141–76.

Kuno, H. (1969) Pigeonite-bearing andesite and associated dacite from Asio, Japan, *Am. J. Sci.*, **Schairer Vol., 267-A**, 257–68.

Kushiro, I. (1972) Effect of water on the composition of magmas formed at high pressures, *J. Petrol.*, **13**, 311–34.

Kushiro, I. (1974) Melting of hydrous upper mantle and possible generation of andesitic magma: An approach from synthetic systems, *Earth Planet. Sci. Lett.*, **22**, 294–9.

Kushiro, I. (1975) On the nature of silicate melt and its significance in magma genesis: regularities in the shift of the liquids boundaries involving olivine, pyroxene and silica minerals, *Am. J. Sci.*, **275(4)**, 411–31.

Kushiro, I. (1980) Viscosity, density, and structure of silicate melts at high pressures, and their petrological applications; Ch. 3, pp. 93–120 in Hargraves, R. B. (ed.), *Physics of Magmatic Processes*, Princeton Univ. Press, Princeton, New Jersey, USA.

Kushiro, I. & Yoder, H. S. (1966) Anorthite-forsterite and anorthite-enstatite reactions and their bearing on the basalt-eclogite transformation, *J. Petrol.*, **7**, 337–62.

Kushiro, I., Yoder, H. S. & Mysen, B. O. (1976) Viscosities of basalt and andesite melts at high pressures, *J. Geophys. Res.*, **81**, 6351–6.

Kyle, P. R. (1981) Mineralogy and geochemistry of a basanite to phonolite sequence at Hut Point Peninsula, Antarctica, based on core from Dry Valley Drilling Project drill holes 1, 2 and 3, *J. Petrol.*, **22(4)**, 451–500.

Lacroix, A. (1905) Sur un nouveau type pétrographique representant le forme de profondeur de certaines leucotéphrite de la Somma, *Acad, Sci. (Paris) C.R.*, **141**, 1188–93.

Lacroix, A. (1922) *Minéralogie de Madagascar*, **Vol. 2**, A. Challamet, Paris.

Lacroix, A. (1939) Sur un nouveau type de roches metamorphiques (sakenites) faisant partie des schistes cristallins du sud de Madagascar, *Acad. Sci. (Paris), C.R.*, **209**, 609–12.

Larsen, E. S. (1948) Batholith and associated rocks of Corona, Elsinore, and San Luis Rey Quadrangles, southern California, *Geol. Soc. Am., Mem.*, **29**, 1–182.

Larsen, G., Gronvold, K. & Thorarinssen, S. (1979) Volcanic eruption through a geothermal borehole at Namafjall, Iceland, *Nature*, **278**, 707–10.

Le Bas, M. J. (1977) *Carbonatite-Nephelinite Volcanism: An African Case History*, John Wiley & Sons, London.

Le Bas, M. J. (1980a) Alkaline magmatism and uplift of continental crust, *Geol. Assoc. (Lond.), Proc.*, **91(1)**, 33–8.

Le Bas, M. J. (1980b) The East African Cenozoic Magmatic Province, *Atti Acad. Lincei (Roma)*, **47**, 111–22.

Le Bas, M. J. (1981) Carbonatite magmas, *Mineral. Mag.*, **44**, 133–40.

Le Bas, M. J. & Sabine, P. A. (1980) Progress in 1979 on the nomenclature of pyroclastic materials, *Geol. Mag.*, **117(4)**, 389–91.

Lebedev, A. P. & Pavlov, N. W. (1957) Dzhugdzhurskii anortozitivy massiv, *Akad. Nauk SSSR Inst. Geol. Rudn. Mestorozhd. Petrol. Mineralog. Geokim. Trudy*, **15**, 34–82.

Le Maitre, R. W. (1962) Petrology of volcanic rocks, Gough Island, South Atlantic, *Geol. Soc. Am., Bull,*, **73**, 1309–40.

Le Maitre, R. W. (1976a) The chemical variability of some common igneous rocks, *J. Petrol.*, **17(4)**, 589–637.

Le Maitre, R. W. (1976b) Some problems of the projection of chemical data into mineralogical classifications, *Contrib. Mineral. Petrol.*, **56**, 181–9.

Le Maitre, R. W. (1981) Genmix: A generalised petrological mixing model program, *Comput. Geosci.*, **7**, 229–47.

Le Pichon, X. (1968) Sea-floor spreading and continental drift, *J. Geophys. Res.*, **73**, 3661–97.

Le Pichon, X., Francheteau, J. & Bonnin, J. (1973) *Plate Tectonics*, Elsevier Sci. Pub. Co., Amsterdam, The Netherlands.

Lewis, H. C. (1887) On a diamondiferous peridotite, and the genesis of the diamond, *Geol. Mag.*, **4**, 22–4.

Lindgren, W. (1900) Granodiorite and other intermediate rocks, *Am. J. Sci.*, **4th series**, **9**, 269–82.

Lippard, S. J. (1973a) The petrology of phonolites from the Kenya Rift, *Lithos*, **6**, 217–34.

Lippard, S. J. (1973b) Plateau phonolite lava flows, Kenya, *Geol. Mag.*, **110**, 543–9.

Loewinson-Lessing, F. Y. (1899) Studien uber die Eruptivgesteine, *7th Int. Geol. Congr.*, St Petersbourg (1897), 191–464.

Loewinson-Lessing, F. Y. (1954) *A Historical Survey of Petrology* (trans. from the Russian by S. I. Tomkeiefe), Oliver and Boyd, Edinburgh.

Lofgren, G. (1980) Experimental studies on the dynamic crystallization of silicate melts; Ch. 11, pp. 487–551 in Hargraves, R. B. (ed.), *Physics of Magmatic Processes*, Princeton Univ. Press, Princeton, New Jersey.

London, D. & Burt, D. M. (1982) Chemical models for lithium aluminosilicate stabilities in pegmatites and granites, *Am. Mineral.*, **67**, 494–509.

Lovering, T. S. (1935) Theory of heat conduction applied to geological problems, *Geol. Soc. Am., Bull.*, **46**, 69–94.

Lowman, P. D. & Frey, H. V. (1979) *A geophysical atlas for interpretation of satellite-derived data*, NASA Tech. Mem. **79722**, Goddard Space Flight Center, Greenbelt, Maryland, USA.

Lubimova, E. A. (1958) Thermal history of the Earth, *Geophys. J. (R. Astronom. Soc.)*, **1**, 115–34.

Luth, W. C. (1976) Granitic rocks; pp. 335–417 in Bailey, D. K. & MacDonald, R. (eds), *The Evolution of the Crystalline Rocks*, Academic Press Inc., London.

Maaløe, S. & Aoki, K. (1977) The major element composition of the upper mantle estimated from the composition of lherzolites, *Contrib. Mineral, Petrol.*, **63**, 161–73.

Maaløe, S. & Jakobsson, S. P. (1980) The PT phase relations of a primary oceanite from the Reykjanes Peninsula, Iceland, *Lithos*, **13**, 237–46.

Macdonald, G. A. (1960) Dissimilarity of continental and oceanic rock types, *J. Petrol.*, **1**, 172–7.

Macdonald, G. A. (1967) Forms and structures of extrusive basaltic rocks pp. 1–61 in Hess, H. H. & Poldervaart, A. (eds), *Basalts: The Poldervaart Treatise on rocks of basaltic composition*, Interscience Pub., New York, USA.

Macdonald, G. A. (1968) Composition and origin of Hawaiian lavas, *Geol. Soc. Am., Mem.*, **116**, 477–522.

Macdonald, G. A. & Katsura, T. (1964) Chemical composition of Hawaiian lavas, *J. Petrol.*, **5**, 82–133.

Macgregor, A. M. (1928) The geology of the country around the Lonely Mine, Bubi District, *S. Rhodesia (Zimbabwe) Geol. Surv., Bull.*, **11**.

MacKenzie, W. S. (1972) The origin of trachytes and syenites; pp. 46–50 in *Progress in Experimental Petrology*, UK, NERC Pub. **Ser. D, No. 2/1972.**

Makarenko, G. F. (1977) The epoch of Triassic trap magmatism in Siberia, *Int. Geol. Rev.*, **19(9)**, 1089–1100.

Mansfield, G. R. & Ross, C. S. (1935) Welded rhylitic tuffs in southeastern Idaho, *Am. Geophys. Union, Trans.*, **16th Ann. Mtg.** pt. 1, 308–21.

Manson, V. (1967) Geochemistry of basaltic rocks: major elements; pp. 215–69 in Hess, H. H. & Poldervaart, A. (eds), *Basalts: The Poldervaart Treatise on Rocks of Basaltic composition*, Vol. 1, Interscience Pub., New York, USA.

Marsh, B. D. (1982) The Aleutians; pp. 99–114 in Thorpe, R. S. (ed.), *Andesites: Orogenic Andesites and Related Rocks*, John Wiley & Sons, Chichester.

Marshall, P. (1932) Notes on some volcanic rocks of the North Island of New Zealand, *NZ J. Sci. Technol.*, **13**, 198–202.

Mason, B. (1965) The chemical composition of olivine-bronzite and olivine–hypersthene chondrites, *Am. Mus. Novitates*, **2223**, 1–38.

Mason, B. & Moore, C. B. (1982) *Principles of Geochemistry*, John Wiley & Sons, New York, USA.

Mathias, M., Siebert, J. C. & Rickwood, P. C. (1970) Some aspects of the mineralogy and petrology of ultramafic xenoliths in kimberlite, *Contrib. Mineral. Petrol.*, **26**, 75–123.

Matson, D. L., Ransford, G. A. & Johnson, T. V. (1981) Heat flow from Io (J1), *J. Geophys. Res.*, **86**, 1664–72.

McBirney, A. R. (1963a) Conductivity variations and terrestrial heat-flow distribution, *J. Geophys. Res.*, **68(23)**, 6323–9.

McBirney, A. R. (1963b) Factors governing the nature of submarine volcanism, *Bull. Volc.*, **2(26)**, 455–69.

McBirney, A. R. (ed.) (1969) Proceedings of the Andesite Conference, *Oregon Dep. Geol. Mineral, Ind., Bull.*, **65**, 193p.

McBirney, A. R. (1979) Effects of assimilation; Ch. 10, pp. 307–38 in Yoder, H. S. (ed.), *The Evolution of the Igneous Rocks: Fiftieth Anniversary Perspectives*, Princeton Univ. Press, Princeton, New Jersey, USA.

McBirney, A. R. (1980) Mixing and unmixing of magmas, *J. Volcanol. Geotherm. Res.*, **7**, 357–71.

McBirney, A. R. & Gass, I. G. (1967) Relations of oceanic volcanic rocks to mid-oceanic rises and heat flow, *Earth Planet. Sci. Lett.*, **2**, 265–76.

McBirney, A. R. & Nakamura, Y. (1974) Immiscibility in late-stage magmas of the Skaergaard intrusion, *Carnegie Inst. Wash., Yearb.*, **73**, 348–52.

McBirney, A. R. & Noyes, R. M. (1979) Crystallization and layering of the Skaergaard Intrusion, *J. Petrol.*, **20(3)**, 487–554.

McBirney, A. R. & Williams, H. (1969) Geology and petrology of the Galapagos Islands, *Geol. Soc. Am., Mem.*, **118**.

McGee, P. E., Warner, J. L. & Simonds, C. H. (1977) *Introduction to the Apollo Collections: Part 1, Lunar igneous rocks*, NASA Houston, Texas, USA.

McGetchin, T. R. & Head, J. W. (1973) Lunar cinder cones, *Science*, **180**, 68–71.

McGregor, V. R. (1979) Archaean Gray Gneisses and the origin of the continental crust: evidence from the Godthab Region, West Greenland; Ch. 6 in Barker, F. (ed.), *Trondhjemites, dacites and related rocks*, Elsevier Sci. Pub., Amsterdam, The Netherlands.

McIver, J. R. & Ferguson, J. (1979) Kimberlitic, melilitic, trachytic and carbonatite eruptives at Saltpetre Kop, Sutherland, South Africa; pp. 111–28 in Boyd, F. R. & Meyer, H. O. A. (eds), *Kimberlites, Diatremes, and Diamonds: their geology, petrology and geochemistry*, Proc. 2nd Int. Kimerlite Conf., Am. Geophys, Union, Washington, DC, USA.

McKenzie, D. P. & Morgan, W. J. (1969) Evolution of triple junctions, *Nature*, **224**, 125–33.

McKie, D. & Frankis, E. J. (1977) Nyerereite: a new volcanic carbonate mineral from Oldoinyo Lengai, Tanzania, *Z. Kristallogr.*, **145**, 73–95.

McLennan, S. M., Nance, W. B. & Taylor, S. R. (1980) Rare earth element – thorium correlations in sedimentary rocks, and the composition of the continental crust, *Geochim. Cosmochim. Acta*, **44**, 1833–9.

Meijer, A. (1980) Primitive arc volcanism and a Boninite Series: Examples from Western Pacific Island Arcs; pp. 269–82 in Hayes, D. E. (ed.), The tectonic and geologic evolution of southeast Asian seas and islands, *Am. Geophys. Union, Geophys. Monogr.*, **23**.

Melson, W. G., Hart, S. R. & Thompson, G. (1972) St. Paul's Rocks equatorial Atlantic: Petrogenesis, radiometric ages, and implications on sea-floor spreading, *Geol. Soc. Am., Mem.*, **132**, 241–72.

Melson, W. G., Jarosewitch, E., Bowen, V. T. & Thompson, G. (1967) St. Peter and St. Paul Rocks: A high temperature, mantle-derived intrusion, *Science*, **155**, 1532–5.

Melson, W. G. & Thompson, G. (1971) Petrology of a transform fault zone and adjacent ridge sediments, *Phil. Trans. R. Soc. Lond.*, **A.268**, 423–41.

Menard, H. W. (1964) *Marine Geology of the Pacific*, McGraw-Hill Book Co., New York, USA.

Menzies, M. & Murthy, V. R. (1980) Mantle metasomatism as a precursor to the genesis of alkaline magmas – isotopic evidence, *Am. J. Sci.*, **280-A**, 622–38.

Metais, D. & Chayes, F. (1963) Varieties of lamprophyre, *Carnegie Inst. Wash., Yearb.*, **62**, 156–7.

Metais, D. & Chayes, F. (1964) Kersantites and vogesites; a possible example of group heteromorphism, *Carnegie Inst. Wash., Yearb.*, **63**, 196–9.

Michot, P. (1955) Anorthosites et anorthosites, *Acad. R. Belgique, Bull., Cl. Sci.*, **41**, 275–94.

Middlemost, E. A. K. (1972) A simple classification of volcanic rocks, *Bull. Volc.*, **36(2)**, 382–97.

Middlemost, E. A. K. (1974) Petrogenetic model for the origin of carbonatites, *Lithos*, **7**, 275–8.

Middlemost, E. A. K. (1975) The basalt clan, *Earth-Sci. Rev.*, **11**, 337–64.

Middlemost, E. A. K. (1980) A contribution to the nomenclature and classification of volcanic rocks, *Geol. Mag.*, **117(1)**, 51–7.

Middlemost, E. A. K. (1981) The Canobolas Complex, N.S.W., an alkaline shield volcano, *Geol. Soc. Aust., J.*, **28**, 33–49.

Miesch, A. T. (1976) Q-mode factor analysis of geochemical and petrologic data matrices with constant-row sums, *US Geol. Surv., Prof. Pap.*, **574-G**, 1–47.

Mills, A. A. (1984) Pillow lavas and the Leidenfrost effect, *Geol. Soc. Lond., J.*, **141**, 183–6.

Mitchell, R. H. (1970) Kimberlite and related rocks – A critical reappraisal, *J. Geol.*, **78**, 686–704.

Mitchell, R. H. (1981) Titaniferous phlogopites from the leucite lamproites of the West Kimberley Area, Western Australia, *Contrib. Mineral. Petrol.*, **76**, 243–51.

Mitchell-Thomé, R. C. (1970) *Geology of the South Atlantic Islands*, Beitrage zur Regionalen Geologie der Erde, **Band 10**, Gebruder Borntraeger, Berlin.

Mitchell-Thomé, R. C. (1976) *Geology of the Middle Atlantic Islands*, Beitrage zur Regionalen Geologie der Erde, **Band 12**, Gebruder Borntraeger, Berlin.

Miyashiro, A. (1974) Volcanic rock series in island arcs and active continental margins, *Am. J. Sci.*, **274**, 321–55.

Miyashiro, A. (1975) Classification, characteristics and origin of ophiolites, *J. Geol.*, **83**, 249–81.

Miyashiro, A. (1978) Nature of alkalic volcanic rock series, *Contrib. Mineral. Petrol.*, **66**, 91–104.

Mohr, P. A. & Wood, C. A. (1976) Volcano spacing and lithospheric attenuation in the Eastern Rift of Africa, *Earth Planet. Sci. Lett.*, **33**, 126–44.

Moorbath, S., O'Nions, R. K., Pankhurst, R. J., Gale, N. H. & McGregor, V. R. (1972) Further rubidium-strontium age determinations on the very early Precambrian rocks of the Godthab District, West Greenland, *Nature*, **240**, 78–82.

Moore, J. G., Phillips, R. L., Grigg, R. W., Peterson, D. W. & Swanson, D. A. (1973) Flow of lava into the sea 1969–1971, Kilauea Volcano, Hawaii, *Geol. Soc. Am., Bull.*, **84**, 537–46.

Moore, R. (1957) *The Earth we live on: The story of geological discovery*, Jonathan Cape, London.

Moore, R. B. (1983) Distribution of differentiated tholeiitic basalts on the lower east rift zone of Kilauea Volcano, Hawaii: A possible guide to geothermal exploration, *Geology*, **11**, 136–40.

Moores, E. M. & MacGregor, I. D. (1972) Types of Alpine Ultramafic Rocks and their implications for fossil plate interactions, *Geol. Soc. Am., Mem.*, **132**, 209–23.

Morgan, J. W. & Anders, E. (1980) Chemical composition of the Earth, Venus, and Mercury, *Natl Acad. Sci. USA, Proc.*, **77**, 6973–7.

Morgan, W. J. (1971) Convection plumes in the lower mantle, *Nature*, **230**, 42–3.

Morozewicz, J. (1902) Ueber Mariupolit, ein extremes Glied der Elaeolithsgenite, *Tschermaks Mineral. Petrogr. Mitt.*, **21**, 238–46.

Morris, E. C. & Dwornik, S. E. (1978) Geologic Map of the Amazonis Quadrangle of Mars: Atlas of Mars, **M 5B 15/158G**, US Geol. Surv., Arlington, VA, USA.

Morris, L. D., Simkin, T. & Meyers, H. (1979) *Map of the Volcanoes of the World*, World Data Center A for Solid Earth Geophysics, Boulder, Colorado, USA.

Morse, S. A. (1969) Syenites, *Carnegie Inst. Wash., Yearb.*, **67**, 112–20.

Morse, S. A. (ed.) (1977) The Nain Anorthosite Project, Labrador: **Field Report 1976**, *Contrib. No. 26, Dept. Geol. & Geog.*, Univ. Massachusetts, Amherst, Mass, USA.

Morse, S. A. (1980) *Basalts and Phase Diagrams: An introduction to the quantative use of phase diagrams in igneous petrology*, Springer-Verlag, New York, USA.

Muir, I. D. & Tilley, C. E. (1961) Mugearites and their place in alkali igneous rock series, *J. Geol.*, **69**, 186–203.

Mukherjee, A. (1967) Role of fractional crystallization in the descent: basalt→trachyte, *Contrib. Mineral. Petrol.*, **16**, 139–48.

Murase, T. & McBirney, A. R. (1973) Properties of some common igneous rocks and their melts at high temperatures, *Geol. Soc. Am., Bull.*, **84**, 3563–92.

Murray, C. G. (1972) Zoned ultramafic complexes of the Alaskan type: Feeder pipes of andesitic volcanoes, *Geol. Soc. Am., Mem.*, **132**, 313–35.

Mutch, T. A., Arvidson, R. E., Head, J. W., Jones, K. L. & Saunders, S. S. (1976) *The geology of Mars*, Princeton Univ. Press, Princeton, New Jersey, USA.

Myers, J. S. (1981) The Fiskenaesset Anorthosite Complex – A stratigraphic key to the tectonic evolution of West Greenland Gneiss Complex 3000–2800 M.Y. ago, *Geol. Soc. Aust., Spec. Publ.*, **7**, 351–60.

Mysen, B. O. & Kushiro, I. (1977) Compositional variations of coexisting phases with degree of melting of peridotite in the upper mantle, *Am. Mineral.*, **62**, 843–65.

Mysen, B. O., Ryerson, F. J. & Virgo, D. (1981) The structural role of phosphorus in silicate melt, *Am. Mineral.*, **66**, 106–17.

Naidu, P. R. J. (1963) A layered complex in Sittampundi, Madras State, India, *Mineral. Soc. Am., Spec. Pap.*, **1**, 116–23.

Nash, W. P. & Wilkinson, J. F. G. (1970) Shonkin Sag Laccolith, Montana, Pt 1, *Contrib. Mineral. Petrol.*, **25**, 241–69.

Neal, V. E. (1976) Lahars as major geological hazards, *Int. Ass. Eng. Geol., Bull.*, **14**, 233–40.

Neumann, E. R. (1980) Petrogenesis of the Oslo Region larvikites and associated rocks, *J. Petrol.*, **21(3)**, 499–531.

Neumann, E. R. & Ramberg, I. B. (1978) Paleorifts – Concluding remarks; pp. 407–24 in Ramberg, I. B. & Newmann, E. R. (eds), *Tectonics and Geophysics of Continental Rifts*, D. Reidel Pub. Co., Dordrecht, The Netherlands.

Nielsen, T. F. D. (1981) The ultramafic cumulate series, Gardiner Complex, East Greenland: Cumulates in a shallow level magma chamber of a nephelinitic volcano, *Contrib. Mineral. Petrol.*, **76**, 60–72.

Nielson, D. R. & Stoiber, R. E. (1973) Relationship of potassium content in andesitic lavas and depth to the seismic zone, *J. Geophys. Res.*, **78**, 6887–92.

Niggli, P. (1920) Systematic der Eruptivgesteine, *Cen-*

tralblatt fur Mineral., Geol. und Palaeontologie, Stuttgart, 161–74.

Niggli, P. (1923) *Gesteins-und Mineralprovinzen*, Gebrüder Borntraeger, Berlin.

Niggli, P. (1937) *Das Magma und seine Produkte unter besonderer Berücksichtigung des Einflusses der leichtflüchtigen Bestandteile*, Akademische verlagsgesellschaft, Leipzig.

Niggli, P. (1942) Das Problem der Granitbildung, *Schweiz, Mineral. Petrogr. Mitt.*, **22**, 1–84.

Ninkovich, D. & Hayes, J. D. (1972) Mediterranean island arcs and origin of high potash volcanoes, *Earth Planet Sci. Lett.*, **16**, 331–45.

Ninkovich, D., Sparks, R. S. J. & Ledbetter, M. T. (1978) The exceptional magnitude and intensity of the Toba eruption, Sumatra: An example of the use of deep-sea tephra layers as a geological tool, *Bull. Volc.*, **41**(3), 286–98.

Nisbet, E. G. (1982) The tectonic setting and petrogenesis of komatiites; Ch. 29, pp. 501–20 in Arndt, N. T. & Nisbet, E. G. (eds), *Komatiites*, George Allen & Unwin, London.

Nixon, P. H. (ed.) (1973) *Lesotho Kimberlites*, Lesotho Natl. Dev. Co., Maseru, Lesotho.

Nockolds, S. R. (1954) Average chemical composition of some igneous rocks, *Geol. Soc. Am., Bull.*, **65**, 1007–32.

Nockolds, S. R. & Allen, R. (1953) The geochemistry of some igneous rock series, Pt 1, *Geochim. Cosmochin. Acta*, **4**, 105–42.

Nockolds, S. R. & Le Bas, M. J. (1977) Average calc- (1978) *Petrology for students*, Cambridge Univ. Press, Cambridge.

Nockolds, S. R. & Le Bas, M. J. (1977) Average calc – alkali basalt, *Geol. Mag.*, **114**(4), 311–12.

Obata, M. (1980) The Ronda Peridotite: Garnet-spinel- and plagioclase-lherzolite facies and the P-T trajectories of a high-temperature mantle intrusion, *J. Petrol.*, **21**(3), 533–72.

O'Connor, J. T. (1965) A classification for quartz-rich igneous rocks based on feldspar ratios, *US Geol. Surv., Prof. Pap.*, **525-B**, 79–84.

Oftedahl, C. (1978) Main geologic features of the Oslo Graben; pp. 149–65 in Ramberg, I. B. & Neumann, E. R. (eds), *Tectonics and Geophysics of Continental Rifts*, D. Reidel Pub. Co., Dordrecht, The Netherlands.

O'Hara, M. J. (1965) Primary magmas and the origin of basalts, *Scott. J. Geol.*, **1**, 19–40.

O'Hara, M. J. (1968) The bearing of phase equilibria studies in synthetic and natural systems on the origin and evolution of basic and ultrabasic rocks, *Earth Sci. Rev.*, **4**, 69–133.

O'Hara, M. J. (1977) Geochemical evolution during fractional crystallization of a periodically refilled magma chamber, *Nature*, **266**, 503–7.

O'Hara, M. J. (1980) Non-linear nature of the unavoidable long-lived isotopic, trace and major element contamination of a developing magma chamber, *Phil. Trans R. Soc. Lond.*, **A.297**, 215–27.

O'Hara, M. J. & Mathews, R. E. (1981) Geochemical evolution in an advancing, periodically replenished, periodically tapped, continuously fractionated magma chamber, *Geol. Soc. Lond., J.*, **138**, 237–77.

O'Hara, M. J. & Yoder, H. S. (1967) Formation and fractionation of basic magmas at high pressure, *Scott. J. Geol.*, **3**, 67–117.

Ollier, C. D. & Pain, C. F. (1980) Actively rising surficial gneiss domes in Papua New Guinea, *Geol. Soc. Aust., J.*, **27**, 33–44.

O'Neil, J. R. (1979) Stable isotope geochemistry of rocks and minerals; pp. 235–63 in Jager, E. & Hunziker, J. C. (eds), *Lectures in Isotope Geology*, Springer-Verlag, Berlin.

Osann, A. (1919) Der chemische Faktor in einer natur- lichen Klassification der Eruptivgesteine, *Abh. Akad. Wiss, Heidelberg, Math. Naturw., Kl..* Pt 1, (Pt II 1920).

Osborn, E. F. (1959) Role of oxygen pressure in the crystallization and differentiation of basaltic magma, *Am. J. Sci.*, **257**, 609–47.

Osborn, E. F. (1979) The reaction principle; Ch. 5, pp. 133–69 in Yoder, H. S. (ed.), *The evolution of the igneous rocks: Fiftieth Anniversary Perspectives*, Princeton Univ. Press, Princeton, New Jersey, USA.

Ospovat, A. M. (1971) Translation with an introduction and notes of Abraham Gottlob Werner's, *Short Classification and Description of the Various Rocks*, Hafner Pub. Co., New York, USA.

Oxburgh, E. R. (1980) Heat flow and magma genesis; Ch. 5, pp. 161–99 in Hargraves, R. B. (ed.), *Physics of Magmatic Processes*, Princeton Univ. Press, Princeton, New Jersey, USA.

Oxburgh, E. R. (1981) The engine we call our Earth, *Open Earth*, **15**, 35–8.

Pankhurst, R. J. & Sutherland, D. S. (1982) Caledonian granites and diorites of Scotland and Ireland; Ch. 12, pp. 149–90 in Sutherland, D. S. (ed.), *Igneous Rocks of the British Isles*, John Wiley & Sons, Chichester.

Parks, C. F. (1961) A magnetite 'flow' in northern Chile, *Econ. Geol.*, **56**, 431–6.

Parsons, I. & Butterfield, A. W. (1981) Sedimentary features of the Nunarssuit and Klokken syenites, S. Greenland, *Geol. Soc. Lond., J.*, **138**, 289–306.

Peacock, M. A. (1931) Classification of igneous rock series, *J. Geol.*, **39**, 54–67.

Pearce, J. A. (1982) Trace element characteristics of lavas from destructive plate boundaries; pp. 525–48 in Thorpe, R. S. (ed.), *Andesites*, John Wiley & Sons. Chichester.

Pearce, J. A. & Cann, J. R. (1973) Tectonic setting of basic volcanic rocks determined using trace elements analyses, *Earth Planet. Sci. Lett.*, **19**, 290–300.

Peccerillo, A. & Taylor, S. R. (1976) Geochemistry of Eocene calc-alkaline volcanic rocks from the Kastamonu area, northern Turkey, *Contr. Mineral. Petrol.*, **58**, 63–81.

Perera, L. R. K. (1983) The origin of the pink granites of Sri Lanka – Another view, *Precambrian Res.*, **20**, 17–37.

Perrin, R. (1954) Granitization, metamorphism and volcanism, *Am. J. Sci.*, **252**, 449–65.

Perrin, R. (1956) Granite again, *Am. J. Sci.*, **254**, 1–18.

Perrin, R. & Rouboult, M. (1949) On the Granite Problem, *J. Geol.*, **57**, 357–79.

Petersen, J. (1891) Beitrage zur petrographie von Sulphur Island, Peel Island, Hachijo und Mijakeshima, *Jahrbuch der Hamburgischen wissenschaftlichen Anstalten*, Hamburg, **8**, 1–59.

Philpotts, A. R. (1967) Origin of certain iron-titanium oxide and apatite rocks, *Econ. Geol.*, **62**, 303–15.

Philpotts, A. R. (1972) Density, surface tension and viscosity of the immiscible phase in a basic alkaline magma, *Lithos*, **5**, 1–18.

Philpotts, A. R. (1974) The Monteregian Province; Ch. 4.6, pp. 293–310 in Sørensen, H. (ed.), *The Alkaline Rocks*, John Wiley & Sons, London.

Philpotts, A. R. (1981) A model for the generation of massif-type anorthosites, *Can. Mineral.*, **19**, 233–53.

Philpotts, A. R. (1982) Compositions of immiscible liquids in volcanic rocks, *Contrib. Mineral. Petrol.*, **80**, 201–18.

Pichler, H. (1970) Italienische Vulkan-Gebiete 1: Somma-Vesuv, Latium, Toscana, *Sammlung Geol. Fuhrer*, **Bd 51**, 1–258, Gebruder Borntraeger, Berlin.

Piper, J. D. A. (1971) Ground magnetic studies of crustal growth in Iceland, *Earth Planet. Sci. Lett.*, **12**, 199–207.

Pirsson, L. V. (1905) Petrography and geology of the igneous rocks of the Highwood Mountains, Montana, *US Geol. Surv., Bull.*, **237**, 83–9.

Pitcher, W. S. (1978) The anatomy of a batholith, *Geol. Soc. Lond., J.*, **135**, 157–82.

Pitcher, W. S. (1979a) The nature, ascent and emplacement of granitic magmas, *Geol. Soc. Lond., J.*, **136**, 627–62.

Pitcher, W. S. (1979b) Comments on the geological environment of granites; pp. 1–8 in Atherton, M. P. & Tarney, J. (eds), *Origin of Granite Batholiths; Geochemical Evidence*, Shiva Pub. Ltd., Orpington, Kent.

Pitcher, W. S. (1982) Granite types and tectonic environment; Ch. 1–3, pp. 19–40 in Hsü, K. J. (ed.), *Mountain Building Processes*, Academic Press, London.

Pitcher, W. S. & Berger, A. R. (1972) *The Geology of Donegal: A study of granite emplacement and unroofing*, Wiley-Interscience, New York, USA.

Pitcher, W. S. & Read, H. H. (1959) The main Donegal granite, *Q. J. Geol. Soc. (Lond.)*, **114** (for 1958), 259–305.

Playfair, J. (1802) *Illustrations of the Huttonian Theory of the Earth*, printed for Cadell & Davies, London & William Creech, Edinburgh.

Poldervaart, A. (1955) Chemistry of the Earth's Crust, *Geol. Soc. Am., Spec. Pap.*, **62**, 119–44.

Poldervaart, A. & Parker, A. B. (1964) The crystallization index as a parameter of igneous differentiation in binary variation diagrams, *Am. J. Sci.*, **262**, 281–9.

Presnall, D. C. (1969) The geometrical analysis of partial fusion, *Am. J. Sci.*, **267**, 1178–94.

Presnall, D. C., Dixon, S. A., Dixon, J. R., O'Donnell, T. H., Brenner, N. L., Schrock, R. L. & Dycus, D. W. (1978) Liquidus phase relations in the join diopside-forsterite-anorthite from 1 atm. to 20 kbar: their bearing on the generation and crystallization of basaltic magma, *Contrib. Mineral. Petrol.*, **66**, 203–20.

Presnall, D. C., Dixon, J. R., O'Donnell, T. H. & Dixon, S. A. (1979) Generation of mid-ocean ridge tholeiites, *J. Petrol.*, **20(1)**, 3–35.

Prider, R. T. (1960) The leucite lamproites of the Fitzroy Basin, Western Australia, *Geol. Soc. Aust., J.*, **6**, 71–118.

Pyatenko, I. K. & Saprykina, L. G. (1976) Carbonatite lavas and pyroclastics in the Paleozoic sedimentary volcanic sequence of the Kontozero District, Kola Peninsular, *Dokl. Akad. Nauk. SSSR.*, 185–7.

Quick, J. E. (1981a) Petrology and petrogenesis of the Trinity Peridotite, an upper mantle diapir in the Eastern Klamath Mountains, Northern California, *J. Geophys. Res.*, **86(B12)**, 11837–63.

Quick, J. E. (1981b) The origin and significance of large, tabular dunite bodies in the Trinity Peridotite, Northern California, *Contrib. Mineral. Petrol.*, **78**, 413–22.

Raguin, E. (1965) *Geology of Granite*, Interscience Pub., London.

Ramberg, H. (1948) Titanic iron ore formed by dissociation of silicates in granulite facies, *Econ. Geol.*, **43**, 553–70.

Ramberg, H. (1967) Model experimentation of the effect of gravity on tectonic processes, *Geophys. J. (R. Astronom. Soc.)*, **14**, 307–29.

Ramberg, H. (1970) Model studies in relation to intrusion of plutonic bodies; pp. 261–86 in Newall, G. & Rast, N. (eds), *Mechanism of Igneous Intrusion, Geol. J. Spec. Issue*, **2**, 261–86.

Ramsay, W. (1896) Urtit, ein basisches Endglied der Augitsyenit – Nephelinsyenit – Serie, *Geol. Fören. Stockh., Förh.*, **18**, 459–68.

Ramsay, W. & Berghell, H. (1891) Das Gestein vom Iiwaara in Finland, *Geol. Fören. Stockh. Förh.*, **13**, 300–11.

Rea, W. J. (1982) The Lesser Antilles; pp. 167–85 in Thorpe, R. S. (ed.), *Andesites: Orogenic Andesites and Related Rocks*, John Wiley & Sons, Chichester.

Read, H. H. (1948) Granites and granites, *Geol. Soc. Am., Mem.*, **28**, 1–19.

Read, H. H. (1951) Metamorphism and granitization, Alex. L. du Toit Memorial Lecture, No. 2, *Geol. Soc. S. Afr., Trans.*, **Annex. to 54**, 1–17.

Read, H. H. (1957) *The Granite Controversy*, Thomas Murby & Co., London.

Read, H. H., Sadashivaiah, M. S. & Haq, B. J. (1961) Differentation in the olivine gabbro of the Insch, mass, Aberdeenshire, *Geol. Assoc. (Lond.), Proc.*, **72**, 391–413.

Reaumur, R. A de (1726) Que le fer est de tous les métaux celui qui se moule le plus parfaitement; et quelle en est la cause, *Mém. Acad. Sci., Paris*, 273–87.

Reynolds, D. L. (1947) The granite controversy, *Geol. Mag.*, **84**, 209–23.

Reynolds, D. L. (1954) Fluidization as a geological process and its bearing on the problem of intrusive granites, *Am. J. Sci.*, **252**, 577–614.

Rhodes, F. H. T. & Stone, R. O. (1981) (eds) *Language of the Earth*, Pergamon Press, New York, USA.

Rice, A. (1981) Convective fractionation: A mechanism to provide cryptic zoning (macrosegregation), layering, crescumulates, banded tuffs and explosive volcanism in igneous processes, *J. Geophys. Res.*, **86**, 405–17.

Richardson, W. A. & Sneesby, G. (1922) The frequency distribution of igneous rocks, *Mineral. Mag.*, **19**, 303–13.

Rickwood, P. C. (1981) The largest crystals, *Am. Mineral.*, **66**, 885–907.

Ringwood, A. E. (1962) A model for the upper mantle, *J. Geophy. Res.*, **67**, 857–66.

Ringwood, A. E. (1974) The petrological evolution of island arc systems, *Geol. Soc. Lond., J.*, **130**, 183–204.

Ringwood, A. E. (1975) *Composition and Petrology of the Earth's Mantle*, McGraw-Hill, New York, USA.

Ringwood, A. E. (1982) Phase transformations and differentiation in subducted lithosphere: implications for mantle dynamics, basalt petrogenesis, and crustal evolution, *J. Geol.*, **90(6)**, 611–43.

Rittmann, A. (1936) *Vulkane und ihre Tätigkeit*, Ferdinand Enke, Stuttgart, W. Germany.

Rittmann, A. (1962) *Volcanoes and their activity* (trans. from the 2nd German edn by E. A. Vincent), Interscience Pub., New York, USA.

Rittmann, A. (1970) The probable origin of high-alumina basalts, *Bull. Volc.*, **34(2)**, 414–20.

Rittmann, A. (1973) *Stable mineral assemblages of igneous rocks*, Springer-Verlag, Berlin.

Robertson, I. D. M. & van Breemen, O. (1969) The southern satellite dykes of the Great Dyke, Rhodesia, *Geol. Soc. S. Afr., Spec. Publ.*, **1**, 621–44.

Roche, H. de la & Leterrier, J. (1973) Transposition du tetraedre mineralogique de Yoder et Tilley dans un diagramme chimique de classification des roches basaltiques, *Acad. Sci. (Paris), C.R.*, Ser. D., **276**, 3115–18.

Roche, H. de la, Leterrier, J., Granclaude, P. & Marchall, M. (1980) A classification of volcanic and plutonic rocks using R1, R2 diagram and major element analyses; its relationship with current nomenclature, *Chem. Geol.*, **29**, 183–210.

Rock, N. M. S. (1977) The nature and origin of lamprophyres: some definitions, distinctions, and deviations, *Earth-Sci. Rev.*, **13**, 123–69.

Roddick, J. A. (ed.) (1983) Circum-Pacific Plutonic Terranes, *Geol. Soc. Am., Mem.*, **159**, 1–316.

Roedder, E. (1951) Low temperature liquid immiscibility in the system K_2O–FeO–Al_2O_3–SiO_2, *Am. Mineral.*, **36**, 282–6.

Roedder, E. (1979) Silicate liquid immiscibility in magmas; Ch. 2, pp. 15–57 in Yoder, H. S. (ed.), *The Evolution of the Igneous Rocks: Fiftieth Anniversary Perspectives*, Princeton Univ. Press, Princeton, New Jersey, USA.

Roedder, E. & Weiblen, P. W. (1970) Lunar petrology of silicate melt inclusions, Proc. Apollo 11 Lunar Sci. Conf., *Geochim. Cosmochim. Acta*, **Suppl. 1, (1)**, 801–37.

Roedder, E. & Weiblen, P. W. (1977) Compositional variation in late-stage differentiates in mare lavas, as indicated by silicate melt inclusions, Proc. 8th Lunar Sci. Conf., *Geochim. Cosmochim. Acta*, **Suppl., 8(2)**, 1767–83.

Rogers, D. P. (1968) The extrusive iron oxide deposits, 'El Laco', Chile, *Geol. Soc. Am., Abstr. Programs*, 252–3.

Rogers, G. S. (1911) Geology of the Cortlandt series and its emery deposits, *NY Acad. Sci., Ann.*, **21**, 11–86.

Romey, W. D. (1968) An evaluation of some 'differences' between anorthosite in massifs and in layered complexes, *Lithos*, **1**, 230–41.

Ronov, A. B. & Yaroshevskiy, A. A. (1976) A new model for the chemical structure of the Earth's crust, *Geochem. Int.*, **13(6)**, 89–121.

Rose, G. (1842) *Mineralogisch-geognostische Reise nach dem Ural, dem Altai und dem Kaspischen Meere*, **II**, Berlin.

Rose, W. I., Grant, M. K. & Easter, J. (1979) Geochemistry of the Los Chocoyos Ash, Quezaltenango Valley, Guatemala, *Geol. Soc. Am., Spec. Pap.*, **180**, 87–99.

Rosenberg, P. E. (1967) Subsolidus relations in the system $CaCO_3$–$MgCO_3$–$FeCO_3$ between 350 °C and 550 °C, *Am. Mineral.*, **52**, 787–96.

Rosenbusch, H. (1877a) Die Steiger Schiefer und ihre contactzone an den Granititen von Barr-Andlau, *Abhandlungen zur geologischen Specialkarte von Elsass-Lothringen*, **Bd. 1, H.2**, Druck und Verlag von R. Schultz & Cie, Strassburg.

Rosenbusch, H. (1877b) *Mikroskopische Physiographie der massigen Gesteine* (1st edn), Schweizerbart'sche Verlagshandlung, Stuttgart, Germany.

Rosenbusch, H. (1887) *Mikroskopische Physiographie der massigen Gesteine* (2nd edn), Schweizerbart'sche Verlagshandlung (E. Koch), Stuttgart, Germany.

Rosenbusch, H. (1908) *Mikroskopische Physiographie der massigen Gesteine* (4th edn), Schweizerbart'sche Verlagshandlung, Stuttgart, Germany.

Rosenbusch, H. & Osann, A. (1923) *Elemente der Gesteinslehr*, von Dr A. Osann, E. Schweizerbart'sche Verlags buchhandlung, Stuttgart, Germany.

Roth, J. L. A. (1861) *Die Gesteinsanalysen in tabellarischer übersicht und mit kritischen erläuterungen, von Justus Roth*, W. Hertz (Bessersche buchhandlung), Berlin.

Roth, J. L. A. (1879) *Allgemeine und chemische Geologie*, 3 vols, W. Hertz (Bessersche buchhandlung), Berlin.

Rothstein, A. T. V. (1981) The primary crescumulates of the Lizard peridotite, Cornwall, *Geol. Mag.*, **118(5)**, 491–500.

Rubie, D. C. & Gunter, W. D. (1983) The role of speciation in alkaline igneous fluids during fenite metasomatism, *Contrib. Mineral. Petrol.*, **82**, 165–75.

Rüegg, N. R. (1975) *Modelas de variacáo quimica na provincia basaltica do Brasil Meridional*, Vols 1 & 2, Inst. de Geociencias, Univ. de Sao Paulo, Brazil.

Runcorn, S. K. (1956) Palaeomagnetic comparisons between Europe and North America, *Geol. Assoc. Can., Proc.*, **8**, 77–85.

Rutherford, E. & Soddy, F. (1902) The cause and nature of radioactivity, *Philos. Mag.*, **6(4)**, 569–85.

Sabine, P. A. (1960) The geology of Rockall, North Atlantic, GB, *Geol. Surv., Bull.*, **16**, 156–78.

Sabine, P. A. (1965) Rockall: An unusual occurrence of Tertiary Granite, *Geol. Soc. Lond., Proc.*, **1621**, 51.

Sabine, P. A. & Sutherland, D. S. (1982) Petrography of British igneous rocks; Appendix A, pp. 479–544 in Sutherland, D. S. (ed.), *Igneous Rocks of the British Isles*, John Wiley & Sons, Chichester.

Sagan, C. (1981) *Cosmos*, Macdonald Future Pub., London.

Sahama, T. G. (1962) Petrology of Mount Nyiragongo, *Geol. Soc. Edinb., Trans.*, **19**, 1–28.

Sakuyama, M. (1981) Petrological study of the Myoko and Kurohime Volcanoes, Japan: Crystallization sequence and evidence for magma mixing, *J. Petrol.*, **22(4)**, 553–83.

Saunders, A. D., Tarney, J. & Weaver, D. (1980) Transverse geochemical variations across the Antarctic Peninsular: implications for the genesis of calcalkaline magmas, *Earth Planet. Sci. Lett.*, **46**, 344–60.

Scarfe, C. M. (1981) The pressure dependence of the viscosity of some basic melts, *Carnegie Inst. Wash., Yearb.*, **80**, 336–9.

Scarfe, C. M. & Hamilton, T. S. (1980) Viscosity of lavas from the Level Mountain Volcanic Center, Northern

British Columbia, *Carnegie Inst. Wash., Yearb.*, **79**, 318–20.

Scarfe, C. M., Luth, W. C. & Tuttle, O. F. (1966) An experimental study bearing on the absence of leucite in plutonic rocks, *Am. Mineral.*, **51**, 726–35.

Schairer, J. F. (1950) The alkali feldspar join in the system NaAlSiO₄–KAlSiO₄–SiO₂, *J. Geol.*, **58**, 512–17.

Scott, B. H. (1979) Petrogenesis of kimberlites and associated potassic lamprophyres from central West Greenland; pp. 190–204 in Boyd, F. R. & Meyer, H. O. A. eds), *Kimberlites, Diatremes, and Diamonds: Their Geology, Petrology and Geochemistry*, Proc. 2nd Int. Kimberlite Conf., Am Geophys. Union, Washington, DC, USA.

Scott, D. H. & Carr, M. H. (1978) Geologic Map of Mars. *US Geol. Surv., Misc. Invest. Series*, **Map I-1083**, Arlington, VA, USA.

Scrope, G. P. (1825) *Consideration on Volcanoes, the Probable Cause of their Phenomena, the Laws which Determine their March, the Disposition of their Products, and their Connexion with the Present State and Past History of the Globe; leading to the Establishment of a new Theory of the Earth*, J. Murray, London.

Scrope, G. P. (1862) *Volcanoes: their phenomena, share in the structure and composition of the Earth's surface, and relation to its internal forces, with catalogue of all known volcanoes*, Longman, Green, Reader & Dyer, London.

Sears, J. H. (1891) Elaeolite – zircon – syenite and associated granitic rocks in the vicinity of Salem, Essex County, Massachusetts, *Bulletin of the Essex Institute*, Salem, Mass., USA, **23**, 146.

Sederholm, J. J. (1907) Om granit och gneiss, *Bulletin de la commission geologique de Finlande, Helsingfors*, **23**.

Sekine, T., Katsura, T. & Aramaki, S. (1979) Water-saturated phase relations of some andesites with application to the estimation of the initial temperature and water pressure at the time of eruption, *Geochim. Cosmochim. Acta*, **43**, 1367–76.

Self, S & Sparks, R. S. J. (eds) (1981) *Tephra Studies*, D. Reidel Pub. Co., Dordrecht, The Netherlands.

Shand, S. J. (1942) Phase petrology in the Cortland Complex, New York, *Geol. Soc. Am., Bull.*, **53**, 409–28.

Shand, S. J. (1945) The present status of Daly's hypothesis of the alkaline rocks, *Am. J. Sci.*, **243A**, 495–507.

Shand, S. J. (1950) *Eruptive Rocks, their genesis, composition, classification, and their relation to ore-deposits with a chapter on meteorites* (4th edn), Thomas Murby & Co., London.

Shaw, H. R. (1980) The fracture mechanism of magma transport from the mantle to the surface; Ch. 6, pp. 201–64 in Hargraves, R. B. (ed.), *Physics of Magmatic Processes*, Princeton Univ. Press, Princeton, New Jersey, USA.

Shaw, H. R. & Jackson, E. D. (1973) Linear island chains in the Pacific: Result of thermal plumes or gravitational anchors?, *J. Geophys. Res.*, **78**, 8634–52.

Shaw, H. R., Smith, R. L. & Hildreth, W. (1976) Thermogravitational mechanisms for chemical variations in zoned magma chambers, *Geol. Soc. Am., Abstr. Programs*, **8**, 1102.

Shee, S. R., Gurney, J. J. & Robinson, D. N. (1982) Two diamond-bearing peridotite xenoliths from the Finsch kimberlite, South Africa, *Contrib. Mineral. Petrol.*, **81**, 79–87.

Shiraki, K., Kuroda, N. & Urano, H. (1977) Boninite: An evidence for calc-alkalic primary magma. *Bull. Volc. Soc. Japan*, **Series 2, 22**, 257–61.

Sigurdsson, H. & Sparks, R. S. J. (1981) Petrology of rhyolitic and mixed magma ejecta from the 1875 eruption of Askja, Iceland, *J. Petrol.*, **22(1)**, 41–84.

Sillitoe, R. H. (1976) Andean mineralization: a model for the metallogeny of convergent plate margins; in Strong, D. F. (ed.), *Metallogeny and Plate Tectonics, Geol. Assoc. Can., Spec. Pap.*, **14**, 59–100.

Silva, L. C., Le Bas, M. J. & Robertson, A. H. F. (1981) An oceanic carbonatite volcano on Santiago, Cape Verde Island, *Nature*, **194**, 644–5.

Simkin, T., Siebert, L., McClelland, L., Bridge, D., Nehall, C. & Latter, J. H. (1981) *Volcanoes of the World: A regional directory, gazetteer, and chronology of volcanism during the last 10 000 years*, Hutchinson Ross Pub. Co., Stroudsburg, Pennsylvania, USA.

Simkin, T. & Smith, J. V. (1970) Minor-element distribution in olivine, *J. Geol.*, **78**, 304–25.

Simmons, E. C. & Hanson, G. N. (1978) Geochemistry and origin of massif-type anorthosites, *Contrib. Mineral. Petrol.*, **66**, 119–35.

Simmons, G. (1964) Gravity survey and geological interpretation, northern New York, *Geol. Soc. Am. Bull.*, **75**, 81–98.

Simms, F. E. (1965) Hypabyssal alkaline bodies and structure of part of the northwestern Crazy Mountains, Montana, *Am. Mineral.*, **50**, 291–2.

Simpson, E. S. W. (1970) The anorthosite of southern Angola: a review of present data; Ch. 5, pp. 89–96 in Clifford, T. N. & Gass, I. G. (eds), *African Magmatism and Tectonics*, Oliver & Boyd, Edinburgh.

Smith, B. H. S. & Skinner, E. M. W. (1984) A new look at Prairie Creek, Arkansas; pp. 255–83 in Kornprobst, J. (ed.), *Kimberlites 1: Kimberlites and related rocks*, Elsevier, Amsterdam, The Netherlands.

Smith, C. B. (1984) What is a kimberlite?; pp. 1–2 in *Kimberlite Occurrence and Origin: A basis for conceptual models in exploration*, Geology Dept, Univ. Western Australia.

Smith, R. L (1960) Ash flows, *Geol. Soc. Am., Bull.*, **71**, 795–842.

Smithson, S. B. & Brown, S. K. (1977) A model for lower continental crust, *Earth Planet. Sci. Lett.*, **35**, 134–44.

Smithson, S. B. & Decker, E. R. (1974) A continental crustal model and its geothermal implications, *Earth Planet, Sci. Lett.*, **22**, 215–25.

Sobolev, N. V. (1977) *Deep-seated inclusions in kimberlites and the problem of the composition of the Upper Mantle*, Am. Geophys. Union, Washington, DC, USA.

Sood, M. K. (1981) *Modern Igneous Petrology*, John Wiley & Sons, New York, USA.

Sorby, H. C. (1858) On the microscopic structure of crystals, indicating the origin of minerals and rocks, *Q. J. Geol. Soc. (Lond.)*, **14**, 453–500.

Sørensen, H. (1955) Anorthosite from Buksefjorden, West Greenland, *Medd. Dansk Geol. Foren*, **13**, 31–41.

Sørensen, H. (ed.) (1974) *The Alkaline Rocks*, John Wiley & Sons, London.

Spallanzani, L. (1794) *Viaggi alle Due Sicilie ed in alcuni parti dell' Appennino.*, Pavia, Italy.

Sparks, R. S. J., Self, S. & Walker, G. P. L. (1973) Products of ignimbrite eruptions, *Geology*, **1**, 115–18.

Speight, J. M., Skelhorn, R. R., Sloan, T. & Knaap, R. J. (1982) The dyke swarms of Scotland; Ch. 33, pp. 449–59 in Sutherland, D. S. (ed.), *Igneous Rocks* *of the British Isles*, John Wiley & Sons Ltd., Chichester.

Spera, F. J. (1980) Aspects of magma transport; Ch. 7, pp. 265–323 in Hargraves, R. B. (ed.), *Physics of Magmatic Processes*, Princeton Univ. Press, Princeton, New Jersey, USA.

Spera, F. J. (1981) Carbon dioxide in igneous petrogenesis: II. Fluid dynamics of mantle metasomatism, *Contrib. Mineral. Petrol.*, **77**, 56–65.

Steinhauer, Rev Mr (1814) Notice relative to the geology of the coast of Labrador, *Geol. Soc. Lond., Trans.*, **2**, 488–91.

Steinmann, G. (1906) Geologische Beobachtungen in den Alpen (II). Die Schardtsche Überfaltungstheorie und die geologische Bedeutung der Tiefseeabsätze und der ophiolithischen Massengesteine, *Ber. Natf. Ges. Freiburg* **i.B. 16**, 1–49.

Steinmann, G. (1927) Die ophiolithischen Zonen in dem mediterranean Kettengebirge, *14th Int. Geol. Congr., Madrid*, **2**, 638–67.

Stormer, J. C. & Nicholls, J. (1978) XLFRAC: A program for the interactive testing of magmatic differentiation models, *Comput. Geosci.*, **4**, 143–59.

Strache, G. (1863) pp. 56–72 in von Hauer, F. & Strache, G., *Geologie Siebenburgens*, Wien, Austria.

Streckeisen, A. L. (1967) Classification and nomenclature of igneous rocks (Final report of an inquiry), *Neues Jahrb Mineral., Abh.*, **107**, 144–240.

Streckeisen, A. L. (1973) Plutonic rocks: Classification and nomenclature recommended by the I.U.G.S. subcommission on the systematics of igneous rocks, *Geotimes*, **18(10)**, 26–30.

Streckeisen, A L. (1974) Classification and nomenclature of plutonic rocks, *Geol. Rundsch.*, **63(2)**, 773–86.

Streckeisen, A..L. (1976) To each plutonic rock its proper name, *Earth-Sci. Rev.*, **12**, 1–33.

Streckeisen, A. L. (1978) Classification and nomenclature of volcanic rocks, lamprophyres, carbonatites and melilitic rocks, *Neues Jahrb. Mineral., Abh.*, **134(1)**, 1–14.

Streckeisen, A. L. (1979) Classification and nomenclature of volcanic rocks, lamprophyres, carbonatites, and melilitic rocks: Recommendations and suggestions of the I.U.G.S. subcommission on the systematics of igneous rocks, *Geology*, 7, 331–5.

Streckeisen, A. L. (1980) Classification and nomenclature of volcanic rocks, lamprophyres, carbonatites and melilitic rocks, IUGS Subcommission on the Systematics of Igneous Rocks, *Geol. Rundsch.*, **69**, 194–207.

Strom, R. G., Schneider, N. M., Terrile, R. J., Cook, A. F. & Hansen, C. (1981) Volcanic eruptions on Io, *J. Geophys. Res.*, **86(A10)**, 8593–620.

Subramaniam, A. P. (1956) Mineralogy and petrology of the Sittampundi Complex, Salem district, Madras State, India, *Geol. Soc. Am., Bull.*, **67**, 317–90.

Sugisaki, R. (1972) Tectonic aspects of andesite line, *Nature*, **240**, 109–11.

Sugisaki, R. (1976) Chemical characteristics of volcanic rocks: relation to plate movements, *Lithos*, **9**, 17–30.

Sun, S. S., Nesbitt, R. W. & Shataskin, A. T. (1979) Geochemical characteristics of mid-ocean ridge basalts, *Earth Planet. Sci. Lett.*, **44**, 119–38.

Swanson, D. A., Casadevall, T. J., Dzurisin, D., Malone, S. D., Newhall, C. G. & Weaver, C. S. (1983) Predicting eruptions of Mount St Helens, June 1980 through December 1982, *Science*, **221(4618)**, 1369–76.

Sykes, L. R. (1969) The new global tectonics (Abstract), *Am Geophys. Union, Trans.*, **50**, 113.

Takeuchi, H. & Uyeda, S. (1965) A possibility of present-day regional metamorphism, *Tectonophysics*, **2**, 59–68.

Taljaard, M. S. (1936) South African melilite basalts and their relations, *Geol. Soc. S. Afr., Trans.*, **39**, 281–316.

Tarney, J., Wood, D. A., Saunders, A. D., Cann, J. R. & Varet, J. (1980) Nature of mantle heterogeneity in the North Atlantic: evidence from deep sea drilling, *Phil. Trans. R. Soc. Lond.*, **A297**, 179–202.

Tayler, R. J. (1966) The origin of the elements, *Rep. Pro. Phys.*, **29**, 489–538.

Tayler, R. J. (1972) *The origin of the chemical elements*, Wykeham Pub. (Lond.) Ltd., London.

Taylor, H. P. (1967) The zoned ultramafic complexes of Southeastern Alaska; Ch. 4.3, pp. 97–121 in Wyllie, P. J. (ed.), *Ultramafic and Related Rocks*, John Wiley & Sons, Inc., New York, USA.

Taylor, S. R. (1969) Trace element chemistry of andesites and associated calc-alkaline rocks; pp. 43–63 in McBirney, A. R. (ed.), Proceedings of the Andesite Conference, *Oregon Dep. Miner. Ind., Bull.*, **65**.

Taylor, S. R. (1979) Chemical composition and evolution of the continental crust: the Rare Earth Element evidence; pp. 353–76 in McElhinny, M. W. (ed.), *The Earth: Its origin, structure and evolution*, Academic Press, London & New York.

Taylor, S. R. (1982) *Planetary Science: A lunar perspective*, Lunar & Planetary Institute, Houston, Texas, USA.

Teal, J. J. H. (1888) *British Petrography: with special reference to the Igneous Rocks*, Dalau & Co., London.

Termier, P. (1904) Les schistes cristallins de Alpes occidentales, *9th Int. Geol. Congr.*, Vienne, 571.

Thayer, T. P. (1967) Chemical and structural relations of ultramafic and feldspathic rocks in Alpine Intrusive Complexes; Ch. 7.4, pp. 222–39 in Wyllie, P. J. (ed.), *Ultramafic and Related Rocks*, John Wiley & Sons Inc, New York, USA.

Thiessen, R., Burke, K. & Kidd, W. S. F. (1977) Are African-plate topography and vulcanism simply related to underlying mantle structure?, *EOS, Am. Geophys. Union, Trans.*, **58(5)**, 503.

Thom, R. (1975) *Structural stability and morphogenesis: An outline of a general theory of models*, The Benjamin/Cummings Publishing Co. Inc., Reading, Mass., USA.

Thompson, G., Bryan, W. B. & Frey, F. A. (1973) Petrology and geochemistry of basalts and related rocks from DSDP leg 22 sites 214 and 216, Ninety-East Ridge, Indian Ocean, *EOS: Am. Geophys. Union, Trans.*, **54(11)**, 1019–21.

Thorarinsson, S. (1944) Tefrokronologiska studier pa Island, *Geogr. Ann. Stockh.*, **26**, 1–217.

Thorarinsson, S. (1969) The Lakagigar eruption of 1783, *Bull. Volc.*, **33**, 910–29.

Thorarinsson, S. (1981) Tephra studies and tephrochronology: A historical review with special reference to Iceland; pp. 1–12 in Self, S. & Sparks, R. S. J. (eds), *Tephra Studies*, D. Reidel Pub. Co., Dordrecht, The Netherlands.

Thornton, C. P. & Tuttle, O. F. (1960) Chemistry of igneous rocks, 1, Differentiation index, *Am. J. Sci.*, **258**, 664–84.

Thorpe, R. S. (ed.) (1982) *Andesites: Orogenic Andesites and Related Rocks*, John Wiley & Sons, Chichester.

Tilley, C. E. (1947) Mylonites of St Paul Rocks (Atlantic), *Am. J. Sci.*, **245**, 483–91.

Tilley, C. E. (1950) Some aspects of magmatic evolution, *Q. J. Geol. Soc. (Lond.)*, **106**, 37–61.

Tilley, C. E. (1957) Problems of alkali rock genesis, *Q. J. Geol. Soc. (Lond.)*, **113(3)**, 323–60.

Tilley, C. E. & Muir, I. D. (1964) Intermediate members of the oceanic basalt-trachyte association, *Geol. Fören. Stockh. Förh.*, **85**, 434–43.

Tobi, A. C. (1971) The nomenclature of the charnockitic rock suite, *Neues Jahrb. Mineral., Monatsh.*, **Jg. 1971, H.5**, 193–205.

Tomita, T. (1935) On the chemical compositions of the Cenozoic alkaline suite of the circum-Japan Sea region, *Shanghai Sci. Inst., J.*, Sect. 2, **1**, 227–306.

Toulmin, P. (1960) Composition of feldspars and crystallization history of the granite-syenite complex near Salem, Essex County, Massachusetts, U.S.A., *21st Int. Geol. Congr., Norden*, **13**, 275–88.

Tröger, W. E. (1935) *Spezielle Petrographie der Eruptivghesteine: Ein Nomenklatur – Kompedium,* Schweizerbart'sche Verlangsbuchhandlung, Stuttgart, Germany.

Tschermak, G. (1866) Felsarten von ungewöhnlicher Zusammensetzung in dem Umgebungen von Teschen und Neutitschein, *Sitzungsberichte der mathematisch-naturwissenschaftlichen Klasse der kaiserlichen Akademie der Wissenschaften, Wien*, **53**, 260–74.

Turcotte, E. R. & Oxburgh, E. R. (1973) Mid-plate tectonics, *Nature*, **244**, 337–9.

Turner, F. J. & Verhoogen, J. (1951) *Igneous and Metamorphic Petrology,* McGraw-Hill Book Co., Inc., New York, USA.

Turner, J. S. & Gustafson, L. B. (1978) The flow of hot saline solutions from vents in the sea floor – some implications for exhalative massive sulfide and other ore deposits, *Econ. Geol.*, **73**, 1082–1100.

Tuttle, O. F. (1955) Classification of granites, syenites and nepheline syenites, *Geol. Soc. Am., Bull. (Abs.)*, **66**, 1629.

Tuttle, O. F. & Bowen, N. L. (1958) Origin of granite in the light of experimental studies in the system Na-AlSiO$_3$O$_8$–KAlSi$_3$O$_8$–SiO$_2$–H$_2$O, *Geol. Soc. Am., Mem.*, **74**, 1–153.

Tuttle, O. F. & Gittins, J. (eds) (1966) *Carbonatites,* John Wiley & Sons, New York, USA.

Tyrrell, G. W. (1912) The Late Palaeozoic alkaline igneous rocks of the West of Scotland, *Geol. Mag.*, **9**, 69–80 & 120–31.

Tyrrell, G. W. (1916) The picrite-teschenite sill of Lugar, Ayrshire, *Q. J. Geol. Soc. (Lond.)*, **72**, 84–129.

Tyrrell, G. W. (1926) *The Principles of Petrology: An Introduction to the Science of Rocks.,* Methuen & Co. Ltd., London, Dutton & Co. Inc., New York, USA.

Tyrrell, G. W. (1937) Flood basalts and fissure eruption, *Bull. Volc.*, **2(1)**, 89–111.

Uebel, P. -J. (1977) Internal structure of pegmatites, its origin and nomenclature, *N. Jb. Miner. Abh.*, **131(1)**, 83–113.

Upton, B. G. J. (1971) Melting experiments of chilled gabbros and syenogabbros, *Carnegie Inst. Wash., Yearb.*, **70**, 112–18.

Utnasin, V. K. A., Abdurakhmanov, A. I., Anosov, G. I., Budyansky, Y. A., Fedorchenko, V. I. & Markhinin, Y. K. (1976) Types of magma foci of island arc volcanoes and their study by the method of deep seismic sounding in Kamchatka; pp. 123–37 in Aoki, H. &

Iizuka, S. (eds), *Volcanoes and Tectonosphere*, Tokai Univ. Press, Tokyo, Japan.

Vallari, L. (ed.) (1980) The Aeolian Islands: An active volcanic arc in the Mediterranean Sea, *Rend. Soc. Italiana Mineral. Petrol.*, **36, Fasc. 1**.

Van Bemmelen, R. W. (1949) *Geology of Indonesia,* Vol. 1, The Hague Gov. Print. Office, The Netherlands.

Vanuxem, L. (1837) *New York Geol. Surv., 2nd Annu. Rep.*

Varlamoff, N. (1954) Transitions entre les aplites et les pegmatites dans les zones de contact des massifs granitiques due Maniema, *Soc. Geol. Belg., Ann.*, **77**, 101–16.

Vartianinen, H. & Paarma, H. (1979) Geological characteristics of the Sokli Carbonatite Complex, Finland, *Econ. Geol.*, **74**, 1296–1306.

Vermaak, C. F. (1976) The Merensky Reef – Thoughts on its environment and genesis, *Econ. Geol*, **71**, 1270–98.

Vermaak, C. F. & Hendriks, L. P. (1976) A review of the mineralogy of the Merensky Reef, with specific reference to new data on the precious metal mineralogy, *Econ. Geol.*, **71**, 1244–69.

Verschure, R. H. (1966) Possible relationships between continental and oceanic basalt and kimberlite, *Nature*, **211**, 1387–9.

Verwoerd, W. J. (1966) South African carbonatites and their probable mode of origin, *Stellenbosch, Univ., Ann. (S. Afr.)*, **41.A(2)**, 113–233.

Viljoen, M. J. & Viljoen, R. P. (1969a) The geology and geochemistry of the Lower Ultramafic Unit of the Onverwacht Group and a proposed new class of igneous rocks, *Geol. Soc. S. Afr., Spec. Publ.*, **2**, 55–86.

Viljoen, M. J. & Viljoen, R. P. (1969b) Evidence for the existence of a mobile extrusive peridotitic magma from the Komati Formation of the Onverwacht Group, *Geol. Soc. S. Afr., Spec. Publ.*, **2**, 87–112.

Viljoen, R. P. & Viljoen M. J. (1982) Komatiites – an historical review; pp. 5–17 in Arndt, N. T. & Nisbet, E. G. (eds), *Komatiites*, George Allen & Unwin, London.

Vine, F. J. & Matthews, D. H. (1963) Magnetic anomalies over oceanic ridges, *Nature*, **199**, 947–9.

Vinogradov, A. P. (1962) Average contents of chemical elements in the principal types of igneous rocks of the Earth's crust, *Geokhimiya (Geochemistry)*, **7**, 641–64.

Vinogradov, A. P., Surkov, Y. A. & Kirnozov, F. F. (1973) The contents of uranium, thorium, and potassium in the rocks of Venus as measured by Venera 8, *Icarus*, **20**, 253–9.

Virlet d'Aoust (1844) Note sur les roches d'imbibition, *Geol. Soc. France, Bull.*, Ser. 2, **1**, 845.

Visser, W. & Koster van Groos, A. F. (1979) Effect of pressure on liquid immiscibility in the system K$_2$O–FeO–Al$_2$O$_3$–SiO$_2$–P$_2$O$_5$, *Am. J. Sci.*, **279**, 1160–75.

Vitaliano, D. B. (1973) *Legends of the Earth: Their geologic origins,* Indiana Univ. Press, USA & The Citadel Press, Secaucus, NJ, USA.

Vogt, P. R. (1974) Volcano spacing, fractures, and thickness of the lithosphere, *Earth Planet. Sci. Lett.*, **21**, 235–52.

Vollmer, R., Johnston, K., Ghiara, M. R., Lirer, L. & Munno, R. (1981) Sr isotope geochemistry of megacrysts from continental rift and converging plate margin alkaline volcanism in South Italy, *J. Volcanol. Geotherm. Res.*, **11**, 317–27.

Vom Rath, G. (1864) Beitrage zur Kenntniss der eruptiven Gesteine der Alpen, *Zeitschrift der deutschen geologischen Gessellschaft, Berlin*, **16**, 250.

Von Buch, L. (1802) *Geognostische Beobachtungen auf Reisen*, Abt. 1, III (1802) (Date on title-page 1809).

Von Buch, L. (1836) Uber Erhebungskrater und Vulkane (read before the Akad. Wiss, Berlin, 26, March 1835), *Annalen der Physik, Leipzig* (ed. J. C. Poggendorff), **2nd series**, 37, 169–90.

Von Eckermann, H. (1938) The anorthosite and kenningite of the Nordingra – Rödö Region: A contribution to the problem of the anorthosites, *Geol. Fören. Stockh., Förh.*, **60**, 243–84.

Von Eckermann, H. (1948) The alkaline district of Alnö Island, *Sveriges Geol. Unders.*, **Ser. Ca. 36**.

Von Fritsch, K. (1865) Notizen uber geologische Venhattnisse im Hegau, *Neues Jahrb. Mineral.*, **663**.

Von Fritsch, K. & Reiss, W. (1868) *Geologische Beschreibung de Insel Tenerife*, Wurster & Co., Winterthur.

Von Gruenewaldt, G. (1973) The modified differentiation index and the modified crystallization index as parameters of differentiation in layered intrusions, *Geol. Soc. S. Afr., Trans.*, **76**, 53–61.

Von Knorring, O. & Du Bois, C. G. B. (1961) Carbonatitic lava from Fort Portal area in western Uganda, *Nature*, **192**, 1064–5.

Von Leonhard, K. C. (1823) *Charakteristik der Felsarten*, Heidelberg.

Von Michaelis, H., Ahrens, L. H. & Willis, J. P. (1969) The composition of stony meteorites II: The analytical data and assessment of their quality, *Earth Planet. Sci. Lett.*, **5**, 387–94.

Von Richthofen, F. (1860) Studien aus den ungarisch-siebenburgischen Trachytgebirgen, *Jahrbuch der kaiserlich-königlichen geologischen Reichsanstalt, Wien*, **11**.

Wade, A. & Prider, R. T. (1940) The leucite-bearing rocks in the West Kimberley area, Western Australia, *Q. J. Geol. Soc. (Lond.)*, **96**, 39–98.

Wadia, D. N. (1975) *Geology of India* (4th edn), Tata McGraw-Hill Pub. Co., New Delhi, India.

Wadsworth, W. J. (1982) The major basic intrusions; Ch. 30, pp. 415–25 in Sutherland, D. S. (ed.), *Igneous Rocks of the British Isles*, John Wiley & Sons Ltd., Chichester.

Wager, L. R. (1963) The mechanism of adcumulus growth in the layered series of the Skaergaard intrusion, *Mineral. Soc. Am., Spec. Publ.*, **1**, 1–19.

Wager, L. R. & Brown, G. M. (1968) *Layered Igneous Rocks*, Oliver & Boyd, Edinburgh.

Wager, L. R. & Deer, W. A. (1939) Geological investigations in East Greenland, Pt III, Petrology of the Skaergaard intrusion, Kangerdluzssuaq, East Greenland *Medd. Grønland*, **Bd 105(4)**.

Wagner, P. A. (1914) *The Diamond Fields of Southern Africa*, The Transvaal Leader, Johannesburg, South Africa.

Wahl, W. (1946) Thermal diffusion-convection as a cause of magmatic differentiation, 1, *Am. J. Sci.*, **244**, 417–41.

Walker, F. (1930) The geology of the Shiant Isles (Hebrides), *Q. J. geol. Soc. (Lond.)*, **86**, 355–98.

Walker, F. (1940) Differentiation of the Palisade diabase, New Jersey, *Geol. Soc. Am., Bull.*, **51**, 1059–106.

Walker, F. (1952) Mugearites and oligoclase basalts, *Geol. Mag.*, **89**, 337–45.

Walker, F. & Poldervaart, A. (1949) The Karroo dolerites of the Union of South Africa, *Geol. Soc. Am., Bull.*, **60**, 591–706.

Walker, G. P. L. (1975) A new concept of the evolution of the British Tertiary intrusive centres, *Geol. Soc. Lond., J.*, **131**, 121–41.

Walker, G. P. L. (1980) The Taupo Pumice: Product of the most powerful known (Ultraplinian) eruption?. *J. Volcanol. Geotherm. Res.*, **8**, 69–94.

Walker, G. P. L. (1981a) New Zealand case histories of pyroclastic studies; pp. 317–30 in Self, S. & Sparks, R. S. J. (eds), *Tephra Studies*, D. Reidel Pub. Co., Dordrecht, The Netherlands.

Walker, G. P. L. (1981b) Volcanological applications of pyroclastic studies; pp. 391–403 in Self, S. & Sparks, R. S. J. (eds), *Tephra Studies*, D. Reidel Pub. Co., Dordrecht, The Netherlands.

Walker, G. P. L. (1982) Eruptions of andesitic volcanoes; pp. 403–13 in Thorpe, R. S. (ed.), *Andesites: Orogenic andesites and related rocks*, John Wiley & Sons, Chichester.

Walker, G. P. L. & Croasdale, R. (1971) Two Plinian-type eruptions in the Azores, *Geol. Soc. Lond., J.*, **127**, 17–55.

Washington H. S. (1906) The Roman comagmatic region, *Carnegie Inst. Wash., Publ.*, **57**, 1–199.

Washington, H S. (1917) Chemical analyses of igneous rocks, *US Geol. Surv., Prof. Pap.*, **99**.

Washington, H. S. (1920) Italite, a new leucite rock, *Am. J. Sci.*, **4th Series**, 50, 33–43.

Washington, H. S. (1922) Deccan Traps and other plateau basalts, *Geol. Soc. Am., Bull.*, **33**, 765–804.

Washington, H. S. (1925) The chemical composition of the Earth, *Am. J. Sci.*, **9**, 351–78.

Wasserburg, G. J., Lee, T. & Papanastassiou, D. A. (1977) Correlated O and Mg isotopic anomalies in Allende inclusions: II, Magnesium, *Geophys. Res. Lett.*, **4**, 299–302.

Waters, A. C. (1962) Basalt magma types and their tectonic associations: Pacific northwest of the United States, *Am. Geophys. Union, Geophys. Monogr.*, **6**, 158–70.

Watkinson, D. H. & Wyllie, P. J. (1969) Phase equilibrium studies bearing on the limestone-assimilation hypothesis, *Geol. Soc. Am., Bull.*, **80**, 1565–76.

Watson, J. V. (1980) Metallogenesis in relation to mantle heterogeneity, *Phil. Trans., R. Soc. Lond.*, **A.297**, 347–52.

Watson, T. L. & Taber, S. (1913) Geology of the titanium and apatite deposits of Virginia, *Virginia Geol. Surv. Bull.*, **3**.

Watt, G. (1804) Observations on basalt, and on the transition from the vitreous to the stony texture, which occurs in the gradual refrigeration of melted basalt; with some geological remarks, *R. Soc. Lond., Philos. Trans.* **94(2)**, 279–314.

Webb, P. K. & Weaver, S. D. (1975) Trachyte shield volcanoes: a new volcanic form from south Turkana, Kenya, *Bull. Volc.*, **39(2)**, 294–312.

Wedepohl, K. H. (1969) Composition and abundance of common igneous rocks; Ch. 7, pp. 227–71 in Wedepohl, K. H. (ed.), *Handbook of Geochemistry*, Vol. 1, Springer-Verlag, Berlin.

Wedepohl, K. H. (1971) *Geochemistry* (trans. from the German by E. Althaus) Holt, Rinehard & Winston, Inc., New York, USA.

Wedepohl, K. H. & Muramatsu, Y. (1979) The chemical composition of kimberlites compared with the average composition of three basaltic magma types; pp. 300–12 in Boyd, F. R. & Meyer, H. O. A. (eds), *Kimberlites, diatremes and diamonds: their geology, petrology and geochemistry*, Proc. 2nd Int. Kimbelite Conf., Am. Geophys. Union, Washington, DC, USA.

Weed, W. H. & Pirsson, L. V. (1896) Missourite, a new leucite rock from the Highwood Mountains of Montana, *Am. J. Sci.*, **4th Series, 2(11)**, 314–23.

Wegener, A. L. (1915) *Die Entstehung der Kontinente und Ozeane*, F. Vieweg & Sohn, Braunschweig, Germany.

Wegmann, C. E. (1935) Zur Beutung der Migmatite, *Geol. Rundsch.*, **26**, 305–50.

Weibe, R. A. (1980) Anorthositic magmas and the origin of Proterozoic anorthosite massifs, *Nature*, **286(5773)**, 564–7.

Weinberg, S. (1977) *The first three minutes: A modern view of the origin of the universe*, Andre Deutsch, London.

Werner, A. G. (1780) *Axel von Kronstedts Versuch einer Mineralogie*, Crusius, Leipzig.

Werner, A. G. (1786) Kurze Klassifikation und Beschreibung der verschiedenen Gebürgsarten, *Abhandlungen der Böhmischen Gesellschaft der Wissenschaften*, Dresden.

Werner, A. G. (1788) Vermischte Nachrichten, *Bergmännisches Journal (Freiberg)*, **2**.

Westerveld, J. (1952) Quaternary volcanism on Sumatra, *Geol. Soc. Am., Bull.*, **63**, 561–94.

White, A. J. R. & Chappell, B. W. (1983) Granitoid types and their distribution in the Lachlan Fold Belt, Southeastern Australia, *Geol. Soc. Am., Mem.*, **159**, 21–34.

Whitford, D. J. & Nicholls, I. A. (1976) Potassium variation in lavas across the Sunda Arc in Java and Bali; pp. 63–75 in Johnson, R. W. (ed.), *Volcanism in Australasia.*, Elsevier Scientific Pub. Co., Amsterdam, The Netherlands.

Whitford-Stark, J. L. (1982) Factors influencing the morphology of volcanic landforms: an Earth-Moon comparison, *Earth-Sci. Rev.*, **18**, 109–68.

Wiebe, R. A. (1980) Anorthositic magmas and the origin of Proterozoic anorthosite massifs, *Nature*, **286**, 564–7.

Wiener, R. W. (1981) Tectonic setting, rock chemistry, and metamorphism of an Archaean gabbro-anorthosite complex, Tessiuyakh Bay, Labrador, *Can. J. Earth Sci.*, **18**, 1409–21.

Wilcox, R. E. (1944) Rhyolite-basalt complex on Gardiner River, Yellowstone Park, Wyoming, *Geol. Soc. Am., Bull.*, **55**, 1047–80.

Wilcox, R. E. (1979) The liquid line of descent and variation diagrams; Ch. 7, pp. 205–32 in Yoder, H. S. (ed.), *The Evolution of the Igneous Rocks: Fiftieth Anniversary Perspectives*, Princeton Univ. Press, Princeton, New Jersey, USA.

Wilhelms, D. E. & McCauley, J. F. (1971) *Geologic Map of the Near Side of the Moon*, **1–703**, US Geol. Surv., Washington, DC, USA.

Wilkinson, J. F. G. (1968) The petrography of basaltic rocks; pp. 163–214 in Hess, H. H. & Poldervaart, A. (eds), *Basalts: The Poldervaart Treatise on Rocks of Basaltic Composition*, Vol. 1, Interscience Pub., New York, USA.

Willemse, J. (1964) A brief outline of the geology of the Bushveld Igneous Complex; pp. 91–130 in Haughton, S. H. (ed.), *The geology of some ore deposits in southern Africa*, Vol. 2, Geol. Soc. S. Afr., Johannesburg, S. Africa.

Williams, H. (1942) The geology of the Crater Lake National Park, Oregon, with a reconnaissance of the Cascada Range southward to Mount Shasta, *Carnegie Instn. Wash. Publ.*, **540**.

Williams, H. & McBirney, A. R. (1979) *Volcanology*, Freeman, Cooper & Co., San Francisco, USA.

Williams, H., Turner, F. J. & Gilbert, C. M. (1982) *Petrography: An introduction to the study of rocks in thin sections* (2nd edn), W. H. Freeman & Co., San Francisco, USA.

Wilson, C. J. N. & Walker, G. P. L. (1981) Violence in pyroclastic flow eruptions; pp. 441–8 in Self, S. & Sparks, R. S. J. (eds), *Tephra Studies*, D. Reidel Pub. Co., Dordrecht, The Netherlands.

Wilson, J. R., Esbensen, K. H. & Thy, P. (1981) Igneous petrology of the Synorogenic Fongen Hyllingen layered basic complex, South-central Scandinavian Caledonides, *J. Petrol.*, **22(4)**, 584–627.

Wilson, J. T. (1963) A possible origin of the Hawaiian Islands, *Can. J. Phys.*, **41**, 863–70.

Wilson, J. T. (1965a) A new class of faults and their bearing on continental drift, *Nature*, **207**, 343–7.

Wilson, J. T. (1965b) Evidence from ocean islands suggesting movement in the Earth, *Phil. Trans R. Soc. Lond.*, **258A**, 145–67.

Wimmenauer, W. (1973) Lamprophyre, semilamprophyre und anchibasaltische ganggesteine, *Fortschr. Mineral.*, **51(1)**, 3–67.

Wimmenauer, W. (1974) The alkaline province of central Europe and France; Ch. 4.4, pp. 238–70 in Sørensen, H. (ed.), *The alkaline rocks*, John Wiley & Sons, New York, USA.

Windley, B. F. (1969) Anorthosites of southern West Greenland, *Am. Assoc. Pet. Geol., Mem.*, **12**, 899–915.

Windley, B. F. (1970) Anorthosites in the early crust of the Earth and on the Moon, *Nature*, **226**, 333–5.

Windley, B. F. (1973) Archaean Anorthosites: A Review: with the Fiskenaesset Complex, West Greenland as a model for interpretation, *Geol. Soc. S. Afr., Spec. Publ.*, **3**, 319–31.

Windley, B. F. (1977) *The Evolving Continents*, John Wiley & Sons, London.

Winkler, H. G. F. (1960) La Genese du granite et des migmatites par anatexie experimentale, *Rev. Geogr. phys. Geol. dynam. (Paris)*, **3**, 67–76.

Winkler, H. G. F. & Von Platen, H. (1957) Experimentelle Gesteinsmetamorphose, *Geochim. Cosmochim. Acta*, **13**, 42–59.

Wolff, F. von (1922) Die Prinzipien einer quantitativen Klassifikation der Eruptivgesteine, insbesondere der jungen Ergussgesteine, *Geol. Rundsch.*, **13**, 9–19.

Wolff, J. E. (1938) Igneous rocks of the Crazy Mountains, Montana, *Geol. Soc. Am., Bull.*, **49**, 1569–626.

Wones, D. R. (1979) The fractional resorption of complex minerals and the formation of strongly femic alkaline rocks; Ch. 14, pp. 413–22 in Yoder, H. S. (ed.), *The evolution of the igneous rocks: Fiftieth Anniversary Perspectives*, Princeton Univ. Press, Princeton, New Jersey, USA.

Wood, J. A. (1968) *Meteorites and the Origin of Planets*, McGraw-Hill Book Co., New York, USA.

Wood, J. A. (1979) *The Solar System*, Prentice-Hall, Inc., Englewood Cliffs, New Jersey, USA.

Woollard, G. P. (1970) Evaluation of the isostatic mechanism and role of mineralogic transformations from seismic and gravity data, *Phys. Earth Planet. Inter.*, **3**, 62–9.

Woolley, A. R. (1973) The pseudoleucite borolanites and associated rocks of the south-eastern tract of the Borralan Complex, Scotland, *Br. Mus. (Nat. Hist.), Bull., Mineral.*, **2(6)**, 285–333.

Woolley, A. R. (1982) A discussion of carbonatite evolution and nomenclature, and the generation of sodic and potassic fenites, *Mineral. Mag.*, **46**, 13–17.

Wright, J. B. (1969) Olivine nodules in trachyte from the Jos Plateau, Nigeria, *Nature*, **223**, 285–6.

Wright, J. B. (1971) The phonolite-trachyte spectrum, *Lithos*, **4**, 1–5.

Wright, T. L. (1974) Presentation and interpretation of chemical data for igneous rocks, *Contrib. Mineral. Petrol.*, **48**, 233–48.

Wright, T. L. & Peck, D. L. (1978) Crystallization and differentiation of the Alae magma, Alae Lava Lake, Hawaii, *US Geol. Surv., Prof. Pap.*, **935-C**, 1–20.

Wright, T. L., Peck, D. L. & Shaw, H. R. (1976) Kilauea lava lakes: Natural laboratories for study of cooling, crystallization and differentiation of basaltic magma, *Am. Geophys. Union, Geophys. Monogr.*, **19**, 375–90.

Wyborn, D., Chappell, B. W. & Johnston, R. M. (1981) Three S-type volcanic suites from the Lachlan Fold Belt, Southeast Australia, *J. Geophys. Res.*, **86(B.11)**, 10335–48.

Wyllie, P. J. (1961) Fusion of Torridonian sandstone by a picrite sill in Soay (Hebrides), *J. Petrol.*, **2**, 1–37.

Wyllie, P. J. (1965) Melting relationships in the system $CaO-MgO-Co_2-H_2O$ with petrological applications, *J. Petrol.*, **6**, 101–23.

Wyllie, P. J. (1967a) Ultramafic and ultrabasic rocks: Petrography and petrology; Ch. 1.1, pp. 1–7 in Wyllie, P. J. (ed.), *Ultramafic and Related Rocks*, John Wiley & Sons Inc., New York, USA.

Wyllie, P. J. (ed.) (1967b) *Ultramafic and Related Rocks*, John Wiley & Sons Inc., New York, USA.

Wyllie, P. J. (1969) The origin of ultramafic and ultrabasic rocks, *Tectonophysics*, **7**, 437–55.

Wyllie, P. J. (1977) From crucibels through subduction to batholiths; pp. 389–433 in Saxena, S. K. & Bhattacharji, S. (eds), *Energetics of geological processes*, Springer-Verlag, Berlin.

Wyllie, P. J. (1979a) Petrogenesis and the physics of the Earth; Ch. 17, pp. 483–520 in Yoder, H. S. (ed.), *The Evolution of the Igneous Rocks: Fiftieth Anniversary Perspectives*, Princeton Univ. Press, Princeton, New Jersey, USA.

Wyllie, P. J. (1979b) Magmas and volatile components, *Am Mineral.*, **64**, 469–500.

Wyllie, P. J. (1980) The origin of kimberlite. *J. Geophys. Res.*, **85(B.12)**, 6902–10.

Wyllie, P. J. & Huang, W. L. (1975) Influence of mantle CO_2 in the generation of carbonatites and kimberlites, *Nature*, **257**, 297–9.

Wyllie, P. J. & Tuttle, O. F. (1960) The system $CaO-CO_2-H_2O$ and the origin of carbonatites, *J. Petrol*, **1**, 1–46.

Wyllie, P. J. & Tuttle, O. F. (1961) Hydrothermal melting of shales, *Geol. Mag.*, **98**, 56–66.

Yanagi, T. & Ishizaka, K. (1978) Batch fractionation model for the evolution of volcanic rocks in an island arc: an example from central Japan, *Earth Planet. Sci. Lett.*, **40**, 252–62.

Yoder, H. S. (1952) Change of melting point of diopside with pressure, *J. Geol.*, **60(4)**, 364–74.

Yoder, H. S. (1969) Experimental studies bearing on the origin of anorthosite; in Isachsen, Y. W. (ed.), *Origin of anorthosite and related rocks*, New York State Museum and Science Service, **Mem. 18**, Albany, New York, USA.

Yoder. H. S. (1976) *Generation of Basaltic Magma*, Natl. Acad. Sci. (USA), Washington, DC, USA.

Yoder, H. S. (ed.) (1979a) *The Evolution of the Igneous Rocks: Fiftieth Anniversary Perspective*, Princeton Univ. Press, Princeton, New Jersey, USA.

Yoder, H. S. (1979b) Melilite-bearing rocks and related lamprophyres; Ch. 13, pp. 391–411 in Yoder, H. S. (ed.), *The Evolution of the Igneous Rocks: Fiftieth anniversary perspectives*, Princeton Univ. Press, Princeton, New Jersey, USA.

Yoder, H. S. & Tilley, C. E. (1962) Origin of basalt magmas: An experimental study of natural and synthetic rock systems, *J. Petrol.*, **3(3)**, 342–532.

Younker, L. W. & Vogel, T. A. (1976) Plutonism and plate dynamics: the origin of circum-Pacific batholiths, *Can. Mineral.*, **14**, 238–44.

Zirkel, F. (1866) *Lehrbuch der Petrographie*, **Bd 1**, Adolph Marcus, Bonn, Germany.

Zwart, H. J. (1967) The duality of orogenic belts, *Geol. Mijnbouw*, **46**, 283–309.

INDEX

260

East African Rift System 88, 104, 197, 203, 205, 206, 221, 225
Easter Island 90
Eastern Australian Tertiary Volcanic Province 137, 138, 143
eclogite 43, 44, 49, 57, 127, 128, 176, 219
Ellendale Petrographic Province 210
Elysium Volcanic Province 31, 34, 206
emanations 151
emplacement of intrusive rocks 20, 21, 22, 23
enclosures 65, 148, 160, 166, 219
enderbite 153, 171
endogenous dome 145
enstatite chondrite 179
epigranite 161
epizone 21, 155, 161, 208
equilibrium condensation model 231
equilibrium crystallization 55
equilibrium process 229
Erebus Volcanic Province 212
essexite 201
Ethiopian Rift System 88, 143, 203, 205
Etna Volcano 2, 26
eucrite 106, 107, 181
eutaxitic structure 130, 143
exogenous dome 145
experimental petrology 1, 3, 114, 115, 127, 128, 135, 136, 173, 174, 219, 220, 225, 226
extraterrestrial volcanic landforms 30, 31, 32, 33, 34, 35, 36, 37, 38

Faeroe Islands 103
FAMOUS area 102
farsundite 171
fayalite–leucite–silica system 51
Fe₂O₃/FeO ratio 77, 78
Fen Ring Complex 199, 202, 209, 221
fenites and fenitization 137, 139, 141, 205, 213, 221, 223, 224, 225
fergusite 200, 202, 203
ferrocarbonatite 222, 223, 224, 225
ferrodiorite 52, 187
ferronorite–ferrogabbro 191
ferrosyenite 140
ferrosyenodiorite 187
Fiji 119, 142
filter pressing 58, 62, 188
Fiskenaesset Igneous Complex 168, 169, 170
fissure eruptions 23, 24
fitzroyite 210, 211
flood icelandite 119, 121, 129
flood phonolite 203, 206, 207
flood trachyte 134, 135, 206, 207
flowage differentiation 59, 182, 193
flow banding 142, 143
fluidization 22, 24, 220
foid-bearing alkali feldspar syenite 74, 79
foid-bearing alkali feldspar trachyte 79
foid-bearing basalt 79, 95, 196, 205
foid-bearing gabbro 74, 79
foid-bearing latite 79
foid-bearing monzodiorite 74, 79, 200
foid-bearing monzonite 74, 79, 200
foid-bearing syenite 74, 79, 138, 140, 196
foid-bearing trachyte 79, 130, 131, 136
foid diorite 74, 79, 196, 200, 201

foid gabbro 74, 79, 196, 200, 201
foidites 74, 79, 196, 197, 198, 199, 201
foid monzodiorite–monzogabbro 74, 79, 196, 200, 201
foid monzosyenite 74, 79, 196, 199, 200, 201
foidolite 79, 196, 201, 202
foid syenite 74, 79, 196, 200, 202
Fongen–Hyllingen Layered Complex 140
fore-arc 87
forsterite–diopside–nepheline–quartz system 99, 100, 148
forsterite–diopside–pyrope system 15, 113
foyaite 199, 201, 202
fractional crystallization 20, 55, 56, 57, 58, 59, 60, 61, 62, 69, 70, 107, 111, 113, 128, 129, 134, 135, 136, 137, 140, 141, 142, 148, 149, 163, 166, 173, 185, 186, 192, 193, 207, 212, 219, 224, 225
fractional melting 15, 113, 115
fractional resorption 212
Fuerteventura Island 168, 173, 221, 224
fugitive constituents 8, 12

gabbro 52, 62, 72, 74, 75, 76, 79, 82, 84, 85, 92, 112, 128, 139, 140, 150, 156, 160, 164, 169, 171, 172, 186, 187, 189, 190, 191, 192, 193
gabbronorite 75
Gabon 215
Galapagos Islands 102, 119, 123, 143
Gardar Alkaline Igneous Province 112, 140, 141, 205
Gardiner River rhyolite–basalt complex 64, 65
garnet lherzolite 41, 42, 43, 44, 45, 49, 113, 114, 115, 116, 183, 184, 185, 193, 206, 212, 219, 220
gaseous transfer 54, 55, 212
geosutures 91, 190, 191
ghost stratigraphy 163
glimmerite 44, 116, 129, 206, 213, 219
gneiss 65, 86, 92, 150, 155, 156, 159, 160, 163, 168, 169
Godthaab, West Greenland 86, 155
Gough Island 89, 90, 104, 105, 133
Grande Ronde Basalt Formation 104
granite 12, 18, 20, 21, 22, 23, 65, 66, 71, 74, 79, 82, 84, 85, 86, 89, 91, 92, 129, 135, 140, 142, 143, 149, 150–167, 168, 171, 173, 174, 187, 194, 196, 208, 210, 212
granite
  genesis 92, 149, 163–7
  geochemistry 156–9
  modal composition 152, 153, 154, 155
granites of convergent plate margins 91, 160
granitic rocks of Venus 161, 167
granitization 150, 151
granitoid 23, 155
granitoid texture 155
granodiorite 23, 65, 74, 79, 82, 84, 85, 91, 129, 142, 143, 150, 152, 153, 154, 155, 156, 157, 158, 159, 160, 165, 165, 171
granophyre 62, 155, 161, 187
graphic granite 155, 161
granulite 85, 91, 92, 113, 141, 153, 169
Great Dyke of Zimbabwe 182, 183, 185
Great Serpentine Belt 190, 191
Greenland 51, 52, 58, 60, 86, 103, 112, 113, 140, 155, 168, 169, 170, 171, 172, 182, 183, 194, 205, 209, 210, 211, 214
greenschist 101, 127, 155, 189
greenstone belts 125, 143, 169, 183
Gutenberg discontinuity 5, 6, 176

harzburgite 41, 42, 43, 44, 49, 76, 85, 113, 114, 128, 176, 179, 185, 186, 187, 188, 189, 190, 192, 211